FUNDAMENTALS OF PACKAGING TECHNOLOGY

Fourth Edition

WALTER SOROKA, CPP

Institute of
**Packaging
Professionals**

Published by:
Institute of Packaging Professionals
1833 Centre Point Circle, Suite 123
Naperville, Illinois 60563, U.S.A.
(630) 544-5050
info@iopp.org

Cover design: David Nelson & Associates

ISBN 1-930268-28-9

Printed in the United States of America

For George and Victoria Soroka
Pioneers to this land

They would have been proud.

CONTENTS

ACKNOWLEDGEMENTS   **XIII**

CHAPTER ONE
PERSPECTIVE ON PACKAGING   1

What Is Packaging?	3
Primitive Packaging	4
From Rome to the Renaissance	5
The Industrial Revolution	7
The Evolution of New Packaging Roles	8
Packaging in the Late 20th Century	10
Modern Packaging	11
Environmental and Sustainability Issues	14
The Modern Packaging Industry	25

CHAPTER TWO
PACKAGING FUNCTIONS   29

Introduction	31
The Contain Function	32
The Protect/Preserve Function	33
Food Preservation	33
The Transport Function	48
The Inform/Sell Function	48

CHAPTER THREE
GRAPHIC DESIGN   53

Introduction	55
Demographics and Psychographics	56

The Retail Environment   60

Fundamental Messages   61

Equity and Brand Names   64

Color   67

Graphic Design Basics   68

Package Design and Marketing Studies   73

CHAPTER FOUR

PACKAGE PRINTING AND DECORATING   81

Introduction   83

Color   83

Artwork   90

Preparation for Printing   95

Proofing   98

Printing Methods   99

Relief Printing: Flexography and Letterpress   101

Lithography   104

Gravure Printing   107

Comparing Flexography, Lithography and Gravure   109

Other Package Decoration Techniques   111

Printing Dimensional Packages   114

Labeling   118

CHAPTER FIVE

PAPER AND PAPERBOARD   125

Source and Preparation of Fiber   127

Representative Paper-Making Machines   131

Paper Characterization   136

Paper Types   138

Paperboard Grades   141

Paper Characterization Methods   142

CHAPTER SIX

PAPERBOARD CARTONS   147

Paperboard Package Classifications   149

Folding Carton Design   149

Selecting the Correct Paperboard   153

The Carton Production Process   153

Basic Tube-style Folding Cartons   157

Basic Tray-style Folding Cartons   165

Beverage Baskets and Setup Boxes   166

Paperboard Resources   000

CHAPTER SEVEN

METAL CANS AND CONTAINERS   173

Background   175

Can-making Steels   177

Three-piece Steel Cans   179

Two-piece Drawn Cans   181

Impact Extrusion   184

Can Dimensioning   186

Protective Coatings for Cans   187

Decoration   187

Aerosols   188

CHAPTER EIGHT

GLASS CONTAINERS   197

Glass Types and General Properties   199

Commercial Glass Manufacturing   201

Bottle Manufacturing   203

Bottle Design Features   208

CHAPTER NINE

POLYMER CHEMISTRY FOR THE NONCHEMIST 217

Introduction to Plastics   219

Polarity and Material Properties   222

Hydrocarbons and Polyethylene   223

Other Packaging Polymers   228

Molecular Structure and Properties   230

Thermal Behavior   232

Density and Yield   236

Thermoplastic and Thermoset Polymers   236

CHAPTER TEN

SHAPING PLASTICS 241

Selecting the Material and the Process   243

Plasticating Extruders   244

Profile Extrusion   245

Injection Molding   251

Extrusion Blow Molding   257

Injection Blow Molding   264

Bottle Design   266

Thermoforming   270

Other Forming Methods   274

Recognizing Molding Methods   277

CHAPTER ELEVEN

PLASTIC APPLICATIONS 281

Polyethylene (PE)   283

High-density Polyethylene (HDPE)   284

Low-density Polyethylene (LDPE) and
Linear Low-density Polyethylene (LLDPE)   285

Polystyrene (PS)   287

Polypropylene (PP)   289

Poly(ethylene terephthalate) (PET)   291

Poly(vinyl chloride) (PVC)   292

Poly(vinylidene chloride) (PVDC)   294

Poly(vinyl acetate) (PVAC) and Ethylene-vinyl Acetate (EVA)   294

Polyamide (PA or nylon)   295

Poly(vinyl alcohol) (PVAL) and Ethylene-vinyl Alcohol (EVOH)   296

Ethylene Acid Copolymers and Ionomers   297

Other Packaging Polymers   297

Additives   300

Characterizing Plastic Materials   301

Chemical Properties   310

CHAPTER TWELVE

CLOSURES   315

Selection Considerations   317

Container and Closure Dimensioning   318

Metal Closures   320

Closure Seals   324

Plastic Closures   327

Injection Molds and Closure Design   328

Closure Application   329

Tamper-Evident Closures   333

Child-Resistant Closures   334

Special Closures and Functions   335

CHAPTER THIRTEEN

ADHESIVES   343

Introduction to Adhesives   345

Theories of Adhesion   345

Surface Treatment   347

Solidification   349

Common Classes of Packaging Adhesives   350

Adhesive Application   356

Viscosity   357

Adhesive Selection and Considerations   360

Inspecting Bond Failures   364

CHAPTER FOURTEEN
FLEXIBLE PACKAGING LAMINATES   369

Laminates   371

Aluminum Foil   372

Vacuum Metallizing   377

Other Non-Organic Coatings and Barrier Teatments   380

Laminate Structural and Physical Properties   381

Flexible Bags, Pouches and Sachets   384

Sealability   386

Barrier Properties   388

Aesthetics and Other Properties   391

Laminating Processes   392

Specifying Laminates   396

Examples of Laminates   398

CHAPTER FIFTEEN
CORRUGATED FIBERBOARD   403

Historical Perspective   405

Corrugated Board   405

Properties and Tests   411

Carrier Rules and Regulations   415

Corrugated Boxes   417

Corrugated Box Printing   425

Special Board Treatments   427

Corrugated Container Quality Assurance   429

CHAPTER SIXTEEN

DISTRIBUTION PACKAGING 435

Distribution Packaging: A Systems Approach 437

Tracking Distribution Losses 442

The Warehouse 447

Unit Loads 447

Good Distribution Practice 452

Evaluating Distribution Packaging 454

CHAPTER SEVENTEEN

SHOCK, VIBRATION AND COMPRESSION 467

Shock 469

Quantifying Shock Fragility 472

Cushioning Against Shock 476

Vibration 477

Compression 481

Estimating Required Compression Strength 488

CHAPTER EIGHTEEN

PACKAGING MACHINERY 493

Automated Production 495

The New Production Line 496

Package Design and Machinability 498

Speed 499

Buffers 502

Straight-line and Rotary Systems 504

Changeovers 506

Machine Controls 508

Upgrading Existing Equipment 509

Filling Systems 509

Liquid Filling 511

Dry-product Filling 516

Introduction to Statistical Process control 521

CHAPTER NINETEEN

APPLIED PACKAGING   533

Carded Display Packaging   535

Blister Packaging   536

Carded Skin Packaging   537

Chub Packages   538

Fiber Cans   539

Collapsible Tubes   541

Plastic and Paper Bags   542

Bar Codes   546

Security Labeling   549

Durable Goods Packaging   550

Wood Packaging   551

Pharmaceutical Packaging   553

Creative Designs   557

Molded Pulp Containers and Forms   561

CHAPTER TWENTY

THE PACKAGE DEVELOPMENT PROCESS   565

Managing the Packaging Function   567

Project Scope   569

Package Development Process   571

Specifications   577

Case Study: Redesign of an Oil Battle and Shipping System   585

An Example of Graphic Design Development   591

Package Designer's Checklist   592

INDEX   603

ACKNOWLEDGMENTS

Many people have contributed knowingly and unknowingly to this book. In particular, the author would like to acknowledge the help of the following packaging authorities, who took time to read and critique the original manuscripts. Their comments and suggestions were invaluable in helping to shape and organize a mass of information into *Fundamentals of Packaging Technology*.

Stuart Bolton
Aaron Brody
Joseph Cavanagh
James Chestnut
Robert Cirrotto
Walter Durning
Robert Esse
Robert Fiedler
Robert Forsyth
Jack Giacin
Bob Ginsberg

Roger Griffin
Ted Holloran
Randall House
Kevin Lipsky
George Maltenfort
Ken Marsh
Alfred McKinlay
David L. Olsson
Herb Schueneman
Jim Sims

CONTENTS

What Is Packaging?

A definition of packaging, the many things a package might be asked to do, how packaging changes to meet society's needs.

Primitive Packaging

The origins of packaging, how packaging changed as social structures changed, early packaging materials, the discovery of glass.

From Rome to the Renaissance

The invention of the glass blowpipe, wood barrels, the discovery of paper, ancient printing, the Dark Ages and the Renaissance.

The Industrial Revolution

Characteristics of the Industrial Revolution and the dramatic changes in how we lived.

The Evolution of New Packaging Roles

How the Industrial Revolution affected packaging, the first packaged retail products, the origin of the term "brand" and how it was transferred to unit packages, early brands, early labeling. Quaker Oats—a new idea in branding, changes in the way we traveled and shopped, changes in the retail store, the evolution of selling and informing as vital packaging roles.

Packaging in the Late 20th Century

Changes in demographics, fast food and other institutional markets, the "baby boom" and packaging, legislated changes, the advent of microwave ovens, the vanishing domestic housewife.

Modern Packaging

The trend toward more intensive marketing, globalization, why packaging is important to our food supply, freedom from geographic and seasonal food production, advantages of central processing and prepackaged food, packaging and mass manufacture of durable goods, packaging in less-developed countries, the United Nations and packaging.

Environmental and Sustainability Issues

Consumer perceptions of packaging, materials in the residential waste stream, percentage of residential waste that is packaging, the four Rs hierarchy, recycling realities, global sustainability issues, definitions of sustainability, sustainability and packaging, life cycle analysis, cradle to cradle production, biodegradability.

The Modern Packaging Industry

"Converters and users"—the broad industry divisions, converter and user subdivisions, professional packaging associations, other organizations having a major impact on packaging activities.

PERSPECTIVE ON PACKAGING

WHAT IS PACKAGING?

Packaging is best described as a coordinated system of preparing goods for transport, distribution, storage, retailing and use. It is a complex, dynamic, scientific, artistic and controversial business function. In its most fundamental form, packaging contains, protects/preserves, transports and informs/sells. Packaging is a service function that cannot exist by itself; it needs a product. If there is no product, there is no need for a package.

Packaging functions range from those that are technical in nature to those that are marketing oriented:

Technical Functions		**Marketing Functions**	
contain	measure	communicate	promote
protect	dispense	display	sell
preserve	transport	inform	motivate

Technical packaging professionals need science and engineering skills, while marketing professionals need artistic and motivational understanding. Packaging managers need a basic understanding of both marketing and technical needs, mixed with good business sense. This unusual skill spread makes the packaging industry a unique career choice.

Packaging is not a recent phenomenon. It is an activity closely associated with the evolution of society and as such can be traced back to human beginnings. The nature, degree and amount of packaging at any stage of a society's growth reflect the needs, cultural patterns, material availability and technology of that society. A study of packaging's changing roles and forms over the centuries is, in a very real sense, a study of the growth of civilization.

From an individual perspective, change seems to be that which has already happened, but society is changing daily—meeting new challenges, integrating new knowledge, accommodating new needs and rejecting systems proven to be unacceptable. These changes are inevitably reflected in the way we package, deliver and consume goods.

Because the science of packaging is closely connected to everything we do as a society, it should come as no surprise that the packaging industry is always in a state of change. Entire sectors can become obsolete, or new industries can be generated by the discovery of a new material, process or need. For example, a whole new packaging sector was born with a single tragic tampering incident (the Tylenol episode of October 1982). Society suddenly required tamper-evident closure systems.

Until the 1950s, motor oil was delivered in bulk to service stations, which in turn measured it into 1-quart glass jars. (See Figure 1.1) The advantages of premeasured oil in metal cans swung the entire trade into metal cans. By the late 1960s, foil/fiber composite cans had replaced metal cans, and by the late 1970s, plastic bottles had replaced fiber cans.

Figure 1.1

Packaging of automotive products over the years; refillable glass bottle, metal can, spiral wound fiber can and high density polyethylene bottle.

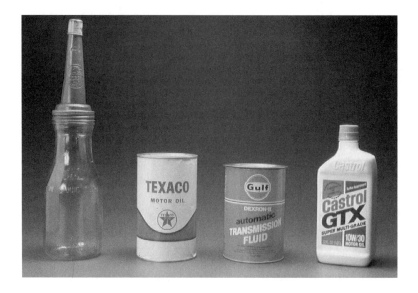

Similarly, milk delivery went from glass bottles to today's variety of plain and aseptic paperboard cartons, plastic bottles and flexible bags, with each packaging method offering its own particular advantages.

How oil or milk will be delivered tomorrow is open to speculation. Packaging choices will probably reflect an increasing need for environmentally acceptable packaging that will generate minimal waste. The relative costs of petrochemicals, wood pulp and metal will likely govern choices. And finally, the way we buy and consume oil or milk will have a significant impact. No option can be ignored.

PRIMITIVE PACKAGING

We don't know what the first package was, but we can certainly speculate. Primitive humans were nomadic hunters/gatherers; they lived off the land. Such an existence has severe limitations. It takes considerable land area to support the wild animals and vegetation needed to feed a single person. Social groupings were small, mostly restricted to extended family units.

These early humans would have been subject to the geographical migrations of animals and the seasonal availability of plant food. This meant that humans followed their food sources around and quite often went hungry. Such an extreme nomadic existence does not encourage property accumulation beyond what can be carried on one's back.

Nonetheless, primitive people needed containment and carrying devices, and out of this need came the first "package." It was most likely a wrap of leaves, an animal skin, the shell of a nut or gourd, or a naturally hollow piece of wood. Fire was carried from camp to camp, and evidence suggests that the role of fire-bearer and the "packaging" of fire carried a mystical significance.

Let's jump ahead to 5000 B.C., a time of some domesticated plants and animals. While the forage or hunt was still important, a reasonable food supply was available in a given vicinity. This evolutionary stage, which supported larger social groups, gave birth to small tribal villages. Storage and transport containers

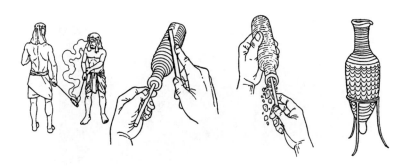

Figure 1.2

Forming a hollow glass vessel around a core. (Source: P. Copeland and H. Martin, *Story of Glass*, Dover Publications, New York, 1)

were needed for milk, honey, seed grains, nuts and dried meat. Villages with access to different resources traded with their neighbors, requiring transport containers.

Fabricated sacks, baskets and bags, made from materials of plant or animal origin, were added to the primitive packaging list. Wood boxes replaced hollow logs. Clay from a riverbank would have initially been shaped into shallow bowls and allowed to dry in the sun. This was fine for dry products, but wet products quickly reverted such containers back to mud. Some impatient Neolithic genius, probably trying to hurry the slow process of sun-drying, placed a clay bowl in a fire. Much to his or her pleasure, the fire-dried clay pots were more durable and held their shape when filled with water. Thus was born the pottery and ceramic trade.

Legend has it that Phoenician sailors who used salt blocks to protect their fire from wind on the sandy Mediterranean coast, discovered a hard inert substance in the fire's remains. By 2500 B.C., glass beads and figures were being made in Mesopotamia (today's Iraq). The earliest hollow glass objects appeared in Mesopotamia and Egypt in about 1500 B.C.

Ancient Egyptian glass containers were core-formed. Hot strands of glass were wrapped around a core of clay and dung. (See Figure 1.2) Wavy patterns could be introduced by dragging a stick across the soft hot glass. Rolling the glass against a smooth surface flattened and smoothed the strand lines. When the glass was cool, the core was dug out of the container.

Along with metal, these glass containers were the ancient packaging materials. Many centuries would pass before modern materials such as paper and plastics expanded the packager's portfolio.

While the printing arts and extensive packaging laws were still in the distant future, laws that affected packaging were being enacted as early as the Greek city-state period (about 250 B.C). For example, olive oil, at that time packaged in amphora (large clay jugs with elongated or pointed bottoms), was marked with a stamp identifying the city-state where it was produced, the time of pressing and the person responsible for it. (See Figure 1.3)

FROM ROME TO THE RENAISSANCE

As time went on, cities were established, trade flourished across the European and Asian continents, and conquering armies frequently sallied forth to plunder

Figure 1.3

A portion of a Greek amphora handle dated 220–189 B.C. The stamped image shows a rose, indicating that the olive oil was pressed on the island of Rhodes. The symbol is encircled with the Greek words "in the tenure of Ariston, month of Hyakinthios." (Courtesy Royal Ontario Museum.)

some other region's wealth. While the world witnessed many societal changes, the corresponding changes in packaging related mostly to the quality and quantity of existing packaging practices.

An important packaging event, attributed to the Romans in about 50 B.C., was the invention of the glass blowpipe. The blowpipe was a hollow metal rod on the end of which was placed a gob of molten glass. By blowing into the opposite end, the glassblower could inflate the gob into a hollow vessel in a variety of shapes and sizes. The glassblower could shape the vessel freehand by alternately blowing and shaping, or blow the glass bubble into a cup mold with pre-existing decorations.

The blowpipe's invention brought glass out of noble households and temples. Roman glass beakers decorated with chariots and gladiator contests—apparently sold as souvenirs and mementos of such events—are reasonably common.

The origin of the first wooden barrel is not clear, but it also probably had its start at this time, possibly in the Alpine regions of Europe. The barrel was destined to become one of the most common packaging forms for many centuries.

With the Roman Empire's collapse in about 450 A.D., Europe was reduced to minor city-states and squabbling kingdoms at best, and downright barbarity at worst. Many established arts and crafts were forgotten or became stagnant. The 600 years following the fall of Rome were so devoid of significant change that historians refer to them as the Dark Ages. Any progress came from the Far East and from Arabic nations newly inspired by the Muslim faith.

As early symbolic markings on stones and mud tablets evolved into a more formal alphabet, there was a need for a lighter, more portable media to write on. The Egyptians produced one of the earlier forms of writing material by weaving together the split stalks of papyrus reeds. By pounding, pressing and drying the woven strips, they created a useful sheet material. Papyrus is not classed as being a true paper, but centuries later, the name "paper" was given to the Chinese invention made of matted plant fibers.

The earliest existing texts on papyrus are dated to about 500 B.C.

Ts'ai Lun (China) is credited with making the first true paper from the inner bark of mulberry trees about 105 A.D., although more recent archeology has found samples of paper made from hemp and ramie fiber in a tomb dated 140–87 B.C. When the Muslims sacked Samarkand in about 950, they brought three Chinese papermakers and the secret, back to Spain. From there, the art of papermaking spread slowly throughout Europe.

Printing from woodcuts—the ancient parent of the printing process known as flexography—also originated in the Far East. The oldest existing printed objects are Japanese Buddhist charms dated to 768. The oldest existing book is the *Diamond Sutra*, found in Turkistan and printed in 868.

The European world awoke in about 1100. Neglected crafts were revitalized, learning and the arts were revived and trade increased. Gutenburg printed a Bible using a modified wine press and moveable type in 1455. By the 1500s, the great age of exploration was well under way.

Fundamental social structures had not changed significantly. Most of the population lived off the land, sometimes as freeholders, but more typically as serfs who owed their existence and part of everything they produced to a higher power. For the most part they ate what they raised, found or caught. At this level, consumer needs were nonexistent.

Shops and stores where a person could buy goods did not exist as we know them. Although money as an exchange medium was available, much of the population never saw any. Manufacturing was strictly a custom business, and what we have called packages to this point were personally crafted, as were most goods. Packages, where they existed, were valuable utensils, and were rarely disposable in the manner of a modern package.

Since there was no retail trade, concepts of marketing, advertising, price structures and distribution were irrelevant. Population levels were not large enough to support mass production, even in the most limited sense.

THE INDUSTRIAL REVOLUTION

Encyclopedia Britannica describes the Industrial Revolution as "the change that transforms a people with peasant occupations and local markets into an industrial society with world-wide connections." This new type of society makes great use of machinery and manufactures goods on a large scale for general consumption.

The Industrial Revolution started in England in about 1700 and spread rapidly through Europe and North America. Some characteristics of this revolution included the following:

- Rural agricultural workers migrated into cities, where they were employed in factories.

- Inexpensive mass-produced goods became available to a large segment of the population; the consumer society was born.

- Factory workers needed commodities and food that were previously produced largely at home.

- Many new shops and stores opened to sell to the newly evolving working class.

- By necessity, some industries were located in nonagricultural areas, requiring that all food be transported into the growing urban settings.

These changes increased the demand for barrels, boxes, kegs, baskets and bags to transport the new consumer commodities and to bring great quantities of food into the cities. The fledgling packaging industry itself had to mechanize in order to keep up with the growing demand. With large segments of the population living away from food production points, it became necessary to devise ways of preserving food beyond its natural biological life.

THE EVOLUTION OF NEW PACKAGING ROLES

For most of recorded history, people lived in rural communities and were largely self-sufficient. Bulk packaging was the rule, with the barrel being the workhorse of the packaging industry. Flour, apples, biscuits, molasses, gunpowder, whiskey, nails and whale oil were transported in barrels. Packaging served primarily to contain and protect during transport. Individual packaging was of little importance until the Industrial Revolution spurred the growth of cities. The new industrial workers needed to be fed by a separate agricultural system and supported in most of their nonfood needs by the manufacturing skill of others.

City dwellers did not have a farm's storage facilities, and so quantities purchased tended to be small and trips to the shop more frequent. This was an open opportunity to create individual packages in the amounts that people preferred to purchase. In practice, it took many years for this to happen, and even today the transformation is not complete.

Initially, shops simply adapted the bulk delivery system to consumer selling. The shopkeeper received apples and biscuits in barrels, cheese in large rounds and herbs or medicines in glass jars. He or she would measure and portion these items, often into a container provided by the purchaser. The shopkeeper sold mostly unfinished product.

Medicines, cosmetics, teas, liquors and other expensive products were the first prepackaged products, along with awkward items such as tacks or pins. The latter were often wrapped in paper, and the expression "a paper of pins" accurately described the product. In time, many products were sold in a "paper."

Products were sold generically. Cheese was cheese, oatmeal was oatmeal and lye soap was lye soap. Sometimes identifying marks were made with a blackening brush or with a hot branding iron on the barrel or cask to show origin or manufacturer. In time, certain brand marks became associated with quality products. As individual packaging began to develop, quality producers wished to identify their particular product as a guarantee of quality or composition. The brand mark was carried from the bulk package to unit packages or labels. It was an early form of product branding, as well as the origin of the term "brand name."

The first brand names were inevitably those of the maker. Yardley's (1770), Schweppes (1792), Perrier (1863), Smith Brothers (1866) and Colgate (1873) are a few of the personal names that have survived to this day.

Most packages that existed in the mid-1800s were for higher cost goods, and the evolving printing and decorating arts were applied to these early "upscale" packages. Similarly, it was realized that the papers used to wrap products for sale were easily imprinted with a brand mark, with some message of instruction or with a description of the product's virtue. Many early decorations were based on works of art or national symbols. Labels were printed with ornate and elaborate scrolls, wreaths, allegorical figures or impossibly flawless and shapely ladies (some things are difficult to change!). These often combined typography in a dozen type styles.

Early food can labels had to appeal to simple country folk, so pictures of pastoral life, barnyards and fruit on a branch were commonly used. Sometimes the label graphics had little to do with the contents, and sometimes the same graphic was used on unrelated products. Another popular practice was to display the gold medals won at one or another of the great national and international fairs held frequently at the time. Many early labels were so attractive that they were saved for decorative use.

A packaging milestone was set in 1877 when the American Cereal Company chose a symbol to represent or trademark its product. The Quaker personage (See Figure 1.4) represented purity, wholesomeness, honesty and integrity—values that by extension also applied to the product. It was perhaps one of the earliest forms of what designers refer to as the "persona," a description of the package or product as if it were a person.

After an intense advertising campaign, the company convinced a fair proportion of the population to ask for Quaker Oats rather than just oatmeal. The Quaker figure's success possibly inspired other companies to adopt fictitious persons to represent their products, among them were Aunt Jemima (1889) and the Cream of Wheat smiling chef (1893).

Package decoration follows national art styles and trends. Between 1890 and about 1920, decoration followed the art nouveau style popular in that period. This was followed by a period of art deco graphics and designs.

The first plastic, based on cellulose, was made in 1856, but packaging applications were still a long way off. In 1907, phenol formaldehyde plastic, later known as Bakelite, was discovered. Bakelite's major packaging application was for closures. A few years later, in 1911, a machine was built to manufacture continuous cellulosic film. DuPont chemists perfected the cellulose casting process in 1927 and called their product cellophane. Cellulose films dominated the

Stands Alone!
THE PERFECT CEREAL FOOD FOR ALL SEASONS

Figure 1.4

The Quaker personage as it appeared in 1896. Such images have to change with time as perceptions and styles change. One hundred years later, the modern Quaker image is not as stern and somewhat younger in appearance.

Figure 1.5

A typical store in the middle 1900s. A general store such as this likely stocked well under a thousand product choices. Compare that to a modern grocery supermarket with 80,000 stock keeping units.

clear film market until the advent of polyethylene and polypropylene. Bakelite was largely displaced by the newer thermoplastics in the 1960s.

In earlier days, craftspeople sold their own wares and were able to explain the available choices and how best to use a product. Over time, general merchandise stores selling a variety of products from different producers became the norm; but there was still a counter between the customer and the shopkeeper. (See Figure 1.5). In 1916 the Piggly Wiggly grocery store in Memphis TN, started a whole new trend by introducing the self serve concept. Now, the shopkeeper was not there to aid or influence the consumer's purchase. Stores with thousands of products were staffed by people who had little or no knowledge of the products and their applications. The consumer was face to face with the package, and the package's motivational and informational roles became critical:

- The package had to inform the purchaser.
- The package had to sell the product.

Package design and graphics were suddenly much more than a pretty picture, and a whole new profession, the package design**er**, was born. The transformation from bulk packaging to individual packaging and from general stores to supermarkets continued, interrupted only briefly by the shortages of the Second World War.

PACKAGING IN THE LATE 20TH CENTURY

The 1950s birth rate was so imposing that it earned its own name: the baby boom. Demographics, the study of population structure and trends, was universally realized to be an important factor in designing products and packages.

Fast-food outlets made their appearance in the 1950s and created a demand for new kinds of packaging. The consumer met disposable single-service packaging for the first time, while the fast-food outlets demanded the bulk delivery of ready-to-cook food portions in their own special type of packaging. Later, two other factors joined the fast-food outlet boom to influence packaging: increased levels of public health care and a rapidly growing trend toward eating out rather than at home. Today, this market is large enough to form its own sector, sometimes called the HRI (hospital, restaurant and institutional) market.

The 1950s also saw the growth of convenience and prepared food packages, such as cake mixes, TV dinners, boil-in-bag foods and gravy preparations. A rapidly growing technology added petroleum-derived plastics to the package designer's selection of packaging materials.

The coming-of-age baby boomers were the largest identifiable population segment in the late 1960s, and this was reflected in a major youth orientation in packaging and products. Sexual morality shifted significantly in the 1960s to allow more suggestive and provocative messages. In the 1960s, this was mostly confined to "cheesecake," images of scantily clad women aimed at selling products to men. Its counterpart, "beefcake," did not become common until the more liberated 1980s. Today, the practice continues despite protests that such tactics are inappropriate methods of promoting goods.

Consumerism and a concern for the environment became important factors at this time for those who watched for future trends.

The 1970s and early 1980s brought numerous changes, many of them legislated. Child-resistant closures were mandated for some products. Tamper-evident closures were brought in for others. Labeling laws required listing of ingredients. International agreements were signed to phase out the use of ozone-depleting chlorofluorocarbons (CFC). Standards for the acceptance of new packaging materials were raised.

Microwave ovens became a common household feature, and a significant effort went into devising products and packaging specifically for the microwave. A new health awareness meant not only changes in consuming habits and nutritional labeling but also opportunities for entire new food lines. Yogurt became the "in" food. Bottled water became big business.

The last decades of the 20th century witnessed rapid change. The population aged, and many social habits changed. Families became smaller. Single-person households became common. The domestic housewife became a relic of the past as both partners in a marriage sought professional careers and higher income levels. For the modern urban dweller, "convenient" and "fast" became the operative words. Marketers recognized a whole subclass of people who know only how to boil water or turn on the microwave. If it wasn't ready in five minutes, they didn't want it. If it took more than one dish, their interest wandered.

MODERN PACKAGING

Changing Needs and New Roles

Looking back, historical changes are understandable and obvious. That all of them impacted the way products are bought, consumed and packaged is also obvious. What is not so obvious is what tomorrow will bring. Yet, it is to the needs, markets and conditions of tomorrow that packaging professionals must always pay their attention to.

The forces that drove packaging during the Industrial Revolution continue to operate today. The consumer society continues to grow and is possibly best described by a 1980s bumper sticker, "Born to Shop." We consume goods today at a rate four to five times greater than we did as recently as 1935. Most of these goods are not essential to survival; they constitute the so-called "good life."

In the second half of the 20th century, the proliferation of goods was so high that packaging was forced into an entirely new role, that of providing the major purchase motivation rather than just presenting the good itself. On a shelf of 10 competing products, all of them similar in performance and quality, the only method of differentiation became the package itself. Marketers aimed at life-styles, emotional values, subliminal images, features and advantages beyond the basic product itself—anything that would make a shopper's hand reach for *their* product rather than the competitor's. In some instances, the package has become the product, and occasionally, packaging has become entertainment.

Globally, the trend toward urbanization continues. Providing increased tonnages of high-quality food to massive city complexes at affordable prices is a problem that continues to challenge packagers. A new concern is the removal of the debris generated by a consumer society and the impact that these consumption rates have on the planet's ecology.

The makeup, needs, styles, perceptions and wishes of the consuming public are always changing. The packaging professional must be aware of and keep up with these changes or be lost to history.

Packaging and the Modern Industrial Society

The importance of packaging to a modern industrial society is most evident when we examine the food-packaging sector. Food is organic in nature, having an animal or plant source. One characteristic of such organic matter is that, by and large, it has a limited natural biological life. A cut of meat, left to itself, might be unfit for human consumption by the next day. Some animal protein products, such as certain seafood, can deteriorate within hours.

The natural shelf life of plant-based food depends on the species and plant part involved. Pulpy fruit portions tend to have a short life span, while seed parts, which in nature have to survive at least until the next growing season, have a longer life. Stalks and leaves separated from the living plant are usually short-lived.

In addition to having a limited natural shelf life, most food is geographically and seasonally specific. Thus, potatoes and apples are grown in a few North American geographical regions and harvested during a short maturation period. In a world without packaging, we would need to live at a point of harvest to enjoy these products, and our enjoyment of them would be restricted to the natural biological life span of each.

It is by proper storage, packaging and transport techniques that we are able to deliver fresh potatoes and apples, or the products derived from them, throughout the year and throughout the country. Potatoes—whole, canned, powdered, flaked, chipped, frozen and instant—are available anytime, anywhere. Global trade brings fresh lettuce, tomatoes and tropical fruit to those in colder climes throughout their winter. This ability gives a society great freedom and mobility. Unlike less-developed societies, we are no longer restricted in our choice of where to live, since we are no longer tied to the food-producing ability of an area. Food production becomes more specialized and efficient with the growth of packaging. Crops and animal husbandry are moved to where their production is most economical, without regard to the proximity of a market. Most important, we are free of the natural cycles of feast and famine that are typical of societies dependent on natural regional food-producing cycles.

Central processing allows value recovery from what would normally be wasted. By-products of the processed-food industry form the basis of other sub-industries. (See Figure 1.6) Chicken feathers are high in protein and, when properly milled and treated, can be fed back to the next generation of chickens. Vegetable waste is fed to cattle or pigs. Bagasse, the waste cane from sugar pressing, is a source of fiber for papermaking or can be used as the base feedstock for making ethanol fuel stock.

The economical manufacture of durable goods also depends on good packaging. A product's cost is directly related to production volume. A facility building 10,000 bicycles per year for local sale could not make bicycles as cheaply as a 3-million-unit-a-year plant intended to capture the national market. Both would fail in competition against a 100-million-unit, world-market facility. But for a national or international bicycle producer to succeed, it must find a way of getting the product to a market, which may be half a world away. Again, sound packaging, in this case distribution packaging, is a key part of the system.

Some industries could not exist without an international market. For example, Canada is a manufacturer of irradiation equipment, but the Canadian market (which could account perhaps for one unit every several years) could not possibly support such a manufacturing capability. However, by selling to the world, a manufacturing facility becomes viable. In addition to needing packaging for the irradiation machinery and instrumentation, the sale of irradiation equipment requires the safe packaging and transport of radioactive isotopes, a separate challenge in itself.

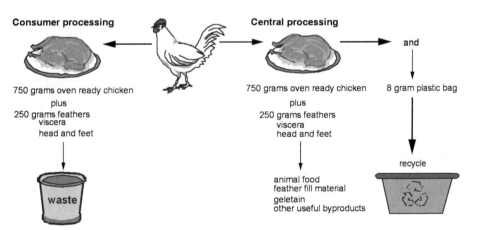

Figure 1.6

By-products collected with central processing can be converted into useful materials.

World Packaging

This discussion has referred to primitive packaging and the evolution of packaging functions. However, humankind's global progress is such that virtually every stage in the development of society and packaging is present somewhere in the world today.

Thus, a packager in a highly developed country will agonize over the choice of package type, hire expensive marketing groups to develop images to entice the targeted buyer and spend lavishly on graphics. In less-developed countries, consumers are happy to have food, regardless of the package. At the extreme, consumers will bring their own packages or will consume food on the spot, just as they did 2,000 years ago.

Packagers from the more-developed countries sometimes have difficulty working with less-developed nations, for the simple reason that they fail to understand that their respective packaging priorities are completely different. Similarly, developing nations trying to sell goods to North American markets cannot understand our preoccupation with package and graphics.

The significant difference is that packaging plays a different role in a market where rice will sell solely because it is available. In the North American market, the consumer may confront five different companies offering rice in 30 or so variations. If all the rice is good and none is inferior, how do sellers create a preference for their particular rice? How do they differentiate? The package plays a large role in this process.

The package-intensive developed countries are sometimes criticized for overpackaging, and certainly overpackaging does exist. However, North Americans also enjoy the world's cheapest food, requiring only 11 to 14% of our disposable income. European food costs are about 20% of disposable income, and in the less-developed countries food can take 95% of family income.

It is simplistic to say that the less-developed countries do not have adequate land to raise enough food, although in some few instances this is true. United Nations' studies have shown that many countries in which hunger exists actually raise enough food for their population. However, without adequate means of preservation, protection and transportation, up to 50% of the food raised never survives for human consumption. Food goes beyond its natural biological life, spoils, is lost, is infested with insects or eaten by rodents, gets wet in the rain, leaks away or goes uneaten for numerous reasons, all of which sound packaging principles can prevent. Furthermore, in a poor economy that can afford no waste, no industries recover secondary value from food by-products.

This is a tragic waste. The United Nations maintains staff whose purpose is to increase packaging level and sophistication in less-developed countries. Packaging is perceived to be a weapon against world hunger.

ENVIRONMENTAL AND SUSTAINABILITY ISSUES

A discussion of packaging today means eventually turning to related environmental issues. Packaging is often blamed for a host of ills, and a perception exists in some circles that if only the packaging industry would stop doing something, or conversely start doing something, all our landfill and pollution problems would go away. Packaging waste is far less than the typical consumer imagines. In fact, residential waste is much less than half of what is in a typical landfill.

Unfortunately, consumers see the package as that part of the shopping trip that gets thrown away. Hence, packaging is garbage. No home decorator would dispute the necessity of a paint can or a caulking tube. Yet when empty, these, along with other household packages that have fulfilled their function, are suddenly perceived as garbage—unnecessary and a problem.

The greater part of what goes into a landfill is construction and demolition, commercial and industrial waste.

The measure of what exactly is going into landfills and what is being recycled or otherwise diverted is a significant problem. Individual waste management jurisdictions have various ways of measuring the waste stream and do not necessarily even agree on what should be measured.

One problem is whether waste should be measured by weight or volume. Residential waste removal trucks pick up at the curb by volume. The waste is delivered to the landfill site by weight, but when it is compacted and buried, it again occupies volume. This weight-volume issue is sometimes used to support a company's or an environmental association's platform.

For example, the volume of uncompacted residential garbage bags was used to support the proposition that as much as 80% of residential waste was packaging—a myth offered to the general public in the late 1990s that continues today. Fortunately, for general discussion purposes, the average amount of packaging in typical residential waste is very close whether described by weight or by compacted volume (EPA data):

Proportion packaging by weight	29.6%
Proportion packaging by compacted volume	31.6%

In considering the breakdown of residential waste shown in Table 1.1, one could observe that it would be possible to recycle or compost almost the entire list. This is true if economics do not enter into consideration.

Environmentalists will maintain that recycling is an issue of the environment, not of economics. This is quite true. However, money expended to recycle a material represents an investment in energy, water and other resources. When the resource investment to recover a material exceeds the value of the material recovered, then the harm to the environment is greater, not less. The process of recycling cannot ignore market economics.

The Four Rs

The guiding principles for designing environmentally responsible packaging developed in the early 1990s are embodied in the four Rs hierarchy and are still valid today:

1. **Reduce** Packaging designs should use the minimum amount of material consistent with fulfilling their basic function. A reduction in material use

Table 1.1

Average materials mix by weight in residential solid waste. These are national averages ... local proportions can vary significantly. (Source: EPA.)

Material	*Packaging*	*Nonpackaging*
Paper	12.7%	19.6%
Wood	4.6%	—
Metal	2.0%	5.7%
Glass	5.7%	0.8%
Plastic	4.1%	5.5%
Other misc.	0.1%	12.0%
Food waste	—	8.1%
Yard waste	—	19.0%
Totals	29.2%	70.7%

will diminish further considerations of reusing, recycling or recovering other value.

2. **Reuse** Where practical, containers or packaging components should be reused.

3. **Recycle** Where practical, packaging should be collected and the materials recycled for further use.

4. **Recover** Finally, before consigning packaging to a landfill, some thought should be given to possibly recovering other value from the waste.

Recycling is the R that has caught the imagination and devotion of great parts of the consuming public. Despite its many problems, few public figures would risk anything other than positive commentary. However, many public myths exist about recycling, perhaps the greatest being that placing material in a collection box constitutes recycling. Recycling does not occur until someone uses the material collected.

A second myth presupposes that since the recycled material is recovered from discards, it should be economical. In most instances, using recycled material offers little if any economic advantage. The cost of land-filling municipal solid waste (MSW) is still less than that of recycling in most areas. The bulk of the recovered material is paper and has low value. Aluminum, the material with the highest value, is as little as 2% of the collected weight. Revenues generated from the sale of recyclable materials do not always recover collecting and recycling costs. Obviously, someone has to make up the shortfall.

Other myths propose that one or another of the packaging materials is more environmentally friendly. There is no magic material. Packagers select appropriate materials to contain, protect/preserve, efficiently transport and sell the product

Figure 1.7

A code identifies the main packaging plastic families. PETE is usually abbreviated PET and V is usually abbreviated PVC. Less commonly used plastics and mixed-plastic constructions are classified as "other." (Source: SPI.) Note: PET is a registered company trademark. When appearing on a package, the acronym PETE was selected to avoid a trademark infringement. PETE is not different from PET.

in the most cost-effective manner. Laminate constructions, a favorite target, are designed to combine the best characteristics of several different materials, offering properties not available with any single material. Their design is based on the most cost-effective and material-efficient method of achieving the needed result. They are, in fact, environmentally preferable.

Other impediments are the development of markets for post-consumer recycled (PCR) materials and the guarantee of a consistent and reliable supply of the recovered material.

Paper products vary considerably in their fiber makeup and quality. However, reasonably efficient sorting systems are in place and some cross-contamination of paper types is not a serious problem. On the negative side, paper fiber quality deteriorates with every recycling, and so paper cannot be recycled indefinitely.

Plastic materials pose a number of serious recycling problems. Many different plastics are used in packaging, and many are not mutually compatible. Identifying and sorting the plastic materials by appearance alone is beyond the abilities of even a conscientious consumer. The plastic industry developed a code for identifying the six most commonly used packaging plastics, plus an "other" category as a seventh code. (See Figure 1.7) The code identifies only the general plastic family: Significant variations can occur within each family.

While the SPI code specifically identifies six plastic material families, only PET and HDPE are collected and recycled in most municipal recycling programs. The reason is that they represent the bulk of plastic packaging. The remaining four together represent only a small fraction of the plastics used in packaging. The economics of collecting and sorting these small quantities are prohibitive at this point in time.

The frequently used phrase "plastic will last a thousand years in a landfill" has introduced a perceptual problem in the eyes of the general public. Glass will also last a thousand years in a landfill, but that does not seem to be a problem. It would be nice if all plastic (or glass) could be composted into mulch, but the fact they can't is not necessarily a major problem.

Most waste management issues fall under local and regional jurisdictions rather than national jurisdiction. The problem this poses for industry is that every state or province can pass its own packaging regulations or mandates, which can take many forms. Examples of past and current regulations in North America include:

- Recycling mandates/recycle content requirements

- Material bans or restrictions; for example: heavy metals or poly(vinyl chloride)

- Green labeling requirements/prohibitions

- Purchasing preference mandates

- Tax incentives/penalties

- Deposit laws/advance disposal fees

- Volume-based household garbage removal fees, such as paying by the bag or can

- Extended producer responsibility/stewardship laws where the producer is responsible for the product and package up to and including proper disposal

Developing packages able to meet dozens of differing waste management requirements would present a formidable challenge.

Energy is one value that is recovered from waste in many parts of the world. (As high as 70% in some countries). However, with not-in-my-backyard attitudes and a negative position held by environmental groups, incineration has become highly politicized in North America. It is not likely that this useful technology will be employed in the near future, even though many authorities agree that incineration can make a positive contribution to waste management problems.

A life cycle that includes incineration of polyolefin plastics such as polyethylene and polypropylene is referred to as the cascade model. (See Figure 1.8) Polypropylene, for example, is made by joining together molecules of a gas related to propane. It can be regarded as propane in a solid form. Propane gas can be burned for its energy value directly, or it can be reformed into polypropylene.

Figure 1.8

The cascade model proposes that monomer gases such as ethylene and propylene can be used to make useful plastics, recycled several times and still have most of their energy value when incinerated.

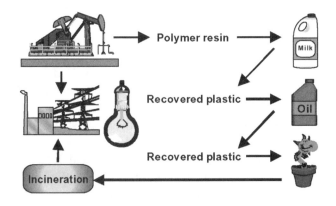

The plastic can be used as a food container and recycled perhaps to become an office letter tray. After several useful reincarnations, when incinerated, it will still have a large percentage of its original propane energy content. Combustion by-products are water and carbon dioxide.

Germany's Packaging Ordinance was the first national action where extended producer responsibility (EPR) was enacted. The ordinance's basic principle is that manufacturers or distributors must take back used packaging for reuse or recycling. The collection could be done by the company or the company could contract an outside source to do this for them. Industry established a comprehensive collection system for those who have paid a collection fee, as signified by a green dot on the package. Because of the two ways of collecting used packages, it is described as the "Dual System" (DS or DSD). European Union countries have since adopted variations or elements of the DSD system. In Europe, the EPR concept is being applied to other products as well as packaging.

In Canada, the provinces of Ontario and Quebec have recently started versions of EPR where brand owners pay a levy for packaging materials based on the cost of collecting and recycling a given material minus the revenue generated by the sale of the recycled material. If the recycling rate for a given material increases or if revenue from the sale of recycled product go up, then the material levy will be reduced proportionately. In the instance of Ontario, the generated revenues will be used to pay for 50% of municipal collection and recycling costs.

Many authorities concede that, in the long term, we will move to similar extended producer responsibility programs.

The dilemma of packaging and waste management is a complex one, not amenable to simplistic solutions. Every packaging professional should be involved in educating the public to the real and vital benefits of packaging. Inflexible environmentalism needs to be replaced with a keen awareness of packaging's legitimate role and the difficult decisions that must be made. In the final analysis, the consumer makes the choices and will direct the course of the industry. The consumer deserves to have the correct information to make those choices.

Sustainability

Recycling packaging materials is an important issue that has occupied the public's attention for the last 20 years, but another, more serious issue, has crept up on in more recent times: the issue of sustainability. The focus in the general press has tended to be on global warming and green-house gas (GHG) emissions, but this is only a small part of the picture.

- Despite replanting, global forest coverage is shrinking every year.

- Global fisheries are being depleted. Those such as the Grand Banks off North America's east coast as well as others have already been essentially fished out.

- Changing weather patterns have caused severe water shortages. (The U.S. and Canada's mid-west, U.S. southeast, Africa's Sahel region and Australia, to name a few).

Figure 1.9

Sustainability is the striking of a balance between what resources the environment can supply and absorb back into itself and humanity's levels of consumption.

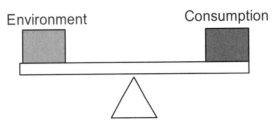

Environment   Consumption

Sustainability is a balancing act

- Arable crop land is being reduced. Food shortages are on the increase.

- Petrochemicals, a primary global energy source, are becoming harder to come by, as are many other minerals essential to modern industry.

- Air, water and soil pollution are increasing as is global temperature.

- The global economic model is based on continuous growth, while global resources are fixed.

Our consumption of resources has gone beyond the balance point at which the environment can accommodate and regenerate them. (See Figure 1.9). Meanwhile, global population will grow by 1.7 billion people by 2025. Put in perspective, that's about the population of six United States. How are we going to feed, clothe and shelter 1.7 billion more people when we are unable to do so today.

In summary:

Consumption of life sustaining resources is going up while the availability of life supporting resources is going down.

This is not sustainable.

Sustainability Definitions

The original definition of sustainability and sustainability development was issued by The Bruntland Commission (From Our Common Future) as: *"The concept of meeting the needs of the present without compromising the ability of future generations to meet their needs."*

The Oxford Concise Dictionary of Ecology defines sustainability as *"Economic development that takes full account of the environmental consequences of economic activity and is based on the use of resources that can be replaced or renewed and therefore are not depleted."*

Global Warming

The role of the scientist is to quantify the universe around us. Those measurements must be peer reviewed and must be accepted by the general scientific community as being correct before they are accepted as a truth. The scientific community is rarely wrong in their measurement; where debate occurs, it usually concerns implications of the new knowledge or its impact on future events. It should be noted that predicting the future is, strictly speaking, not science.

Global warming is not an issue that suddenly caught the scientific community by surprise. Swedish chemist Svante Arrehenius, made the following statement in 1890:

"If you keep pumping carbon dioxide into the air the way humanity has been doing since the dawn of the industrial age you can double the level of the heat-trapping gas in the atmosphere, raising temperatures dramatically."

He spent a full year calculating what the global temperature would be when the carbon dioxide level doubled. His answer was within fractions of a degree to that developed by today's sophisticated measuring devices and computers.

Today the Intergovernmental Panel on Climate Change, an international scientific community of some 1,000 scientists is unanimous in its conclusion that human activities are the cause of recent increases in average global temperatures. They may not be unanimous in some of the details, but on the matter of climate change, they were in total agreement. Unfortunately, many of the world's leaders (few of who have scientific training) have chosen to disregard or even dispute the seriousness of the findings, and to varying degrees have not fully responded.

As a result of this many states, provinces and even cities, as well as assorted industries and industry associations have taken lead positions in developing programs that are sustainable for the long term.

Unlike programs related to waste management and recycling, sustainable development is not about some particular material, activity or location: it is a global problem and concerns all human activities. As such, its resolution requires a comprehensive and global response.

The difficulty of forming a global consensus is partly because of the great disparity in national economic states and populations of the globe's individual countries. The higher the per capita income, the higher the consumption rate of products and services, and therefore the higher the per capita carbon dioxide footprint. For example according to the Carbon Dioxide Information Analysis Center, the per capita carbon dioxide footprint for an American is about 20 tons per year and for a Canadian about 17 tons per year. Compare this to developing countries: China at about 3 tons per capita and India at about one ton per capita.

If countries are compared on total emissions as nation, then a country like China ranks as a major global contributor of green house gases (GHG). Understandably, such countries protest when it is suggested that they should reduce their carbon dioxide emissions, while the citizens of developed countries are producing per capita GHG gases six or seven times that of a Chinese citizen.

Sustainability and Packaging

The packaging industry is a major consumer of materials and as a result is a significant producer of waste material. Furthermore, it is a significant user of energy, both in the production of materials and packaging, and for transportation in a trade economy that transports goods and foodstuffs around the globe.

Figure 1.10

Manufacturing in accordance with sustainability principles requires that every phase of a product's manufacture be considered from the initial raw materials inputs to the final proper disposal at the product's end-of-life. No harmful waste or by-products should be released to the environment.

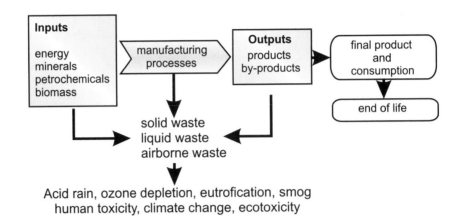

As such there is considerable focus, perhaps even a disproportionate focus, on the packaging industry to "do something."

Sustainability in its fullest sense is a management philosophy whose object is to strike a balance between what resources nature is capable of providing, and using those resources in a manner that doesn't deplete a resource or cause other harm.

In the not too distant past, a product manufacturer was concerned only with the manufacture of the product (See Figure 1.10). In the late 1980's, waste management became an issue, and manufacturer's needed to concern themselves with end-of-life treatments of the package and product residues. Manufacturers did not concern themselves very much with raw materials inputs, the conversion of these into useful materials, and the conversion of these into packaging.

Solid waste, liquid waste and airborne emissions were treated casually for the most part. The casual disposal of solid waste has resulted in ecotoxic and human toxic soils, leachable land-fills that contaminated water sources and the emission of methane, a potent greenhouse gas amongst other problems.

Similarly liquid effluents introduced a myriad of man-made chemicals into the environment, many of them carcinogenic (polychlorobiphenyl), some toxic (solutions containing heavy metals), and some biologically active (medications of various sorts, bisphenol-A). Some, such as the excessive release of phosphate containing cleaning compounds in the 1950's resulted in the eutrophication of lakes and rivers.

The gas of greatest concern is carbon dioxide, being identified as the principle greenhouse gas. Other greenhouse gases such as methane, nitric oxides, halogenated hydrocarbons (CFCs), nitrous oxide and sulfur dioxide are much more potent GHGs than carbon dioxide but are not as plentiful. Together these gases have given us acid rain, ozone depletion, human and ecological toxicity, smog and climate change.

Life Cycle Analysis (LCA)

A life cycle is a plotting of the complete material, energy and process flow path from raw materials to the end of life for a particular product. The plot will also detail by-products and solid waste, liquid effluent, and atmospheric releases. (See

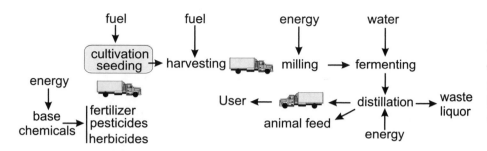

Figure 1.11

A simplified life cycle. Transportation fuel is part of the life cycle. The illustration approximates the life cycle for manufacturing ethanol from corn.

Figure 1.11) The quantities of each input and release are determined and added to this diagram to make a life cycle inventory. Using this complete picture, a life cycle analysis is conducted to identify opportunities for increasing the sustainability level. LCA is useful for focusing on the overall picture and as a means of eliminating over-sights.

A not uncommon situation is where an apparently positive change in one part of the life cycle causes a more negative condition in another part. Good LCA circumvents this problem.

A great number of sustainability benefits are being claimed for various products that are marginal at best and deceptive at worst. (So-called green washing). Down-gauging or light-weighting a package is certainly laudable, but such work has always been done as part of a corporation's continuous improvement program. It is not an innovative step forward into a new paradigm ... it's just doing what we've always done but giving it a different name. In terms of an LCA, it's just one small bit in a complex flow of materials, energy, manufacturing practices and so on.

International concern led the International Organization for Standardization (ISO) to develop the ISO 14000 series of standards. These documents do not set recycling target levels or mandate package types. Rather, the ISO 14000 series provides guidance for suitable management policies, auditing methods, environmental labeling practices, corporate environmental performance evaluations and LCA protocol guides amongst other subjects.

Cradle to Cradle

The old cradle to grave paradigm that proposed that a producer should be responsible for a packaging material until it has been properly disposed of has been replaced by the new cradle to cradle paradigm. In this scenario, the objective is to recover used packaging material and return it into the manufacturing cycle to be manufactured into new packaging. (See Figure 1.12) Failing this, to recover some other useful values such as energy or composting from the residues. Land-filling should be the option of last resort.

Energy considerations are an important part of an LCA. The cost of transport fuel is a large part of this cost and the exhaust gases are a major source of GHG. A large percentage of electricity is generated by coal-fired generating stations, and in the United States, these contribute more GHG to the atmosphere than transportation fuel.

Figure 1.12

The use of packaging materials should ideally be within a closed loop system where at the end of life the material is returned into the loop to be reborn again as another package.

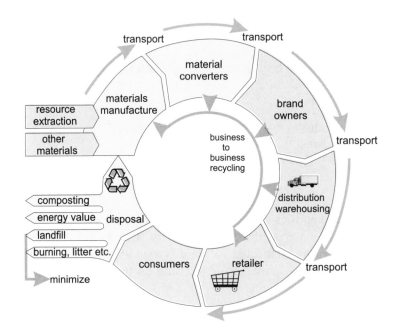

Biodegradability

Biodegradation is the process by which a material is converted by microorganisms into basic elements and compounds such as carbon dioxide, water and mulch that can be safely absorbed into the ecosystem. Biodegradability is a positive sustainability attribute.

In the context of packaging materials, glass and metals are not biodegradable but since they are easily recycled, this is not viewed as a problem. Paper is biodegradable and is also not viewed as a problem.

The traditional plastic materials however are not biodegradable and furthermore, although in principle they can be recycled, in practice there are many obstacles and problems to be resolved; the most significant being sorting the collected plastics into their respective families and sometimes sub-groups within that family. Another problem concerns the product residues that get absorbed into the plastic.

Recent developments have launched a group of plastics that are biodegradable; leading among these new polymers is polylactide (PLA) made from starch. (Polylactide is frequently referred to as polylactic acid)

When selecting a plastic for an application, the package designer will determine what group of performance criteria (properties) will be required to contain and protect the product through production and distribution. (properties such as stiffness, barrier qualities, machinability, coefficient of friction, printability, product compatibility, glass transition temperature, biodegradability and so on. The choice is made on the basis of which plastic will provide the greatest number of these properties at the lowest cost. No plastic can fulfill all these requirements, and so it is often necessary to make multi-layered structures that include several plastics. In making this choice, primacy will always be given to the safety and security of the product itself at an acceptable cost. Biodegradability will always be a secondary choice.

Another factor that must be considered is how and where biodegradation will take place. Some biodegradable plastics biodegrade best in industrial composters that operate at elevated temperatures. Biodegradation at the ambient conditions of a back-yard composter is marginal at best. This would suggest that a means of separating biodegradable plastics would have to be put in place. This is not a likely prospect for the immediate future. As a minority plastic, it would join the other minority plastics that are not recycled to any extent simply for the reason that there isn't enough of them to make it economically viable to do so. The majority will still end up in landfill.

The sealed and capped environment inside a modern landfill is not conducive to aerobic biodegradation.

This is not to say that biodegradable plastics have no applications in packaging. There are many expanding niche markets where they are already in use and others will be found. Further development will broaden their application window to make them more suitable for additional applications.

However, they are not a silver bullet that will solve all the problems of using and recycling plastic materials.

THE MODERN PACKAGING INDUSTRY

Drawing clear-cut boundaries around the packaging industry is difficult. Obviously, those actually manufacturing the physical package (cans, bottles, wraps) are part of the packaging industry. Their function is to take various raw materials and convert them (hence the general classification of this part of the industry as "converters") into useful packaging materials or packages. Viewed from this perspective, packaging becomes a materials application science.

In many instances, the company forming the physical package will also print or decorate the package. Thus, part of the printing industry and all its attendant suppliers is also viewed as part of the packaging industry.

Many user-sector companies, the firms that package products, are also regarded as part of the packaging industry. Package users can be divided into a number of categories, (See Figure 1.13) and each of these can be further subdivided. Each subsector has its own unique package design requirements.

The supplier sector, manufacturers of machines for the user sector and the suppliers of ancillary services, such as marketing, consumer testing and graphic design, are also important sectors of the packaging industry.

Serving these industry sectors are a large number of professional associations. Some are broad-based general-interest associations that cover the entire gamut of packaging concerns. Prominent among these are the Institute of Packaging Professionals (IoPP) and the Packaging Association of Canada (PAC). Other associations are more specialized in their packaging focus. Examples are the Packaging Machinery Manufacturers Institute (PMMI), the Flexible Packaging Association (FPA) and Association of Independent Corrugated Converters.

International packaging activities are often coordinated by the World Packaging Organization (WPO). The International Organization for Standardization

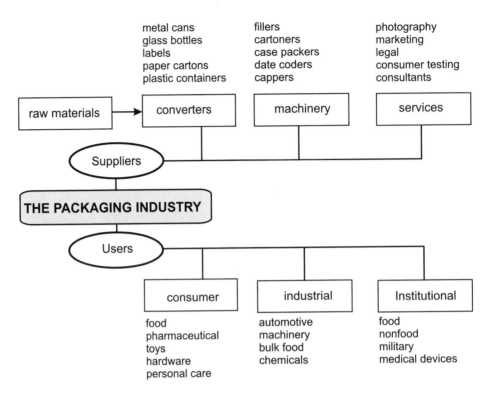

Figure 1.13

The packaging industry can be divided into those that use packaging for their products and those that supply to these users.

(ISO) is an international standards body that issues many international standards affecting packaging.

Some associations are not specific to packaging, but their activities are important to the packaging industry. The American Society for Testing and Materials International (ASTM) and the Technical Association of the Pulp and Paper Industry (TAPPI), for example, supply the bulk of material and package-testing procedures. The International Safe Transit Association (ISTA) is concerned with loss prevention and the safe transit of goods. The decisions of various retailing associations can also greatly impact packaging.

The industry is served by a large number of trade journals. Like associations, trade journals are either broadly based or more specifically focused on a particular package type, material, process or product category.

Lastly, the modern packaging industry is highly regulated. Added to the basic complexity of the industry are the jurisdictional complexities of the political world. Various aspects of packaging are governed by authorities ranging from the federal to the local, and it is not always entirely clear which authority has jurisdiction over a particular issue. Ensuring that all legal requirements are met can be an especially challenging task.

REVIEW QUESTIONS

1. Define "packaging."

2. Although packaging has existed from primitive times, the Industrial Revolution is generally considered as the time when modern packaging was born. What changes at that time lend validity to this statement?

3. What is the origin of the term "branding"?

4. Although there were earlier brand markings, the Quaker Oats brand mark set a new precedent in 1877. What was it?

5. As shops changed from specialized proprietor-owned outlets to today's large department stores, packaging needed to assume different roles. What were they?

6. What significant social trends and changes affected the way goods were packaged in the decades between 1950 and 1970?

7. Packaging plays a vital role in modern society. Explain the significance of that role for: a) food products and b) mass-manufactured durable goods.

8. Why is food loss so high in less-developed countries?

9. Why is the United Nations so interested in packaging?

10. What differences might you expect if you compared products and packages from developing countries with ours?

11. About what proportion of municipal waste is classified as packaging?

12. The four Rs are used as the guiding principles for managing the waste problem. What are the four Rs, in the correct order?

13. Give examples that illustrate the "recovery" item in packaging waste management.

14. What are the two major divisions within the packaging industry? Name two subcategories in each major division.

15. About what percent of the residential waste stream is plastic material?

16. Discuss the advantages of the cascade model for plastic usage.

17. Looking at the residential solid waste material mix (Table 1.1), we can see that nearly all residential waste is either recyclable or compostable. Why is this not so in practice?

18. The Quaker personage was one of the earliest uses of an imaginary person. How many other fictitious persons can you think of who were invented to represent a product or company?

19. Define "sustainability."

20. Discuss five conditions that are driving the need for sustainability.

21. What is a "life cycle analysis" (LCA)? Why is it important to use LCA when assessing the sustainability of a product?

22. What is implied by the "cradle-to-cradle" model?

Assignment

Benchmarking is a tool used to compare the effectiveness of a practice compared to a peer group. For example: How many grams of packaging is needed to hold one litre of drinking water? It is a way of identifying the best practice.

Choose a category with at least five competitors, and determine who has the best practice for that category. Note that the quantity of product contained has an impact on the amount of material that will be used. Some suggested categories are:

motor oil	household vinegar	shampoo	laundry detergent
bottled water	jam	spaghetti	

CONTENTS

Introduction

The four main functions of a package and definitions of different packaging levels.

The Contain Function

Considerations pertaining to the contain function of packaging.

The Protect/Preserve Function

Considerations related to the protect/preserve function. Examples of protective packaging problems, examples of preservation packaging problems.

Food Preservation

The nature of food, spoilage mechanisms, microorganisms and their preferred environments for propagation, extending shelf life by reduced temperature and freezing, thermal processing, water reduction, chemical preservation, modified atmosphere, irradiation.

The Transport Function

The transport function and examples of transport modes.

The Inform/Sell Function

Package communication roles, "persona," how a package communicates.

PACKAGING FUNCTIONS

INTRODUCTION

In Chapter 1, "Perspective on Packaging," the functions of a package were given as:

- Contain
- Protect/Preserve
- Transport
- Inform/Sell

When discussing packaging functions, keep in mind the different packaging levels:

Primary package	The first wrap or containment of the product that directly holds the product for sale.
Secondary package	A wrap or containment of the primary package.
Distribution package (shipper)	A wrap or containment whose prime purpose is to protect the product during distribution and to provide for efficient handling.
Unit load	A group of distribution packages assembled into a single unit for the purpose of mechanical handling, storage and shipping.

Figure 2.1 illustrates some of these levels. In addition, packages are often defined by their intended destination:

Consumer package	A package that will ultimately reach the consumer as a unit of sale from a merchandising outlet.
Industrial package	A package for delivering goods from manufacturer to manufacturer. Industrial packaging usually, but not always, contains goods or materials for further processing.

The basic packaging functions have different levels of importance depending on the particular packaging level and intended destination. It is common for several packaging levels to contribute to a single function.

The primary package for a breakfast cereal is the inner undecorated bag. Its main function is to contain and preserve the product, and to a lesser extent, protect it. The secondary package, a paperboard carton, provides physical protection, informs the consumer and motivates the purchase decision. Twelve cartons are packed into a corrugated shipping container to protect the product and to facilitate

Figure 2.1

Packaging can have many
levels. All levels of the
system must work together.

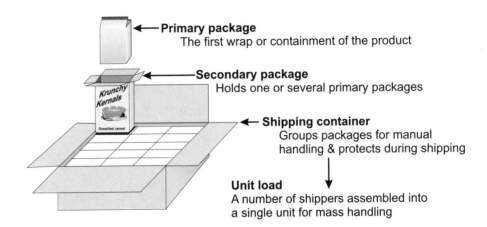

Primary package
The first wrap or containment of the product

Secondary package
Holds one or several primary packages

Shipping container
Groups packages for manual
handling & protects during shipping

Unit load
A number of shippers assembled into
a single unit for mass handling

manual handling and warehousing. The information printed on the corrugated
shipper primarily identifies the product for distribution purposes. Finally, corrugated shippers are assembled into a unit load, whose primary purpose is to
facilitate mechanical handling during distribution.

In some instances, a package will be required to assume all the functions. The
primary package for a power tool may be strong enough to protect the product
and withstand the rigors of shipping. This single package may feature all the
necessary information to inform and motivate the consumer.

Typically, the inform/sell function plays a less significant role in industrial
packaging.

THE CONTAIN FUNCTION

The first step in preparing a packaging design is to consider the nature of
the product and the kind of packaging needed to contain the product. These
considerations include:

- The product's physical form:

mobile fluid	viscous fluid	solid/fluid mixture
gas/fluid mixture	granular material	paste
free-flowing powder	non-free-flowing powder	solid unit
discrete items	multicomponent mix	

- The product's nature:

corrosive	corrodible	flammable
volatile	perishable	fragile
aseptic	toxic	abrasive
odorous	subject to odor transfer	easily marked
sticky	hygroscopic	under pressure
irregular in shape		

Throughout this discussion, we will examine the characteristics of various packaging materials and how their qualities influence effective containment packaging design.

THE PROTECT/PRESERVE FUNCTION

In the context of this discussion, "protect" refers to the prevention of physical damage, while "preserve" refers to stopping or inhibiting chemical and biological changes.

To provide physical protection, specifics on what will cause loss of value (damage) must be known. Specifics means knowing not only the general condition, but also a quantified measure of the level at which unacceptable damage starts to occur. (See Table 2.1)

Details of providing suitable product protection appear in Chapter 17, "Shock, Vibration and Compression," and to a lesser degree in Chapter 15, "Corrugated Fiberboard," and Chapter 16, "Distribution Packaging."

The preservation function most often refers to the extension of food shelf life beyond the product's natural life or the maintenance of sterility in food or medical products. Like the protective function, the preservation function needs to be defined and quantified. (See Table 2.2)

FOOD PRESERVATION

The Nature of Food

Food is derived from animal or vegetable sources. Its organic nature makes it an unstable commodity in its natural form. Left on their own, foodstuffs can deteriorate rapidly, sometimes becoming unfit for human consumption within

Table 2.1

Examples of protective packaging problems and concerns.

Condition	Quantification or Design Requirement
Vibration	Determine resonant frequencies
Mechanical shock	Determine fragility factor (drop height)
Abrasion	Eliminate or isolate relative movement
Deformation	Determine safe compressive load
Temperature	Determine critical values
Relative humidity	Determine critical values
Water	Design liquid barrier
Tampering	Design appropriate systems

Table 2.2
Typical preservation packaging problems and concerns.

Condition	Qualification or Design Requirement
Oxygen	Determine required barrier level
Carbon dioxide	Determine required barrier level
Other volatiles	Determine nature and barrier level
Light	Design opaque package
Spoilage	Determine nature/chemistry
Incompatibility	Determine material incompatibilities
Biological deterioration	Determine nature
Deterioration over time	Determine required shelf life

hours. Various means are used to increase the natural shelf life of foods, thus reducing dependence on season and location. To understand how the natural life of foodstuffs is prolonged, it is necessary to understand how food products deteriorate. Food spoilage can occur by three means: internal biological deterioration, external biological deterioration and abiotic deterioration.

"Internal biological deterioration" describes biological functions that continue even though the food has been harvested. Fruits continue to ripen and vegetables continue to respire. Fresh meat exhibits many of the processes associated with living tissue. For example, myoglobin, which gives meat its red color, continues to interact with atmospheric oxygen.

In some instances, internal biological factors are used to advantage. Fruit, for example, is often picked green or in a firm state; final ripening is a controlled process allowed to take place on the way to the market. Beyond a certain point, however, all biological activity will lead to spoilage and loss of product.

"External biological deterioration" refers to the action of microorganisms. What is food to us is also food to a host of other organisms. Molds, bacteria and yeasts are present in most foods. Often they are harmless and even beneficial. In other instances, they can be deadly.

"Abiotic deterioration" describes those changes that are chemical or physical in nature and that are not dependent on a biological agent. For example, atmospheric oxygen will chemically react with (oxidize) many substances. Vitamin C is no longer a useful nutrient once oxidized. Oxidized oils and fats have a rancid taste.

What is generally described as "taste" more correctly refers only to the sweet, sour, salty and bitter sensations that we detect with the taste sensors located on our tongue. Other mouth sensations are texture or "mouth-feel," temperature and chemical burning such as the effect of pepper.

We are also capable of detecting complex volatile substances, variously known as essential oils or "sensory active agents." We detect essential oils when minute quantities, in gaseous form, pass over sensors located in our nasal passages. Our sense of smell is highly developed, and we are capable of differentiating thousands of smells or aromas compared to the four tastes we detect in our mouths.

What we perceive as a food product's flavor is a combination of what we detect with our sense of taste combined with what we detect with our sense of smell. Because essential oils are volatile, they are easily lost through evaporation or oxidation. Preservation of essential oils retains the food's full flavor at retail.

Volatiles from outside the package can permeate a packaging material. Many food products are virtual blotters for any stray volatiles in the atmosphere. Absorption of even part-per-million quantities of undesirable volatiles can impart unpleasant odors and off-flavors to a food product. Contamination from improperly dried or cured inks and adhesives are common sources of this problem.

The above discussion addresses the importance of controlling the gain or loss of essential oils in food products. Similarly, it is equally important to retain essential oils in the many nonfood products whose appeal lies partly or entirely on the smells associated with that product. Perfumes, colognes and room fresheners are blends of pure essential oils. Most health and beauty aids such as cosmetics, soaps, shampoos and toothpastes also contain essential oils in their formulations.

Water vapor is similar to an essential oil in that it readily permeates many packaging materials. Moisture loss or gain can be a deteriorating factor, depending on the nature of the food. A snack food loses quality as it gains moisture while a cake loses quality as it loses moisture.

Temperature can promote undesirable changes that are abiotic in nature. The most common of these are the irreversible changes encountered when some fruits are frozen. The formation of ice crystals puncture the fruit's fragile cell walls, and the fruit loses its desirable character.

Meat Products

Meats are an ideal medium for microorganisms because they contain all the necessary nutrients to sustain growth. In addition to biological action, fatty tissue is susceptible to oxidation, and the entire mass can lose water.

Reduced temperature retards microorganism activity and slows evaporation and chemical reactions such as those associated with oxidation. At 0°C (32°F) and 85% relative humidity (R.H.), beef carcasses keep for about twenty-one days. Pork and lamb keep about fourteen days. Beef retail cuts on open display at 5°C (41°F) keep for one or two days. Proper packaging and storage of retail cuts can increase this to ten days.

An important marketing factor with red meat is the bright red color associated with freshness. This color results from different oxidation states of myoglobin. Fresh-cut beef tends toward a purplish red color that comes from a slightly oxygen-deficient state. Exposure to controlled amounts of oxygen produces the bright cherry red of oxymyoglobin so desired by the consumer in North America. (Consumers in most other countries do not have an aversion to beef that is not bright red.)

In fact, neither state is wrong. Since North American consumers prefer the bright red appearance, packagers use plastic films that allow the correct amount of oxygen into the package to maintain a bright red appearance.

Fish

The preservation of fresh fish is a difficult challenge because of three main factors:

- Psychrophilic bacteria may be present.
- Many fish oils are unsaturated and are easily oxidized.
- Typical fish proteins are not as stable as red meat proteins.

Chilling does not affect the activity of psychrophilic bacteria to the extent it does mesophilic types, so the "keeping quality" of fresh fish is limited. Frozen fish is typically kept at much lower temperatures ($-30°C/-22°F$) than other frozen foods to ensure the control of psychrophilic bacteria.

Produce

Harvested fruits and vegetables continue to respire and mature. Furthermore, they contain large amounts of water and will wither if water loss is excessive. No two fruits or vegetables are alike, and the rate at which biological and abiotic changes occur varies with the species. Peas, green beans and leafy vegetables have high respiration rates compared with those of apples, oranges and pears. Potatoes, turnips and pumpkins respire slowly and are easy to store. Moisture loss is more rapid with lettuce than with a turnip because of the large available surface area.

Most fruits have an optimum ripening temperature, usually about $20°C$ ($68°F$), and a threshold temperature that will prohibit ripening. Few fruits will ripen below $5°C$ ($41°F$). As a rule of thumb, a $10°C$ ($18°F$) temperature drop will typically increase shelf life by a factor of three (providing freezing is avoided). Freezing of many produce items will damage cell structure, and breakdown is very rapid after thawing.

The growth, maturation and ripening of a fruit or vegetable is controlled by various hormones and gases. Increasing the amount of carbon dioxide while reducing the amount of oxygen slows the respiration rates. However, some oxygen must always be present to keep the fruit alive. These techniques are used in modified atmosphere packaging.

Ethylene gas, produced by plant tissues, is associated with the ripening of many fruits, and its control is effectively used to retard or accelerate the ripening process.

Bananas are particularly sensitive to the atmosphere around them. However, they can remain in a mature but green state for up to six months in atmospheres of 92% nitrogen, 5% oxygen, 3% carbon dioxide and no ethylene. The bananas will ripen normally when transferred to "ripening rooms" containing a few parts per million of ethylene.

As the above brief discussion illustrates, atmosphere and temperature control are key requirements for extending the shelf life of fresh produce. Packaging for these products must be tailored to the individual product's needs, and trade-offs are necessary. The ideal humidity for most produce is about 90%. At these levels bacterial and fungal growth is greatly encouraged. Furthermore, sealed plastic bags are subject to condensation and wetting, which will only aggravate the problem. The compromise seen for many produce items is a perforated or vented plastic wrap. This allows respiration while providing for some containment and restraint to loss of moisture. Another option is to select packaging films with high gas-transmission rates.

Some recently developed plastic films have excellent moisture barrier and very low oxygen barrier. One application of this film is for precut salad bags. The high moisture barrier keeps bagged produce from drying out, while the good supply of oxygen allows the produce to respire naturally. The shelf life of precut salads packaged with this material is about ten days.

Barrier Packaging

We have noted that the movement of gases into or out of a package can lead to undesirable changes in the product. An important factor in the preservation of products that contain gaseous or volatile components or that are susceptible to change through the action of such components is the ability to control the movement of these gases and volatiles. (See Figure 2.2)

Stopping or reducing gas permeation requires barrier packaging. This packaging construction either retains desirable gases and volatiles inside the package or prevents undesirable gases and volatiles from entering the package. Often, barrier packaging must address both conditions. Of the materials a packager can choose from, only glass and metal provide absolute barriers to all gases and volatiles. While glass and metal are superior in this property, they have associated disadvantages, and packagers frequently seek plastic material alternatives. However, all plastics have a measurable permeability. The actual permeability varies widely depending on the plastic selected and the nature of the permeant gas or volatile. It is important to understand both the nature of the permeant and the properties of the candidate plastics. The term "high barrier" plastic is a relative, nonspecific term and should not be taken to mean "absolute" barrier. Furthermore since any given plastic can be a good barrier to some gasses and very poor to others, the term must be further qualified by identifying the gas to which the statement applies. Barrier properties of specific plastics will be further discussed in the chapters on polymer chemistry and plastics (Chapters 9 and 11) and flexible packaging (Chapter 14).

Barrier packaging is not always desirable. Fresh produce, for example, continues to respire after harvesting and would shortly consume all the oxygen in an oxygen-barrier package. This would lead to reduced shelf life. Plastic bags for

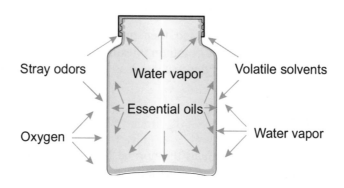

Stray odors

Water vapor

Volatile solvents

Essential oils

Oxygen

Water vapor

Figure 2.2

A barrier packaging material is one that slows down or stops the movement of selected gaseous substances into or out of a package.

produce commonly have vent holes punched in them to allow for a free exchange of atmospheric gases.

Microorganisms

A large part of food preservation depends on the control of microorganisms. These can be present in various forms. Bacteria or microbes are unicellular microscopic organisms that reproduce by splitting into two identical cells (binary fission). Bacteria grow exponentially and can divide as fast as every twenty minutes. Certain bacterial species can form spores that are highly resistant to killing.

Molds or fungi are multicellular and unicellular plantlike organisms. Neither is capable of producing chlorophyll or carbohydrates. Instead, they depend on outside sources for nutrients. Molds form filamentous branching growths called mycelia and reproduce by spores. Yeasts are similar organisms that reproduce by budding. The propagation and spread of molds and yeasts is typically slower than for bacteria because of the reproduction method.

Typical of any living entity, each microorganism type has a preferred environment in which to exist and propagate and other environments under which it will not. Manipulating the four principal environmental factors that regulate microorganism growth—temperature, moisture, acidity (pH) and nutrient source—controls or eliminates microorganisms. Microorganisms are often classified by their preferred reproduction environment, the most important being the following:

Mesophilic	Prefer ambient conditions, 20–45°C (68–113°F)
Psychrophilic	Prefer cool conditions, 10–25°C (60–77°F)
Thermophilic	Tolerate heat; will propagate at 30–75°C (86–167°F)
Aerobic	Need oxygen to propagate
Anaerobic	Propagate only in the absence of oxygen

Some microorganisms act only on the food. They or their by-products may change the nature of the food to either its benefit or detriment, but they do little harm when ingested. Pathogenic organisms, on the other hand, cause sickness or death. Pathogens fall into two basic classes:

- Those that produce harmful toxins as by-products in the food they infest. Examples of toxin-producing organisms are shown in Table 2.3.

- Those that infest the food and then grow in the human gut to produce illnesses. Examples of common infesting organisms are Salmonella, Shigella dysenteria, Staphylococcus aureus, and Escherichia coli.

Extending Shelf Life

Six basic methods are used to extend the normal biological shelf life of food. The methods are used alone or in combination. They are:

Table 2.3
Toxin-producing microorganisms and the illnesses they cause.

Organism	*Toxin-induced illness*
Clostridium botulinum	Botulism
Claviceps purpurea	Ergotism
Aspergillus flavus	Aflatoxin poisoning

- Reduced temperature
- Thermal processing
- Water reduction
- Chemical preservation
- Modified atmosphere
- Irradiation

Each method requires its own unique combination of packaging materials and technology.

Reduced Temperature and Freezing

Reducing temperatures below the ambient temperature has many beneficial effects that will lead to a longer shelf life. Doing so:

- Slows chemical activity
- Slows loss of volatiles
- Reduces or stops biological activity

While chilling a food product increases its shelf life, actual freezing provides the greatest benefits. Bacteria and molds stop developing at about $-8°C$ ($-18°F$), and by $-18°C$ ($0°F$) chemical and microorganism activity stops for most practical purposes. Freezing kills some microorganisms, but not to the extent of commercial usefulness.

Ice crystal formation is greatest between 0 and $-5°C$ (32 and $23°F$). Ice crystals can pierce cell walls, destroying the texture of many fruits and vegetables. Rapid freezing reduces this damage somewhat by reducing the size of the ice crystals.

Freezer conditions will cause ice to sublimate, and serious food dehydration, commonly known as freezer burn, will occur. Snug, good moisture-barrier packaging with a minimum of free air space will reduce freezer dehydration. Complete filling of the package is desirable because ice will sublimate inside the package, dehydrating the product and leaving ice pieces in the voids.

Frozen food package materials must remain flexible at freezer temperatures, provide a good moisture barrier and conform closely to the product. When paperboard is used as part of the package, it should be heavily waxed or coated with polyethylene to give protection against the inevitable moisture present in the freezing process.

Poultry packaging in high-barrier poly(vinylidene chloride) (saran) bags is an excellent example of an ideal freezer pack. Prepared birds, placed into bags, pass through a vacuum machine that draws the bag around the bird like a second skin. The tight barrier prevents water loss and freezer burn for extended periods, as well as preventing passage of oxygen that would oxidize fats and oils.

Thermal Processing

High temperatures will destroy microorganisms. The degree of treatment depends on the:

- Nature of the microorganism to be destroyed
- Acidity (pH) of the food
- Physical nature of the food
- Heat tolerance of the food
- Container type and dimension

In some instances, it is not necessary to kill all microorganisms. Pasteurization, a mild heat treatment of 60 to 70°C (40 to 158°F), kills most, but not all, microorganisms present. Pasteurization is used when:

- More severe heating would harm the product
- Dangerous organisms are not very heat resistant (such as some yeasts)
- Surviving organisms can be controlled by other means
- Surviving organisms do not pose a health threat

"Hot filling" refers to product filling at temperatures up to 100°C (212°F). Hot filling is used to maintain sterility in products such as jams, syrups and juices.

Some products can tolerate high temperatures but only for short time periods. Ultra-high temperature (UHT) processing of milk and fruit juices uses temperatures in the range of 135 to 150°C (275 to 302°F), but for a few seconds or less. The high temperature is enough to kill most pathogens but the exposure period is not long enough for chemical reactions that would alter food taste to occur. UHT is the basis of most flexible aseptic drink packaging. The term "aseptic" as applied to packaging has come to refer to any system wherein the product and container are sterilized separately and then combined and sealed under aseptic conditions. (See Figure 2.3) Metal cans were sterilized and then filled with puddings, sauces and soups (the Dole process) in the 1940s. In the 1970s, aseptic packaging was adapted to institutional bag-in-box systems.

Sterilizing package and product separately eliminates the need for the elevated temperatures and pressures used in conventional canning methods. Eliminating the need for extreme sterilizing conditions allows aseptic packaging materials to have lower physical strengths and lower temperature tolerance. Commercial systems, such as Tetra Pak, Combibloc and Bosch, use hydrogen peroxide to sterilize simple paper, foil and polyethylene laminates, and then the formed package is filled with UHT-treated product.

Several aseptic systems use the heat of forming plastic as a "free" sterilant. Thermoformed plastic containers can be kept sterile until after they are filled and

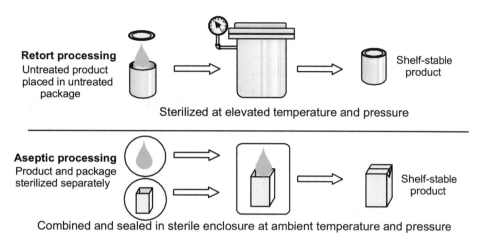

Figure 2.3
Conventional retort process (top) and aseptic filling process (bottom).

sealed. Sterile solutions are filled into blow-molded plastic bottles at the molding machine as a guarantee of sterility.

Unlike aseptic packaging, normal canning maintains only nominal cleanliness in the food and the can. After the food is sealed in the can, it is subjected to temperatures high enough to kill pathogens and achieve commercial sterility. Temperatures of 110 to 130°C (230 to 265°F) are typical. The actual cook time depends on many factors, calculated in advance to ensure commercial sterility. One of the most important factors is the rate of heat penetration to the farthest and most insulated portion of the product, usually the container's geometric center.

Sealed cans are an oxygenless environment. At pH levels above 4.5, conditions are conducive to the growth of Clostridium botulinum, a particularly dangerous anaerobic bacterium that produces heat-resistant spores. Generally, the less acid the food, the longer the cook times needed to ensure destruction of Clostridium botulinum. Foods with acidities high enough to prevent harmful pathogens from propagating can be heat-processed by immersion in boiling water.

Most canned-food cooking takes place in large pressure cookers, or retorts, that raise temperatures considerably above the atmospheric boiling point. Keeping food at these temperatures for a long time results in overcooking and gives some foods their "canned" taste or texture. Canning is not successful for many foods because the cooking cycle would produce objectionable changes in taste or texture.

Cans are subjected to alternating positive and negative pressure effects as they are heated and cooled. They suffer mechanical abuse, too. The rigorous temperature and pressure conditions needed to achieve commercial sterility restricted retorting to rigid metal cans and glass jars for many years. As flexible materials became more heat resistant and stronger, other constructions became feasible alternatives to rigid containers.

The retortable pouch is a laminate of poly(ethylene terephtalate), foil (for an oxygen barrier) and a heat-sealable polyolefin. Retortable pouch material is shipped in roll form, creating significant transport and storage savings. Since pouches can be as little as 12 mm (1/2 in.) thick, thermal processing time can be reduced, thus improving food texture and nutritional qualities. There are also attractive implications for waste disposal. Despite these advantages, North

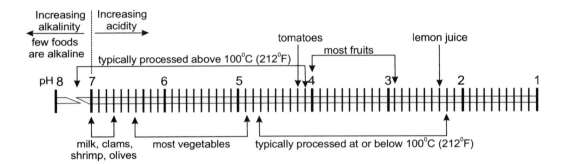

Figure 2.4

Food pH levels and typical related processing temperatures.

Americans have not readily accepted retort pouching. The largest customer is the military.

Figure 2.4 shows the pH level of a number of foods and food classes, along with the likely temperature processing ranges. Figure 2.5 shows the effect of temperature on molds, yeasts and bacteria.

Water Reduction

Drying is an old and well-established method of preserving food. The essential feature of drying is that the moisture content is reduced below that required for the support of microorganisms. An added advantage is less bulk and reduction of other chemical activity. Available moisture can be reduced by simple heat drying or, less obviously, by the addition of salt or sugar. Concentrated salt and sugar solutions tie up free water and make it unavailable to microorganisms. Jams and marmalades having high sugar contents do not require refrigeration for this reason.

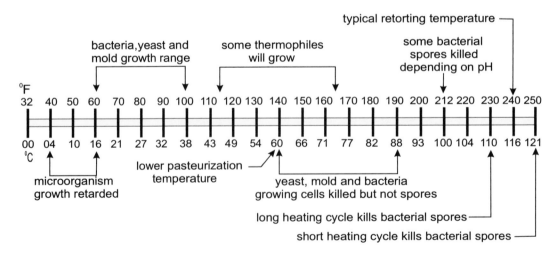

Figure 2.5

Temperature levels and the growth and destruction of microorganisms.

Figure 2.6

The equilibrium moisture content of a representative cereal product at three humidity levels.

In addition to managing moisture content as a method for controlling microorganisms, moisture control is important for keeping many foods at their most desirable moisture levels.

Most foods are hygroscopic and exist in a state of equilibrium with the relative humidity (R.H.) in the immediate atmosphere. If a food is sealed in a closed container (see Figure 2.6), the food will either gain or lose moisture until equilibrium with the moisture content in the air space is reached.

Equilibrium relative humidity (ERH) is the atmospheric humidity condition under which the food will neither gain nor lose moisture to the air. This value is often expressed as A_w, the water activity, defined as:

$$A_w = \frac{\text{food vapor pressure}}{\text{water vapor pressure}}$$

A food with an A_w of 0.5 will be at equilibrium at a relative humidity of 50%. Table 2.4 lists the moisture content and the desired ERH for some common foods. Sorption isotherms (a plot of food water content against ERH at a specific temperature) can be drawn to show the moisture contents of a food at any RH (See Figure 2.7)

Ambient R.H. ranges from very low to very high during the course of a year, and a food's moisture content will be changing continuously as it adjusts to the current R.H. However, the best mouthfeel for many foods is at a specific moisture content.

The snack food moisture content curve shown in Figure 2.7 shows food's moisture content over an R.H. range. However, usually the most enjoyable crispness, or mouthfeel, is when the snack food has a moisture content no higher than 5%. The curve shows that the snack will have a moisture content above 5%

Table 2.4

Representative moisture content and ranges.

Product	Typical Moisture	Percentage
Potato chips, instant coffee	3% or less	10–20%
Crackers, breakfast cereals	3–7%	0–30%
Cereal grains, nuts, dried fruit	7–20%	30–60%
Salt	75%	
Sugar	85%	

Figure 2.7

The moisture content of a representative snack food at various relative humidity levels. The most desirable crispness, or mouth-feel, occurs when the food has 5% or lower moisture content.

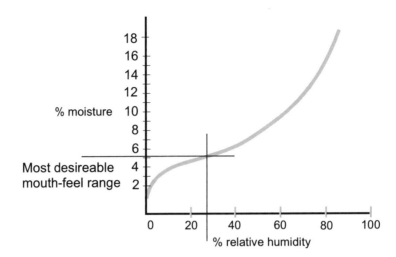

any time it is exposed to a humidity above 28%. A properly designed package for this snack food would seal the snack in a water-vapor barrier material that will keep the snack at a humidity below 28% until the package is opened for consumption.

The A_w for sugar is 0.85, which explains why sugar rarely cakes. Salt is somewhat lower at 0.75, and it does take up moisture on the most humid days. Both would present problems at conditions of 90% humidity.

Knowledge of a food's ERH or A_w provides a good indication of the package required by the food. Very low-ERH foods are hygroscopic and will draw available moisture from the air. These foods require a barrier package that will not permit the entry of atmospheric moisture.

Dried foods such as potato chips and instant coffee require a moisture content of 3% or lower and an E.R.H. of 10 to 20%. Since ambient relative humidity is rarely this low, there is a great tendency for these products to take up water. They require packaging materials with high moisture-barrier properties. Potato chips are also rich in oil (about 30%), so they also need a high oxygen barrier. In-package desiccants and oxygen scavengers are sometimes used to increase the shelf life of very sensitive products.

Dried foods with ERH values of 20 to 30% have less stringent moisture-barrier requirements and are easier to package. Depending on the food, oxygen or other barriers may still be needed. Many crackers, biscuits and breakfast cereals fall into this category.

Foods with an ERH of 30 to 60% can often be stored for long periods with little or no barrier packaging since their ERH corresponds to typical atmospheric conditions. Cereal grains, nuts and dried fruits are in this group. Again, if the food has a high oil content, an oxygen barrier may be needed. Bacteriological activity is rarely a problem with low- or reduced-moisture foods since one of the essentials of bacterial growth has been removed.

High-ERH foods lose moisture under typical atmospheric conditions. At first thought, it may seem that effective packaging would include a good barrier to stop the loss of moisture; however, a cake with an ERH of 90% would soon establish a relative humidity of 90% inside a sealed package, creating ideal conditions for mold growth. The packaging challenge is to control moisture loss, retarding it as much as possible, but not to the extent that a high humidity is established within the package.

Chemical Preservatives

Various natural and synthetic chemicals and antioxidants help to extend the keeping quality of foods. Generally insufficient by themselves, they are used in conjunction with other preservation methods. The use of most of them is strictly controlled by law, although what is allowed varies from country to country.

Chemical preservatives work in various ways. Some, such as lactic, acetic, propionic, sorbic and benzoic acids, produce acid environments. Others, such as alcohol, are specific bacteriostats. Carbon dioxide, found in beers and carbonated beverages, creates an acid environment and is also a bacteriostat. Smoking and curing of meat and fish is partly a drying process and partly chemical preservation. Aliphatic and aromatic wood distillation products (many related to creosote) are acidic and have variable bacteriostatic effects. Varying amounts of salt pretreatment accompanies most smoking.

Antioxidants and oxygen absorbers can reduce oxidation. Some oxygen absorbers have been used indirectly, contained in separate pouches within the sealed package. The absorber, usually a fine iron powder, scavenges any available oxygen still in the package. Oxygen absorbers may also be incorporated into the packaging material.

Modified Atmosphere Packaging

Ambient air is about 20% oxygen and 80% nitrogen, with traces of carbon dioxide and other gases. Altering these proportions alters product response. This is the basis of modified atmosphere packaging (MAP). For example, one mode of degradation is removed if a product prone to oxidation is packaged in an atmosphere free of oxygen. MAP involves the introduction of a gas mixture other than air into a package; that mixture is then left to equilibrate or change according to the nature of the system.

A related process, controlled atmosphere storage (CAS) is used in storage and warehousing where the atmosphere is continuously monitored and adjusted to keep the atmospheric conditions constant. The process is often referred to as controlled atmosphere packaging (CAP), but since it is a warehousing technique, the term is not technically accurate.

Vacuum packaging is one type of MAP. It has the effect of eliminating some or all oxygen that might contribute to degradation. However, the method is not universally useful, since products such as fruits and vegetables have respiratory functions that must be allowed continue. Another difficulty is that red meat will turn brown or purple without oxygen. Pressures created by the external atmosphere surrounding a vacuum-packaged product can physically crush delicate products or squeeze water out of moist products. Other types of MAP solve these problems.

Table 2.5 lists atmospheric combinations for some common food products. With few exceptions, MAP works with the atmospheric gases as follows.

Table 2.5
Typical modified atmospheres for selected food products.

Product	Oxygen	Carbon Dioxide	Nitrogen
Red meat	40%	20%	40%
White meats/pasta	—	50%	50%
Fish	20%	80%	—
Produce	5%	—	95%
Baked goods	1%	60%	39%

Oxygen is biologically active, and for most products, is associated with respiration and oxidation. Oxygen is normally reduced to slow down the respiration rate of produce and reduce oxidation activity. Red meat is the single exception, where high oxygen levels are used to keep the bright red "bloom" associated with freshness. Some oxygen is required in situations where anaerobic bacteria may be present in order to reduce the possibilities of propagation.

With most other meats, baked goods, pastas and dairy products, oxygen is reduced to the absolute minimum consistent with not creating an oxygenless atmosphere that would encourage the growth of anaerobic bacteria. Produce needs at least some oxygen to continue natural respiration.

Carbon dioxide in high concentrations is a natural bacteriostat. Levels of 20% and higher are used to create conditions unfavorable to most microorganisms. Carbon dioxide is highly soluble in water, creating a mild acid, and moist products can dissolve enough carbon dioxide to create a partial vacuum. In some instances, the resulting external pressure is undesirable.

Nitrogen, unlike the previous two gases, is biologically inert. Its solubility in water is negligible, and it is tasteless. Nitrogen is used as a "filler" gas or to displace oxygen.

Most packaging materials used in MAP for everything other than produce must have good gas-barrier properties to all three gases. This is true even if the package does not contain the gas. A package containing only carbon dioxide and nitrogen is a system where atmospheric oxygen is trying to penetrate the package and establish an equilibrium partial pressure. The integrity of all seals is of paramount importance.

The natural respiration of a fruit or a vegetable consumes oxygen and produces carbon dioxide and moisture. Ventilated or low-barrier packaging is needed to ensure a supply of oxygen and to rid the package of excess moisture.

MAP has increased natural shelf life by two to ten times. Cooked pasta, for example, will keep for up to twenty-one days in an atmosphere of 50% carbon dioxide and 50% nitrogen. The atmosphere used must be tailored specifically to the food item and the type of package being used.

Irradiation

Radiation is energy categorized by wavelength and includes radio waves, microwaves, infrared radiation, visible light, ultraviolet light and X rays. These types of radiation increase in energy from radio to X rays; the shorter the wavelength, the greater the energy. Given sufficient energy, waves can penetrate substances. With more energy still, they will interact with the molecules of the penetrated substance.

Short-wavelength radiations have enough energy to cause ionization of molecules, mainly water. Ionization can disrupt complex molecules and leads to the death of living organisms. Enzymes, vitamins and other similar complex molecules can also be destroyed. Excessive exposure will produce enough chemical changes that the taste of food or the chemistry of an enclosing container will be altered.

Irradiation has been used to increase the keeping quality of various foods. Cobalt 60, a radioactive isotope, is the principal source of ionizing radiation (gamma rays). Since the cobalt source is radioactive, it must be shielded with about 1.8 meters of concrete and lowered into a pool of water when not in use. All safety precautions pertaining to radioactive hazards must be observed. It should be noted that while the energy source is radioactive, gamma rays cannot make other substances radioactive. Irradiation is a unique process in that it is carried out at ambient temperatures and can penetrate packaging materials or products.

Low irradiation doses have been used to reduce microbial or insect populations. In addition, irradiation has been found to inhibit sprouting in onions and potatoes and delay opening of mushroom caps. A common use is to reduce microbial loadings on such heat-sensitive items as herbs and spices. In addition to treating food, gamma rays can sterilize packaging materials. A significant proportion of hospital supplies are sterilized with gamma irradiation.

Not all packaging materials are sufficiently stable for higher levels of gamma treatment. Polystyrene and polyethylene can tolerate high exposures. Poly(vinyl chloride) discolors (brown) and with extended exposure may start to decompose and release chlorine. Glass is also prone to browning. Paperboard products lose mechanical strength and polypropylene becomes brittle.

In another application, light irradiation induces cross-linking in some polymers to yield tougher films, some of them with attractive heat-shrink properties.

Irradiation of consumable food is an issue that is not fully resolved, and the process is carefully controlled in most countries. Critics argue that irradiation causes chemical change and that we are unsure of prolonged effects of consuming irradiated food. Proponents reply that normal heat processing also causes significant chemical changes in a food whose details we are also unsure of, but that this has never been viewed as a problem. On this basis, food irradiation is prohibited in some countries and highly regulated in most. However, the use of irradiation to achieve sterility for medical devices, packaging materials and personal care products does not present a problem and is a useful technology.

Labeling is another contentious issue. The irradiation symbol (see Figure 2.8) must be accompanied by a statement such as "treated by irradiation" or "irradiated." The term "ionizing energy" is being touted to replace the more dangerous sounding "irradiation." Some claim that the design of the irradiation symbol is misleading.

Canada has given product clearances for irradiation of potatoes, onions, wheat flour and spices. The United States has given product clearance for potatoes, wheat flour, spices, fresh fruit and vegetables, pork, chicken, ground meats and

Figure 2.8

The international food irradiation (radura) symbol.

dehydrated vegetables. Israel and the Netherlands have the broadest range of food irradiation clearances.

THE TRANSPORT FUNCTION

The transport function entails the effective movement of goods from the point of production to the point of final consumption. This involves various transport modes, handling techniques and storage conditions. In addition to the general physical rigors of distribution, there are a number of carrier rules that will influence package design. Examples of some of the information required to design successful distribution packaging appear in Table 2.6.

Transportation and distribution is generally regarded as an activity that is hazardous to the product being moved. In many instances, the stresses that the product will experience are greater than the durability of the unprotected product. In such instances, it will be necessary to design additional packaging to isolate or cushion the product from the external forces.

Packaging contributes to the safe, economical and efficient storage of a product. Good package design takes into account the implications of transport and warehousing, not just for the distribution package and unitized load, but for every level of packaging.

Preparation of goods for effective transport and warehousing appear in detail in Chapter 16, "Distribution Packaging."

THE INFORM/SELL FUNCTION

The communication role of packaging is perhaps the most complex of the packaging functions to understand, measure and implement because of the many levels at which this communication must work. Laws and customs dictate certain messages, without much leeway in their presentation. Examples of such messages are:

- Specific name of the product (what is this?)
- Quantity contained
- Address of the responsible body

Table 2.6

Typical transport, handling and storage information.

truck	rail	aircraft
cargo ship	storage duration	storage conditions
handling methods	unitizing methods	specific shipping unit
weight considerations	stock picking	dimension limits
carrier rules	environmentally controlled storage	

However, to promote the contained product effectively, a package must appeal to the potential customer at all levels. A good package creates a "persona," or personality. If the designer has done an effective job, that persona will appeal to the targeted audience.

The targeted audience itself needs to be identified and studied. This is the realm of demographics and psychographics.

The package itself communicates by many channels such as:

- Selected material
- Shape and size
- Color
- Predominant typography
- Recognizable symbols or icons
- Illustrations

A brand of peanut butter aimed at family consumption might come in a plastic tub with a snap-on lid. The text may simply state that it is an economy peanut butter. The tub would have minimal or no illustrations. A gourmet peanut butter, on the other hand, would more likely come in a glass jar with an old-fashioned-looking screw-on closure. The label would have an upscale name in a carefully selected old-fashioned font. Features such as embossing or gold stamp printing would further promote the gourmet persona. The whole package might be offered in a wooden box or wicker basket. Similar products, two totally different packaging treatments and resulting personas.

All of the communication channels must balanced and supportive of one another to produce a persona with appeal and instant recognition. All supporting material, such as promotions and advertisements, must agree with the image projected by the package.

Developing the information and incorporating this information into a package's surface design is the subject of Chapter 3, "Graphic Design."

Producing a well-balanced package persona requires an intimate familiarity with not just the structural qualities of packaging materials, but also the emotional qualities that they project. A thorough understanding of the various printing processes and the specialized decorating techniques used to create particular effects or decorate unusual surfaces is essential. These topics appear in Chapter 4, "Package Printing and Decorating."

REVIEW QUESTIONS

1. Name the four principal functions of a package.

2. Define primary package, secondary package and distribution package.

3. Containment is a primary packaging function. List 12 product characteristics that will affect your choice of material and package design.

4. What conditions or events might cause physical damage and loss of value? Where are these conditions likely to be encountered?

5. In providing for the protect/preserve function, it is essential to know and quantify what factors?

6. Describe two biological spoilage mechanisms.

7. Give three examples of food-spoilage mechanisms that are not biological in nature.

8. In most food packaging, we try to eliminate or reduce oxygen levels. There are, however, three situations where we would want the presence of oxygen. What are they?

9. Microorganisms are controlled by manipulating four conditions. What are they?

10. What is an essential oil? Why is it necessary to preserve essential oils?

11. What specific protection must be given to extend the keeping quality of oily foods?

12. Why are some vegetables never found in a can?

13. What MAP gas can act as a bacteriostat?

14. Why aren't high water-activity foods packaged in high-barrier materials to prevent them from drying out?

15. Name the six ways of extending the natural shelf life of foods. For each of the methods, briefly note the mechanisms by which the keeping quality of a food product is increased.

16. What are the gases used in controlled-atmosphere packaging?

17. Why is it difficult to extend the shelf life of fresh fish?

18. What is meant by the term "barrier material"?

19. What is an essential difference between a mold and a bacteria?

20. What is a characteristic of microorganisms that are: mesophilic, psychrophilic, thermophilic, anaerobic and aerobic?

21. One anaerobic bacterium is of special concern to humans. What is it, why is it of such concern and in what packaging type is it most commonly found?

22. What is a pathogen?

23. What are the levels of food heat treatment, and where are they used?

24. What does the term "aseptic packaging" describe?

25. A cake will lose quality by drying out, yet we never put a cake into a high-moisture barrier package in order to extend shelf life. Why not?

26. A particular food has an Aw of 0.3. What does this mean, and what kind of package might this suggest to you?

27. What is one purpose behind vacuum packaging of cheese and prepared meat products?

28. What are the advantages of a retortable pouch?

29. What details are needed to provide good design information for creating distribution packages that will provide for efficient handling, transport and storage?

30. What is a unit load?

31. A package communicates in many ways besides the actual written text. Name six avenues of communication.

32. What is meant by the "persona" of a package?

33. What are the advantages of aseptic processing of food?

34. What two packaging materials offer absolute barrier properties?

35. List five means by which a package communicates its persona to the observer.

CONTENTS

Introduction

Technical and communication roles compared.

Demographics and Psychographics

Importance of having demographic and psychographic information, definition of psychographics, examples of psychographic population groups. Example of demographic/psychographic study of shopping habits. Package features that appeal to consumers, knowing the competition's targets, strengths and weaknesses.

The Retail Environment

A sea of choices, the final confrontation is between consumer and package, how long you have to motivate a purchase decision, merchandising methods. Changing loyalties, shopping habits, merchandising methods.

Fundamental Messages

The three messages: what is this, what is it going to do for me, who guarantees this? Real and imagined points of difference, the importance of point-of-difference messages, examples of points of difference for modern shampoos. "All new" and "old-fashioned" points of difference.

Equity and Brand Names

Definitions of equity and icons, leading brand names, examples of contrived brand names that failed.

Color

The first thing an observer sees, color and emotions, how color influences perception, cultural associations.

Graphic Design Basics

Basic design elements, balance and unity, direction, proportions. Examples of good and poor graphic organization and dominance. Typography principles, uppercase and lowercase, serif and sans serif, font choice, persona.

Package Design and Marketing Studies

New product launches. Focus groups, recall, findability, eye tracking, S-scope methodology, example of S-scope study, virtual reality.

GRAPHIC DESIGN

INTRODUCTION

The objective of any package design is to realize the strategic objectives that will sell the product.

A package design is composed of two separate components:

- The structural component encompasses the features and characteristics that fulfill the package's technical and physical requirements: containment, protection/preservation, convenience and the qualities that facilitate transport and distribution.

- The graphic component encompasses the features and characteristics that attract and inform the consumer and motivate a purchase decision. A great part of this concerns surface decoration, although form, material and shape can be equally important.

Structural and graphics components must compliment each other in order to produce a holistic (the end result is greater than the sum of the parts) and coherent form. While this chapter is going to discuss the graphic images portrayed on a package, the physical shape and the choice of material are very important factors in establishing a believable persona.

For example, a peanut butter positioned as a no frills economy product might come in a plastic tube with minimum graphics. In no way could this presentation be positioned as an upscale product. If the corporation elected to offer the peanut butter in airport boutiques as a gift item for busy executives returning home, a completely different approach would be needed (See Figure 3.1).

The plastic tub would be replaced by a glass jar. The label would be in rich colors with possibly special effects such as embossing, metallic trim and so on. It wouldn't just be "peanut butter" but rather gourmet peanut butter and be supported by phrases such as Old South, Grandma Lee's, or Authentic Carter Family Recipe. The closure might have a gingham cloth held on with a ribbon, or have a ribbon across the closure held on with a wax seal. All of these would serve to increase the perceived value of the contained product.

Attention should be given to the product prior to any consideration of the package design. No amount of clever packaging will sell a product that the

Figure 3.1

A basic packaging treatment for an economy grade of peanut butter and one for an upscale presentation of the same product.

consumer does not want. Sophisticated graphics and misleading statements may motivate a first purchase, but once the consumer realizes that the contained product is inferior to the claims, it is the last sale that will be made.

A packaging graphic project starts with a clear definition of what the package is supposed to achieve:

- With what product
- At what targeted demographic/psychographic audience
- In what marketplace
- By what means
- Against what competition
- In conjunction with what other activities

The overall guiding plan is formalized in a formal planning document. (For example see packaging design brief, Chapter 20). The graphic designer must have amongst other information:

- A clear description of the goal
- A schedule of the identified icons that must appear and can't be changed
- A schedule of all legally required information
- A clear positioning statement (who is going to buy this product and why)
- An identified unique selling proposition statement
- A clear understanding of the market in which the product competes
- A clear understanding of the competition's positioning
- Graphic constraints related to printing

This chapter provides an overview of the information and methods used to create packages that successfully communicate information to the potential buyer.

DEMOGRAPHICS AND PSYCHOGRAPHICS

For correct structural design, we need to know facts about the product and the physical world that it will encounter. Designing correct communication requires, first of all, an understanding of the intended receiver of the communication.

Consumption habits and motivations of targeted audience segments are different, sometimes dramatically so. It is important to understand who a package design is supposed to appeal to and the best manner in which to motivate a purchase decision in that targeted audience. Information about the consuming public usually falls into the realms of demographics and psychographics.

Demography is a numerical count of how many of us there are in specific, easily quantifiable classifications. Much demographic information is derived from a country's national census and might include such information as:

gender	age	occupation
residence	cultural background	ethnic background
education level	marital status	family size
socioeconomic status	geographic factors	religious beliefs

Packaging is always anticipating tomorrow's market, and demographic trends are the first place to look when trying to anticipate future packaging needs. One major demographic trend is the "graying of America." The average age of a North American is slowly increasing. In the 1970s the population was mostly under 30 years of age. Today most of the population is older than 30, and with the highest percentage of retirees ever. There is a continuing trend to smaller family size and an increase in single-parent and nontraditional family households.

Some demographic trends can be difficult to project. For example, North American birth rates are low, and a significant part of the population growth comes from immigration. Simply saying that there will be a large ethnic market is not useful. The specific influence these newcomers will have on living, working and consumption habits must be determined.

Broad demographic categorizations, while useful, are rarely enough to identify a group with similar motivational triggers. Not all 26-year-olds are interested in, or motivated by, the same thing.

Psychographics is the study of how groups of people are motivated and how they behave. Unlike demographics, it is not a precise study. Psychographic terms are common in everyday usage, although they are often not recognized as such. When we say "redneck," "yuppie," or "baby boomer" we are identifying a real or imagined group of people who supposedly have a characteristic behavior.

Recent terms used to describe modern population groups include the DINK family. "Double income no kids" describes the older baby boomer. The kids are gone, the mortgage is paid, both partners work and draw a good professional salary. In short, they have a high disposable income with accompanying purchasing habits. GIZIGI describes the modern approach to dining: "grab it, zap it, gulp it." Modern eating on the run has also been described as grazing and as having "eating episodes."

There is a continuous effort to identify tomorrow's hot trend or an unfulfilled need. The objective is to discover the purchasing preference or need of a significant consumer block. Many studies seek to identify behavioral patterns that may help in the design of packaging that will appeal to specific groups.

An example of psychographic groups is in a study by the Grocery Products Manufacturers of Canada (GPMC). The study identified five major characteristic attitudes and behavioral patterns in terms of eating habits and nutrition. The five groups, and each group's percentage of the total population, are:

Laissez-faires (18%)

- Not concerned with nutrition. The lowest interest of the five groups in nutritional labeling.

- Not worried about additives or calories, and they are not into "natural."

- Eating habits are driven by taste rather than concern for a balanced diet. In short, they eat whatever they feel like eating.

- They are snackers, and balanced meals are not a priority.

- Most rate ease and convenience of preparation very high.

- The group tends to be younger and most have children.

- Express more concern about what their children eat than about their own eating habits.

Mature moderates (17%)

- The group is older; it is likely that laissez-faires grow up to be mature moderates.

- Don't find nutritional labeling interesting, but are more careful of what they eat than the laissez-faires.

- More health conscious than weight conscious. Not unduly concerned about sugar or calories, and don't generally buy low-calorie products.

- Fiber, salt, preservatives and pesticides are what this group watches.

Three squares (21%)

- Have a commonsense approach to eating.

- Committed to three square meals a day and have a strong desire to avoid snack foods.

- Very concerned about the eating habits of their own—and everybody else's—children.

- After freshness and taste, they are most concerned about additives, preservatives, pesticides, salt content, vitamin content and mineral content.

- Of the five groups, they are the least likely to buy a low-calorie product.

Fat phobics (22%)

- Concerned about their appearance.

- Strongest interest in nutrition, but primarily to avoid high-calorie and high-fat foods. They are big purchasers of calorie-reduced products.

- Not concerned about food additives and certainly don't question additives such as aspartame. Fat, sugar, cholesterol and calories are top concerns.

- To some extent they are willing to give up good taste in order to restrict calories.

- Expressed the greatest concern of the five groups about what children eat.

Trend trackers (22%)

- Typical trend trackers are 25 to 44 years in age.

- The "all-natural" group ... or whatever else is in style.

- Nutrition is the important current topic for trend trackers but they are all talk and no action.

- Seventy-five percent want to see lists of ingredients, preservatives and additives.

- Will pay more for natural food products.

- At the same time, they place less emphasis on the need for nutritionally balanced meals.

- Readily admit to eating too many snack foods.

- Follow nutrition issues, but their own eating habits are open to question.

Another example of psychographic groups emerges in a study by Yankelovich Partners. The study compiled the following eight adult life-style categories:

- Stressed by life   Parents with heavy burdens.

- Up and comers   Young, upbeat and childless. The largest Gen-X group and likely to tell the marketers what to do.

- Young materialists   Cynical, single, think money equals happiness.

- New traditionalists   Upscale, family oriented, progressive: they set the agenda for boomers.

- Family limiteds   Parents totally concentrated on their families.

- Detached introverts   Successful but lonely geeks.

- Renaissance elders   Mature, enjoying life, have deep pockets.

- Retired from life   Mature, uninvolved. They hear you knocking but you can't come in.

Obviously, each of these psychographic groups would be looking for different information on a package and would be motivated to a purchase decision—or discouraged from a purchase decision—by the received information.

The public's mood can be difficult to define, and apparent psychographic trends should be carefully analyzed. It would appear, for example, that there is a great desire amongst the majority of the population to have environmentally friendly packaging. Various surveys have suggested that upwards of 90% of the population would give purchasing preference to packages made from recycled material, or that they would be willing to pay more for more environmentally responsible packaging. In practice, this has proved not to be the case. "Bright greens," those willing to change habits and spend extra time and money in aid of environmental beliefs, appear to be a minority.

In addition to basic demographic/psychographic information, there is other information about the consumer that is essential. At first sight these other pieces of the motivational puzzle do not seem to be related to demographics/psychographics. However, they are affected by the relationship between the product and the way the consumer views it. Packagers need to ask:

What is the preferred purchase unit? Is this an impulse item? Is it a seasonal purchase? Is it a durable good? A staple item? A gift item?

Facts about how the product is used can also be helpful in determining the extra features that will attract a potential customer's attention. Packagers need to evaluate:

easy opening features	reclosure features	dispensing features
measuring aids	table packs	attractiveness level
instructions	cautions	disposal methods
use quantities	returnable packages	secondary uses
storage methods	special features	environmental status

Since your package will be in direct competition with other brands for the consumer's attention, you must know almost as much about your competition as you do about your own product.

target markets	strengths	weaknesses
package types	unit	sales volumes
market share	pricing structure	marketing strategy

Targeting a market dominated by a single large competitor serving a population with high brand loyalty is a high-risk venture. In many instances, selling to a smaller niche market not served by the major players has proved to be a good strategy. Better to have 90% of a small market than fight for 2% of the large market.

THE RETAIL ENVIRONMENT

The modern retail establishment is a sea of choices. A food supermarket can have upwards of 40,000 products on display, each one clamoring for the consumer's attention. Hardware outlets may have even more items. It is said that the typical consumer sees fewer than 100 of these and leaves the store with about 14.

Individual products present an equally astonishing number of choices. A supermarket may have upwards of 100 different hair care preparations and 50 varieties of potato chips. The challenge facing the package designer is this: How do I get my potato chip bag, the 51st offering on the shelf, to be seen? And if my chip bag is seen, how do I convince the viewer that, with 50 other choices, my brand is the one to purchase?

The only medium left to influence the purchase is the package itself. Regardless of advertisements and promotions outside the store, the final confrontation is between the consumer and the package. Depending on the information source and the nature of the product, between 68 and 80% of purchase decisions are made in the store while the consumer is facing the product itself.

Furthermore, today's consumer rarely has a specific shopping list. The shopper scans aisles for general classes of products or simply cruises the aisles for ideas that trigger impulse buys. Measurements suggest that a product has the consumer's attention for about seven seconds. In this time it must convey a message that will motivate a purchase decision.

Cluttered graphic designs and contradictory messages cannot deliver the buying message in those critical seven seconds. Such products are simply not seen by the potential purchaser. And unseen is unsold.

There are many merchandising methods, and the specific method or methods by which you deliver a product to the consumer will have bearing on the final design:

self-serve	sales clerks	pegboard display
shelf display	mail order	vending machine
door-to-door	warehouse outlets	department stores
specialty stores	inspection before purchase	

Merchandising methods and the way consumers relate to products are undergoing rapid change. National brand loyalty has been dropping significantly. The image of many store brands has changed from that of the second-choice economy option to as good as or better than the national brand at a better price.

UPC codes and computers have put an enormous bank of information in the hands of savvy merchandisers. They have instant access to what is selling and what is not. This instant wealth of information on purchasing habits and trends has given retailers the power to tell suppliers what is needed, rather than simply accepting what is offered.

FUNDAMENTAL MESSAGES

What is the very first thing shoppers want to know about a package when their eyes comes across a package on a market shelf? The answer to this question is simpler than most people would suppose. What if a shopper actually spent seven seconds on every package in a store having 18,000 stock-keeping units (SKUs)? It would take 35 hours to get out of the store. Shoppers do not go to a store to read, and so the most important first item of understanding that must be delivered in a flash is:

What is this?

Recognizing that the shelf is displaying 100 varieties of shampoo is only the first part of the story. For many products, a consumer cannot recognize a tangible difference in the performance of the product itself. Often, it is the package that must provide the tangible difference. The customer needs information on which to make a purchasing decision. With a hundred options clamoring for the customer's attention, the customer will want to know:

What is it about this product that makes it better than the others?

Or maybe more specifically: "What are you going to do for me?" This point is variously known as "the significant point of difference" or "the unique selling proposition." It is the statement that differentiates one product from another.

A last factor that may contribute to the purchase decision is the answer to the question:

Who guarantees that?

In some instances a highly respected company or brand name may influence the purchase decision.

Designers use these messages in various proportions, depending on the nature of the product.

The first message, What is this? (the chord of familiarity), is the single most important element. The consumer must be able to instantly recognize what he or she is looking at. Direct common names are the most familiar. For example:

alkaline batteries   rice   paper clips   light bulbs   cough medicine

Appropriate chords of familiarity are especially important with new products. They give consumers a reference point on which to base an understanding of the product. For example:

glue stick (not office helper, magic stick, etc)
solid paint (not easy-wipe, spread-on, Gerry's Easy Paint)

Some products have established brand names that have become synonymous with the product. Procter & Gamble's Tide package for example, states that it is a detergent in the smallest possible letters simply to meet the legal requirement. The brand name alone identifies it.

The second message, What is it going to do for me?, is the point of difference. Consumers must recognize some benefit or virtue that will come to them if they purchase the product. In a choice of 12 different kinds of rice, the chord of familiarity is "rice." The points of difference that characterize them might be:

instant rice	long-grain rice
added vitamins rice	Cajun-style rice
rice and tomato	free recipe book with this rice
win a trip to Florida rice	famous person eats this rice

Without a point of difference, your product is just another package on the shelf.

Stringent rules cover the adjectives that can be used with common names in order that the consumer not be misled. The following terms, for example, suggest specific virtues:

Organic strawberry jam	all natural strawberry jam	pure strawberry jam
Fresh orange juice	orange drink with real juice	orange drink
Diet bread	no sugar added	lite
Chocolate milk	chocolate drink	chicken soup

The virtue implied by the point-of-difference statements may be real:

Vitamin-enriched apple juice	long-life light bulbs
Biodegradable garbage bags	instant soup mix

The virtue may also be purely imaginary. Perfumes and cosmetics are sold on the basis of romance. A popular breath mint implies that you will get kissed. A cigarette brand is sold on a "macho man" basis. (Ironically, the macho cigarette was originally promoted as a "ladies" brand.) Table 3.1 lists some point-of-difference statements that have been made for shampoos.

Note that the stated points-of-difference listed for the shampoos in Table 3.1 are not specific; the meaning is left for the customer to decide. For example, what does "deep-cleaning" actually mean? What is the definition of "frequent use?" What is it about the "continentals," the "Swiss" or the "Aussies" that makes their shampoo better? The answer is "whatever you think." These decisions are invariably based on emotional interpretations rather than facts or observable performance differences.

Some beverage advertisements imply that users of their product will partake in a particular life-style. Other images deal with insecurities or a desire to be part of a group. Hence, there are products that are endorsed by media stars, royalty, sports figures and just about anyone who can lay claim to fame.

Table 3.1

Examples of "point of difference" statements that have been made for shampoos.

Stated Difference	Presumed Appeal
Dry hair formula	Consumers who think their hair is dry
Gives extra body	Consumers who think they need extra body
For stressed hair	Consumers who think they have stressed hair
For fine hair	Consumers who think they have fine hair
Medicated formula	Consumers who think they have a hair problem
Scalp treatment	Consumers who think they have a scalp problem
Continental formula	Consumers who think Europe is more sophisticated
Frequent-use formula	Consumers who wash every day, or twice a day or whatever
Herbal shampoo	Consumers who believe in plant power
Replenishing formula	Consumers who believe something is missing
Deep-cleaning shampoo	Consumers who think they get extra dirty
Oily hair shampoo	Consumers who believe they have oily hair
Aussie formula	Consumers who believe Australians know something we don't
Swiss formula	Then again, maybe the Swiss know the secret
Papaya moist	Consumers who believe the tropics have it
Removes build up	Consumer who believe something is building up in their hair

"All New" and "Old-Fashioned" are two popular images used to sell product, both invoking unspecified product qualities. Products tend to be associates with one or the other, and market studies may be needed to determine which describes the persona of the product as the consumer understands it. Declaring a wine as a "new, improved formula" is not likely to inspire a purchase decision from a dedicated wine lover.

"All New" and "Old-Fashioned" messages need not be delivered in text. Quality wine labels are examples of presentation that suggest tradition and old-fashioned values. Many upscale products create old-fashioned personas by using older or even technically obsolete packaging materials and forms. Wooden presentation boxes, metal biscuit boxes, lightning-style bottle closures and woven vegetable-fiber baskets are examples of upscale treatments that can be found in almost any boutique or gift store.

A final message that may be used successfully—"Who guarantees this?"—is the name and reputation of the maker:

Kellogg's Corn Flakes	Clorox Bleach	Kodak Ektachrome 200
Nestle's Cocoa	Campbell's Soup	IBM Computer

A serious homemaker is much more likely to try a new household cleaner by Clorox than one labeled Dr. Plum's All-New Heavy-Duty Cleaner. Similarly, the consumer is more likely to try a new food offering by a reputable national company.

Not all companies use their name as a selling aid. Most pharmaceuticals are known only by their brand names. (Quick, who makes Tylenol and Alka Seltzer?) In other instances the name becomes the purchase rationale: witness the success of the many clothing designers who have lent their names to products, and the rush to get endorsements from any Olympic gold medalists or any other sports hero of the day. Hollywood stars tend to be avoided as product endorsers on account of their marked tendency to become involved in scandalous behavior.

Inexperienced companies often place their vanity on the package, giving major prominence to their company or personal name, when in fact the name has no significance to the purchaser.

The three basic messages are used in various proportions and can be delivered by text, graphics, shape or color. The weight given to each message and the medium through which the message is delivered should be determined by careful and thorough market research. Particular care must be given to keeping the messages consistent in choice of the package structure, graphic presentation and advertising message.

EQUITY AND BRAND NAMES

Over time, certain products and companies have built superior reputations. Typically such products have graphic elements or icons that the customer easily identifies and relates to, hopefully, in a favorable way. These may be the company name itself, a brand name, a symbol, a typographic style, a color or color pattern or any combination of these.

Kellogg's "K," Coca-Cola's bottle shape and color pattern, Campbell's soup's red-and-white label, the Heinz "tombstone" logo and McDonald's golden arches are icons that can be identified long before any text details can be recognized. Such icons are said to have equity. Equity is built by establishing a reputation for consistently good product and service over a long time period. Icons are highly recognizable symbols that have major motivational impacts on a consumer's purchasing decision. Icons with high equity are carried on new product lines in order to immediately establish the heritage and trust.

Brand names can have a great deal of equity and this equity can be an invaluable purchase motivator. Some of today's valuable brand names are:

Anacin	Ajax	Ritz	Oreos
Maxwell House	Marlboro	Tide	Band-Aid
Tylenol	Realemon	Elmer's	Drano
Bufferin,	Cheerios	Kleenex	Kotex
Jell-O	Perrier	Quaker Oats	WD-40

Established brand names are valued possessions. The Coca-Cola trademark is probably worth as much as the company's other assets. Great care is taken to protect such names with trademarks or copyrights. Brand names, icons or any other representations may not create the impression that they have some real or implied relationship to another company or brand. At its lowest level, some companies will produce identical or counterfeit products passing themselves off as the real thing. This of course is a criminal offence.

Others are more subtle in their presentations and walk a very fine line between what is acceptable and what is legally an offence. The packages illustrated in Figure 3.2 are clearly different and yet the house brand on the right suggests that it is essentially the same composition as the national product. The house brand is

Figure 3.2

While clearly different in design the house brand on the left effectively communicates that it is similar to the national brand but at substantially lower cost. Another example is The Crispy Rice brand positioned against the Rice Crispies brand.

always shelved next to the national brand so that it is easy to see that the house brand is almost half the price of the national brand.

High equity brands are treated more generously than national brands. A purchaser who tries Elmer's Cola because it costs less than Coca Cola and finds that it is rather flat tasting, will never buy another bottle of Elmer's. But if a customer finds that the Coca Cola seemed rather flat, they presume that perhaps the closure was slightly loose and would still remain loyal to the brand.

Good brand names describe a virtue of the product or invoke some image. Clever names don't work; the public will not be talked down to. These brand names were doomed from the moment they hit the shelf:

Greese-off (a dishwashing product)
I Hate Peas (French fries made from peas)
Gorilla Balls (vitamin-enriched malt balls for athletes)
Fluff-off (static cling eliminator)

In a world that sometimes seems obsessed with "New!" it is easy to forget that some top brands have been that for a long time. (See Table 3.2.) Two other 1925 leaders, Hershey and Colgate, have yielded top positions to Mars/M&M and Crest, but still command a respectable market.

It is a mistake to invent brand names for new products and attempt to sell them solely on that basis. "Turbo-dyne" may be a dynamic name invoking modern

Table 3.2
Market leaders from 1925 that are still in a leadership position today.

Product	Company or Brand
Bacon	Swift
Dessert	Jell-O
Batteries	Eveready
Biscuits	Nabisco
Breakfast cereal	Kellogg's
Gum	Wrigley
Mints	Life Savers
Paint	Sherwin-Williams
Razors	Gillette
Shortening	Crisco
Soap	Ivory
Soft drinks	Coca-Cola
Canned soup	Campbell's
Tea	Lipton
Tires	Goodyear

imagery, power and so forth, but "turbo-dyne" means absolutely nothing to a consumer until identified as spark plugs, a car-wash detergent or a computer game. Selling on the virtue of a brand name can succeed only if the name is promoted by a substantial advertising and promotional campaign. The cost of establishing a new brand name nationally can be $100 million and more.

COLOR

Color is the first thing an observer notices about a package. It is recognized before shape, and the graphic or text content is recognized last. As such, color is one of the most important motivators of a purchase decision.

Color evokes an emotional response from the observer. Color is associated with moods, feelings, places and things. That we relate color to emotions is evidenced by the use of colors to describe particular emotional states. We say we are "feeling blue," "saw red," are "green with envy," had a "purple rage" or are in a "black mood." Red, orange, yellows and brown shades are "warm" colors, while greens and blues are "cool" colors. (See Table 3.3)

Color has weight, size and movement. Generally, brighter colors will appear larger than darker colors in bars of the same size. A yellow circle tends to move or radiate outward, while a blue circle conveys inward movement.

Color can influence perceptions such as size, quality, value and flavor, to name a few. To demonstrate differences in product perception based on color alone, matched groups of people were asked a number of questions about crackers. The crackers were actually identical, the only difference being the package color. Package color was shown to have a significant influence on perception of flavor. (See Table 3.3)

Color has ethnic and social associations. For example, in some Asian countries white is the color of mourning. Green and orange combinations, rarely used in North America, are common in India, as they are the national colors. Red, white and green combinations are used on packages trying to create an Italian flavor.

Table 3.3
Color and flavor perception. (Source Opatow Associates Inc.)

	Package Background Color	
	Red Shade	Yellow Shade
Far too much flavor	13%	2%
A little too much flavor	11%	7%
About right	66%	50%
Not quite enough flavor	5%	23%
Not enough at all	3%	18%
Not sure	2%	0%

Although there is some tendency for colors to come in and out of fashion, certain colors tend to dominate the marketplace. A supermarket check will show a predominance of reds, browns and blues and an almost total absence of purple.

There are few universal rules when deciding on what colors to make a package. For every stated rule for selecting colors, a package can be found that successfully defies the rule. Suffice it to say that colors must be selected to represent the persona of the package design and the perceptions of the targeted audience.

GRAPHIC DESIGN ELEMENTS

A complete graphic design must communicate a mass of information on many levels (See Figure 3.3). Some information such as product descriptor, contents, manufacturer's domicile, National Drug Codes, ingredient lists and nutritional information is legally required and in many instances their location on the package is specified. Depending on the product, the legally required information will vary. The designer has the challenge of fitting the company's promotional messages in amongst the required text.

A packager works with basic design elements to create the desired package appearance:

Shape	The actual package outline, or the outline of an illustration or body of text. Be aware of positive and negative shapes. Length-to-width proportions of 2:3 and 3:5 are the most pleasing. Length-to-width proportions of 1:1 and 1:2 are boring.
Size	How large or small the object or design is. Size can be physical or perceptual.
Color	Color can attract attention and affects the moods or persona of the package. Color can also add expense to the package.
Texture	Perceived or real smoothness or roughness. It involves the sense of touch. Consider the difference between a plastic bag and a paper bag. Texture can be created using graphic patterns or textured substrates.
Tone	The lightness or darkness. Darker colors appear heavier than lighter ones.
Line	Lines can be straight or curved, heavy or light, rough or smooth, continuous or broken. Certain line orientations can create different feelings: Horizontal: calm Vertical: dignity Diagonal: vitality Curved: grace Converging: distance shadows: suggest volume
Icons	Graphic design elements or symbols that convey meanings or messages. The most important icons are those that have equity.

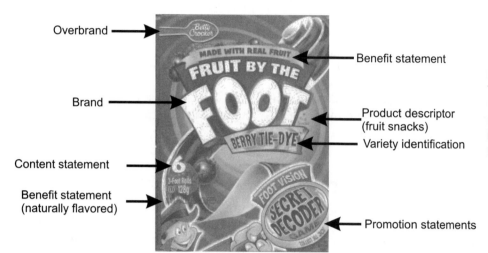

Overbrand

Brand

Content statement

Benefit statement
(naturally flavored)

Benefit statement

Product descriptor
(fruit snacks)

Variety identification

Promotion statements

Figure 3.3

In addition to the information on the front panel, other panels carry the company's domicile, the UPC code, ingredient list, nutritional information, a kosher symbol, an Olympic logo and use instructions.

Design principles are used to organize design elements into a composition having balance and unity. They apply to each element and to the design as a whole. A composition is a specific arrangement of design elements.

BALANCE AND UNITY

Each element of a composition has an optical weight. Lightness, darkness, size, shape and color control weight. The designer must recognize optical weight and be able to determine when two elements are balanced.

In addition, the following considerations contribute to a package's balance and unity:

- Symmetrical or formal balance centers elements geometrically. The elements of one side of the vertical center are repeated on the other, Symmetrical balance is easy but rather formal, although it can sometimes be used to create a particular persona.

- Asymmetrical or informal balance arranges elements by optical weight from left to right.

- Weight must be correctly distributed vertically. The bottom is normally given more weight to avoid a top-heavy look. This can be done optically by having lighter colors at the top and darker colors at the bottom. (A panel's optical center is slightly above the geometric center.)

- A theme or mood can create unity. This includes color, typography, substrate material and so on. A border can be used to create unity, but borders can act to reduce optical size.

- All elements must tie together in a sense of harmony or belonging. (Gestalt or holistic: the whole is greater than the sum of the parts.) Every element has to fit so that if one part is removed, it will be missed.

- White space can be a "negative" design element. If there is too much white space inside the design, it "falls apart." Use it around the outer edges. However, white is a common element in pharmaceutical packaging where it is associated with cleanliness and sterility.

- The combined elements must unite to create a persona. The created persona should match the psychographic/demographic profile (persona) of the targeted customer.

DIRECTION AND DOMINANCE

In Western society, people see things in a set order: top to bottom, left to right, large to small, black to white, color to no color and unusual to usual. Designs like A in Figure 3.4 that break up the normal flow of reading are not likely to be as readily identified as design C. Good organization can lead the eye from one element to the next.

The designer can control eye movement and can direct the eye in a circular path, diagonally or whatever. Designers direct the observer by using real or implied lines. Pictures have a direction in which they face, almost as an arrow does. Borders can sometimes be used to contain several items and mass them into one element.

Packages must be kept simple because they typical modern consumer will not spend the time to hunt through busy or cluttered designs. Designs should have one dominant element that stands out from the rest of the design. This element can be emphasized by being larger, brighter, darker, faced in a different direction or anything else that will single it out from the background.

When designing product packages for a range of sizes, it's best to design the smallest size first. It's much easier to scale up to a larger size than to compress a large design down to a smaller facing.

In Figure 3.5, the design on the left gives major prominence to "Frank's," not likely to be a significant purchase motivator in this instance. In the normal order of reading, "Enjoy a cup every day" is also given prominence, although the reader may still wonder what is going to be enjoyed. Actual product identity is given less importance, and a significant point of difference is relegated to the

Figure 3.4

Design A interrupts the normal reading pattern by splitting the text with a product illustration. Design B reduces the perceived size of the illustration, and detracts from it, with a framing device. Design C is clean and uncluttered.

A

B

C

Figure 3.5

Examples of a poor (left) and a good (right) arrangements of text messages.

bottom of the package. The improved design (right) gives major prominence to the product identity and its point of difference.

Single design examples might look good on the designer's monitor screen, but they should also be reviewed in real or simulated displays (See Figure 3.6) The candidate designs should also be compared with the competitor's offerings in similar real or simulated display settings.

TYPOGRAPHY

There are a great many typographical fonts from which to choose. However, for some applications, such as logos and trade names, a unique design will be prepared.

The basic fonts can be classified as serif and sans serif, and for most packaging purposes, sans serif fonts are preferred. (Serifs are the small, decorative extensions at the ends of a line.) Serif fonts have fine lines that tend to fill during printing, particularly with reversed-out printing of text. (See Figure 3.7, right side) A larger serif font size could overcome this problem somewhat.

Another font category may be loosely described as the decorative fonts. Such fonts are usually designed to project a certain character or mood. Script fonts, for example, may be considered as feminine or romantic, and they are popular for personal care products. Elaborate script fonts can be difficult to read; relatively simple script designs in a larger size are preferred. Figure 3.8 shows a number of type treatments designed to convey a message beyond the actual textual message.

Figure 3.6

Actual on-the-shelf displays sometimes create unfortunate color or incomprehensible word patterns (left) that may confuse or make reading difficult. The right-hand design is preferred.

Figure 3.7

Examples of (top to bottom)
sans serif, serif and script
fronts. At the right is
reversed-out type.

SANS SERIF FONT

SERIF FONT

SCRIPT FONT

The following considerations are important when deciding on typography for a package:

- Typography must match the persona of the package and product. Each typographical style carries its own persona and message.

- Dominant typography must be readable from the normal observer distance at the point of recognition. For a retail display, this may be several feet.

- The population contains a significant number of people who are functionally illiterate and a large number who should wear glasses when shopping but don't. Text and typography should be selected with these facts in mind.

- Be cautious of reversed-out type, particularly on poor-quality substrates where ink tends to fill in. If reversed-out type must be used, increase its size and select fonts with wide strokes that won't fill in during printing.

- Avoid using text over illustrations or color areas that do not have enough contrast over some or all of the area to make the type readable.

- Avoid long stretches of small type. The optimal line length for easy readability is about 39 characters. Use columns to break up long lines.

- Uppercase does not necessarily make a message easier to read. (See Figure 3.9)

- In some situations, such as the U.S. Food and Drug Administration's "Drug Facts" rules, typography is determined by regulations.

- Text and illustrations that cross over package joints or seams may be difficult to register. (See Figure 3.10)

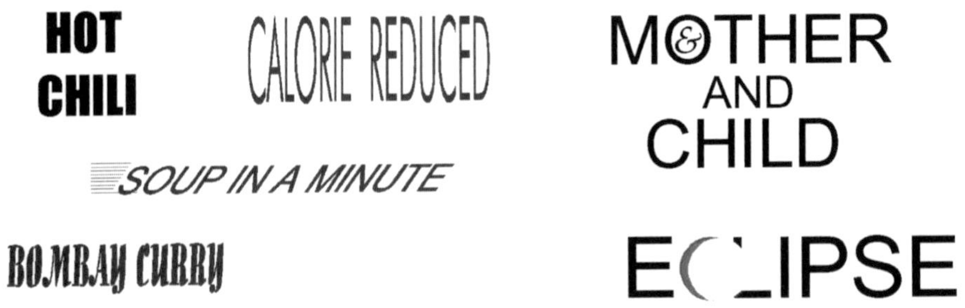

Figure 3.8

Typography can be
designed to communicate
more than just the word
itself.

HOT CHILI

CALORIE REDUCED

M&THER AND CHILD

SOUP IN A MINUTE

BOMBAY CURRY

ECLIPSE

ALAYTMINIOM
Alaytminiom

Figure 3.9

Typographic styles must be chosen for legibility. Long, unfamiliar words are generally easier to read in lowercase. (Source: H. Bossard.)

PACKAGE AND MARKETING STUDIES

Numerous reports have discussed the risks of a new product launch. Although the numbers and experiences vary, they are clear on one thing: launching a new product is a high-risk activity. One general rule of thumb says that for every 100 new products that development time is spent on, only ten make it as far as test marketing (a limited offering in a few locations to assess consumer response). Of these ten, five get a full commercial launch, and only two survive beyond a few years.

Katrina Carl of Mark Oliver Inc. reports that 58% of new product launches fail because the consumer cannot recognize a significant point of difference between the new product and an existing one. A further 32% failure is attributed to poor product positioning. Product performance accounts for only 12% of the failures. The obvious message is that designing a good package presents a greater challenge than designing a good product.

There are several methodologies used to evaluate a package design's effectiveness, each of which has its strengths and limitations. Understanding exactly what you are looking for is key to selecting the correct methodology.

Whatever the methodology, care must be taken to remove all bias in communicating with prospective buyers. Words and questions must be carefully chosen.

- The dictionary meaning is not necessarily the emotional meaning. (A "cheap" computer is not the same as an "economical" computer.)

- Response to the question "Would you be interested in a vacation in the Greek Islands?" will be different than to "Would you spend $4,899 for a vacation in the Greek Islands?"

- Leading questions must be eliminated. ("Would you be willing to pay a few cents more if this package was made from recyclable material?"

Figure 3.10

Graphics and text must take package seams and closures into account. Avoid arrangements with text or drawings that cross a joint, such as in the example at left.

elicits a positive answer from most people, but it is not necessarily true at the point of sale.)

- Response should be primarily emotion-based rather than a reasoned. Most purchasing decisions are made at an emotional or intuitive level. They are rationalized after.

Responses should be numerical to remove any word ambiguity.

- Numerical data can be tabulated and averaged as necessary. Word answers cannot. How would you tabulate "fair," "good," "average," and "OK"?

- A preferred question format would be "Rank the (appearance, brand name, design, environmental friendliness, price, etc.) of the exhibited designs on a scale of 1 to 10."

- An indirect way of doing the same thing would be: "Arrange the order of the five samples according to how much you think they cost."

Select your panelists carefully. They must represent some demographic/psychographic group that has relevance to your product and package.

- A panel of college students will tell you they associate mushrooms with pizza. The folks at the retirement home associate mushrooms with soup.

- If you want to evaluate the design of a computer software package, then your panelists should own computers.

- If your design objective is to take market share from the dominant category leader, your panelists should be users of that leader's product.

There significant regional differences that must be taken into consideration for any market or package design evaluation

MARKET AND PACKAGE EVALUATION METHODOLOGY EXAMPLES

Here are some of the most commonly used methods of evaluating the marketing effectiveness of packaging:

- **Test market auditing:** The actual product is offered for sale in selected regions and outlets. It is an expensive process that is sometimes hard to control and hard to interpret. (The product didn't sell ... I wonder why?). Test marketing is usually done after other more precise studies are completed. For example you would use a focus group rather than a test market study to evaluate a brand name.

- **Mall intercepts questioning:** These are usually very subjective and do not offer many opportunities for objective package design information.

- **Focus group:** Focus groups are selected panels that are assembled to discuss, rank, evaluate and otherwise consider some subject at hand. They are useful for gathering general broad-based information and for judging the overall appeal of a package design.

- **Recall questioning:** One recall methodology shows panelists a picture of a marketplace shelf with an assortment of product. After a brief observation period, the panelists write down the product names they can recall. Recall questioning is good for judging a package design's shelf impact, but won't tell you what you should change.

- **Findability tests:** There are several approaches to findability testing. A broad-based test might measure the time it takes a subject to locate a product in the store. This version is useful for determining where a product should be displayed (Where did the subject go to look for dried tomatoes?) as well as finding it on the shelf. The more specific test would time how long it took a subject to locate a specific product when in the general product area. (In the breakfast cereal section, find a box of Jordan's Harvest Crunch.) The latter is a form of shelf impact evaluation.

- **Eye tracking studies:** Unlike the previous methodologies, eye tracking can be used to judge the individual elements of a package design. Eye tracking uses instrumentation that can follow exactly what the eye is focusing on when observing an individual package design. When looking at a package, the observer's eye will immediately focus on some design element and then wander over the package, pausing on some elements and skimming over others. The subject is not conscious of these actions. In subsequent recall questioning, the subjects have poor recall of elements where the eye skimmed rather than paused. Eye tracking provides detailed information on individual design elements and their placement. Similar procedures can be used viewing a full product shelf. Eye tracking has the advantage of being objective rather than subjective and of being able to provide information on the relevance of individual design elements.

- **S-scope studies:** S-scope studies are similar to eye-tracking in that they provide detailed information on the individual graphic design elements. Subjects are shown an image of the package, flashed at 1/100-, 1/50-, 1/25-, 1/10- and 1-second intervals. After each interval, the subject notes what they have recognized. For example, at 1/100 of a second, the subject may have seen a "red box." The averaged results provide a good understanding of the order in which the information is received and sometimes what information is not noticed.

S-scope study of the Hardwood Hills cereal package (See Figure 3.11) showed, among other things, that a subdued background image of a log cabin was hardly noticed even after a one-second observation. The new design increased the visibility of most graphic elements by eliminating this background component and increasing the prominence of the company's name with a diamond-shaped

Figure 3.11

An S-scope study on a
cereal package design and
a redesign. (Information
from H. Bossard Design.)

Original
package
design

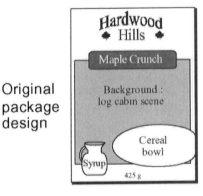

Hardwood Hills - Maple Crunch	
Element	**1 Sec.**
Company name	53 %
Bowl	42 %
Cereal	56 %
Maple Crunch	49 %
Maple leaf	06 %
Pitcher of syrup	13 %

First
redesign

Hardwood Hills - Maple Crunch		
Element	**1 Sec.**	**Up by**
Company name	70 %	17 %
Bowl	75 %	33 %
Cereal	80 %	24 %
Maple Crunch	32 %	-17 %
Maple leaf	20 %	14 %
Pitcher of syrup	20 %	07 %

framing device. Although only one maple leaf was used rather than two, its location at the very top of the design gave it increased visibility. The Maple Crunch flavor identifier was reduced in visibility because of its location at the bottom of the package.

Even though the redesigned Hardwood Hills package improved the visibility of the most graphic elements, the analysis does not actually determine whether a package design is good or bad. It only determines the order in which we recognize graphic elements. For example, even though the company's name had a 17% visibility increase, this would only be a benefit only if the name had a high enough equity value to influence a purchase decision. Since Hardwood Hills makes a number of different Harvest Crunch flavors, the loss of prominence of the flavor identifier would make it more difficult for the customer to select their favorite. And finally, the absence of a definitive point-of-difference statement—for example, "Made with all-natural maple sugar"—makes the product just another "nothing-special" cereal product on a crowded shelf.

Virtual Reality

Designers are able to create virtual reality scenes on their screens that simulate what the product will look like on a shelf surrounded by other products. There is value in this capability but it should be understood that the word "virtual" in this context means "almost real", that is, not the real thing.

Many leading retailing organizations have simulated stores in which they duplicate the display shelving, access aisles, sight lines and lighting of an actual store. These provide a good opportunity to see proposed packaging in a real three-dimensional environment.

Actual test marketing with real product in cooperating retail outlets is the final test before a national market launch. Such test market studies would normally be done in five or so locations, each representing some regional difference. As well as providing sales numbers, test markets provide information that can be used for associated advertising campaigns. Final decisions on a national launch are based on the results of these studies conducted in the real world.

1. A total package design is made of two separate components. What are they, and what are the primary roles played by each component?

2. Define demographics and give six examples of demographic information. Where might you find demographic information?

3. Define psychographics and give examples of psychographic information.

4. Why is psychographic/demographic information important to a package designer?

5. Consider a breakfast cereal package designed to appeal to each of the shopping patterns described in the GPMC Study. What design elements, icons, colors and other information would go on a package designed to appeal to each of the described shoppers?

6. What percentage of purchase decisions are made by consumers in the store while considering product choices? About how much time do you have to deliver a motivation to purchase?

7. What are the two main messages that the consumer always looks for? What third piece of information might have a major influence on a decision to purchase?

8. Explain the importance of having an effective point-of-difference message.

9. How can the basic communication message be delivered to the viewer?

10. Define equity and icon.

11. What is the first thing a consumer notices about a package?

12. What is the human observer's typical relationship to color? Give examples.

13. Give examples of attributes that are influenced by color.

14. What design elements does a designer manipulate to create a final package presentation?

15. What is meant by the term "persona" and why is the concept important in package design?

16. How does a typical Western person "read" a package?

17. What errors might we make if we do not perceive the package as it might be displayed in groups?

18. What is the difference between serif and san serif fonts, and which is more common in packaging?

19. Describe some good practices when selecting a package's typographic components.

20. Market studies can take many forms. Discuss methodology of the following methods and the kind of information generated: Focus groups, recall questioning, findability tests, eye tracking and S-Scope studies.

Assignments

Assignment 1 Competing Retail Designs

1. Bar soap (for example Dial, Irish Spring, Zest, Dove and others)

2. Beer

3. Hair shampoos as sold in large grocery chain stores

4. Prepared breakfast cereals (for example corn flakes, Wheaties, Rice Krispies)

5. Cooking oil, as sold in large grocery chain stores. Note the sizes as well as the brands.

6. Potato chips, party pack size, as sold in large grocery chain stores.

7. Adhesives for wood as sold in a hardware store.

8. Vitamin Pills

9. Women's or men's perfumes or colognes

10. Ground coffee brands

11. Ice cream brands

12. Spices and condiments

13. Toothpastes

14. Vinegar as sold in large grocery chain stores.

Select a product category from the above list. For that category: determine how many choices the consumer has in a typical shopping environment. List the product names as far as is practical. Note the price ranges within which the product sells.

Submit a report outlining the unique selling proposition of three products selected to represent a variety of approaches, or targeted at different demographic/psychographic groups. In considering the targeted buying group, you may need to refer to advertising and promotional material as well as the physical package. How are the "points of difference" and icons used? What can be said about the brand's equity? Typography and color should be mentioned where it plays a significant role. What persona does the whole package design project?

Be prepared to give a five-minute verbal summary of your findings. You should have samples or photos of the packages you will be focusing on.

Assignment 2 Package Design Assessment

Locate a package that you consider to be poorly designed. Poor design may relate to graphic components, structural components or both. Bring it or a photograph of it to class, and be prepared to give a 5 minute oral presentation on this package on how you might improve the design.

CONTENTS

Introduction

Objective, definitions of printing and decorating as used in this text.

Color

Human perception, what the eye actually detects, sensitivity, electromagnetic spectrum, additive synthesis, subtractive synthesis, hue, brightness, value, saturation. Viewing color, light source, graphic arts light standard. Reproducing color, pigments.

Artwork

Line art, color selection, continuous-tone and halftone illustrations, screens and color density, typical screen ranges and applications. Process printing, primary process colors, creating infinite color ranges, steps in process printing, moiré patterns, key color.

Preparation for Printing

Prepress work, keylines or mechanicals, color bleeds, trapping, number of plates needed for basic process printing, where additional plates are used, registration.

Proofing

Purpose of prepress proofs, differences between digital and analog proofing, examples and applications of common proofing methods.

Printing Methods

Relief (flexographic), lithographic, gravure. Printing presses, general components and configurations, web-fed and sheet-fed presses, printing stations. Process selection factors.

Relief Printing: Flexography and Letterpress

Definition of relief printing, nature of the plate, rubber and photopolymer plates, general characteristics and applications of flexography printing, typical printing deck, stack and central impression press configurations. Applications and limitations.

Lithography

Basic principles, printing plates, typical lithography station, characteristics, applications.

Gravure Printing

Basic principles, gravure cylinders, typical station, characteristics, applications.

Comparing Flexography, Lithography and Gravure

Identifying the printing method, flexography strengths and limitations, lithography strengths and limitations, gravure strengths and limitations, press types and typical packaging applications, wet ink thickness.

Other Package Decoration Techniques

Reflective metallics, heat transfer and hot-stamp printing, embossing, gloss, reverse printing, laser marking, ink-jet printers.

Printing Dimensional Packages

Letterpress and offset letterpress, stencil or screen printing, applications and limitations; pad printing.

Labeling

Cut and glued-on labels, pressure sensitive labels, shrink sleeves, in-mold labeling.

PACKAGE PRINTING AND DECORATING

INTRODUCTION

The objective of package printing and decorating is to consistently create a visibly identifiable image for a large number of impressions. Printing or decorating requires the ability to separate image and nonimage areas. This is done with a printing plate; the various printing or decorating methods are named after the nature of the printing plates used. Many techniques and variations have been developed. For the sake of this discussion, these techniques have been divided into two groups:

- "Printing," in the context of this discussion, will refer to flexography, lithography and gravure—the methods that account for the vast majority of all packaging graphic art. Each of these methods has a number of variations.

- "Decorating" is used to describe a number of special methods such as screen printing, hot-foil stamping, embossing and pad printing. In volume, these methods account for a small proportion of packaging graphic art. However, each can create decorative values not available by the mainline methods or can decorate substrates not readily decorated by other means.

Color is an important visual element of package design. Since the majority of package printing concerns the development of colored images, this discussion will start by reviewing the basic physics of color.

COLOR

The Electromagnetic Spectrum

The electromagnetic spectrum is described as a wave phenomenon. Waves at the long end of the spectrum are used in radio broadcasting and radar. Infrared radiation, perceived by the human body as heat, is shorter and is the region immediately before visible light. Visible light describes that part of the electromagnetic spectrum perceived by the human eye, and is about midpoint in the wave spectrum between infrared and ultraviolet. (See Figure 4.1)

Ultraviolet, the next shorter wavelength after violet, is not detected by the human eye. X-rays are shorter yet, and powerful enough to penetrate matter and expose photographic plates. Gamma rays are powerful enough to disrupt molecular structures. They are used to eliminate microorganisms in some food products and ensure sterility of many hospital supplies.

Color Perception

The eye is a complex organ that receives light and sends stimuli to the brain for interpretation. Color perception, therefore, depends on the eye's receptors and the psychology of how the brain interprets the message. We "see" with our brains, not with our eyes.

The normal human eye has a retinal structure with individual receptors sensitive to red, green and blue parts of the spectrum. (People who are said to be color blind have reduced sensitivity in one or several color receptors.) As well as detecting differences in wavelength, the human eye is thought to have a separate function that determines brightness or contrast levels. Any color in the spectrum can be matched by combining these stimuli in the proper proportions.

The human eye can differentiate several million colors. The problem of verbal color communication can be appreciated when you consider that there are only about a dozen specific color names. Furthermore, we have no "color memory." We can recall telephone numbers and recite poetry, but our color memory is vague. At best, we can recall the general name of a color and perhaps qualify it as light blue or greenish-blue, but we could never walk into a paint store a week later and precisely match a previously observed color.

The human eye does not detect all colors equally. Sensitivity falls off at either end of the visible spectrum. Yellows are the brightest colors to the human eye. The greatest perceived contrast is between black and yellow, not black and white, as might be supposed.

Perceived color depends on the proportion of stimulation given each color receptor. When all receptors are fully and equally stimulated, we experience the sensation of "white." If no receptors are stimulated, we experience black, the absence of color. (For convenience, black is called a color.)

Additive Synthesis

Additive synthesis describes the addition of different light wavelengths to create a new color. (See Figure 4.2) Thus, if a red light and a green light were projected onto a white screen, the overlapping area would appear yellow. The various combinations of the three primary additive colors—red, green and blue—are as follows:

> Blue + green = cyan
> Red + blue = magenta
> Red + green = yellow

Cyan, magenta and yellow, the products of additive synthesis, are the three primary process colors used in color printing. Other colors are produced by manipulating these three colors.

Color television screens use additive synthesis. The picture tube has separate generators for blue, green and red light. The eye receives and mixes them according to the laws of additive synthesis to give the entire color spectrum.

Table 4.1

Colors produced when different wavelengths are subtracted from white light.

Absorbs	Reflects	Color Seen
Red	Blue and green	Cyan
Blue	Red and green	Yellow
Green	Blue and red	Magenta
All wavelengths	Nothing	Black

Subtractive Synthesis

Subtractive synthesis (see Figure 4.3) is the synthesis of printing inks where colors are produced by subtracting wavelengths from white light. Subtractive synthesis is achieved by using pigments that have the ability to subtract or absorb certain wavelengths while reflecting others. Thus a transparent cyan ink printed over a transparent yellow ink will appear green; the yellow ink printed over a transparent magenta ink would appear red; and magenta printed over cyan would appear blue. All three colors overprinted would subtract almost all wavelengths and would appear almost black. Subtractive synthesis is further illustrated in Figures 4.4 through 4.6.

A colored object is one that reflects some wavelengths but not others. (See Figure 4.5) Thus, if an object absorbed all the green light waves and reflected back only the red and blue components, then by the rules of subtractive synthesis, the observer would see magenta. A cyan object is one that will absorb all red components, and reflect those that combine to give the sensation of cyan. Similarly, yellow is produced when blue is absorbed and red and green are reflected. Table 4.1 shows how light absorption produces reflected color.

Subtractive synthesis is the synthesis of the paint box. When red and green light are mixed, we synthesize yellow. However, if red and green pigments are mixed, most wavelengths would be absorbed and the resulting color would be a dull brownish-black.

Color Terminology

Hue   The color's position in the spectrum. The quality that differentiates between named colors such as red, yellow, green, blue and purple.

Value   The lightness or darkness of a color relative to a gray scale starting at jet black at one end and ending with white at the other. A black-and-white photograph converts all colors to some shade of gray. Colors with similar values would be hard to differentiate in a black-and-white photograph.

Saturation   How strongly colored the object is or how much the color differs in its strength of color from a gray sample of the same value. Sometimes referred to as chroma.

Saturation and value reflect the color differences when a base color is mixed progressively with more white for a lighter, less saturated color (a tint), and mixed with progressively more black for a darker value (a tone).

Brightness, when used to describe colors, describes the total amount of reflected wavelength particular to a color. When used to describe paper, brightness refers to the total amount of white light reflected back compared to pure magnesium oxide, which was assigned a value of 100 units in days when it was assumed to be the whitest and brightest substance in existence; it is not a percentage. Since then pigments such as titanium dioxide were found to have brightness values over 100. Photographic paper for example has brightness values in the order of 108 or 110. (See Figure 4.6) Brightness is a key attribute when considering a substrate for printing. Most package printing inks are transparent; light passes through them and is reflected from the substrate surface back to the observer. If the substrate surface is bright, then all wavelengths not absorbed by the pigment are reflected back. However if the substrate absorbs some percentage of red, green and blue, then the perceived reflected color will not appear as bright.

Viewing Color

Color perception is highly subjective and depends on the:

- Light source illuminating the object
- Nature of the object itself
- Observer of the object

Light source. Light from different sources has different wavelength compositions. For example, incandescent lights are rich in the red end of the spectrum, while most fluorescent lights are deficient in reds. (See Figure 4.7) Since color is an attribute of incident light, colors will appear different under these two light sources.

To reduce color-matching problems, graphic arts industries have standardized viewing illumination to a light source that approximates northern daylight at about noon. This illumination is specified as a color temperature of 5,000°Kelvin (K). (At low temperatures, a heated object radiates energy in the infrared range, detected as radiated heat. As the temperature rises, more radiation occurs in the shorter wavelengths, and the eye detects a dull red. At high temperatures, the object radiates across a broad spectral band covering all visible wavelengths, and the eye sees "white heat.") All visual color comparisons should be done under these industry standardized conditions.

Object. The object itself influences color perception. Surface texture, gloss, geometry and surrounding or adjacent colors will all affect judgment of the subject color. Some object effects promote optical illusions.

Observer. The greatest variable of all is the person viewing the color. Even eliminating those who have poor sensitivity in certain wavelengths (i.e., color blindness) still leaves questions of personal emotions and preferences. A male genetic trait causes reduced reception of the red wavelength in about 8% of the

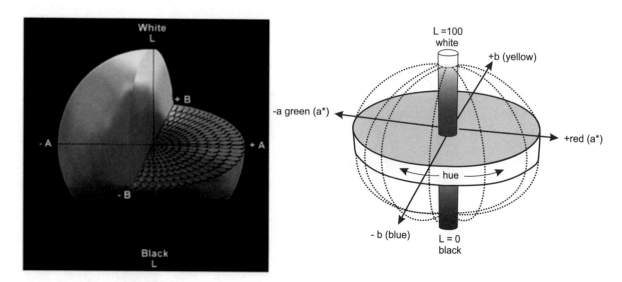

Figure 4.7

Visualizing and quantifying the multi-dimensional attributes of color is difficult. The L*ab (pronounced lab star) globe is one of several methods that organize colors in a scheme that can be easily quantified. The globe has three axes: the A axis goes from green (−A) to red (+A), and the B axis goes from blue (−B) to yellow (+B). The perpendicular goes from black (L=0) to white (L=100) (white).

If the globe is sliced in half at its equator, the outer perimeter of the disk would be made up of pure colors or hues. If other wavelengths other than the ones needed to make up the pure color are present, they reduce the level of saturation and the pure color will begin to lose its brilliance and will move towards the central L axis. Eventually it will lose all traces of color and end up on the L axis as some level of gray.

If we decrease the spectral intensity of the wavelengths, the pure colors will become darker as we move downwards through the globe's successive slices until there is no light (L=0) ... that is we will have black.

If the spectral distribution amongst the wavelengths becomes more even, the effect is that of adding white to the pure color. As we go upward from the equatorial layer, the colors become lighter. Eventually there will be an exact balance of high intensity wavelengths and L will be 100 (white). Figures 4.8 through 4.11 illustrate various saturation distributions and L values and the resulting colors.

Any color can be identified as to its position in the globe with three digits using the L*ab system.

male population. Deficiencies in other wavelengths is rare. Women in general have better color acuity than men.

The brain makes adjustments based on experience to the signals received from the eyes. An object viewed under a fluorescent light that has little red component will be color-corrected by the brain to make it look normal according to our experience. Photographs taken under the same fluorescent light tell the truth: The scene will have an overall green cast.

The brain alters color perceptions in ways that cannot be controlled, and the eye as the primary receptor suffers from a number of irregularities such as after-image and fatigue. For this reason, the most objective color measurements are

Figure 4.8

Saturation levels determine the lightness or darkness of a color. A flat curve will not favor any hue resulting in levels of gray. The light gray (left curve) would have a high L value while the right curve would represent a darker gray and a lower L value.

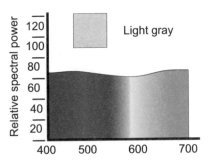

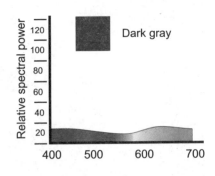

Figure 4.9

The location of the wavelength distribution curve's peak relative to other wavelengths determines the hue.

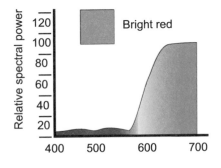

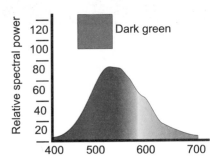

Figure 4.10

The amplitude of the spectral distributions high points determines the lightness or darkness of a color.

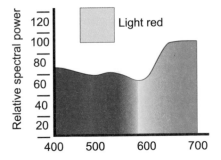

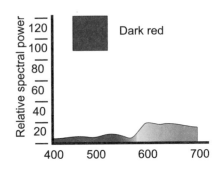

Figure 4.11

Saturation and hue is determined by the amplitude difference of the dominant high point and the remaining colors. This would represent a movement from the globe's perimeter towards the L axis.

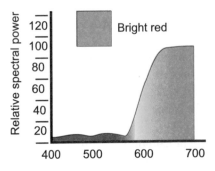

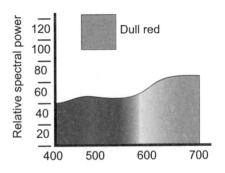

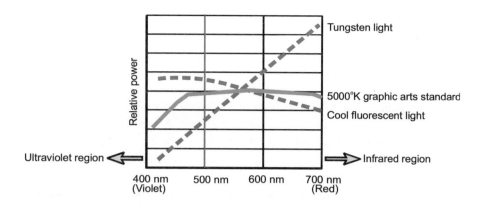

Figure 4.12

Relative wavelength distributions (in nanometers) for common light sources.

done instrumentally with colorimeters or densitometers. These instruments assign numerical values to the amount of each color component reflected. Figures 4.7 through 4.11 illustrate the L*ab (pronounced L-star) system for numerically describing colors.

The problem with "objective" instrumental color measurement, however, is that the instrument makes no allowance for shapes, adjacent colors, textures and other factors that will affect human color perception. Such colorimetry will not tell us whether a graphic image "looks right." It can only verify that the inks and papers are the same as those used on the last job or are the same as in a selected control sample. More often a color is first approved by a panel of human observers. Then a colorimetric instrument is used to quantify the color for specification or control purposes.

Reproducing Color

In theory, any color observed in nature can be faithfully reproduced. In practice, this is not so. Printing methods compress tonal and color values. A printing method cannot reproduce all the tones and colors we see in nature, or even the tone and color variation in a well-exposed photograph.

Colored pigments are composed of metal oxides and organic complexes. No ink has perfect absorption and reflectance of the relevant wavelengths. More typically reflectance is spread over a wavelength range. (See Figure 4.13) Of the three pigments used in process color printing, yellow comes closest to the ideal.

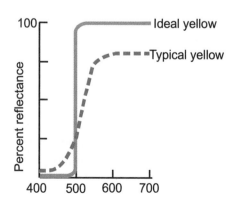 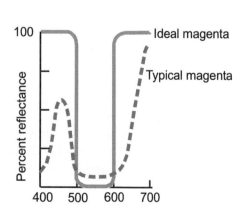

Figure 4.13

A comparison of ideal and typical reflectance curves for yellow and magenta pigments.

An ideal yellow pigment would reflect all green and all red wavelengths and absorb all blue wavelengths. The best yellow pigments, however, do not reflect all of the red and green wavelengths, while a small amount of blue is reflected. Typical yellow pigments have a slight orange cast.

Magenta and cyan pigments are even further from the ideal. An ideal magenta pigment for example should absorb all of the green and reflect all of the red and blue wavelengths. However, this is never the case. A typical magenta pigment absorbs most but not all green and reflects most but not all red and blue. The printer's challenge is to select inks, and apply them in a manner that will minimize interference from these imperfections.

When several pigments are mixed to provide other colors, pigment deficiencies accumulate and can cause the final product to look dull or muddy. For this reason, printers will often use inks other than the three primaries to ensure that a particular hue and brightness are achieved. Thus, print jobs can be made up of seven or more inks, even though in theory three colors should have been sufficient.

Black is an absence of color, and no combination of process colors will give jet black. At best, heavy lay-downs of the three process inks will produce a dark, dirty purple-brown. Because of this difficulty, a printing plate for black or another dark color is added to the cyan, magenta, and yellow already mentioned, in order to bring out shadows and dark lines, and to add more depth and realism to the illustration. This additional printing ink is known as the key color or black printer. Thus, a minimum of four printing plates is needed to create a good full-color illustration using process colors: cyan, magenta and yellow, plus a key color. The four are abbreviated to CMYK.

ARTWORK

Artwork refers to any drawing, illustration or graphic effect imparted to a substrate. Printed matter is divided into three general categories: line art, halftone art and process-printed art, based on how the color or colors are presented in the finished work. The different art categories need to be considered when preparing the printing plates that will pattern the ink and transfer the art to the surface to be printed.

Line Art

Line art consists of solid or monolithic ink lay-downs of a single hue, where hue and saturation are determined solely by the ink color used. A line-art illustration can contain several colors, but the colors are not mixed or superimposed to give color variations. Type copy, diagrams, line illustrations and illustrations with solid color blocks are line art.

Line art is the simplest and most economical image to produce. If done in one color, only one printing plate is required. Printing is accomplished simply by ensuring that the inked printing plate is in the correct location, or "register," with the sheet or object to be printed. A solid block of ink is transferred to the substrate.

Figure 4.14
Color chart for four-color process printing.

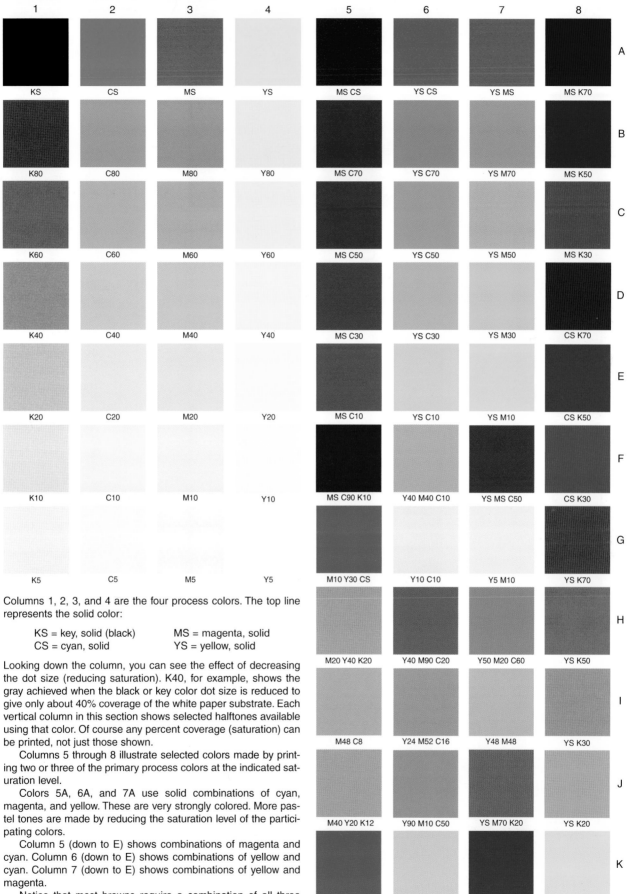

Columns 1, 2, 3, and 4 are the four process colors. The top line represents the solid color:

KS = key, solid (black)   MS = magenta, solid
CS = cyan, solid   YS = yellow, solid

Looking down the column, you can see the effect of decreasing the dot size (reducing saturation). K40, for example, shows the gray achieved when the black or key color dot size is reduced to give only about 40% coverage of the white paper substrate. Each vertical column in this section shows selected halftones available using that color. Of course any percent coverage (saturation) can be printed, not just those shown.

Columns 5 through 8 illustrate selected colors made by printing two or three of the primary process colors at the indicated saturation level.

Colors 5A, 6A, and 7A use solid combinations of cyan, magenta, and yellow. These are very strongly colored. More pastel tones are made by reducing the saturation level of the participating colors.

Column 5 (down to E) shows combinations of magenta and cyan. Column 6 (down to E) shows combinations of yellow and cyan. Column 7 (down to E) shows combinations of yellow and magenta.

Notice that most browns require a combination of all three process colors.

Figure 4.15
The components of a full-color
illustration, showing the effect
of different screens.

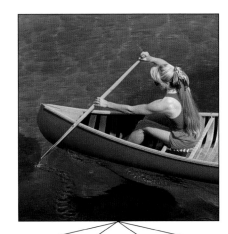

Process color reproduction of a full-color
original photograph. This one is printed
with a 133-line screen.

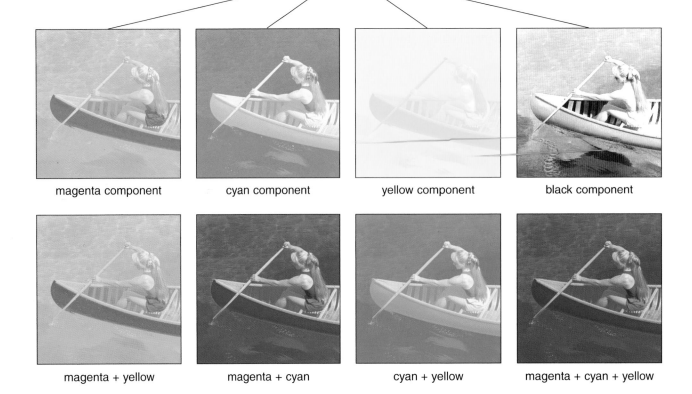

magenta component   cyan component   yellow component   black component

magenta + yellow   magenta + cyan   cyan + yellow   magenta + cyan + yellow

Illustration printed with a 65-line screen.

Illustration printed with a 100-line screen.

If the artwork has more than one color, a printing plate is needed for each color. In addition to registering the additional printing plates with the sheet or object being printed, the plates must also register with the colors already put down.

Colors for line art are usually chosen from books of color chips, much as you would choose house paint. The Pantone Matching System (PMS) is the most frequently used system for specifying colors for packaging graphic line art. PMS color guide books have a selection of more than a thousand colors, each identified by a number and an ink formulation key. Designers can conveniently communicate their color needs to printers with PMS numbers.

Specifying a PMS color does not guarantee that the final printed color will be exactly as in the sample book. Although PMS color guides are available printed on several different substrates, the packager's choice of substrates far outnumbers those in the PMS books. Since substrates will affect color appearance, a final adjustment of the PMS recipe is done at the printers. A draw-down is a step where the correct thickness of the specified formula is applied (drawn down) the actual substrate to be printed. This color swatch is compared to the desired PMS color chip and the recipe is adjusted to bring it closer to the desired color. A great number of other variables occur in the printing process, and in general, a printer will be able to replicate a PMS color exactly only about half of the time.

Continuous Tone and Halftone Illustrations

Black-and-white photographs are continuous-tone images that use only black pigmentation. By varying the amount of black, a gray scale, going from white (an absence of pigment) to jet black, is created. In actuality, this process is combining varying amounts of black with the white of the paper to produce a range of gray values.

In printing, it is not practical to premix white and black inks in infinite ranges to produce a scale of gray values. However, the eye can be tricked. Artists discovered that by laying down fine patterned lines of black ink that covered varying percentages of the white substrate (paper), an optical illusion could be created that would fool the eye into seeing a range of grays.

Using fine lines or other intermittent ink patterns to create a scale of color saturations is the basis of single-color halftone printing. The engraved art on paper money is an example of colored halftone images using line patterns and several inks to create a range of colors. In package printing, it has been found that patterns of ink dots are more versatile than lines for creating varying color saturations and densities. Black-and-white newspaper illustrations are a common example of halftone printing using dot patterns.

Halftones can be printed in any color. Figure 4.14 (left-hand section) illustrates halftone dot patterns. Column 1 in Figure 4.14 illustrates a range of gray values obtained by varying the density of the black at the top of the column. The "K" initial stands for "key color," the designation used in the graphic arts industry for black or sometimes another dark color. The numbers following the K refer to the density or percentage of the white substrate that is colored with black ink. (The letter "S" following K stands for solid or 100%.)

Table 4.2
Typical screen ranges for different printing processes.

Printing Method	Typical Screen Range
Screen printing	40 to 110 dpi
Flexography	60 to 150 dpi
Lithography/gravure	133 to 200 dpi

Columns 2, 3, and 4 illustrate the effect of reducing density or saturation levels of cyan, magenta and yellow. For illustration purposes, only six halftones are shown. Modern computers can create a gamut of 256 halftone steps. No printing press is capable printing such a gamut. Converting a continuous-tone photographic image into a halftone dot pattern was formerly done by exposing a photonegative through a screen or grid, hence the term "screen" when referring to dot patterns. Today, screens are imposed electronically. When a picture is broken up into a series of dots, a small part of the picture is lost, and the eye is asked to interpret the remainder. Obviously, the finer the dots, the less the eye is aware of them, and the better the resolution of fine details in a reproduction.

Screens are specified by the number of dots per linear inch (dpi.) (In metric, the number of dots in a linear centimeter is specified.) A 65-line screen, for example, means that the image has been created using 65 dpi. While the entire image has 65 dpi, the size of the individual dots varies depending on the saturation, or color density, required at that spot in the illustration. A density of 20 would indicate that about 20% of the substrate surface is covered with the ink in question.

Substrate, illustration type and printing method dictate screen density. However, each printing method has other inherent characteristics that affect final image quality. Finer screens require smoother substrate surfaces. Rough surfaces such as kraft linerboard are usually printed using coarse screens. Smooth clay-coated paper is normally used to optimize appearance when using very fine screens. The general industry standard for full-color process printing is 133 dpi or 150 dpi screen. Gravure printing and on occasion lithography will print 200 dpi. Screens with more than 200 dpi are mostly used for extremely fine printing such as coffee table books and art reproductions.

Typical screen ranges representing the most common packaging applications are shown in Table 4.2. Finer screens have been used for special applications, but these are less common. Lithography and gravure printing plates can be made in screens having more than 400 dpi.

Ink colors for halftone printing are selected from PMS color selection books.

Screen Variations

Screen dots may be round, elliptical or another shape. In most instances, the shape of the dot has no great significance; however, some graphic features will print better using a particular dot shape.

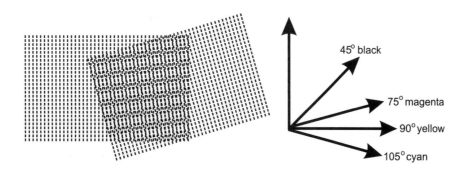

Figure 4.16

Moiré patterns (left). To avoid moiré patterns, the lines of dots for each process color are set at different angles.

Standard industry practice uses a fixed number of dots per linear inch and varies dot size (amplitude modulated) to produce different density halftones. An alternative is stochastic screening where a very small fixed-size dot is used. The number of dots is increased or decreased (frequency modulated) in random patterns to produce different density halftones. An advantage of stochastic screening's random dot placement is that moiré pattern (see Figure 4.16) problems are eliminated. Stochastic screening is sometimes used to create difficult vignettes.

Process Printing

The most complex printing task is to create a full-color illustration. This is referred to as process color reproduction or process printing.

Artists create infinite color variations by physically mixing paint on a palette. Physically mixing inks for printing is not technically possible, so the printer again resorts to fooling the eye with an optical illusion similar to halftone printing. Recall that with halftone printing, the eye in effect mixes individual black ink dots, which it can't actually discern, with the white background paper to give shades of gray. Similarly, a person observing a fine pattern of cyan dots printed over an equal pattern of yellow would not discern individual color dots, but rather some shade representing a mix of the two. A broad range of colors can be achieved by mixing the CMYK primary process colors in varying proportions. Columns 5 through 8 in Figure 4.14 show a selection of colors that can be created by combining the indicated densities of the primary process colors shown in columns 1 through 4. (Individual screen patterns can be discerned with a low power magnifying glass.)

To achieve the full-color effect, the photographic original must be separated into the three component colors plus the key color (CMYK). Depending on the technology being used, either a photonegative or digital record is made for each color. A screen pattern, as is done for halftone printing, is imposed on each of the photonegative or digital images. The color-separated and screened records are used to develop what is essentially a halftone printing plate for each process color. Thus, a cyan printing plate is made to print the cyan component, a magenta plate will lay down the correct amount of magenta ink and a yellow plate will do the same for yellow ink. Printed alone, each plate would produce a halftone of the respective color. However, when the individual halftone images are superimposed over one another, the eye blends the CMYK colors to give the illusion of a full-color continuous-tone image. The eye cannot discern the millions of tiny individual dots that go into making the colors.

Figure 4.15 summarizes the entire process. The full-color illustration represented by the image at the top of the figure, is separated into its four halftones representing the three color components and the black component of the original image. (The image representing the original photograph is actually printed with a 133-line screen, typical of package printing.) These separations are used to produce the four respective printing plates, one for each color component. If printed separately, they would produce the images shown on the second line of the figure.

Combining two or three of the colors would produce the variations shown in the third line. Finally, by printing all four components in perfect register over each other, a reproduction of the original can be made. The reproductions in the bottom row of Figure 4.15 have been printed in 65- and 100-line screens to illustrate the difference in appearance associated with different screen selections.

The difference in resolution and image quality can be readily seen by comparing the top image at 133 dpi to the bottom 100 dpi image. Note that a ripple in the water can be clearly seen off the tip of the paddle and some bubbles in the water below the paddler's leg in the 133 dpi image. The resolution at 100 dpi is not good enough for these details to appear. In the 65 dpi image, the dots are large enough that they can be seen with the unaided eye. Note also in the black component image, that the ripple is actually defined by the black printing plate.

With the rapid changes that microprocessor technology has introduced, a mix of traditional and advanced technologies is available in packaging graphics and printing. Most, but not all, packaging graphic production uses digital workflow. Analog workflow using photonegative films for plate-making is becoming rarer and will in the near future vanish completely.

Computer-to-plate (CTP) digital technology is rapidly replacing photonegatives. Digital workflow imposes the graphic record directly onto the printing plate, eliminating all intermediate steps and photographic materials. Gravure printing cylinders have been produced using CTP technology since the early 1990s. With the resolution of some complex problems, CTP technology is now being used for both flexographic and lithographic platemaking.

Direct-to-press (DTP) technology, where the plate is formed directly inside the press, is the next step up. Direct-to-press technology can be likened to giant desktop printers where the designer presses a "print" key and the press immediately prints 10,000 labels. The printing of small numbers of packages that will be used for test marketing and consumer studies is one application as are small runs of labels and tags. The ink used in such presses is costly and, to date, these presses would be classed as narrow web presses, typically up to 610 mm (24 inches) wide. Printing a large order of labels at 10 images per cycle is very slow compared to a lithographic press that might carry 200 labels on a single press sheet. Current costs restrict these presses to special applications where speed is of the essence and the number of impressions required is small. However, it may be expected that as costs come down, the use of this technology will grow.

Simply superimposing the four colors as described would not produce a high-quality image. Dot rows in the different colors would periodically line up in orderly formations called moiré (pronounced "mow-*ray*") patterns that would interfere with proper product appearance. (See Figure 4.16) To minimize moiré patterns, screens for each component color are placed at angles as shown in Figure 4.16 to minimize pattern formation.

Earlier in this chapter, it was mentioned that printing inks are not perfect and that printers can match a specified PMS color exactly only about half of the time. A similar situation exists with the CMYK-based four-color process printing system. The Hexachrome system is an alternative that adds a vivid orange and green to an enhanced CMYK set. It is claimed that the Hexachrome system can provide a good match for upward of 90% of PMS colors. Some publications are using Hexachrome, but it is not as yet common in packaging although there is interest in it for certain applications. Two reasons for this limited packaging use concern the added cost of two additional printing plates, and that the six-color process would occupy most or all printing stations on common package printing presses. This would allow little leeway for additional PMS and other special colors.

PREPARATION FOR PRINTING

Prepress

Creating a printed package requires the cooperation of many separate groups of people. For printing specifically:

- The graphic design department that develops the art

- The prepress department that converts the art into a form ready for plate-making

- The printer who will actually print the package

Regardless of the printing method or design composition, the art department must be supplied with a "keyline" layout showing the exact position and size of each element in a proposed design. The keyline tells the designer where the package borders are. For a folding carton the keyline would also show the creases, windows and other features that the graphic would have to accommodate.

As artists, graphic designers prefer not to have constraints put on their imaginations. A design on the computer screen for a cosmetic carton may be a thing of creative genius; bringing that design into being meets the limitations of the real world and what can actually be done on a printing press.

Prepress is the critical work of turning a concept on the computer screen into a form that can be satisfactorily and economically printed by the millions. It is at the prepress stage where we may realize that the cosmetic carton as proposed will require 11 printed colors, when the available press can only print eight, or that the metallic gold border will be impossible to print using lithography.

Digital workflow will direct the work through a number of computers, and checks must be made to make sure that the information is flowing correctly. The first of these is a preflight check of the digital graphic as it arrives from the graphics department.

Figure 4.17

Some printed colors are overlapped slightly to compensate for printing press movement. Traps can range from 100 micrometers (0.004 inch) for lithography to 350 micrometers (0.014 inch) for flexography. Gravure trap allowance is about 175 micrometers (0.007 inch).

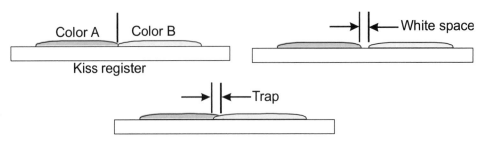

The moving parts of any machine must have some slack or play for them to be able to move. The practical printing implication of this slack is that you cannot achieve perfect register. If you tried to print a single dot on a hundred sheets, you would find not one dot but a group of dots within, for example, a 125-micrometer (0.005-inch) circle.

Each printing method and press has a tolerance within which it will be able to register a color. For example, the plates in a lithographic printing press might move 100 micrometers (0.004 inch) about the set position during printing. If two colors are positioned so that they just touch, or "kiss," at the proper press setting, then as the plates move during the print run, a white unprinted line will periodically appear between the two colors. (See Figure 4.17) A "trapping" allowance is a slight extra margin of color where two colors come together so that the inks overlap even at the extremes of plate movement. ("Trapping" is also used to describe the ability of a wet ink to adhere and transfer to a previously applied undried ink.)

A similar registration problem occurs when the printed sheet is put through a die-cutting machine. Color "bleeds" are margins of color that extend beyond the package borders (see Figure 4.18), so that full color will always be visible within the tolerance of the printing press and die-cutter. A decision on how large the bleeds should be is another prepress responsibility.

Figure 4.18

"Bleed" compensates for printing plate, substrate and cutting-die movement. The printed area on the paperboard carton blank "bleeds," or extends, slightly beyond cut or visible edges.

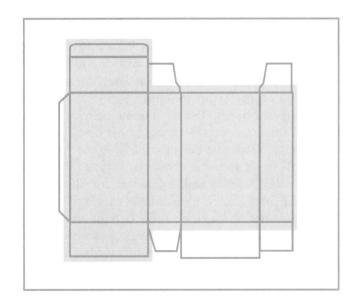

Printing is not placed over gluing areas or areas that will be concealed when the package is assembled.

Package designs composed entirely of line art need only to have the number of colors counted and specified. The only provision is that the available printing press must have sufficient printing stations. (There must be one station for each ink color.) Common configurations have six or eight printing stations and a few will have 10. A composition that had more colors than the number of available stations would need two passes through the machine with the attendant increased costs.

Most packaging graphics have both line art and process color segments. The CMYK process colors will be used for the process art segment, and these colors can also be used in the line copy, if appropriate. However, large single-color blocks will be more consistent if applied as a specified PMS ink rather than as a process ink mix.

Additional printing plates might be needed for other special colors and effects. For example, fluorescent colors and metallic inks must be applied as separate inks. Browns require blending of at least three and possibly all four of the process inks. This is hard to control at the printing press, and it requires a heavy ink lay-down. Thus, brown inks are often applied with a separate printing plate in order to control color consistency. Graphics requiring colors that are particularly bright or pure are also applied from a separate plate. For example, brilliant greens and bright oranges are often best achieved with PMS colors rather than process ink colors.

Some corporations have taken ownership of a color. Since it is part of their corporate identity, it is especially important to them to maintain a consistent color. Corporate colors rarely rely on the art of mixing at the printing press and are usually a specified ink formula.

Sometimes designs are created that require more than one printing or decorating method. The majority of printing machines are dedicated to one type of printing plate. A design that needs both lithography and gravure will need the services of one of the few printing companies that feature a mixed-station printing press, or will require two passes through separate machines. In most instances, decorating processes are also done off line on a different machine.

Each off-line operation needs a separate press setup, or "make ready," and a number of printing trials to register and bring the machine up to production readiness. Additional make-readies can add significantly to project cost and should be considered at a design's inception. A folding carton that is hot-stamped with gold foil, embossed and windowed will likely need three additional make-readies with all their associated costs.

The platemaker must know the intended printing method in order to give the right orientation to the plate. For example, a conventional flexographic plate image is reverse reading so that when the inked image is applied to the substrate, a proper reading image is produced. (Think of an ordinary office stamp.) However, when printing clear plastic films, it is common to put the ink on the side opposite from the one that will be viewed (referred to as reverse printing). A plate intended to reverse print a clear film would be made to read correctly. Offset lithographic plates for printing on paper are always right reading. Some elements such as universal product codes (UPC) must have special distortions built in so that the final product falls within exact finished dimensional tolerances.

PROOFING

The electronic image on a designer's computer is made up of red, green and blue light imposed on a glass or plastic screen whereas the final printed product will be made up from CMYK plus assorted PMS colors printed on plastic, paper or metal. Not surprisingly the graphic will appear quite different when finally printed on the intended substrate and viewed under actual use conditions. Accordingly, a variety of prepress proofing systems have been developed to produce a hard copy that offers a level of approximation of what the customer will finally see. In most instances, a customer will want to see several proofs at various stages of the design's travel through prepress activities.

Typically, proofs are wanted:

- During the design stage to approve copy and position. This proof is used primarily to ensure that the graphic fits the project's keyline, that the text is correct (including spelling and postal codes), the placement of the colors is correct, and all legal declarations requirements have been met. This first proof is frequently printed in black and white.

- During the design stage to verify general color correctness and placement. After copy and position have been verified as correct, another proof in full color might be made. Depending on the system being used, the colors will be close approximations of what will be printed but not necessarily exactly the same.

- For a final contract proof before printing plates are made. Again depending on the system being used and the customer's wishes, there may be a more advanced color proof that is signed off for approval to print. In some instances, a final approval is given at the press after a few repeats have been printed.

- For a press proof and approval before commitment to production

The cost of producing too many proofs can be considerable, and judgment needs to be made as to which proofs are essential. Generally, the cost of a proof goes up the closer it gets to production.

Creating a digital proof that closely matches what will come off the press is a challenge because:

- Digital printers use CMYK inks while press images may include a range of PMS colors.

- Digital printing employs line patterns whereas process-printed halftones use dots.

- The proofing image might be applied to a different substrate material.

- Digital proofing may not accurately duplicate some press characteristics such as gain and trapping.

- Individual printing presses have their own variables that will affect the final outcome.

The problem is not whether the digital color proofs are good; some of them look better than what can be printed on a press. The problem is to have an image that will provide a high confidence level of what you will realistically see off the press.

The elimination of photonegative film for platemaking made it essential to have a digital proofing system that offers print buyers a high level of confidence in the final result. DuPont's Digital WaterProof, or AQ4 and Kodak Approval system, for example, fingerprint individual presses by having them print a test sheet with up to 1,000 color-specific blocks. A scanner analyzes the printed color blocks to determine exactly how that press produces each color and incorporates that information into its file when it makes the digital proof. In essence, the digital proof is altered to imitate the actual colors that the press will be able to print.

Color Keys. A Color Key, despite appearances, is not really a proofing system. Approximate colors are exposed onto relatively thick clear base sheets that are overlaid (not laminated) in register. Some press operators find them useful for setting up the printing press because they allow the operator to see what each plate is supposed to print. The use of Color Keys is likely to decline with the advent of more advanced proofing and printing technologies.

Printers include a variety of printed devices on the press sheet, usually along trim margins or in areas that will be covered by a seal, that help make the initial setup easier and that serve as monitoring targets during the print run. Registration marks are usually crosses that appear on each printing plate. When all printing plates are in perfect register, the plates will print directly on top of one another and the cross will appear black. If any color is visible, it means that a color printing plate is out of register. Other devices are tonal scales and gray balance charts in various screens, star-shaped elements to show "slur and drag," and devices to record gain for UPC code monitoring.

It is common practice for the printer and customer to agree on the acceptable print quality during the first press run, and for specimens showing the desired print quality and color tolerance ranges to be retained as references.

PRINTING METHODS

Printing an image requires the ability to transfer fluid ink or another marking medium onto the substrate in the desired pattern. There are many of ways of doing this, but the bulk of package printing can be grouped into three basic categories based on the fundamental geometry of the printing plate:

Relief   Variations include flexography (commonly referred to as flexo), letterpress and offset letterpress (commonly referred to as dry offset).

| Planographic | The process is known as offset lithography and commonly referred to as lithography, offset or litho. |
| Gravure | The process is rotogravure, sometimes called roto and occasionally referred to as intaglio. |

Each printing method has a different way of creating, carrying and transferring ink patterns onto a substrate. In most instances, the device used to create the ink pattern is for lithography and flexography is generally called the printing plate. In the instance of flexography and lithography, the plates are made in the flat but then attached to round rolls inside the printing press. The print image for gravure is engraved directly into the surface of a round metal roll or cylinder and referred to as the gravure cylinder.

Printing presses have the following features in common regardless of the actual printing method used:

- An accurate material feed system that presents substrate to the printing station in precise register.

- An ink reservoir or ink fountain and a method of introducing ink into the printing train.

- A means of metering ink so that the amount applied is consistent over the print run.

- A way of configuring the ink to the required pattern. This is done by the printing plates, one for each color.

- A means of transferring ink to the substrate by pressing the substrate between the ink-bearing surface and an impression roll.

- Since inks are applied as fluids, a means of drying or solidifying them.

Printing presses are variously configured, depending on the print method and on whether the machine is fed with individual sheets or by a continuous length of material unwound from a large roll. The latter is known as a roll-fed or web-fed press.

Light materials—and those that are extensible (very stretchy) or have low strength or dimensional stability (tissue, for example)—must be web fed; the material is supplied from a roll and is usually rewound into a roll after it is printed. Web-fed machines typically run faster than sheet-fed machines.

Printed materials in roll form fit nicely into packaging operations. The many varieties of form-fill-seal filling machines and most wrapping machines must be supplied with packaging material from a roll. These materials will usually require registration marks, or "eye marks," that indicate cutting or sealing points.

Most papers can be either web or sheet fed, in which case other factors must be considered. For instance, corrugated board and other stiff or rigid materials that cannot wrap around feed rolls must be sheet fed.

In-line presses, typical of lithography and gravure applications, arrange the individual printing stations in a straight line. Stack presses, more typical of flexography, cluster printing stations on vertical frames.

While in principle most art can be printed with four stations, printing presses with eight or more printing stations are not unusual. The added stations allow the printer more options and flexibility on how to produce exacting designs of the highest quality. Examples where added stations may be used are:

- Fluorescent and metallic colors that cannot be printed with standard CMYK inks

- Line art, or process art combined with line art, that requires a large number of PMS colors

- Double applications of the same color needed to develop desired depth

- Corporate colors that are often specified PMS or proprietary formulations

- Protective or decorative coatings such as high-gloss lacquers or varnishes

- Difficult to duplicate colors such as orange, dark browns and some greens

- Exceptionally bright color, if needed

- Large solid (line art) areas

- Pattern-applied adhesives

The printing process that is selected for a particular task depends on many factors:

- The volume or number of impressions desired (10,000 or 10 million impressions)

- The art type and desired effect (line art, process color, vignettes, metallic sheen)

- The substrate (paper, plastic film, surface quality, colored, porous, flexible, rigid)

- The substrate's physical shape (roll stock, sheets, discrete items, round, irregular)

- Special package process or use conditions (chemical resistance, thermal resistance)

RELIEF PRINTING: FLEXOGRAPHY AND LETTERPRESS

Plate Production

Relief printing, the earliest printing method, uses a raised surface (one that stands out in relief) to hold the ink. The raised surface is inked by passing an inked roller over it or by pressing the plate against an inking pad. The simple office rubber stamp is an example of relief printing. The first relief plates were hand-carved from wood. Later versions were engraved into metal or used movable metal type.

Figure 4.19

UV light projected through the image photonegative will cure photopolymer. Uncured photopolymer can be washed away, leaving the raised image areas.

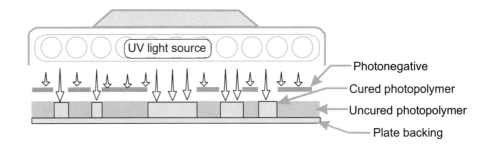

Relief printing plates have been made from rubber, photopolymer or occasionally metal, depending on the application. Rubber printing plates are the oldest of the flexographic plate technologies and their use is slowly declining. The majority of modern flexographic plates are made from photopolymer, a polymeric material that cures or hardens where exposed to ultraviolet (UV) light. Unexposed areas are soluble and can be washed away. Plates are modest in cost and can be made quickly. (See Figure 4.19)

New ablation technology using digital computer-to-plate processing is replacing traditional photonegative-based image imposition. Ablation technology uses conventional photopolymer except that the surface of the photopolymer sheet is coated with an opaque, carbon-based black coating. A laser "ablates" or burns away the carbon following digital design information. In effect, an ultrathin photonegative is created attached to the photopolymer. The sheet is then exposed to UV light, (see Figure 4.19) and the uncured photopolymer removed by washing.

Photopolymer plates are able to hold a smaller screen than rubber plates and generally produce better process art images.

Another laser engraving technology is able to engrave a rubber sleeve mounted on a metal cylinder to produce a seamless printing cylinder. The methodology is used mostly where a continuous repeat is desired.

Completed printing plates are mounted with adhesive onto a metal cylinder that rotates against the substrate during printing. Of necessity, a joint exists where the ends of the plate meet on the cylinder.

Printing by Flexography

In a typical flexographic printing station (see Figure 4.20) excess ink is applied to an engraved transfer or anilox roll. The engravings on the anilox roll meter the correct amount of ink, depending on the engraving geometry and depth. The ink is transferred to the raised surfaces of the printing plate attached to the plate cylinder. Line-art printing plates have a solid, smooth surface. Halftone and process printing plate surfaces are composed of small dots standing out in relief. The substrate is passed between the plate cylinder and the impression cylinder to achieve ink transfer.

Flexography, by definition, uses a flexible printing plate and pressure to create an image. Accordingly, flexography tends to be sensitive to small pressure changes, which can cause images to spread or "gain." Pressure variations appear as color variations in finished work.

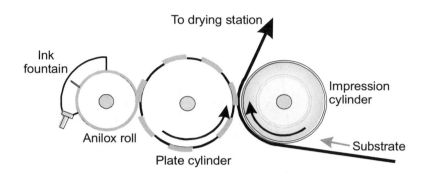

Figure 4.20

A typical flexographic print deck. Here, a chambered doctor blade ink fountain applies ink to the anilox roll. In other systems, ink is applied with rolls rotating in the ink fountain.

The flexible plate material used in flexography limits the screen that can be used for process printing and the reproduction of fine lines. Flexographic screens are normally between 65 and 133 dpi although improved plate-making materials and techniques can make 150 dpi plates. Ink squeeze-out, producing a light "halo" effect along solid edges (line art), is a common characteristic of flexography and letterpress.

Fine screens or fine copy and blocks of solid color on the same plate should be avoided when designing packages to be printed with flexography. The pressure needed to print the solid area will squeeze and distort the fine screens and lines. Vignettes or gradations (images in which color gradually fades to the paper), soft-focused images and subtle, moody subject matter are also more difficult to reproduce using flexography because of screen limitations and pressure differences between dark and highlighted areas.

Flexography's rubber-stamp nature, being more forgiving of surface irregularities, makes it the process of choice for rough or textured surfaces. Most corrugated fiberboard and kraft linerboard is printed with flexography. Flexography is usually the choice for printing flexible plastic web roll stock intended for package-forming machines, pressure-sensitive adhesive labels and wrapper stock. The soft polymer inking surfaces do not cut or damage the substrate.

Recent flexographic printing improvements have encouraged growth in printing paperboard stock for folding cartons, an area that was dominated by lithography. Presses for these applications usually have an in-line configuration. (See Figure 4.21). The advantages over sheet fed lithography are:

- Speed. Roll-fed presses are faster than sheet fed.

- Ink is dried in the press allowing printed material to go directly to post-print operations.

- Die-cutting can be done directly in-line with the printing press.

Flexographic press stations can be arranged in different ways. (See Figure 4.22) The stack press has individual color stations stacked one above the other, with drying zones between the stations. Each plate cylinder has its own impression cylinder. Stack presses are an older design and have been replaced by central impression presses in most applications. The central impression (CI) press has printing stations grouped around a single, large central impression drum.

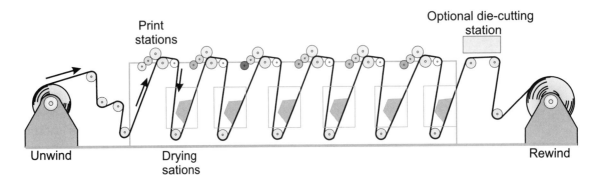

Figure 4.21
An in-line flexographic press.

Extensible webs such as polyethylene are best printed on a CI press, since the central impression drum keeps web distortion to a minimum.

The strengths and limitations of flexographic printing are summarized in Table 4.3.

LITHOGRAPHY

Lithography is a planographic process, meaning that printing and nonprinting areas are on the same plane. Unlike a relief plate, a lithographic printing plate is flat and smooth. Lithographic principles were discovered when a greasy crayon was used to write on a porous stone. The stone was then soaked with water, wetting everything except the greased area. An ink made from oil, wax and lampblack, applied to the stone's surface, was naturally repelled by the water-wetted area and adhered to the greasy area.

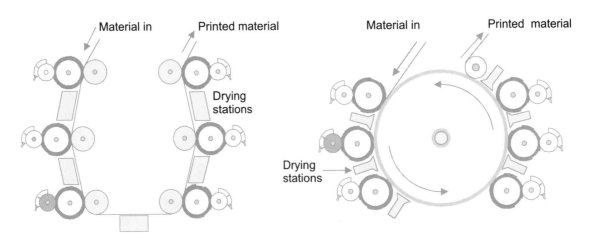

Figure 4.22
A six-color flexographic stack press (left) and a six-color flexographic common impression (CI) press (right). Common impression presses are also called central impression presses.

Table 4.3
Strengths and limitations of flexographic printing.

Flexography Printing Strengths

Prints well on rough and uneven substrates.

Able to print low strength and lightweight substrates.

Has wide ink formulation latitude, including good water-based inks.

Prints large solids evenly and with good color consistency.

Printing plates are low in cost (slightly more than lithographic plates but considerably less than gravure) and are readily made.

Considered to be better than lithography for printing large solids, but not as good as gravure.

Flexography Printing Limitations

Sensitive to changes in printing pressure.

Subject to halo effects around the edges of line copy.

Screen dot sizes cannot be as fine as available with lithography or gravure.

Halftone dot gain is greater than in lithography and gravure.

Highlight halftone dots tend to disappear, while shadows tend to fill in.

Difficult to make smooth transitions of dot size in vignettes.

Considered to be not as good at reproducing fine lines as lithography but better than gravure.

The mutually exclusive nature of oil and water forms the basis of modern lithography. Lithographic ink is, by definition, always oil based. It is a heavy paste and is metered to the plate cylinder by a train of inking rollers. Another group of rollers applies a thin film of water to the water-receptive areas. (See Figure 4.23)

Aluminum alloy plates with chemically developed oil-receptive and water-receptive areas have replaced stones. Plate costs are lowest of the three printing processes, and lead times are short. Lithographic printing plates are mounted onto a plate cylinder similar to that used in flexography. The inked metal image plate is not resilient enough to follow minute substrate surface irregularities. Transferring, or "offsetting," the ink image from the metal plate to a rubbery blanket roll provides for better ink transfer to the substrate and reduces wearing of the plate. An impression cylinder provides the contact pressure required for transferring ink from the blanket to the substrate.

Offset lithography is the most common paper-printing process, used to print folding carton stock and can and bottle labels. Labels are often produced in composite sheets, sometimes carrying a dozen or more orders on one press sheet. Small buyers pay only for the plate area used for their label, thereby reducing printing costs. This practice is not permitted for pharmaceuticals to avoid the possibility of mixing labels.

Figure 4.23

A lithographic printing
station.

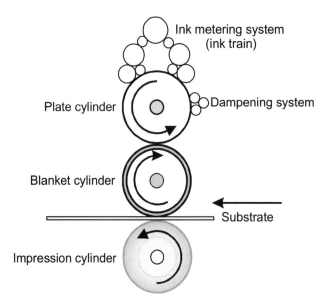

Paper for lithographic printing needs to have a certain amount of water resistance since some water may be transferred from the plate-dampening system. Paper stocks also need a strong, clean surface with good anchorage of surface fiber and clay coatings to resist being picked or pulled apart by the heavy paste inks as the blanket roll lifts from the substrate surface. Any fiber or contaminating material adhering to the blanket will mar the printed image. The oil-base nature of lithographic inks and the necessity of dampening the printing plate with water makes printing on plastic substrates difficult.

Unlike flexographic and gravure inks, lithographic inks are not dried between printing stations. Good trapping of an ink applied over a previously applied ink that is still wet is very important. The press sheet exits the press with the ink still wet, and usually a stack of printed sheets is left to dry for 24 hours before further processing. The heavy paste nature of the wet ink minimizes smearing. Many lithographic printers coat the printed sheet with an aqueous surface varnish that is instantly UV cured as the sheet leaves the press. The varnish protects the ink layer and also allows for immediate further handling of the sheet even though the lithographic inks are still wet under the cured varnish.

Most lithographic presses for packaging applications are sheet fed, although there are some web-fed presses. The planographic nature (having a smooth plate rather than a raised surface) of the process requires that the substrate surface be reasonably smooth in order to get good ink transfer. Lithographic plates can be made with 200-line and finer screens, although 133 and 150 are more common in packaging. Accordingly, the lithographic image is sharp and has excellent detail. It does not have the problems with ink squeeze and halo effect that flexography has. The edges of line art are sharp and straight. A unique advantage of lithography not available with the other methods is that some color adjustment can be made on-press.

A particular application of offset lithography is the printing of flat metal sheets destined to be formed into metal containers. The inks used in this application are heat cured, or solidified, by being treating with UV light.

Table 4.4

Strengths and limitations of offset lithography printing.

Lithographic Printing Strengths

Plates are economical and readily made.

Replacement or corrected plates are easily made.

Economical for small runs.

Capable of fine lines and of holding highlight halftone dots better than flexography or gravure.

Capable of exceptionally fine halftone screens.

Prints well on metal surfaces.

Low halftone dot gain and excellent registration.

Some color adjustment available on-press.

Lithographic Printing Limitations

Paper stocks need to be exceptionally clean.

Heavy paste inks make printing of lightweight substrates (thin papers or films) difficult.

Oil-based inks dry slowly.

Ink formulations are limited because the operating principle is based on the mutual repellency of oil and water.

Color can vary across a sheet or from sheet to sheet.

Oil-based inks and the requirement for dampening can make the printing of plastic substrates difficult.

Relatively complicated compared to flexography and gravure, requiring higher press crew skill levels.

Does not produce large solids as well as flexography or gravure.

Sheet-fed lithography is slower than web flexography or gravure.

The strengths and limitations of printing by offset lithography are summarized in Table 4.4.

GRAVURE PRINTING

Gravure printing uses engraved copper-plated steel cylinders to measure and apply patterns of ink to the substrate. (See Figure 4.24) In the most common process, a stylus controlled directly by digital information engraves the desired cell pattern into the cylinder's soft copper surface. The cylinder is then chrome plated to give it a hard wear-resistant surface.

While flexograhic and lithographic printing processes are limited in the ink thickness that can be applied to a substrate, gravure can provide heavier ink lay-downs. Cell patterns are simply cut deeper to hold more ink. This is an advantage where a heavy ink lay down is desired in order to achieve good hiding

Figure 4.24

A gravure cylinder may have millions of tiny cells or wells whose volume can be controlled to carry different amounts of ink.

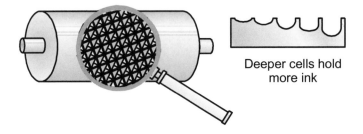

Deeper cells hold
more ink

Figure 4.24

A gravure cylinder may have millions of tiny cells or wells whose volume can be controlled to carry different amounts of ink.

and depth of color. Metallic gold or silver ink formulations also must have heavy applications for a good effect.

Normal gravure printing is always done from rolls and in web form. The gravure cylinder's entire surface is flooded with low-viscosity ink and then wiped clean with a straight-edged metal doctor blade. After the cylinder has been wiped, only the ink inside the recessed cell pattern remains on the cylinder. (See Figure 4.25) The substrate to be printed is nipped between the impression roll and the gravure cylinder, and the ink is pulled out of the cells and deposited on the substrate. Often the substrate and the gravure cylinder are given opposite electrical potentials in order to give ink removal an added electrostatic assist. Gravure printing needs a smooth substrate surface to ensure contact with the minute ink cells.

Unlike the other printing methods, gravure always lays down ink as a dot pattern, even for line art. Gravure can typically be recognized by the slightly ragged edge on the borders of line art. Very fine lines such as scrolls or pin-striping are difficult to achieve for this reason.

Gravure printing gives superior print quality and unmatched control over long production runs. The amount of ink delivered by a gravure cylinder is metered and fixed by the engraving itself, and therefore, gravure printing is not as subject to operator and environmental variables as other processes. Make-ready is simple. Since there is no plate joint on a gravure cylinder, it is possible to print continuous patterns.

Figure 4.25

A gravure print station is mechanically simpler than either flexography or lithography.

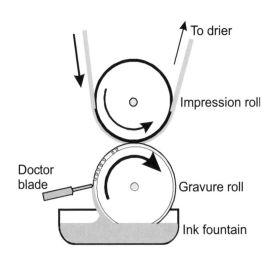

To drier

Impression roll

Doctor blade

Gravure roll

Ink fountain

Table 4.5
Strengths and limitations of gravure printing.

Gravure Printing Strengths

Very high printing speeds and productivity are possible.

Exceptionally fine halftone screens are possible.

Excellent color consistency over long print runs.

Ink cells can be engraved to different depths allowing for the application of different ink thicknesses.

Heavy ink applications can be used to produce exceptionally bright and glossy colors.

Can print heavily pigmented metallic inks.

Considered to be superior for printing skin colors and uniform heavy solids.

Gravure cylinders are capable of printing several million repeats; flexographic or lithographic plates might need to be replaced several times for long runs.

Press make-ready is fast and production costs are modest.

Gravure cylinders can be stored and remounted for repeat runs.

Continuous repeat is readily available.

Gravure Printing Limitations

Cylinder preparation requires a long lead time.

Cylinders are several times the cost of flexographic or lithographic plates, making the process economical only for long runs.

Does not print well on rough substrates such as uncoated paperboard.

Does not give good resolution of small type, fine lines and other small details.

Inventory and storage of base and engraved cylinders is costly.

Gravure cylinder preparation is an exacting and time-consuming procedure, so lead times for gravure printing are longer than for other print methods. The cost of a set of gravure cylinders is several times that of plates for flexographic or lithographic printing. However, a gravure cylinder will last for several million impressions, whereas flexographic and lithographic plates will need to be replaced well under a million impressions. A prime requisite of gravure printing is a large enough production run to offset the higher initial cylinder costs. Gravure printing is used on a variety of high-volume web-printing applications such as labels, cartons, carton wraps and flexible packaging materials.

The strengths and limitations of gravure printing are summarized in Table 4.5.

COMPARING FLEXOGRAPHY, LITHOGRAPHY AND GRAVURE

The quality of printed images varies widely among flexography, lithography and gravure. It is easy to distinguish between the three processes when the

Figure 4.26

The printing method can often be determined by examining the edges of line art under magnification.

Flexo Printing
"halo" effect

Litho Printing
smooth edges

Gravure Printing
saw-tooth edges

printing is not done to the highest of standards (see Figure 4.26), but the process is identifiable only by careful examination with a magnifying glass when the printing is of the first quality. The UPC code is usually the best line art to examine for print identification.

Competition between the three printing industry segments is fierce, and as each segment incorporates a more advanced technology, predictions are made regarding the ascendancy of that segment at the expense of another. The end result of this competition has been a remarkable improvement in graphic quality and turnaround time, but relatively small changes in market share.

The most typical press configurations and applications for relief and offset lithographic printing are shown in Table 4.6. Gravure printing presses are always web-fed and are used primarily for large volume runs on any smooth-surfaced stock. There are a limited number of combination presses available that combine

Table 4.6

Typical flexographic and lithographic press configurations and applications.

Press Type	*Typical Applications*
Flexographic, web	Most plastic films used for bags and wrappers, paper wraps, some pressure-sensitive labels, gable-top milk cartons, some paperboard folding carton stock, preprinted linerboard for corrugated boxes.
Flexographic, sheet	Post-printed corrugated board stock.
Letterpress, web	Mostly narrow web label and tag applications. Not common.
Offset letterpress (dry offset)	Round containers such as metal cans, plastic tubs and collapsible tubes.
Offset lithography, sheet	Most common press for printing paper stocks used for cut labels, folding cartons, and other paper and paperboard constructions.
Offset lithography, sheet	Most common press for printing flat metal stock for three-piece metal cans.
Offset lithography, web	Used in applications similar to sheet-fed offset lithography. Not as common.

Table 4.7

Wet ink film thickness for typical printing methods.

	Wet Ink Film Thickness	
Printing Method	*Inch*	*Micrometer*
Offset lithography	0.0002 to 0.0005	5 to 12
Flexography	0.0004 to 0.0008	10 to 12
Gravure	0.001 to 0.0015	25 to 40
Screen	0.001 to 0.005	25 to 130

lithography and gravure or flexography and gravure in order to take advantage of the strengths of two processes.

Each printing process deposits a different thickness of ink on a substrate. (See Table 4.7) Heavy ink lay-downs increase ink consumption and cost on the one hand, but they can also provide better opacity and greater depth of color and gloss. Table 4.8 is a summary comparison of the printing processes.

OTHER PACKAGE DECORATION TECHNIQUES

Not all package decorating and marking requirements can be met with flexography, lithography or gravure. For distinctive effects, special substrates or irregular

Table 4.8

Printing processes compared.

	Lithography	Flexography	Gravure
Short runs	best	good	not suitable
Long runs	good	good	best
Plate lead time	shortest	medium	longest
Fine lines	best	good	poor
Large solids	good	better	best
Register	best	lowest	intermediate
Gain	lowest	most	intermediate
Uncoated paper	good	best	not suitable
Plastic film	not suitable	good	good
Screen range	200+	133 to 150	200+
Ink formulation	oil-based paste	widest latitude	low viscosity

shapes, a number of additional processes and variations can be called into use. Some decorating processes are almost exclusive to the plastics industries, where preformed parts need to be decorated.

Additional decorating of printed stock is rarely done in-line with the printing press. This means that conventionally printed material would be moved to a separate operation if it required hot-stamping. Still another operation would be needed if the design also called for embossing. Some of the already printed material would need to be used to set up each added feature, and a method of registering between machines is essential.

Reflective Metallics

No printing ink is able to produce glossy reflective metallic. All such effects are based on aluminum either in its foil form in a vacuum metallized form. Only a continuous metal surface can provide a reflective glossy metallic sheen. In the instance of printed aluminum foil, the graphic will have a hard, glossy surface even in those areas printed with opaque ink.

Golds and other reflective metallic colors are created by coating aluminum with a transparent yellow or other appropriate color varnish.

In most decorative applications where localized reflective metallics are called for, the aluminum layer will be transferred from an aluminum vacuum-metallized sheet. (See Chapter 14) Metallizing is a full-web process; metallized designs and patterns are not practical.

There are several ways of creating patterned reflective metallics. Hot-stamp printing is the most common method usually used where only small areas of metallic print are needed. In this application, a metallized carrier or release sheet (typically polypropylene or poly(ethylene terephthalate) is coated with a heat activatable adhesive material. The carrier is brought into contact with the substrate and the hot die is applied to the back of the carrier sheet. The adhesive material melts and in adhering to the substrate, pulls the aluminum metallizing with it. As with aluminum foil, gold and other reflective metallics are produced by transparent inks of the desired color over the metallized surface.

Another option is to preprint a web prior to metallizing, thus providing for colored art with a metallic background. As a final option, a demetallizing process using a caustic solution applied by a printing type roll will dissolve away the aluminum and open up clear windows in a metallized film.

Hot-stamp and Heat-transfer Printing

In some instances, printing ink or other material is applied to a carrier sheet by conventional printing methods and then the ink or material is transferred to the container:

Hot-stamp and heat-transfer printing are similar in that they both use heat to transfer images from a carrier web to the substrate to be decorated. They are both clean processes since there are no inks to dry. Both processes require a substrate that is reasonably heat tolerant.

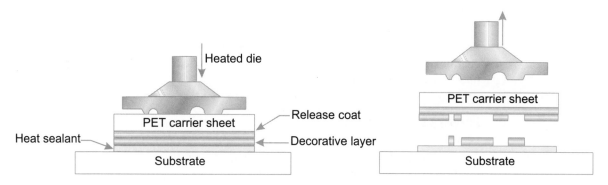

Figure 4.27

Hot-stamp printing uses a heated die that has the image engraved into its surface. Hot-stamp printing transfers only one color.

Hot-stamp printing (sometimes called leaf printing) uses a carrier web made of release-coated PET. Decorative and protective coatings are applied against the release-coated carrier web, and then covered with a final layer of heat-activated adhesive. The web is placed against the substrate to be decorated, with the adhesive side facing the substrate. A hot, engraved die is brought against the back of the PET carrier web, activating the adhesive that then adheres to the substrate. The adhesive pulls an image duplicating the die profile from the release-coated carrier web and bonds it to the substrate. (See Figure 4.27)

Metallic decoration is the principal hot-stamp application. To produce the metallic sheen, the decorative coating is created with a vacuum metallized aluminum layer. (See Chapter 14, Flexible Packaging Laminates)

Unlike hot-stamp printing, heat-transfer printing has a full, preprinted image applied to the carrier web. The desired design is printed with thermoplastic inks on the carrier web by whatever process is most suitable, thus giving substantial design flexibility. The heated die does not have an image engraved into it; it only has to conform to the overall design shape. Heat-transfer printing is primarily used for decorating plastic bottles and articles. Therimage, Di-Na-Cal and Electrocal are proprietary names for heat-transfer printing.

Embossing

Embossing is the practice of pressing a substrate, usually paper, so that a design stands out in relief. A key requirement of embossing is that the substrate be capable of deforming under pressure and holding the newly created contour.

Embossing dies are made by direct engraving or by casting from a master engraving. The embossing die is pressed against the substrate that is in turn backed by a resilient material or by a matching anvil. Most embossing is done in register with a printed pattern already laid down in previous steps. Web stock can be embossed continuously by embossing rolls to impart an overall texture to the substrate. Aluminum foils are often embossed in this way.

Gloss Coatings

Printing inks alone do not normally have a high-gloss surface. Clear surface coatings are applied where such an effect is needed. Ultraviolet-cured coatings have particularly good surface sheen.

Reverse Printing

Clear plastic films are often "reverse printed," or printed on the back so that the image shows through the film. The film surface provides gloss as well as protecting the ink from surface abrasion. In most reverse-printing applications, the reverse-printed film is laminated to a backing film or sheet. The backing film can be clear or colored. Many snack food packages back the reverse-printed sheet with a metallized film to provide a reflective metallic background for the print.

Laser Marking and Ink-Jet Printers

Laser marking is different from that produced in common office laser printers in that the image is burned into the substrate surface rather than developed by the application of ink. The surface to be marked must be receptive to the laser. Substrate surfaces that are transparent to lasers can be coated with a laser-receptive material. Laser marking is exceptionally fast and is used to mark lot numbers, dates and similar information at speeds up to several thousand per minute. Laser printing, as used in coding, has a limited font size.

Ink-jet printers eject a train of ink droplets that are deflected into the desired patterns when they pass between electrically charged plates. Ink-jet printers are increasingly being used to print variable information on packages and labels.

PRINTING DIMENSIONAL PACKAGES

For those packages that are flat at some point in their manufacture, flexography, lithography and gravure are used to economically print quality-text and graphics directly onto the packaging material at high speeds. Three-dimensional packages such as cans, bottles, jars and boxes cannot be easily decorated by these options. While printing directly on dimensional packages is done, there are usually some limitations. For example:

Letterpress and Offset Letterpress (Dry Offset)

Letterpress refers to relief printing processes that uses stiff polymer or sometimes metal printing plates made in relief. Where flexographic printing inks are fairly fluid and can be metered with engraved rolls, letterpress inks are heavy pastes similar to lithographic inks and must be metered by a complicated series of rollers. Packaging printing by letterpress is not common; the method is used mostly for printing labels and tags. The plate is more durable but more expensive to make than a similar flexographic plate. The stiff plates are dimensionally more

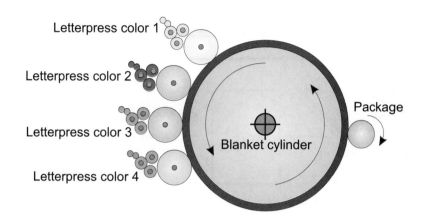

Letterpress color 1

Letterpress color 2

Letterpress color 3

Letterpress color 4

Blanket cylinder

Package

Figure 4.28

Offset letterpress (dry offset) assembles the entire image on a blanket roll and transfers the image to a round container in one rotation of the container.

stable than flexible polymer (flexographic) plates, and a finer screen pattern can be used to provide a better-quality image.

Cylindrical objects such as two-piece metal cans have no circumferential register point against which to register printing stations. This problem is resolved by a process modification variously known as offset letterpress, dry offset or letterset. (See Figure 4.28)

In offset letterpress, the inked images from the letterpress printing plates are transferred onto an intermediate resilient rubber blanket roll, where all the colors can be assembled in complete register. The heavy paste nature of letterpress inks prevents them from running or spreading while the image is being assembled. The blanket roll is then rolled against the round object, and all the colors that make up the image are transferred at one time and in complete register.

The colors applied to the blanket are wet and must stay wet until transferred to the container. Inks used in these applications are cured by heat or by ultraviolet light. Colors cannot be easily printed over other colors with this printing technique, and a fine unprinted line between colored areas can usually be seen with magnification.

Offset letterpress is used to decorate drawn-and-ironed metal cans, round plastic tubs and plastic or metal collapsible tubes. Because of the difficulty of overprinting wet inks, offset-letterpress-printed beverage cans and collapsible tubes are usually decorated with simple line or halftone art. Process color printing, while possible, tends to be restricted for more upscale applications. A characteristic darker margin can be seen on most containers at the point where the printing plate has to overlap itself slightly.

Stencil or Screen Printing (Serigraphy)

Many glass and plastic bottles are screen printed. The heavy ink application provides good opacity where a background color needs to be covered, and the plates are inexpensive. The process is slow and is limited in the complexity of art that can be produced. The advantage of a "no label look" on glass bottles is being successfully reproduced with clear plastic pressure- sensitive labels.

The term "silk screen," while commonly used, is technically incorrect since modern screen printing uses fine metal or plastic screens. The screen is masked

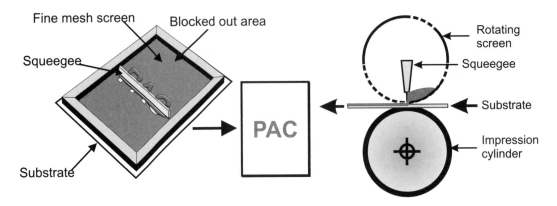

Figure 4.29

Flat framed screens (left) are used for very large area application such as point-of-purchase displays. printing can be done on flat or round objects. Rotary screens (right) are use for smaller higher volume applications.

off into a pattern that leaves porous screen areas where ink is desired and sealed areas where no ink transfer is indicated. The screen is placed against the surface to be printed, and a wiper blade moves an ink puddle across the screen. (See Figure 4.29) Where the screen has been left porous, the ink drops through onto the substrate. Stencil screens are easily and economically made by exposing a screen coated with photosensitive material in a manner similar to that used in lithography and flexography.

Screens can be configured to a variety of shapes and sizes, making it possible to decorate round bottles (see Figure 4.30) and other items that would be difficult to print any other way. Screen printing is best for line art, although process art can be printed. Halftone screens are limited to about 85 dpi, giving fairly coarse halftone reproductions. The strengths and limitations of screen printing are given in Table 4.9.

Screen printing lays down an exceptionally heavy ink layer. Normally, this would be viewed as unfavorable and costly. However, in some instances, heavy ink lay-downs are needed. Applied ceramic lettering (ACL) and decorations applied to glass bottles, for example, need fairly heavy ink applications and are normally screen printed. Heavy ink lay-downs can also be beneficial when printing over colored backgrounds. Colored plastic containers are screen-printed

Figure 4.30

Screen printing is easily done on round containers.

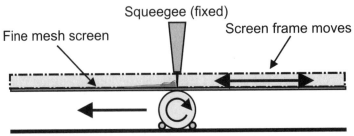

Table 4.9

Strengths and limitations of screen printing.

Advantages of Screen Printing

Image carrier (printing plate) is inexpensive and quickly prepared.

Able to print with the greatest variety of ink formulations.

Can print any substrate including metal plates and some textiles.

Capable of the heaviest ink lay-down of any process and of producing brilliant colors.

Heavy ink lay-down provides high opacity on colored substrates.

Large solid areas are uniformly opaque.

Can be readily adapted to print cylindrical or tapered shapes.

Very large image carriers are possible.

Screen Printing Limitations

Production speeds are very low compared to other printing processes.

Heavy ink lay-downs increase ink consumption and cost.

Not able to produce fine halftones.

in order to provide complete opaque coverage of the substrate color. The brown kraft of corrugated board can be successfully concealed with screen printing.

Textiles, point-of-purchase displays, stiff boards and rigid plastic, and metal parts that cannot be printed in other ways are other typical applications.

Pad Printing

Pad printing is a relative of gravure printing. The inked image is created on a flat etched plate, (the cliché), in a manner similar to gravure. A large, resilient silicone pad is pressed against the inked cliché. The ink pattern is transferred to the pad, which is subsequently pressed against the substrate. (See Figure 4.31)

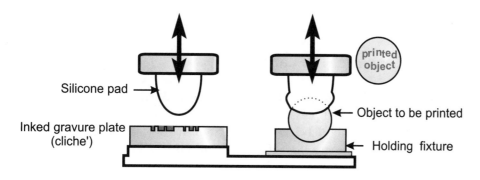

Figure 4.31

Pad printing is used to decorate irregularly shaped objects. The pad is first pressed against the inked cliché and then moved over and pressed against the object to be printed.

A feature of pad printing is the ability to print highly irregular surfaces. The resilient pad transferring the ink can conform intimately to surprisingly asymmetric and uneven surfaces. (Golf balls are printed this way.) Multicolor printing can be accomplished by using several printing stations in sequence. Pad printing is most commonly used to decorate molded plastic parts such as closures and cosmetic containers.

LABELING

Labeling generally refers to communication matter that is printed on a separate material and subsequently attached to a package by means other than direct printing. The entire gamut of decoration and printing methods is available since the actual text and graphic are applied while the label material is in the flat.

Cut and Stack Labels

Cut labels are printed paper or laminate stock sheet, cut to size and stacked for shipment. Coated high quality paper stock allows for high quality graphics. The labels are attached using adhesives applied to them or the container, most commonly in line with filling and closing. The adhesives are usually water-based emulsions, although hot-melts and combinations of adhesives are also used. Their single biggest application is for canned food and similar products. They are the least expensive labels to purchase, however labeling operations using wet glues require constant attention, so that some of these economies can be easily lost.

Nonetheless in mass production situations where a company may be producing 40 or 50 product varieties, inventorying one can type and 50 boxes of labels is more economical than inventorying 50 varieties of prelabeled cans.

Cut and stack labels are not used in the pharmaceutical industry where it is necessary to account for every label and the risk that equal-sized loose labels could be mixed up is not acceptable.

Cut and stack label disadvantages are:

- Limited material options
- In-line gluing is messy
- Longer set-up and clean-up times compared to pressure sensitive labeling
- Potential for label mix-ups

Pressure Sensitive (Ps) Labels

Pressure sensitive (PS) labels can be paper or plastic based. The unprinted side of the label has a pre-applied pressure-sensitive adhesive and the whole is mounted onto a release paper. The label is removed from the release paper immediately before application to expose the adhesive. PS labels avoid the need for adhesive

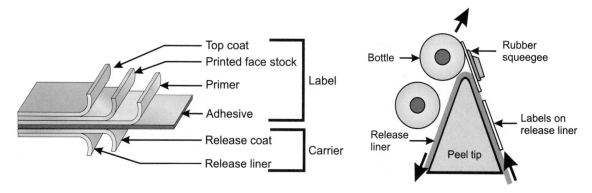

Figure 4.32

Typical pressure sensitive label construction. The label is peels away from the liner when it is passed around a sharply angled peel tip.

application systems at the point of application. Unlike most glued-on labels, PS labels are delivered in rolls or fan-fold form that makes application, inventory counts and auditing more reliable for those industries where this is required. Although initially more costly than glued-on labels, in many instances the overall operation can be more economical.

Clear plastic labels (typically polypropylene or poly(ethylene terephthalate) that produce a "no label" look are a recent development.

There are several methods by which PS labels can be applied to the container. Wipe applicators pull the liner with the attached label around a sharp-nosed peel tip at which point the label peels away from the liner. (See Figure 4.32) A rubber squeegee directs the free end of the label into contact with a bottle and establishes the initial bond. The motion and rotation of the bottle continues to draw the label from the liner while the squeegee wipes out any air pockets. The bottle may be rotated past addition squeegees or pads to ensure a smooth application.

Blow-on or non-contact applicators transfer the label from the liner to a vacuum grid from which a puff of air blows it into contact with the container. Blow-on applicators are able to apply labels to packages that have a recessed label panel. Similar to blow-on applicators, a tamp or pad style applicator transfer the label from the liner to a vacuum pad. However in this instance the pad is mounted on an air cylinder that extends and places the label on the container.

Shrink-Sleeve Labels

Shrinkable labels are printed on a plastic material that shrinks when exposed to heat. Tubular sleeves can be produced by either extrusion blowing the film tube, or by solvent bonding flat extruded PVC or PETG films into a sleeve. Extrusion blown tubes are typically in a single color and are used for shrinkable neck bands and other applications where decorative qualities are not needed.

Table 4.10

Comparison of common shrink-label materials. Source: National Starch and Chemical

Material	Maximum Shrinkage	Cost	
OPP	22%	Lowest cost	Used only for conventional shapes.
PVC	60%	Next higher	Low shrink temperature. Can be solvent welded.
OPS	50%	Next higher	
PETG	70%	Highest cost	Lowest shrink temperature. Can be solvent bonded.

Flat film stock that will be bonded into a sleeve is first printed while in the flat. Printing in the flat allows for using the full gamut of printing methods and multi-color capabilities available, with the caution that excessive heat cannot be used in the ink drying step. The label stock would normally be reverse printed to provide for a glossy label face. Depending on the application, film might be vertically or circumferentially perforated to provide tear strips or other features. Full-body shrink labels can be perforated to accommodate a tamper evident feature.

The tubular shrink sleeve is dropped over the container and heat, typically in the range of 135°C to 149°C (depending on the material) for a few seconds, causes the plastic to shrink and conform to the container's contours. Most often, the container contour is such that label-to-container adhesives are not necessary. Some distortion of the graphics will be necessary where high shrinkage ratios are required. Shrink-on sleeve labels have the advantage of being able to decorate a bottle completely from finish to heel. Shrink-band labeling can be used to consolidate several items into multipacks. Shrink sleeves have also been used to provide the window material to show contents in folding carton designs. It is generally accepted that the labels can be separated for recycling.

Table 4.10 lists the materials most commonly used for shrink labeling. Regional prohibitions may affect material choice. For example PVC represents a major of shrinkable labeling in North America, but many European countries and Japan ether restrict the use of PVC or ban it entirely. Most label stock is between 38 to 75 mm (0.0015 to 0.003 inches) thick.

Shrink sleeve drawbacks are:

- Heat sensitivity can impact on storage
- Printing can require complicated prepress
- Reduced line speeds.

Labeling sleeves are dimensioned in the order lay-flat by cut length, with lay-flat being the dimension in the flat across the sleeve. Length is the dimension between the open ends.

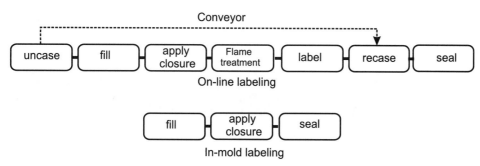

Figure 4.33
In-mold labeling can significantly reduce required production space. The simpler line and the elimination of a labeler will increase line efficiency.

An option to shrink sleeves is stretch sleeves. LDPE based material can be made to stretch up to 30% to fit over a container providing a low cost alternative. Low material cost and no shrink tunnel).

In-Mold Labeling

In-mold labeling describes a process of applying labels to plastic containers during the actual molding process. Fully decorated paper or plastic labels have a heat-activated adhesive (typically based on ethylene-vinyl acetate) on the backside. In a typical operation, robotic pick-and-place devices place the label into the mold where they are held in place by vacuum ports. As the mold closes, the heat of the extruded or injected plastic melts the adhesive material and bonds it firmly to the container. The label displaces a volume of plastic equal to the volume of the label and is flush with the surface of the container

Film labels are more expensive than paper, but have the advantage of being recyclable if they are of the same material as the container. They are unaffected by moisture and the flush surface gives the appearance of not having an applied label. (The "no-label" look). In-mold applied paper labels can cause recycling problems since they cannot be easily separated from the container body material.

In-mold labeling has gained popularity as a method of decorating blow-molded plastic containers. Significant advantages are the elimination of all labeling equipment (see Figure 4.33) including flame-treating, as well as staffing and maintenance costs. Since the label becomes an integral part of the bottle, plastic container gram-weights can often be reduced. In-case filling also becomes an attractive possibility.

The disadvantages of in-mold labeling are:

- Higher tooling cost
- Slower molding cycle rate due to slower cooling
- Regrind is contaminated with label debris
- Bottle shape limitations
- Inventory cost of predecorated containers

REVIEW QUESTIONS

1. White light is beamed onto a surface that absorbs the blue wavelength. What does the eye see?

2. Name two applications of screen printing.

3. Printers can theoretically duplicate all colors using the CMYK process inks, but printing machines often have six or eight stations. Give three examples of how you might use the other stations.

4. List the steps necessary to create a halftone printing plate from a color photograph?

5. What three colors does the human eye detect?

6. Your printer informs you that a 133-line screen will be used for a particular job. What is this telling you?

7. What is "reverse printing"? Why use it?

8. What are some limitations of flexography?

9. What is the minimum number of printing plates needed to print a good-quality process color illustration?

10. A toy box will have a full-color action illustration. The illustration will be framed in a fluorescent orange and green border. How many printing plates are needed?

11. What three factors influence the human perception of color?

12. What is the operating principle of lithography?

13. Dot "gain" is a problem that is particularly associated with what process?

14. Name the four process colors.

15. Name the three principal printing methods.

16. When referring to an illustration, what is line art?

17. Which will produce the better illustration: a 65-line screen or a 100-line screen? What do the numbers represent?

18. Why are printing plates for separate colors set at different angles for printing?

19. What printing problem must be resolved when printing round containers? What is the printing method called?

20. What is the difference between a web press and a sheet-fed press? Which printing processes are most typically web fed and which are most typically sheet fed?

21. What kind of press would be best for printing a highly extensible web such as a thin polyethylene?

22. What decorative effects cannot be achieved with conventional four-color printing processes?

23. What is the "key color," and why is it used?

24. What is meant by a printing process described as being "offset"?

25. What decorating process would you choose for decorating plastic bottles?

26. What is a central impression press?

27. All graphic artwork should be compared under standard light conditions. Why and how is this light specified?

28. Exactly what does the term "brightness" describe? Why is it an important characteristic of a surface being process printed?

29. What are a blanket cylinder, an anilox roll and an impression cylinder?

30. Name one advantage and one disadvantage of gravure printing.

31. An illustration that is printed in one color but that has variations in saturation of that color is called a _____.

32. "Trap" is used to describe what two conditions?

33. Name two advantages of using shrink-sleeve labeling.

34. What printing process would not be suitable for printing plastic bread bags?

35. What two colors provide the greatest contrast to the human eye?

36. Name one advantage and one disadvantage of screen printing.

37. A hard metallic sheen can be printed only by what process?

38. What does "bleed" mean?

39. What are the reasons that make it difficult to get exact replication of a printed image using digital proofing methods?

40. What is a Color Key, and what is it used for?

41. What are the factors that make an analog proof closer to what can be printed than a digital proof?

42. Name one advantage and one disadvantage of in-mold labeling.

43. Which shrink sleeve label plastic offer the least amount of shrink and which offers the highest amount.

44. What printing method would you choose for decorating the top of a dome-shaped plastic closure?

CONTENTS

Source and Preparation of Fiber

Definition of paper, fiber sources, wood composition, fiber length, formation, recycled fiber, pulping methods, relative strengths of various wood pulps, refinement, sizing, other additives.

Representative Paper-Making Machines

Fourdrinier machines, cylinder or vat machines, characteristics imparted by machines, multi-ply boards, twin-wire formers. Fiber alignment, MD and CD, anisotropic properties. Calendering, clay coating.

Paper Characterization

Grammage, basis weight, caliper, ream weight, brightness, moisture content, equilibrium moisture content, hygroscopicity, paper curl, standard test conditions, hygroexpansive properties, viscoelasticity.

Paper Types

Newsprint grades, commercial papers, greaseproof, glassine, parchment, natural kraft, bleached kraft, tissue, label, pouch paper, solid bleached sulphate, linerboard, medium.

Paperboard Grades

Chipboard, cardboard, newsboard, lined chip board, bending chipboard, single white lined, double white lined, clay coated boards, solid bleached sulfate.

Paper Characterization Methods

A listing of the most typical paper characterization methods.

PAPER AND PAPERBOARD

SOURCES AND PREPARATION OF FIBER

Paper is defined as a matted or felted sheet usually composed of plant fiber. Paper has been commercially made from such fiber sources as rags (linen), bagasse (sugar cane), cotton and straw. North American paper is made almost exclusively from cellulose fiber derived from wood.

The paper industry has few definitive terms. For example, paperboard, boxboard, cardboard, and cartonboard are all terms used to describe heavier paper stock. "Paper" and "paperboard" are nonspecific terms that can be related to either material caliper (thickness) or grammage (basis weight). The International Standards Organization (ISO) states that material weighing more than 250 grams per square metre (51 lb. per 1000 sq. ft.) shall be known as paperboard. General U.S. practice calls material that is more than 300 micrometres (0.012 in.) thick paperboard. For the purposes of this text materials over under 300 micrometres will be referred to as paperboard. "Paper" will be used in a generic sense to include all thicknesses and also, more specifically, to those products under 300 micrometres in thickness.

The properties of paper and paperboard are dependent on a large number of variables. To understand paper products, it is best to know the fiber source, how the fiber was extracted and prepared for papermaking, the machine on which the paper was made and treatments given the finished paper.

Fiber Source and Length

Cellulose fiber suitable for making paper can be obtained from many plants. Each forms cellulose into fiber bundles characteristic to the species. The most important characteristic for papermaking is fiber length—the longer the fiber, the better the fiber entanglement and the stronger the resulting paper. (See Table 5.1)

Table 5.1

Approximate fiber length of cellulose used in papermaking.

Fiber Source	Typical Fiber Length
Main Sources	
Hardwood (e.g. poplar, aspen, maple)	2 millimetres/0.08 inch
Softwood (e.g. pine, spruce, hemlock)	4 millimetre/0.16 inch
Other Sources	
Straw, bagasse	< 2 millimetres/0.08 inch
Bast (e.g. linen, cotton)	> 2 millimetre/0.5 inch
Recycled paper	varies depending on source

Figure 5.1

Paper qualities and fiber length.

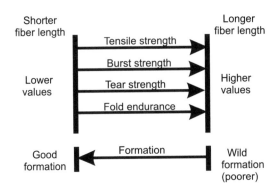

Longer fibers produce paper with proportionately higher tensile, tear, fold and puncture strengths. For example, newsprint made from short-fiber mechanical pulps will fail a standard fold endurance test in fewer than 15 folds. Typical office papers will last 20 or 30 folds, while kraft bag paper will last into the hundreds. Currency paper has a large percentage of bast fiber and will tolerate thousands of folds.

On the negative side, long, coarse fibers produce a rougher surface texture than short fibers. Also, individual fibres in long-fiber pulps tend to entangle and clump together when deposited on the screen of a papermaking machine. The density of the paper will vary across the sheet. Evenness of fiber distribution is referred to as "formation." "Wild formation" refers to a very uneven distribution of fibers. Variations in density resulting from poor formation can lead to such problems as uneven ink absorption during printing or erratic adhesive bonding.

Shorter fibers produce a paper with a smoother surface and a more consistent density. However, short-fiber papers significantly have reduced physical properties. These relationships are illustrated in Figure 5.1.

Package designers must occasionally compromise between the requirement for good folding ability, high tensile strength or high burst strength (qualities requiring a long fiber but resulting in poor formation) and good printability (a quality requiring short fiber, but resulting in a loss of physical strength properties).

Recovered or recycled fiber will have properties inherited from the original fiber source, but with the provision that every repulping process degrades and reduces fiber length. Recycled kraft (discussed next under Pulping Methods) will still have good strength, though not as much as virgin kraft, while recycled newsprint, already a short fiber, will be degraded further. Postconsumer waste may contain a variety of extraneous contaminants, many of which cannot be removed. The principal contaminants are water-insoluble adhesives, plastic debris and nonremovable printing inks. These appear in the finished sheet as tiny bits of color, "grease" spots, and "shiners."

Pulping Methods

Wood, regardless of species, is about 50% cellulose. Carbohydrates and lignin, the other principal components, are unsuitable for papermaking because of their nonfibrous nature. Lignins, the natural adhesive that binds cellulose fiber together, is chemically not as stable as cellulose and discolors readily. Lignins are not water soluble and so can't be easily removed by simple water washing. Water-soluble carbohydrates such as sugars and starches are dissolved and removed during pulping. Softwoods contain significant amounts of rosin-like substances that must be removed.

Cellulose fiber can be separated from the wood mass in a number of ways, and each method produces a different quality of pulp. The fastest and most economical method of extracting cellulose from wood is to mechanically abrade or cut the wood (See figure 5.2). However, the mechanical action breaks fibers and reduces their effective length. These groundwood, or mechanical pulps are used for lower-quality papers such as newsprint, and for blending with other, more expensive pulps to reduce cost or to improve formation.

The least fiber damage occurs when chemicals are used to dissolve away the natural lignin binders in wood, leaving the fiber bundles intact and undamaged. Several chemical processes can be used; the two most common are based on alkali sulfate and acid sulfites. The strongest chemical pulps are produced by alkali sulfate extraction, more commonly known as the kraft (German for strength) process. Sulfate extraction is preferred for softwoods because it is able to emulsify and remove resinous components.

Kraft pulp costs substantially more than mechanical pulp and is used where maximum strength is required. Natural kraft is the mainstay of the corrugated box and multiwall shipping bag industries. Bleached kraft is used for many food and display packaging applications, particularly where the board may be exposed to wet conditions.

Mechanical pulping and chemical pulping represent the two extremes in both cost and resulting pulp quality. Intermediate in cost and properties are pulps made by semichemical processes (the wood mass is partly digested by chemicals before mechanical refining) and by thermomechanical processes, (the wood is softened by heating before mechanical refining). Table 5.2 lists the relative strength of pulps produced by these different processes.

Figure 5.2

Early groundwood pulping simply forced logs against a large stone grinding wheel. Much groundwood pulp today is made from wood chips from the lumbering industry.

Table 5.2

Relative strength of pulps produced by different methods. (Source: Smook G.A., *Handbook for Pulp and Paper Technologists*, TAPPI, Atlanta, GA)

Pulp Type	Relative Strength
Stone groundwood hardwood	3
Stone groundwood softwood (newsprint)	5
Semichemical hardwood	5–6
Thermomechanical softwood	6–7
Semichemical softwood	7
Chemical: sulfite hardwood	7
Chemical: kraft hardwood	7–8
Chemical: sulfite softwood	9
Chemical: kraft softwood	10

Preparing Pulp for Papermaking

Cellulose fiber bundles separated from the wood mass are refined (beaten) in order to release small fiber strands, or fibrils. A small amount of refining produces paper with high tear strength (the paper's resistance to tearing) and high absorbency, but lower burst strength (the paper's resistance to rupturing) and lower tensile strength (the strength of paper in tension). Increased refining decreases absorbency and tear strength but increases burst and tensile strengths. High refining levels also reduce paper opacity.

Paper mills adjust the amount of refining to give an optimum property balance for a given application. Grease-resistant papers are made from highly refined pulps, and glassine is paper that has had the maximum fibril separation.

Natural pulps range from a light to a medium brown. Pulps are whitened by bleaching with chlorine-containing compounds or hydrogen peroxide. Chemical bleaching reduces the strength of the final paper and in those applications where mechanical strength properties are at a premium bleaching would be avoided if possible,

Internal Sizing, Additives and Wet-End Treatments

A variety of additives and sizings are added to the pulp in preparation for papermaking. The various types of additives are as follows:

Sizing Agents: Untreated cellulose is essentially a highly absorbent blotting paper. Sizing consists of a group of additives that help control water and ink penetration. Papers with high sizing levels, or "hard-sized" paper, are very water resistant whereas "slack-sized" paper has little or no water hold-out capability.

Starches, gums: Adding starches or gums improves burst and tensile strength, stiffness and pick resistance (the tendency for fibers to "pick" off the paper surface).

Wet-strength resins: Resins are added to improve wet tensile strength retention under high humidity or damp conditions.

"Furnish" is the mixture of fiber, water, and additives that is fed to the papermaking machine. About 98% of furnish is water. A furnish may be a single pulp type or a blend of different fibers selected to give a balance of desired properties at the lowest possible cost. In addition to mixed-fiber furnishes, paper can also be made of individual layers of different fibers matted together to form a multilayer sheet.

REPRESENTATIVE PAPER-MAKING MACHINES

There are many variations on paper-making machines, each imparting its own character to the resulting paper. Only three representative classes will be discussed here: fourdrinier, cylinder, and twin-wire machines.

Fourdrinier Machine

Fourdrinier machines (see Figure 5.3) pump furnish from a headbox directly onto a moving wire screen through which the water is continuously drained. Fourdrinier machines may have a second headbox situated downstream of the first headbox to add further quantities of furnish onto the partially dewatered initial lay-down.

However, it is impractical to add more headboxes to produce thick paperboard on a fourdrinier machine, since the water from each successive addition must drain through fibers that have already been laid down. This limits the thickness of paper produced on a conventional fourdrinier machine. Heavier caliper boards can be made by bringing together the wet pulp layers laid out by two or more completely separate fourdriner machines and pressing these together before the sheet is sent to the drier.

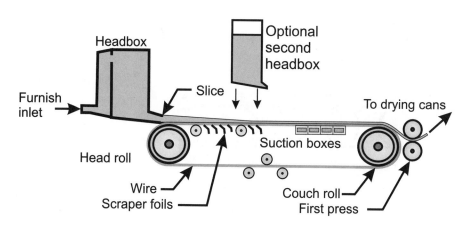

Figure 5.3

Furnish pours out of the headbox of a fourdrinier machine and onto an endless wire or screen where excess water can be drained. The fibers remain trapped on the screen.

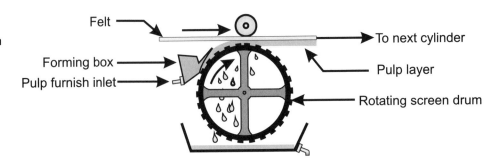

Figure 5.4

A single cylinder station on a cylinder-type machine.

Most free water is removed at the "wet end" of a papermaking machine. At the couch (pronounced "kooch") roll, the wet paper has enough strength to be removed from the wire and passed around a series of heated drying drums where moisture content is brought down to finished-product specifications. The dried paper may go through some further treatments at the dry end of the papermaking process before being wound up into a mill roll.

Cylinder Machines

A cylinder machine (see Figure 5.4) rotates a screen drum in a vat of furnish. (The paper is sometimes called vat lined paper.) As the water pours through the screen, fiber accumulates on the outside of the screen. This thin layer of matted fiber is transferred onto a moving felt belt that passes sequentially over further rotating cylinders, each of which deposits another fiber layer.

Cylinder machines dewater furnish at the cylinder and paste a thin layer of fiber against the felt. (See Figure 5.5) The fibers of subsequent layers do not intermingle and therefore the bond between the layers is weak. The dry end is similar to that of the fourdrinier machine.

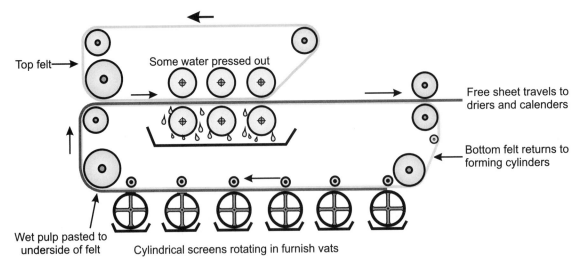

Figure 5.5

A cylinder machine with six cylinders at which paper layers can be formed.

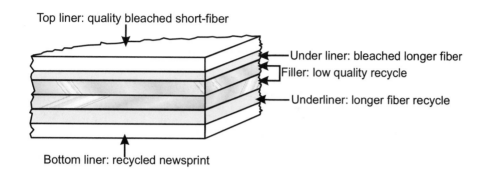

Top liner: quality bleached short-fiber

Under liner: bleached longer fiber

Filler: low quality recycle

Underliner: longer fiber recycle

Bottom liner: recycled newsprint

Figure 5.6

Cylinder boards are multi-ply boards. An advantage is that the plies can all be different.

Cylinder machines don't have the fourdrinier machine's limitation on the number of stations, and six- or seven-station machines are common. Higher-caliper boards for folding and setup cartons are usually cylinder boards. An advantage of cylinder machines is that low-quality fibre can be used to fill or bulk the middle of a board, while higher-quality bleached fibers can be used on one or both liners.

Cylinder board has definite layers, or plies, and individual plies can often be easily separated. Poor interply bonding can produce a variety of packaging problems related to ply delamination. Generally, papers are made on fourdrinier or twin-wire formers, whereas heavier paperboard products are made on cylinder machines. Extremely heavy boards are made by laminating several thinner sheets.

A typical cylinder board construction (see Figure 5.6) may have a top liner composed of good-quality bleached pulp with some short fibers, possibly sized and clay coated to produce a smooth, attractive printing surface. The underliner may also be composed of a good-quality stock, possibly bleached to provide a smooth opaque base for the top liner.

Filler plies use the most economical recycled pulps, since they have little impact on properties such as stiffness. The bottom liner is a better-quality pulp to add stiffness. If appearance is not a factor, the bottom liner may be better quality recycle pulp. If appearance is critical or if the paperboard will be printed on both sides, the bottom liner would also be bleached stock.

Twin-Wire Machines

Vertiformers and twin-wire formers (see Figure 5.7) inject the furnish between two moving wire screens. The advantage is that dewatering takes place on both sides of the paper and is therefore fast. These machines can produce single and multi-ply sheets with identical formation at both faces.

Machine Direction and Cross Direction

Depositing a fiber-and-water slurry onto a moving wire belt tends to align fibers in the direction of travel, known as the machine direction (MD). The direction across the papermaking machine and across the fiber alignment is the cross direction (CD). (See Figure 5.8) Because of this fiber alignment, paper is anisotropic material—measured properties differ depending on the direction in which the

Figure 5.7

Water can be simultaneously removed from both sides of the paper on a twin-wire paper former.

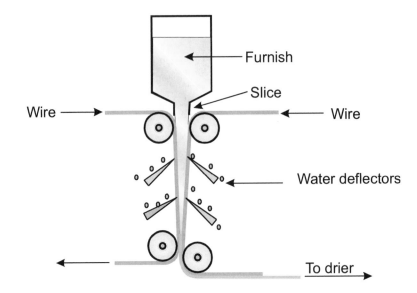

property is measured. Figure 5.9 shows the relationship of tear, stiffness, and fold endurance to machine direction. Paper specification sheets normally show physical values measured in both directions. Package designers need to be aware of paper's directionality. For example, it is much easier to create a tear strip along the machine direction rather than trying to force it in the cross direction.

Cylinder machines tend to align fibers more than fourdrinier machines. Tensile strength ratios in MD and CD for a typical fourdrinier board are about 2:1, while for a cylinder board the ratio might be 4:1 or higher, meaning that the MD tensile strength is four times greater than the CD tensile strength. The greater the degree of fiber alignment, the greater the difference in a given property when measured in MD and CD. The ratio of a property in the two directions is often used as a gauge of fiber alignment.

Surface or Dry-End Treatments and Coatings

After the paper is formed and dried, it is usually passed between multiple sets of heavy rolls. (See Figure 5.10) This "calendering" operation has many variations, but the prime objective is to improve caliper consistency and iron and smooth out the surface of the paper stock to make it more suitable for printing. Calendering also compresses the paper sheet, giving a denser product and glossier surface.

Figure 5.8

Fibers in a manufactured paper sheet tend to align themselves in the machine direction.

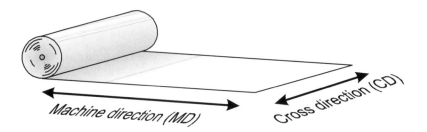

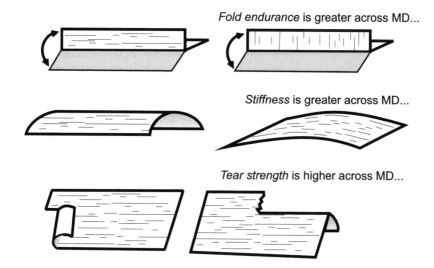

Fold endurance is greater across MD...

Stiffness is greater across MD...

Tear strength is higher across MD...

Figure 5.9

The relationship between MD and tear, stiffness and fold endurance properties.

Finished paper can have a number of surface sizings and/or coatings applied at the dry end in order to further improve surface characteristics. Starch is a typical surface sizing used to bind fibers together and reduce liquid penetration rate. Surface coatings made with pigments such as clay, calcium carbonate and titanium dioxide fill in irregularities between the fibers to produce an exceptionally smooth printing surface as well as improving gloss and brightness. Coated papers are usually called "clay-coated" regardless of the actual formulation. Coated papers are calendered to maintain a high-quality smooth surface.

If clay-coated paper is passed under highly polished chrome drums that are rotating counter to the paper or faster than the paper speed, the clay coatings will be polished. These are referred to as machine glazed or chrome coated papers.

Poorly bonded clay coatings can cause printing and adhesive bonding problems. A common problem experienced in lithographic printing is when the extremely tacky lithographic ink picks off a small particle of clay. This particle adheres to the blanket cylinder resulting in a small spot or "hicky" being printed with every subsequent impression. Clay lift describes a situation where an adhesive has bonded well to a clay surface coating but the bond has separated

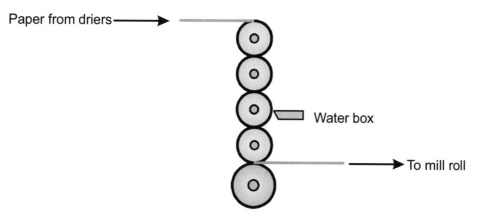

Paper from driers

Water box

To mill roll

Figure 5.10

Calendering consists of passing the formed dried paper between sets of heavy rolls. The paper surface may be dampened to help in smoothing the surface.

because the clay lifted away from the paper base. In addition, highly sized and clay-coated boards can be difficult to bond with water-based adhesive because of poor liquid penetration and the inability of the adhesive to bond to the underlying fibers. Adhesives need to be appropriate to the paper's properties and, where necessary, coated boards should have perforations in the adhesive bond areas so that adhesive can penetrate to the body of the paper.

With such a large number of principal variables (and many lesser ones), it is easy to understand that no two paper mills in the world will produce an identical paper, and that even a single mill might have difficulties producing within a tight tolerance level from day to day.

PAPER CHARACTERIZATION

Caliper and Weight

The prime specifying values for paper or paperboard include caliper, or thickness, and a value expressing a density. Both inch/pound and metric units are used, and different units may be used for different mill products. Care should be taken to know exactly what units are being quoted.

In inch/pound units:

- Caliper is expressed in thousandths of an inch or in "points." One thousandth of an inch is 1 point. (For example, a 0.020-in. board would be 20 points).

- Containerboard for the corrugated board industry and most paperboards are specified by the weight in pounds per 1,000 square feet, the "basis weight."

- Fine papers may be specified by the weight in pounds per ream. A ream is 500 sheets, but the actual sheet size can vary depending on the product. In most instances a ream is taken to be 3,000 square feet.

In metric:

- Caliper is expressed in micrometres (properly abbreviated as "μm" (the symbol is difficult to find on a keyboard, and it is commonly written as "um"). Millimetres are sometimes used, but micrometres have the advantage of eliminating the decimal point.

- Paper mass/unit area relationship is reported as "grammage," defined as being the mass (weight) of paper in 1 square metre regardless of the paper type.

The metric conversion factors are:

> pounds/1000 sq. ft. × 4.88 = grams/per sq. m
> 0.001 inch = 25.4 μm (usually rounded to 25 μm)
> Therefore one point (0.001 inch) = 25 micrometres
> A 20 point paperboard would be 500 micrometres (20 × 25)

Brightness

Brightness is a measure of the total reflectance of white light. Values are expressed on a scale of 1 to 100, with 0 representing black (no light reflection) and 100 the reflection from magnesium oxide, the brightest material known at the time. The value is not a percentage. In more recent times it was discovered that titanium dioxide pigments have an even higher brightness value. Hence some photographic papers are 108 bright and higher. Brightness should not be confused with "whiteness," which is a color description much as red or yellow is. Most packaging papers range between 78 and 84 bright. The cost of higher brightness papers becomes prohibitive. The brighter the board, the more brilliant the graphic possibilities. Paper stock brightness is a specification value for printing papers.

Paper and Moisture Content

Paper is hygroscopic and absorbs and loses moisture according to the ambient relative humidity (R.H.) and temperature. Paper at 20% R.H. will contain about 4% moisture, while at 80% R.H., it will contain about 15% moisture. (Paper equilibrium moisture content will vary slightly depending on whether equilibrium is reached from a lower humidity or a higher humidity. (This effect is known as hysteresis.) By convention, accurate moisture analysis is done by bringing paper to equilibrium from a lower humidity. Table 5.3 shows the equilibrium moisture content of paper and paperboard at different temperatures and humidity levels.

The physical properties of paper vary dramatically with moisture content, and in some applications the moisture content of the paper during processing must be controlled. Where strength is an important design factor, paperboard should be selected to perform at the highest anticipated R.H. Because physical characterization values depend on moisture content, *all paper testing must be*

Table 5.3
Equilibrium moisture content for paper and paperboard.

Temperature					% Relative Humidity					
°C	(°F)	10%	20%	30%	40%	50%	60%	70%	80%	90%
−1.1	(30)	2.5	4.3	6.0	7.3	8.3	9.6	12.3	15.5	22.5
4.4	(40)	2.4	4.3	5.9	7.3	8.1	9.4	12.1	15.4	22.0
10.0	(50)	2.4	4.2	5.8	7.2	8.0	9.2	11.9	15.3	21.5
15.6	(60)	2.3	4.2	5.8	7.1	7.9	9.1	11.7	15.2	21.0
21.1	(70)	2.2	4.0	5.8	7.0	7.8	9.0	11.4	15.0	20.5
26.7	(80)	2.1	4.0	5.7	6.9	7.7	8.8	11.2	14.8	20.0
32.2	(90)	2.0	4.0	5.5	6.7	7.5	8.6	11.0	14.4	19.8
37.8	(100)	1.9	3.8	5.3	6.5	7.3	8.4	10.7	14.0	19.5
43.3	(110)	1.9	3.7	5.1	6.2	7.0	8.2	10.4	13.7	19.1

Figure 5.11

Paper's hygroexpansive nature can cause unwanted curling when paper is bonded to an environmentally stable surface.

Paper/foil laminate at 40% R.H.

Paper/foil laminate at 20% R.H.

Paper/foil laminate at 80% R.H.

done at a precisely controlled temperature and humidity. Internationally, the standard conditions are specified as 23°C and 50% R.H.

Paper is hygroexpansive: when it absorbs moisture, it expands, when it dries; it shrinks. Between 0 and 90% RH, the dimensions can change 0.8% in the MD and 1.6% in CD. A 1% shrinkage over a 1-metre (3-ft.) carton blank is 10 millimetre. (about 0.4 in.) Such a difference can play havoc with printing and die-cutting register.

Whenever a paper sheet is laminated to, or coated with, a material that is not affected by moisture (for example, plastic film, aluminum foil or heavy print or varnish), there is the potential of curling when humidity changes. If the paper gains moisture and expands while the surfacing laminate or coating remains the same, the paper will curl towards the surfacing material. When the paper loses moisture, it will shrink and curl away from the surfacing material. (See Figure 5.11)

Viscoelasticity

Paper exhibits viscoelastic properties meaning that certain strength values will depend on the rate that a load is applied. Simply put, the faster a load is applied, the greater the apparent strength. Over long loading periods, paper fibers move and distort or "creep." Long-term static compressive strength is much less than dynamic compressive strength. For example, corrugated boxes tested at 500-kilogram-load compressive strength in the laboratory (a fast loading rate is dynamic) could be expected to fail in about a year when a 250-kilogram static load is applied in the warehouse.

The tendency for paper fibers to move or acquire a set also means that the longer a knocked-down folding carton blank is kept flat, the greater the permanent set developed at the score lines. The break-open force required to open the carton on a cartoning machine increases, and at some point may reach a level that will cause erecting problems.

PAPER TYPES

One result of the evolution of thousands of small papermaking craft shops into the giant industry of today is an almost complete lack of clarity and consistency in the naming of paper mill products. The Technical Association of the Pulp and Paper Industry (TAPPI) lists no fewer than 479 descriptors of paper mill products—there are 44 descriptors alone for what is called "paperboard" in this text.

Many of these descriptors are confusing or inconsistent. For example, papers made from chemical pulps are described as "wood free," and "boxboard" is described as a material used to make "cartons." Other descriptors are simply historically obsolete. For example, "bristol board" originally described a board produced in Bristol, England, and "manila paper" was made from scrapped manila and hemp rope. Names such as "railroad manila" and "cracker-shell" reflect an original customer or application. In addition, paper manufacturers have proprietary names for paper, and there is little uniformity in the names of the different types and grades.

The terminology chosen in the following lists of paper and paperboard types has been selected to describe, as closely as possible, the actual fiber make-up and construction of the product or a significant current use.

Most papers are made on fourdrinier or twin-wire machines. Unlike multi-ply boards, papers are usually composed of a single pulp type or blend. In a few instances additional layers are laid on from additional headboxes. Some papers are designed for particular printing processes, and it is important for the paper supplier to know which process will be used.

Newsprint and Related Grades. Newsprint is composed of up to 95% economical mechanical or groundwood pulps. Runability is a prime requisite, and higher-quality pulps are sometimes added to improve strength qualities. Standard newsprint is about 49 grams per square metre (10 lb per 1000 sq. ft.). Newsprint has relatively low brightness, typically 55 to 65, and has low physical strength properties. Newspaper inks are primarily oil and carbon, and high oil absorbency is a desirable characteristic in newsprint.

Book Papers. Like newsprint, book and catalogue papers are also mostly based on mechanical pulp, but are sized and clay coated to varying degrees to improve surface appearance and printing qualities. Inexpensive pocket books are printed on heavier calipers of similar paper. The papers used in popular magazines are about 50% mechanical pulp and are coated and calendered to provide good white printing surfaces.

Commercial Papers. Commercial papers cover a broad range of products, many of them specifically designed for particular applications. They are generally based partly on groundwood and they are invariably coated. Such papers are used for higher-quality journals and books and for general office purposes. Brightness usually ranges from 73 to 85. Papers used for photocopying are designed to withstand the heat of the copying process with a minimum of paper curl and distortion. They also must have controlled electrostatic surface resistance to provide uniform image transfer.

Greaseproof Papers. Greaseproof papers are made from chemical pulps that have been highly refined to break up the fiber bundles. The fine fibers pack densely, providing for a structure that does not readily absorb fluids. Glassine papers are supercalendered, semitransparent greaseproof papers. Parchment papers reduce the fibrous quality of paper even further by treating with sulfuric acid, and in doing so, increase water and grease barrier, as well as transparency.

Greaseproof papers are used for snack foods, cookies, butter and lard wraps, and for other oily, or greasy products. Occasionally they will be used for their semi-transparency properties. Greaseproof paper may be treated with fluorochemicals or poly(vinylidene chloride) to further improve water and grease hold-out. Plastic films have replaced these grades for many applications.

Natural Kraft Paper. Natural kraft is the strongest of the common packaging papers and is used wherever maximum strength is needed. The light brown papers are used in industrial bags, in carry-out grocery bags and as inner plies in multiwall bags. Impact strength is imparted to some kraft paper used for industrial bags by crepeing the paper. The slight extensibility gives the paper greater shock resistance (tensile energy absorption). Paper for carry-out bags can be machine finished (calendered) to provide a pleasing surface gloss. The fibrous nature and color of natural kraft paper does not lend itself to fine printing.

Bleached Krafts and Sulfites. Where appearance is important, kraft paper can be bleached. However bleaching will reduce paper strength somewhat. For applications where the material will be printed, the kraft would be coated to smooth the surface. Flour and sugar bags are typical applications. Low-density bleached kraft and sulfite papers are used to produce "dry waxed" paper. Highly calendared bleached kraft and sulfites are used for "wet waxing," where the wax coats the surface and produces a high surface gloss.

Tissue Paper. "Tissue" is a generic term for any light paper. In packaging, tissue is used for protective wrapping and as a laminating component.

Label Paper. Label papers are similar to book papers. Generally, the printing quality required will determine the grade to be used. For example, uncoated papers are used only for line copy and simple text. Machine-finished papers provide good results up to about a 110-line screen, and supercalendered paper is needed for higher line screens.

Most papers used for label printing are clay coated on one or both sides. Coated paper can be made in matte, dull, gloss and high-gloss finishes. Cast-coated paper is made by drying a clay coating in contact with a heated highly polished chromed drum. The process results in a very smooth, extremely glossy surface.

Pouch Papers. Pouch papers are supercalendered virgin kraft papers that have been treated with a plasticizer to make them more pliable. They are high density, are very strong and have a smooth surface finish. Pouch papers treated to have alkali resistance are used for soap wrappers.

Containerboards (linerboard and medium). Containerboard specifically refers to linerboard and medium produced for use in the manufacture of corrugated board. Linerboard is a solid kraft board made specifically for the liners (facings) of corrugated fiberboard. Performance characteristics are governed by carrier specifications. Most linerboard is natural kraft run on a machine with two headboxes. The inner face is somewhat rougher to promote good gluing to the medium. The outer liner of a linerboard is sometimes made of bleached kraft stock. The bleached liner is not heavy enough to totally hide the natural kraft underlayer resulting in a somewhat mottled or off-white appearance.

Medium is the material used to produce the fluted core of corrugated fiberboard. The desired properties are glueability, stiffness, formability and runability. Most medium is made to an industry specification of 127 grams per square metre and 229-micrometres caliper. (26 lb. per 1,000 sq. ft. and 0.009 in.) Medium is made from semichemical hardwood pulps and from recycled kraft containers. Medium board is the one paper product where lignin content is an asset; it imparts thermoformability properties to the board.

PAPERBOARD GRADES

Chipboard, Cardboard, Newsboard. Chipboard is made from 100% recycled fiber and is the lowest-cost paperboard. Colors range from light gray to brown. Chipboard is unsuitable for printing and has poor folding qualities due to its short fiber length. Chipboards often contain blemishes and impurities from the original paper application. They are used for set-up boxes, partitions, backings and other applications where appearance and foldability are not critical.

The term "cardboard" is a depreciated term not commonly used among paper professionals, but occasionally is applied to describe chipboard-type products. Newsboard is a low grade board made mostly with recycled newspapers.

Bending Chipboard. Bending chipboard is a slightly better grade of chipboard. It is still primarily composed of recycled fiber, but with enough higher-quality fiber to allow scoring and folding. Usually a gray or light tan, it is the lowest-cost board used for folding cartons.

Lined Chipboard. Lined chipboard has had a white face-liner applied to improve appearance and print quality. Bending characteristics and filler and back liner colors will vary depending on ply composition. Lined chipboard may or may not be clay-coated. Single white-lined, double white-lined and clay-coated newsback are varieties of lined chipboard. (See below.)

Single White-Lined (SWL) Paperboard. The top liner of single white-lined paperboard is 100% new pulp or high-quality recycled pulp. The back is usually gray or brown. It is a smooth board with a typical brightness of 60 to 85. SWL is used for folding cartons where the appearance of the back is not critical. The board may or may not be clay coated.

Clay-Coated Newsback (CCNB). This is a single white-lined paperboard in which the back and sometimes filler plies are made from recycled newsprint. The back liner has a neutral pale gray color that is judged to be more aesthetically acceptable for some applications than the mixed browns of other SWL boards.

Double White-Lined (DWL) Paperboard. Double white-lined paperboard is similar to SWL except that both front and back have been lined with a bleached white pulp. Usually, the back liner is somewhat less finished than the front. DWL is used where the internal appearance of the box is important or where both sides will be printed. The primary face is usually clay coated.

Solid Bleached Sulfate (SBS). SBS is a strong premium paperboard composed of 100% bleached sulfate pulps. SBS boards are white throughout. They are used in applications where total board appearance is of primary importance and where maximum physical properties are required for the given weight of board. Because SBS boards are made from virgin pulps, properties vary less during a run than for a similar lined chipboard. Many high-speed packaging operations prefer SBS for its consistent line performance even though from other considerations a lined chipboard may have been adequate.

Food Board. Highly sized SBS paperboards are often called food board. These are used for wet foods, frozen food cartons and other applications where good performance under wet conditions is important.

Solid Unbleached Sulfate (SUS). SUS is a maximum strength unbleached kraft paperboard. Where surface appearance is important, the board will be heavily clay-coated, sometimes with a double coat to provide the opacity needed to hide the brown kraft body. Beverage baskets (6-packs) are a major application of clay coated solid-unbleached sulfate.

SELECTED METHODS OF PAPER CHARACTERIZATION

The majority of paper characterization methods are sponsored by The American Society for Testing and Materials (ASTM) or the Technical Association of the Pulp and Paper Industry (TAPPI). A few of the most common standard testing procedures for paper and paperboard are listed below.

Conditioning Paper and Paper Products (ASTM D 685 / TAPPI T 402). All paper products must be tested under controlled temperature and humidity conditions. International conditions for paper testing are 23°C and 50% RH.

Grammage of Paper and Paperboard (ASTM D 646 / TAPPI T 410). Procedure for determining the weight (mass) per unit area, otherwise known as the basis weight. ASTM D 646 contains ream-weight conversion factor tables.

Thickness of Paper, Paperboard and Combined Board (TAPPI T 411). Since paper is compressible, the pressure of the micrometer foot must be accurately controlled. Several readings must be averaged to assign a paper caliper.

Moisture Content by Oven Drying (ASTM D 644). Moisture content is expressed on an oven-dry basis.

Brightness (TAPPI T 452). Brightness measures the total spectral reflectance.

Gloss at 75 Degrees (TAPPI T 480). Glossiness quantifies surface shine.

Opacity (TAPPI T 425 / TAPPI T 519). Opacity is most important for thinner papers where it is important that printing on reverse faces not show through.

Petroleum Wax in Paper (ASTM D 590 / TAPPI T 405). Used to determine the amount of paraffin in waxed papers.

Internal Tearing Resistance of Paper (TAPPI T 414). Use to assign a value to the force required to tear paper in CD and MD. Commonly called the Elmendorf Tear Test.

Water Absorption (TAPPI T 441). Measures the amount of water absorbed by a given paper area in a given time. The Cobb test is intended to be used with sized papers and paperboards.

Tensile Breaking Strength of Paper and Paperboard (ASTM D 828 / TAPPI T 404). A measure of paper strength in tension.

Folding Endurance (ASTM D 2176 / TAPPI T 423 / TAPPI T 511). ASTM's method is the M.I.T. test. TAPPI also has a standard for the Schopper fold endurance test.

Resistance of Nonporous Paper to Passage of Air (ASTM D 726 / TAPPI T 460). Passage of air is governed by a paper's porosity. It is related to absorbency and has been used to indicate rotogravure ink absorption and to gauge filtering ability. Known as the Gurley Porosity test.

Bursting Strength of Paper (ASTM D 774 / TAPPI T 403). Measures the resistance to rupture. Also known as the Mullen Burst test.

Moldabilty (TAPPI T 512). Quantifies crease retention or springback.

Wax Pick Test for Surface Strength of Paper (ASTM D 2482 / TAPPI T 459). An arbitrary assessment of paper surface strength, the test uses a series of waxes having different adhesive values. Poor bonding of surface fibres or coatings can cause printing and gluing problems. Also known as the Dennison Wax Pick Test.

Grease Resistance (TAPPI T 454). Important for greasy product applications.

Water Vapor Transmission (ASTM E 96 / TAPPI T 464). Usually done on barrier-coated or glassine-type papers.

Smoothness (TAPPI T 479). Surface smoothness relates to printability and other surface-influenced characteristics such as coefficient of friction.

Stiffness (TAPPI T 451 / TAPPI T 489). Stiffness is measured in Taber Stiffness units. Stiffness of a paperboard is important in maintaining a flat face on a carton's main display panel.

1. What is the difference between softwood and hardwood as a source of wood pulp for papermaking?

2. Cellulose fiber can be separated from the wood mass by several means. Name the two main methods, and give the advantages and disadvantages of each method.

3. What is the standard international test environment for all paper and paperboard testing? Why is it important to do paper characterization tests under these conditions?

4. Why is it difficult to print a natural kraft paper?

5. Paper is hygroscopic. What does this term mean?

6. What are MD and CD? Why it is important for a carton designer to know them?

7. Discuss the impact of fiber length on paper properties.

8. Paper is made with different machines, each machine imparting certain characteristics. In most discussions, paper is referred to as coming from two types of papermaking machines. What are these machines, and what is the principal characteristic that indicates what kind of machine it came from?

9. What is a 20-point board?

10. How is paper caliper (thickness) correctly specified in (a) metric units and (b) inch/pound units?

11. Paper is often coated at the paper mill. What is the principal coating material and what does it do?

12. What is the difference between a hard sized and a slack sized paper?

13. Discuss the benefits and problems of postconsumer waste paper as a fiber source for papermaking.

14. What is the strongest and what is the weakest papermaking pulp?

15. What kind of paperboard would you select for making a beverage basket? (a six pack holder)?

16. A paperboard specimen can be peeled apart into seven layers. What does this tell you?

17. Is there a difference between "whiteness" and "brightness" when we are describing paperboard? Define these terms.

18. What kind of pulp is kraft paper made from, and what are the distinguishing characteristics of kraft paper?

19. Is there a difference between paper and paperboard?

20. What might give you a clue that a paperboard contained recycled materials?

21. Which paper would be stronger: mechanical softwood or mechanical hardwood?

22. What problem would be encountered if we tried to make a thick paperboard on a conventional Fourdrinier machine?

23. Explain why paper products are typically specified by *both* caliper and grammage (basis weight).

24. Paper is hygroexpansive. What does this term mean, and where might this property affect your packaging?

25. Name two typical softwoods and two typical hardwoods.

26. You want to design a box with a tear strip around the perimeter. What instrument would you use to evaluate the characteristic in question?

27. What problem might be encountered if a highly sized board was used for making a folding carton?

28. What is the probable makeup of chipboard, and where might you use it?

29. The Cobb test measures the level of a particular paper treatment. What is that treatment?

30. What is the makeup of a glassine paper? Where might it be used?

31. What paper properties will calendering affect?

32. What paper properties does refinement affect? Name an application where low refinement is desirable and an application where high refinement is desirable.

33. Which of the following characteristics is highest in MD: tear, fold endurance, or stiffness?

34. What is formation, and what qualities contribute to poor and good paper formation? What is the significance of formation to the paper user?

35. What is the moisture content of paper at standard test conditions?

36. A foil-laminated label stock is causing problems because the labels are curling. What is the cause of this behaviour?

CONTENTS

Paperboard Package Classifications

Common paperboard constructions: folding cartons, beverage baskets, setup cartons, gable-top containers, Tetra Pak and Combibloc systems, tubs, trays.

Folding Carton Design

Design considerations: single or repeated entry, weight, access prior to purchase, siftproof, single or double glued, erection method, tamper resistance, long-term storage, irregular shapes, loading method, machinery restrictions, consumer needs, retailing needs.

Selecting the Correct Paperboard

Physical strength, moisture and grease resistance, machinability, printing requirements, suggested board calipers.

The Carton Production Process

Concept development, hand samples, typical approval points, importance of sign-offs, cutting and creasing dies, crease formation and geometry, folding paperboard, bleed, single and double knifing, press approval and color standards, secondary and finishing operations, prebreaking of creases, paper set.

Basic Tube-style Folding Cartons

Definition, working creases, principal display panels, dimensioning, grain direction, full-overlap seal-end cartons, tuck-end orientation, windowed cartons, press sheet utilization, friction locks and skit locks, typical tube-style carton dimensions, self-erecting closures, tuck-and-tongue locks, gable-top cartons, fifth-panel designs, internal partitions.

Basic Tray-style Folding Cartons

Definition, Beers tray variations, tray grain direction, Brightwood tray variations, mechanical self-locking trays, frame-vue tray.

Beverage Baskets and Setup Boxes

Beverage basket material, partition selection. Setup box definition, advantages, limitations, applications, material selection, coverings, style examples.

Paperboard Resources

Books and associations related to paperboard packaging.

PAPERBOARD PACKAGE CLASSIFICATIONS

Paperboard provides a versatile and economical material not readily matched by other packaging mediums. One significant advantage is the low tooling cost compared with that for materials such as plastics. Effective paperboard package design is based partly on knowledge of paper and product properties and partly on craftsmanship and art. Paperboard packaging can be considered in a number of categories:

Folding cartons. Folding cartons are by far the largest and most important group in paperboard packaging. Folding cartons are made as flat blanks or as preglued forms that can be flattened for shipping. They can be made economically on high-speed production machinery. The majority of folding carton designs can be classified as falling into either the tube-style or tray-style families.

Within these carton families are many highly specialized variations. The gable-top container is basically a tube-style carton that has found many applications, particularly for dairy products and fruit juices. The heavily sized and polyethylene-coated board is erected and heat-sealed at the point of fill. Combibloc and Tetra Pak and are similar-appearing proprietary cartons made from complex paper/poly/foil/poly laminates. A principal application is for aseptic beverage packaging such as juice boxes.

Not all folding cartons are actually box-like containers. Beverage baskets or carriers are typically designed to hold four or six beverage bottles.

Setup boxes. Setup boxes are rigid cartons that are delivered erected and ready for filling. Because they are already "set up," they need as much storage space empty as they do when full. The rigidity of setup boxes creates an upscale image for products. The sturdiness of setup boxes also makes them desirable for applications where the container acts as a storage unit.

Tubs, trays and liquid resistant boxes. Paperboard can be formed into round or square tubs with paper end seals. Such forms, constructed from food board, are used to contain such items as ice cream and frozen foods. Flat sheets with gusseted corners can be folded to form food trays for frozen entrees or other food products. In most wet food applications, the board is coated with either polyethylene or wax. Dual ovenable paperboard trays are coated or laminated with an oven-temperature-tolerant plastic such as poly(ethylene terephthalate).

FOLDING CARTON DESIGN

Good carton designs are not merely inspired creations. They are the product of careful analysis that considers product requirements, retailing factors, production requirements, consumer needs and other inputs essential for a successful package.

Carton design considerations always start with the product itself. Since the product's nature dictates how it will be filled, how it will be sold and how it will be used, product and carton design must be considered together. The first decision is to select the primary carton shape, for example, tube-style, tray-style or some other basic structural shape. After these decisions have been made, a great deal of carton design has to do with selection of the closure type and its location. For tube-style cartons, the following factors may influence the choice of closure:

- Will the carton hold a self-contained package? If the carton is to hold another package, such as a can or bottle, simple tuck flaps (see Figure 6.12) are adequate closures, since the designer need not be concerned with contamination, sifting or infestation. Tuck flaps have the advantage of not requiring a glue station at the fill point.

- Will there be one entry or repeated entry before discarding? If the tuck flap is a one-time-entry item, it should have a slit-lock feature that will provide a more positive and secure closure. (See Figure 6.15) This is particularly useful for heavier products or when the board itself is springy. Well-designed slit locks will tear the carton tuck flap on opening.

   For repeated-entry cartons, a plain friction-lock tuck flap will provide a neater appearance over the carton's use life.

- Will the consumer wish to see the product before purchase? If the consumer wants to see the product, add an opening or window. However, in some instances, the consumer will want to touch the product. For such cases, the closure must allow entry without destroying the package. Plain tuck flaps are indicated.

- Is the product particularly heavy? Heavier products need greater security in the tuck flap. Locking tabs such as the tongue or edge lock provide a positive tuck-flap lock. (See Figure 6.17)

- Does the product require sift-proof construction? If the product is not contained in a separate primary package, the carton requires double-glued end seals. Double gluing puts adhesive bonds on both minor and major flaps, providing a more effective block against sifting or entry of foreign agents. (See Figure 6.1)

- What is the nature of the packaging operation? Manual, semiautomatic and fully automatic operations are best complimented by different de-

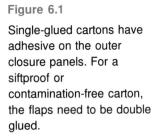

Figure 6.1

Single-glued cartons have adhesive on the outer closure panels. For a siftproof or contamination-free carton, the flaps need to be double glued.

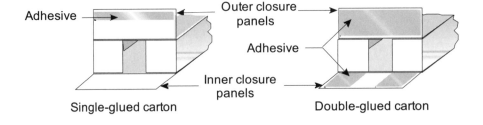

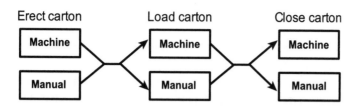

Figure 6.2

Each step in a
carton-packing operation
can be done by machine or
manually. Carton design is
influenced by the parrticular
sequence being used.

signs. (See Figure 6.2) Manual erection could call for preglued or automatic-erecting features such as a Himes lock or 1-2-3 lock for the bottom closure. (See Figure 6.16) Typically, the top closure would be a tuck flap.

- Does the carton need a seal to prevent casual entry? Single-glued flaps close the carton ends with adhesive applied along the major carton flaps. This provides security against casual entry.

- Will the consumer use the box as a storage container? A method of tidy entry, closure for storage and re-entry may be desired for boxes that the consumer will be using over a long time period. Setup boxes with removable lids are useful, provided the added cost is acceptable.

- Is irregular shape an advantage? Rectangular shapes are the most convenient for shipping and displaying, but some products are effectively marketed in other shapes. While irregular shapes may provide unique shelf appearance, they are more difficult to pack and ship. Obtaining machinery that will handle unique shapes can also be a problem. Approach irregular shapes with caution.

- Will the product be loaded by dropping product vertically or by sliding product horizontally into the erected carton? (See Figure 6.3) Horizontal end-loading tube-style cartons are essentially the same as vertical end-

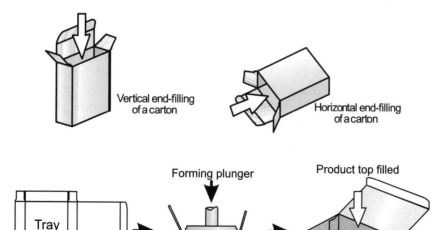

Vertical end-filling of a carton

Horizontal end-filling of a carton

Forming plunger

Product top filled

Tray blank

To filling station

Top fill Brightwood style tray

Figure 6.3

A vertical end-loading
carton, a horizontal
end-loading carton and a
top-loading carton.

loading tube styles, except that the filling orientation has changed. Some attention may have to be given to the direction in which the flaps open.

Vertical end-loading is the preferred loading method, since it is assisted by gravity. Granular or powdered products must be loaded through a vertically oriented end. Most multicomponent products, including primary packages with inserted instructions, are best loaded this way. Products such as convenience dinners, pizzas and cakes have definite horizontal orientations and cannot be dropped vertically. These must be handled gently and pushed horizontally into the carton.

Cartoning machines designed for horizontal end-loading tend to be more complicated than those for vertical end-loading, since a conveyor to transport the product parallel to the cartons and a mechanism to transfer the product into the carton are needed.

- Is the product best loaded through a large opening? Some products are best loaded through the largest possible opening such as that found on a tray-style carton. However, a glued tray in effect becomes a setup box that cannot be knocked down flat for shipping unless additional creases are put into the end panels to allow for the carton to fold flat. These extra creases affect the stiffness and rigidity of the finished tray. In some applications, this is undesirable.

  Where a stiff top-loading tray is required, flat, unglued tray blanks are sent to the filler. The packager uses a carton erector, a relatively simple machine that erects the carton with adhesive or locking tabs. The flat blanks of cartons such as the Brightwood tray (See Figure 6.23) are pressed through a forming frame and glued to a stiff setup-carton shape. (See Figure 6.3) Since top-loading cartons can be shipped as unglued blanks, they have the advantage of being palletized horizontally and flat.

  Dimensionally unstable products such as apparel are best packed in top loaders. Gift boxes that open at the top provide attractive display possibilities and are frequently used to create countertop displays for small items.

- Will machinery restrictions limit design options? A frequently overlooked point is that the carton must be manufactured on existing equipment. The type of erecting and filling machine to be used will also dictate certain design features. Clearances and setbacks are necessary to allow the machine to open cartons and move flaps and closure panels. Dust flaps are usually shorter than a closure panel so that machine "fingers" can pass over the dust flap and fold down the closure panel.

- How will the consumer use the product? Packages must fit conventional storage locations such as medicine cabinets or refrigerators. Convenient entry, carrying handles, pour spouts, tear tapes, dispensing aids and other devices are easily incorporated into paperboard designs.

- How will the carton be retailed? Carton designs can help the retailer. The package should provide stable displays that attract customers. Provision for easy unpacking, shelving and display are obvious features.

If the carton is designed to be suspended from pegboard-type displays, make certain that the board is strong enough to hold the carton for long periods and through nominal abuse. Cartons that have a center of gravity far in front of the pegboard hole will hang at an angle facing away from the consumer and are particularly prone to tearing.

SELECTING THE CORRECT PAPERBOARD

The most important factors in paperboard selection concern structural requirements and printing and decorating needs. Structural considerations deal with the physical strength characteristics needed to hold the product successfully during shipping and display. Puncture resistance, stiffness, tensile strength, z-direction strength (i.e., the direction perpendicular to CD and MD), directionality, glueability and other paperboard characteristics are also important.

Cartons for wet products or products that will experience damp environments such as freezer storage will need hard-sized, waxed or otherwise-treated paperboards. Oily or greasy products will need grease-resistant boards or treatments. Kraft paper is used where maximum board tear or burst strength is needed.

The board's machinability will affect how fast a carton can be selected from a magazine, pulled open and inserted into the flights of a cartoning machine. Coefficient of friction and consistency of physical properties are key factors related to machinability. More costly solid bleached sulfate (SBS) boards are sometimes preferred over lined chipboards; SBS boards exhibit more consistent properties and run more trouble free on high-speed equipment.

Many papers are designed for specific printing processes, and the suitability of the paper to the proposed printing method should be verified. Mechanical condition and uniformity all have a bearing on a paper's runability.

Printing and decorating is concerned primarily with the characteristics of the paper surface finish:

color	brightness	opacity
smoothness	gloss	cleanliness
surface formation	ink compatibility	dimensional stability

Paperboard qualities vary widely and should be verified for every application. No two paper mills make identical papers even though the papers' generic names may be the same. The key properties required for an application should be determined and compared with boards from different suppliers. Table 6.1 provides convenient starting points for selecting board caliper based on the product weight.

THE CARTON PRODUCTION PROCESS

The carton design process starts with an in-depth review of the customer's needs and objectives. It is important at the initiation of any design project for the customer who will be packaging and marketing the product to share all technical

Table 6.1
Product weight and suggested board caliper.

Approximate Weight	Board Stock Thickness
Up to 230 g (1/2 lb.)	380 to 450 μm (.015 to .018 in.)
450 g (1 lb.)	500 to 600 μm (.020 to .024 in.)
900 g (2 lb.)	700 to 800 μm (.028 to .032 in.)
Over 900 g (> 2 lb.)	900 μm (.036 in.) or consider E- or F-flute corrugated

and marketing expectations. Since carton makers do not keep paperboard stocks on hand for possible orders, it is equally important for the customer to contact the carton maker at an early stage so that paperboard orders can be placed.

The carton designer will develop one or several designs that will meet the customer's stated objectives. A hand sample of each candidate design will be cut, scored and manually assembled for the customer's approval. The customer's approval signature on the hand sample authorizes the carton maker to proceed to the next production steps. (The term "hand sample" is still commonly used although computer-aided-design, or CAD, technology has replaced hand cutting and scoring. Some prefer the more accurate term "CAD sample.") The customer inspects the hand sample, and gives the approval, the first of many, to proceed to the next step.

The customer's approval, or sign-off of a hand sample, starts the carton production process summarized in Figure 6.4. During the production sequence, the customer will be asked for more sign-offs to indicate acceptance of work done to date and to authorize the next phase of the production process. It should be clearly understood that each sign-off constitutes a legally binding contract, and it is the customer's responsibility to ensure that every detail is correct at

Figure 6.4

A typical carton production sequence. The most usual sign-off points are indicated. Other sign-offs may be required depending on the nature of the project.

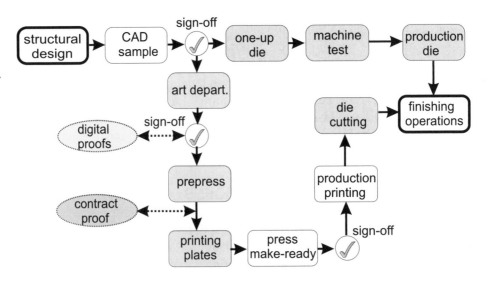

every stage of production. A missed spelling mistake discovered at the end of a production run is the responsibility of the customer not the carton maker.

Digital dimensionally correct records of the approved design are forwarded to graphic arts and die-making departments. Carton layouts are normally shown looking at the outside or printed side.

To produce a folding carton, the flat carton blank must be cut from the press sheet, and the blank must have scores pressed into the board along the lines where the board will be folded to make the carton. Both functions are accomplished by pressing a steel-rule cutting and creasing die into the board. (The terms *crease* and *score* are used interchangeably depending on the region or production plant).

The die maker may produce a one-up die board (i.e., a die that will cut single cartons for design verification purposes). A number of cartons might be produced by hand using the die. These may be used by the customer for cartoning machine or other runability tests, mock-ups, or market tests. Another customer approval may be required before the production die is made. For routine designs, the step of making a one-up die may be eliminated.

Cutting and creasing dies are made by laser-cutting slots into a heavy hardwood plywood base into which the appropriate steel rules are fitted. The blunt, rounded-edge creasing rules must be able to press a valley-like depression into the board. A counter, or tympan, must be placed under the creasing rules to raise the surrounding board and create the relief into which the rule will push the board.

(See Figure 6.5) Cutting rules, on the other hand, need to cut through the paperboard and almost touch the die bed. The final bit of paperboard is split apart by the wedging action of the steel rule much as an axe splits wood. Resilient pads are placed around the cutting rules to act like springs that push the cut board blank off the cutting rules after the cut is made.

A paperboard fold is made with the valley side of the score to the outside of the carton. (See Figure 6.6) As the board is bent, the outside "skin" flattens out, while fiber toward the inside of the fold breaks inward to take up the extra material on the inside radius.

As Figure 6.5 shows, the crease or score along which a carton will be folded can only be formed from one side of the board. Occasionally, a design will require that a board fold toward the die (valley) side rather than away. In these situations, a "cut score," consisting of a series of short perforations cut completely through the board, are used.

Printing plates are designed to print slightly past the edges of a carton. This "bleed" allows for the slight inaccuracies inherent to die-cutting and reduces the possibility of there being an unprinted white streak down a carton's edge. A pair of cutting rules is typically set 6 millimetres (mm) (1/4 in.) apart for separating

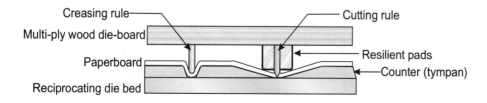

Figure 6.5

Scores are put into the paperboard with blunt-nosed rules. The creasing rule deforms and breaks the paper structure.

Figure 6.6

A paperboard is folded away from the valley side of the score. The distance around the outside of the folded board is greater than around the inside curve. The bead on the inside makes up for this difference.

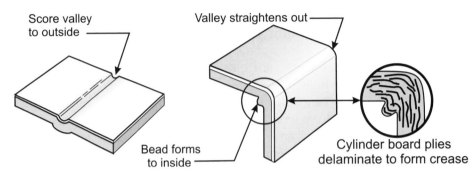

Score valley to outside

Valley straightens out

Bead forms to inside

Cylinder board plies delaminate to form crease

two cartons out of the press sheet. However, if the two cartons are the same color along the entire adjacent edges, a single rule can be used, reducing both die costs and paperboard requirements. (See Figure 6.7).

At the same time as the dies are being made, the art department develops the graphic image that will appear on the carton. When the proofs have been approved, printing plates are made and mounted in the press. The customer is usually called in to give final press approval. The customer and the printer will agree on color standards. Target, lightest acceptable and darkest acceptable carton samples may be filed for control purposes.

After the cartons are printed and secondary operations such as embossing or hot-stamping are completed, the cartons go to be die-cut. Most die-cutting is done on platten presses, but some cartons are cut on faster, but not as accurate, rotary die-cutters. Other finishing operations may include additional carton features such as windows or handholds, or they may simply involve folding, gluing and packing for shipment.

The force needed to erect a carton is a critical value for efficient running on high-speed packaging equipment. The carton manufacturer prefolds or prebreaks all scores on a folding carton so that they can be easily pulled up to the erected shape. (See Figure 6.8) The nature of paper is such that fibers will develop a permanent set over an extended period. Freshly creased cartons have some springiness at the scores and are easily erected. With time, much of this spring is lost, and the cartons become harder to open. As a general rule cartons are best run within 90 days of manufacture.

Improper storage (i.e., cartons that are not kept absolutely flat) will, over time, impart permanent curl or distortion that will interfere with proper carton operation.

Figure 6.7

Single knifing can be used when colors are the same where two carton edges meet. Double knifing is necessary when colors are different.

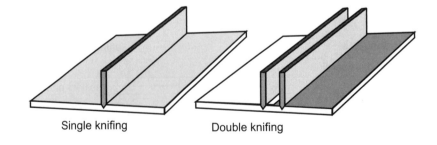

Single knifing

Double knifing

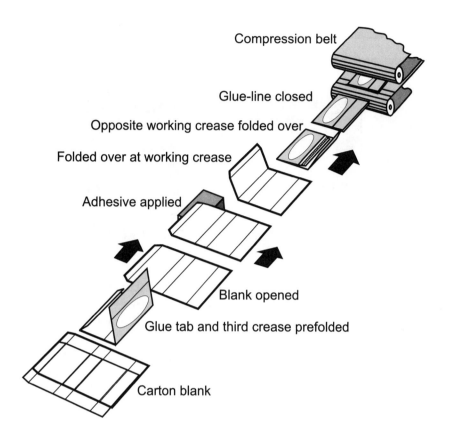

Compression belt

Glue-line closed

Opposite working crease folded over

Folded over at working crease

Adhesive applied

Blank opened

Glue tab and third crease prefolded

Carton blank

Figure 6.8

A carton's body scores are broken by folding and opening inline with the gluing operation. Prebreaking the scores makes it easier to open the carton on filling machines.

BASIC TUBE-STYLE FOLDING CARTONS

The most common carton type is the tube-style folding carton, folded and glued by the carton manufacturer. An open-ended tube can be used as a product sleeve, but more often the tube has some form of top and bottom closure. Cartons are flattened for shipping at the "working scores." (See Figure 6.9) The working

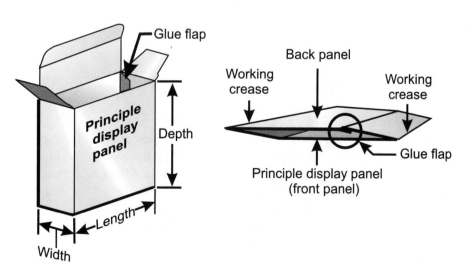

Glue flap

Principle display panel

Depth

Length

Width

Back panel

Working crease

Working crease

Glue flap

Principle display panel (front panel)

Figure 6.9

Carton terminology and placement of the working scores and manufacturer's joint.

Figure 6.10

Carton grain should cross
the corners (right) for
maximum carton stiffness.

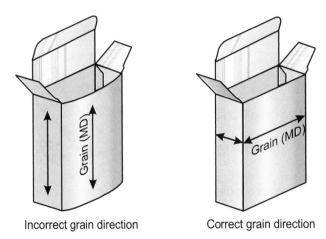

Incorrect grain direction　　　　Correct grain direction

scores are normally the pair not adjacent to the glue flap. Placing the working scores at the glue flap would make folding and flattening of the carton more difficult. The tube is received "knocked down flat" (KDF) by the packager, who erects, fills and closes the carton.

Carton dimensions are always given in the order of length, width and depth, with length and width defined as the carton opening. Depth is perpendicular to the opening. The front, or "principal display panel" (PDP), is the panel situated between the two side panels on the carton blank (i.e., the main panel not adjacent to the glue flap). A normal carton has the glue tab at the right rear corner when viewed from the PDP. (See Figure 6.8)

Grain must be correctly oriented, particularly if the contents are a powder that will bulge the box. (See Figure 6.10) Most tube-style folding cartons have grain, or "paper machine direction" (MD), running around the carton perimeter (i.e., crossing the carton body scores). An end-to-end grain orientation would produce a carton more susceptible to bulging or rounding at the major display panels. Tear strips will be more reliable if they run in the grain direction.

For production purposes, multiple cartons are laid out on a sheet of paperboard (the press sheet) of the size used by the printing and die-cutting presses available. Efficient utilization of the press sheet area is important since paper cost can represent half or more of the finished carton cost. Good designs will minimize board and ink waste.

Sealed-end Cartons

The simplest tube-style folding carton is a full-overlap seal-end (FOSE) carton. The flat blank is essentially a rectangular sheet with appropriate cut-outs for the flaps. FOSE cartons for fine granular or powdered products have the inner and outer closure panels kept at the carton width and the dust flaps cut square. (See Figure 6.11, top closure). The full contact area between the closure panel and the dust flaps allows for full adhesive coverage as used in double gluing (See figure 6.1) to provide a complete, siftproof seal. Where sift proofing or strength are not factors, the closure panels can be cut back to save paperboard. Partial overlap seal end cartons (POSE) cut back closure panels to a point that there is

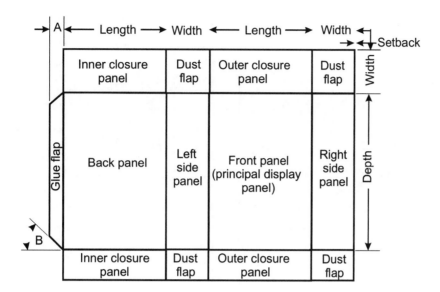

Figure 6.11

A seal-end carton blank. The top end shows a full-overlap seal-end (FOSE), and the bottom shows a partial-overlap seal-end (POSE.)

just enough overlap of the two panels to provide for an adequate glue-line. (See Figure 6.11, bottom closure). POSE closure panels on cereal boxes are typically just slightly over half the carton width. POSE end closures are also known as "economy ends."

Carton dimensions are frequently set back in the order of 0.8 mm (1/32 in.) from the full dimension for aesthetic reasons or to provide a slight clearance to improve machinability. The most common setback is to the carton's right side panel. This improves appearance by moving the cut edge slightly back from the carton corner. Other setbacks on a full-overlap seal-end carton may include narrowing the dust flap slightly so that it does not interfere with the outer closure panel when the carton is sealed.

Tuck Closure Designs

Figure 6.12 shows the four tuck-flap combinations possible on a tuck-end carton. The two reverse-tuck designs are favored because the carton blanks can be better

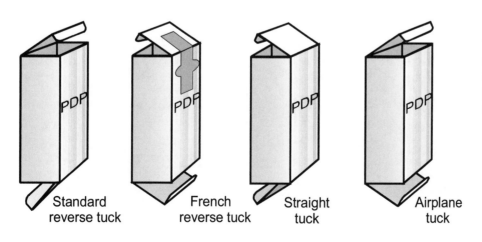

Figure 6.12

Tuck closures can be arranged in various directions relative to the principal display panel (PDP.)

Figure 6.13

A reverse tuck and a straight tuck of identical body dimensions. The reverse-tuck carton (left) has the best board utilization when arranged on a press sheet. A straight tuck (right) is less efficient.

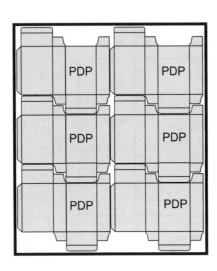
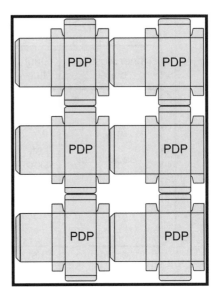

nested into each other on the press sheet (See Figure 6.12) giving the best board utilization. The standard reverse tuck has the top tuck panel tucking toward the carton front. The French reverse tuck is used where a graphic design element continues from the front panel over to the top tuck flap. The French reverse tuck is also favored for upscale products, since it avoids a visible cut edge when viewed from the front.

A straight-tuck design eliminates a visible cut edge at both top and bottom. In those designs calling for a window or cutout on the front panel, a standard reverse tuck could leave an easily damaged, narrow margin of board at the carton top or bottom. Straight-tuck designs avoid this problem by continuing the front panel into the tuck flaps. (See Figure 6.13) Straight tucks may also be preferred for some horizontal end-loading machines where it is necessary to keep both tuck panels clear of the carton openings. Airplane tucks are rarely used.

A carton tuck relying on friction alone to hold it in place does not create a positive closure. Slit-lock closures (See Figure 6.15) incorporate small slits

Figure 6.14

The straight-tuck carton on the right would provide supporting material to the front display panel in those designs that have windows or cutouts. The tuck-flap configuration on the left has less material to support the window, and windowing material glued to the carton interior can interfere with the tuck flap.

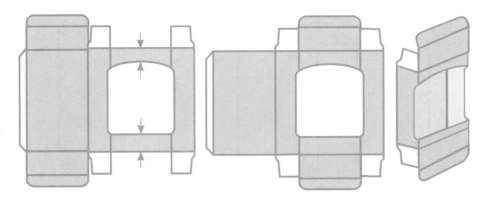

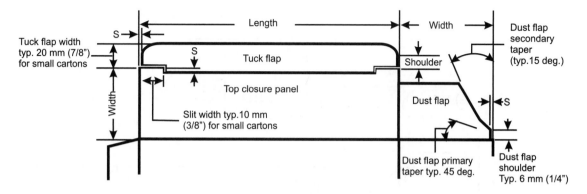

Figure 6.15

Slit-lock tuck closures have slits that engage against the dust flaps to form a more positive closure than a plain friction lock. Slit locks are sometimes called "pie locks." Setbacks (S) are about the board thickness.

between the tuck flap and the top closure panel. When the carton is closed, the slits engage shoulders cut into the dust flaps, securely locking the flap into place. This makes the carton difficult to open without tearing the closure panel. For certain products where the customer wants to open the carton and see the product, a compromise it struck by making a slit lock at the bottom and a friction lock at the top. This is particularly applicable for products such as perfumes or colognes in glass bottles, where it is essential to have a secure bottom closure to ensure the heavy bottle doesn't fall out of the carton while still allowing the customer to inspect the bottle.

Other Closure Variations

Where cartons will be manually erected, variations of snap-lock or Himes bottoms will be used for the bottom closure of the carton. The 1-2-3 snap-lock bottom (See Figure 6.16, top) is the more economical, but requires slightly more time to erect than the Himes bottom lock. (See Figure 6.16, bottom) Himes locks, or crash locks and variations, on them are preglued, automatic bottoms. They are somewhat stronger than the 1-2-3 snap lock.

Tuck-and-tongue locks and edge locks (see Figure 6.17), add security to a tuck flap and allow it to tolerate considerable weight without opening. A tongue discourages opening while still making it possible. Doubled-edge locks provide added security for heavy products and are particularly useful for wide cartons.

The tuck end with an incorporated tear strip (see Figure 6.17) combines the convenience of a tuck end with the security of a glued carton seal. The inner closure panel has been designed with a tuck flap. The outer closure panel is glued over the inner one to provide a secure, tamper-evident carton. The tear strip must be used to open the box.

A gusseted (bellows) closure (see Figure 6.17) can be used to improve carton appearance by eliminating visible cut edges. With frozen food trays and other trays that will hold wet product, gusseted corners rather than glued corners provide a higher level of water resistance.

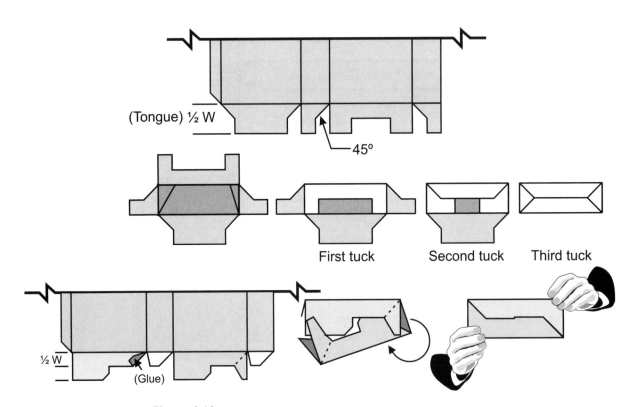

(Tongue) ½ W

—45°

First tuck   Second tuck   Third tuck

½ W

(Glue)

Figure 6.16

Automatic or self-erecting bottoms: a 1-2-3 snap-lock bottom (top) and a Himes lock (bottom).

Gable-top cartons (see Figure 6.18) commonly used for dairy products and fruit juices are a special application of the tube-style carton. Rather than having discreet top and bottom flap closures, all flaps are gusseted. The folded tube is sealed into its finished form by melting and fusing the polyethylene coatings present on both sides of the board. The board can be foil-laminated to improve barrier qualities.

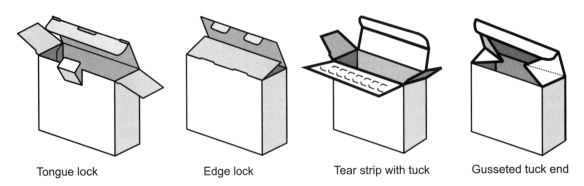

Tongue lock   Edge lock   Tear strip with tuck   Gusseted tuck end

Figure 6.17

Examples of special end closures for tube-style folding cartons.

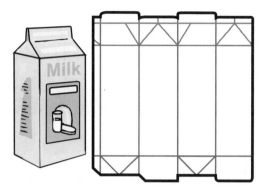

Figure 6.18

A gable-top carton blank and an erected gable-top carton.

The Combibloc carton is a proprietary design similar in many respects to the gable-top carton, except that the top seal is square rather than gabled. While similar in appearance to the Combibloc, the Tetra Pak, another proprietary design, is not a true folding carton because it is delivered as webstock to the user. The material is fed through a form-fill-seal machine, where it is folded into a carton shape, immediately filled and then sealed. Tetra Pak has the advantage over Combibloc and gable-top cartons of being able to create a package with no headspace.

External Design Features and Internal Partitions

A carton design often requires added features that provide support for contents, add merchandising or marketing features and customer appeal. Most of these designs are still based on the tube or tray primary structural shapes, but with added material to provide the desired features. The added material can come from extending any cut edges of the primary shape. Designs that require the assembly of several board components are not favored since they require extra stock-keeping and are more labor intensive.

Fifth panels (see Figure 6.19) can be used as pegboard hangers or to create additional surface area for graphics and information. Usually, they are created by extending one or both edges of board meeting at the manufacturer's joint. Doubled board thickness makes for a more tear-resistant location for the pegboard hole. When the fifth panel is used as a book-style panel for added display area, the carton may have a window or cutout in its face. The fifth panel then acts as a cover for the opening.

Internal partitions serve to provide security, divide cartons into cells, and help display or support the product. Internal partitions are also used to fill space when the carton is holding a product that is significantly smaller than the carton. (This latter purpose is drawing increasing negative comment from consumers and sustainability activists.)

As with fifth panels, most of these internal arrangements are made by extending board from the manufacturer's joint, although some supports are made by extending dust flaps. Figure 6.20 shows three designs that provide support to a bottle or jar based on extending board to the inside of the carton. The design at the left extends the dust flaps to provide a jar base and neck support. The designs on the right extend material from the manufacturer's joint.

Figure 6.19

Examples of external extensions from the glue flap area to provide fifth panels for pegboard retailing (left) or to provide a book-style display (right).

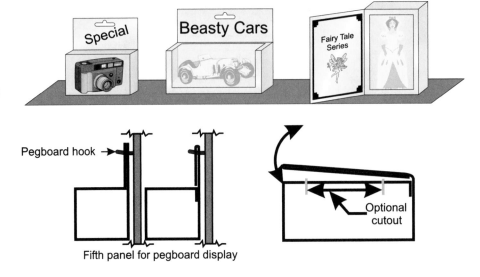

Figure 6.20

Examples of designs that provide internal support for product.

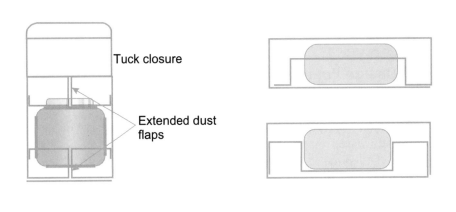

Figure 6.21

Examples of designs creating partitions or cells (left). Another design (right) can be folded together in a book-like form.

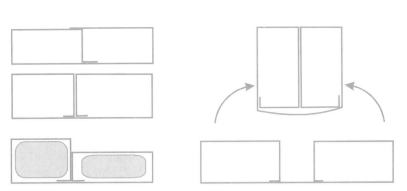

Figure 6.21 shows several ways of creating two partitions, or cells. in a carton. The cells can be the same or different in all dimensions. The cells may be attached (left examples) or separated (right example.) The separated cells can be made to close like a book, providing for a very attractive presentation.

BASIC TRAY-STYLE CARTONS

Trays are top-loading cartons and form the second major folding carton structural family.

Four-corner Beers trays are knocked down flat for shipping. (See Figure 6.22, top) Friction from the glue flaps against the tray's bottom panel holds the erected carton up. The style usually has the angled flattening folds on the carton ends, although they can also be located on the side panels. Four-corner Beers trays are often made in pairs, one slightly larger than the other. The larger tray can then slide over the smaller one to from a notions box, commonly used in many clothing and gift boutiques as a generic container.

The basic Beers tray can be provided with a tuck cover by extending one of the side panels. (See Figure 6.23, bottom) Dust flaps, which usually extend from the body end-panels, increase box stiffness. Flaps can be placed on the cover ends (Charlotte flaps) instead, but the configuration does not permit flaps on both body and cover. Charlotte flaps will stiffen and flatten the cover panel, and if dimensioned to the tray's depth, they will improve top-to-bottom compression strength.

The cover panel of a Beers tray can also be made with glue flaps and angled flattening folds to provide a six-cornered tray with a fully enclosing cover.

Most tray designs have grain running along the long dimension of the tray's bottom panel. Trays with doubled board in the side panels are the exception to this general rule.

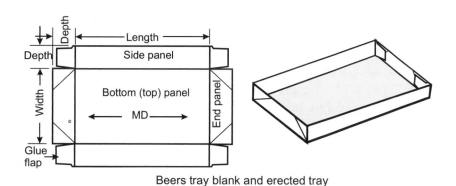

Figure 6.22

Beers tray variations.

Beers tray blank and erected tray

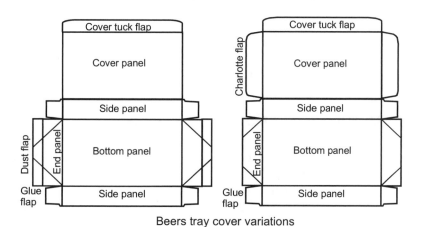

Beers tray cover variations

Figure 6.23

A six-cornered Brightwood tray, flat and assembled.

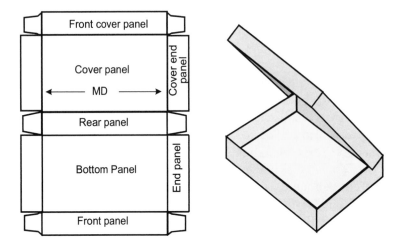

Brightwood trays are similar to Beers trays, but they are nonflattening once erected. As with Beers trays, they can be made in four- and six-cornered variations. A second, slightly larger four-cornered tray of either type can be used as a slide-on cover.

Brightwood trays are machine assembled at the point of fill. A six-cornered Brightwood tray provides a fully enclosing cover. (See Figure 6.23) Because Brightwood trays do not have the diagonal slit scores that allows a Beers tray to be knocked down for shipment, they are much stiffer and hold their shape even when empty. Brightwood trays are used in the confection industry to provide a shipping unit for confections, which at the retailer can be quickly converted into a merchandising unit for the confections they contain.

There are many tray designs intended for manual set-up. The doubled end panels of the Walker tray (see Figure 6.24, top) make a rigid tray. Pinch-lock trays (see Figure 6.24, bottom) have a small foot that locks the panel ends by friction and by engaging a locking slot. Pinch locks can be located on the two end panels or on both the end and side panels. Tray wall stiffness is increased if all four walls have an inner panel. Simplex trays (see Figure 6.25), double material in both end and side panels for greater rigidity.

Gusseted corners are useful for trays that must hold wet products such as frozen foods.

Shadow box refers to designs that have various walls built into the design that are intended to hold and show off upscale products. The frame-vue tray (see Figure 6.26) is one such design. Note that the grain direction for this tray is not along the length of the tray but across the width.

BEVERAGE BASKETS AND SETUP BOXES

Basket carriers or beverage baskets are used for holding bottled beverages. The most common designs hold four or six plastic or glass bottles. The heavy product requires strong kraft-based paperboards, with bleached liners or heavy clay coatings to provide a smooth white printing surface. Where bottle-to-bottle contact must be avoided, partitions between bottle cells will go almost the cell's

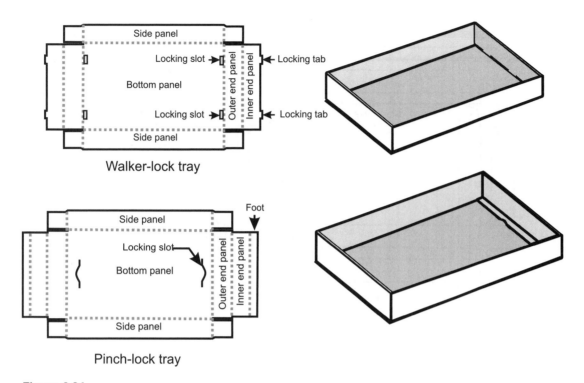

Figure 6.24

The Walker lock and pinch-lock trays are the simplest manual set-up trays.

full depth. Where bottle-to-bottle contact is not objectionable, as might be the case with plastic bottles, the partitions serve mostly to support the side panels and are relatively shallow. (See Figure 6.27)

Unlike folding cartons, setup boxes cannot be knocked down flat. An obvious disadvantage is that a setup box occupies as much space in storage and shipment when empty as it does when full. Furthermore, setup boxes are not as

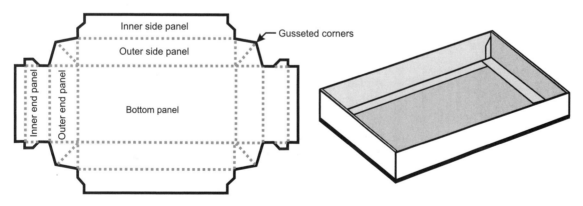

Figure 6.25

The Simplex tray is one of the most popular of manually set-up trays. The double wall thickness at the sides and ends makes it much stiffer than Walker and pinch-lock styles.

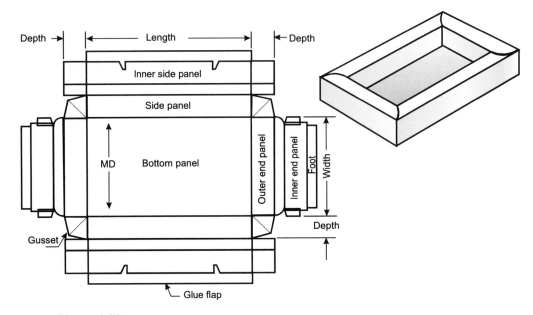

Figure 6.26

A frame-vue tray, flat and assembled.

amenable to high-speed production as folding cartons are, and their manufacture, by comparison, is slow and labor intensive. These factors add significantly to the cost of a setup box.

The rigidity of setup boxes, however, gives them an upscale image, a factor used to advantage by marketers of cosmetics, fancy stationery supplies, quality chocolates, jewelry and other gift items. The setup box makes a convenient long-term storage unit, a feature important in marketing products such as games and jigsaw puzzles. Setup boxes can also serve as low-cost shippers, although this use is now limited almost entirely to the footwear industry.

Setup boxes are typically constructed from heavy, low-grade chipboard, with no particular folding or printing qualities. In its most elementary form, the board is cut to shape, and the sides folded up and taped with stay tape to form a stayed box. (See Figure 6.28) For more upscale applications, a single white-lined board may be used to provide a white internal surface.

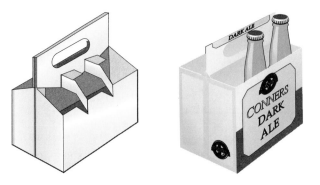

Figure 6.27

A beverage ba
variations.

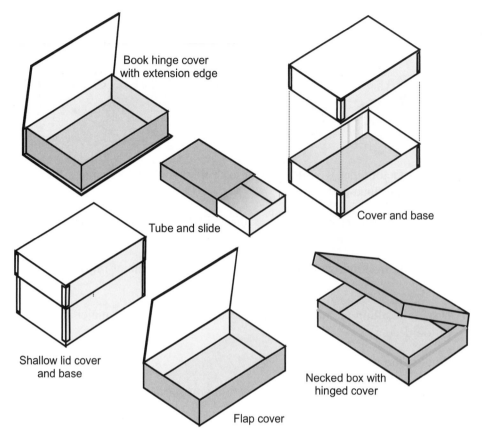

Book hinge cover
with extension edge

Tube and slide

Cover and base

Shallow lid cover
and base

Flap cover

Necked box with
hinged cover

Figure 6.28
Setup boxes start as a cut
flat sheet that is folded to
the box shape and held in
place with stay tape.

The basic setup box consists of a cover and base component. The box base may be the same depth as the cover or considerably deeper. In the tube-and-slide variation (see Figure 6.28), the setup box is inserted into a folding carton sleeve or tube. In a more upscale presentation, the sleeve might also be constructed as a setup form.

Decorative appeal results when a covering material is wrapped around the stayed box. Covering materials can be selected from plain or fancy papers, printed label stock, vinyl, imitation leathers, foils, fabrics or any other material that can be applied over the stayed box base. This broad material selection provides for a wide range of decorative possibilities and appearances.

The covering material can be bonded over the entire surface or only along the perimeter. A soft leather-like texture is created by perimeter-bonding an embossed vinyl imitation leather over a soft expanded plastic material placed over the stayed paperboard.

More complex designs are built up of many inserted pieces either out of paperboard or plastic, and may include such features as flap covers and hinged lids. (See Figure 6.28) Additional sleeves or necks around the box perimeter increase box rigidity, and the extra thickness can be used to hold metal hinges and clasps.

REVIEW QUESTIONS

1. Discuss factors that would lead you to decide whether to design a tuck-end carton or a glued-end carton.

2. Name four product characteristics that will have a major impact on board selection.

3. Name four machining or filling needs that will have a major impact on carton design.

4. Discuss retailing or merchandising needs that will have a major impact on carton design.

5. What is the working score?

6. What is double gluing, and where would you specify it?

7. What paper would you specify for an ice cream box?

8. Which panel on a folding carton is generally regarded as the principal display panel?

9. What are the disadvantages of the airplane-style tuck carton?

10. Himes and 1-2-3 closures are usually put on what kind of cartons?

11. What is the difference between a Beers tray and a Brightwood tray?

12. What are the principal advantages and disadvantages of a setup box?

13. In what direction is a scored paperboard folded: away from the valley or toward the valley?

14. A company has specifications for several folding cartons. One is listed as being 90 mm × 20 mm × 40 mm, and another is listed as being 20 mm × 40 mm × 90 mm. Explain these descriptions.

15. Which will be paper MD in a typical tube-style folding carton?

16. Irregular carton shapes have an inherent disadvantage. What is it?

17. What type of board might be used for a setup box?

18. What is the difference between a vertical end-loading carton, a horizontal end-loading carton and a top-loading carton? Where would you use each?

19. What is a slit lock?

20. At what points is a customer typically asked to sign-off on a carton project?

21. Discuss the nature and critical importance of providing a sign-off.

22. Describe the general process by which a carton design is brought into production.

23. Why is it a good idea to erect and fill folding cartons soon after they have been produced?

CHAPTER SEVEN
METAL CANS AND CONTAINERS

CONTENTS

Background

Early metal packaging, three-piece and two-piece constructions, advantages of two-piece and three-piece cans, common metal can shapes, applications.

Can-making Steels

Black plate steel, tinplating, differential tinplating, tin-free steel, steel alloys, temper, Rockwell hardness, base box measure, base box conversion factors, typical tin-plating weights, typical steel application weights and thickness.

Three-piece Steel Cans

Mechanical seaming applications, adhesive bonding applications, soldered seams, welded cans, welded can manufacture, sidewall beading, can-end expansion rings, compound, double seaming.

Two-piece Drawn Cans

Manufacturing methods, shallow draw, predecorated shallow draw, draw limits, draw and redraw cans, the draw-and-iron process, expanded-wall cans.

Impact Extrusion

Materials, manufacturing sequence, collapsible tubes, dimensioning collapsible tubes, tip styles, advantages and applications, coating and decorating, impact-extruded aerosol cans.

Can Dimensioning

Standard can dimensioning practice.

Protective Coatings for Cans

Purpose, resin types.

Decoration

Can lithography versus paper labeling, plastic sleeves, can lithography for flat sheets, offset letterpress of round shapes, decorating limitations.

Aerosols

Definition, product categories, history, propellants, propellant pressures, product formulations, actuators, mounting cups, valve operation, valve options, other pressurized dispensing systems, regulation, aerosol container specifications.

METAL CANS AND CONTAINERS

BACKGROUND

Steel is one of the older packaging materials and was originally used for round, square and rectangular boxes and canisters. Tea and tobacco were two of the first products packaged in tin-plated, mechanically seamed or soldered steel containers with friction or hinged lids. Today, such labor-intensive metal boxes are limited to custom and upscale applications. The old-fashioned appearance of a fabricated metal box is effectively used by package designers to create nostalgia for specialty and gift-type containers.

Of all the metal packaging forms, none has had as much impact on society as the sanitary food can. Thermal processing of food packed into hand-soldered cylindrical metal cans started in the early 1800s and soon developed into a major industry. Metal cans exhibit advantages of being relatively inexpensive, capable of being thermally processed, rigid, easy to process on high-speed lines and readily recyclable. Metal offers total gas and light barriers. Despite market changes resulting from freezing and plastic-based packaging, metal cans remain an important means of delivering a shelf-stable product.

Originally, all steel containers were fabricated from flat sheets that were cut to size, bent to shape and mechanically clinched or soldered to hold the final shape. Food cans were of three-piece construction—a formed sidewall and a top and bottom end. (See Figure 7.1)

With time, ways of drawing metal (shaping metal by pushing it through a die) were developed. Shallow drawn containers with friction or slip covers were used for pastes, salves, greases and other semisolid products. Later, two-piece shallow drawn cans with double-seamed (folded) ends were used for sardines.

Two-piece cans have a body and bottom in a single piece with a separate attached end. (See Figure 7.1, right) Immediate advantages are reduced metal usage, improved appearance and elimination of a possible leakage location. However, while three-piece cans can easily be changed in length and diameter, two-piece cans require more elaborate tooling that is dedicated to one can form.

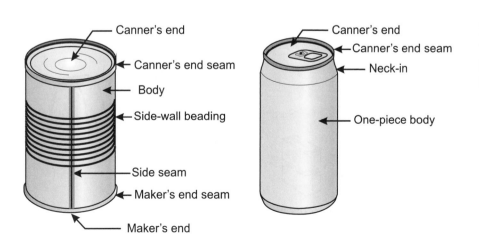

Figure 7.1

Three-piece (left) and two-piece (right) can construction.

Improvements in metallurgy and processing allowed deeper draws and multiple draws, and eventually, they led to a draw-and-iron process in which the walls of a drawn container were made thinner by an ironing step. Aluminum joined steel as a can material.

Ductile metals, such as tin, lead and aluminum, can be formed into tubular shapes by impact extrusion. Originally, only tin and lead were used to make collapsible tubes—a tube that can be collapsed or squeezed to expel the contents. Today, impact-extruded collapsible tubes are made from aluminum, except for a small number of special applications requiring the chemical properties of tin or lead.

Impact-extrusion technology has advanced to the point where heavier-gauge aluminum extrusions can be used to make pressurized aerosol containers.

Common Metal Container Shapes

Stock metal cans come in a great variety of sizes and shapes. A quick list of the most common include:

- Three-piece steel sanitary food cans.

- Aerosol cans made by two methods: (1) Three-piece steel cans with a welded body and two ends, and (2) one-piece, impact-extruded aluminum cans necked-in to accept the valve cup.

- Steel or aluminum two-piece, drawn-and-ironed beverage cans.

- Two-piece steel or aluminum cans made by drawing or by draw and redraw. Full-opening, ring pull-top cans are used for fish products, canned meats and dips. Double-seamed, conventional-top cans are used for many canned food products.

- Cans with hinged lids, usually steel, used for medications, confections, small parts and novelties.

- Flat round cans of drawn steel or aluminum with slip covers. Used for ointments, salves, confections, shoe polish and novelties. (See Figure 7.2)

Figure 7.2

Examples of specialized can shapes.

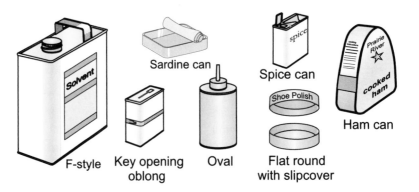

- Three-piece steel or aluminum ovals, typically fitted with a dispensing spout and used for oils. (See Figure 7.2)

- Traditional pear-shaped, three-piece steel ham cans.

- Oblong, steel three-piece F-style cans used mostly to contain aggressive solvents. (See Figure 7.2) The "F" name comes from Flit insecticide, an early, large-volume user. There are no A-, B-, C-, D- or E-style cans. The term has been transferred to plastic jugs with offest necks such such as those for windsield washer fluids.

- Oblong key-opening cans, three-piece steel, used for luncheon meat products. (See Figure 7.2)

- Multiple friction cans of three-piece steel, used primarily by the paint industry. These are variously referred to as double- and triple-tight or doubletite and tripletite.

- Three-piece, square-breasted steel cans. (See Figure 7.2) Larger designs are specific to the talcum, bath and baby powder markets. These have been almost entirely repaced by plastic cans. Spice cans are smaller three-piece cans with a perforated metal or plastic top, used for spices and dry condiments.

- Two-piece, low-profile steel or aluminum ovals, with full-opening ring pull tops for seafood products.

CAN-MAKING STEELS

The name "tin can" is not strictly correct, since low-carbon steel is the predominant can-making material. Bare steel corrodes readily when in contact with moisture or other corrosive agents, and unprotected steel or black plate can be used only for such noncorrosive products as waxes, oils or greases. Normally, a coating is needed to protect the steel. This was first done by dipping black plate sheets into baths of molten tin. The original full term was "tinned canister."

Today, black plate is electrolytically tin-plated, allowing substantial reductions in the amount of tin used, as well as offering the ability to put different thicknesses of tin on either side of a steel sheet. The tin layer is extraordinarily thin, about 0.38 micrometres (0.000015 in).

Manufacturers identify differential tinplate, as to both the amount of tinplating and the side having the thicker plate, by embossing an identifying pattern onto one side of the sheet. The heavier tin deposit goes to the inside of the container where greater protection is needed.

Electrolytic chrome-coated steel (ECCS) use chrome and chrome oxides for corrosion protection. ECCS has a somewhat gray appearance rather than the bright reflectance of tinned steel. ECCS is more economical than tinplate. However, the chrome must be removed to weld the can body. ECCS is most often used for can ends or for drawing, where weldability is not a requirement. ECCS is also known as tin-free steel (TFS).

Alloy and temper are the most important variables when selecting a can maker's quality (CMQ) steel. (See Table 7.1) Alloy type "medium residual"

Table 7.1

Steel alloys used for tin-plated can maker's quality steel.

Designation	Typical Applications
MR	Most general can making where corrosion resistance is not critical
L	Used where high corrosion resistance is needed
D	Highly ductile alloy for producing drawn and drawn-and-ironed containers
N	High stiffness alloy for can ends and aerosol domes

(MR), referring to the amount of residual metal elements other than phosphorous, is the most common can-making steel. Types L and LT have low residuals and are used for acidic foods and other corrosive products. Type D alloy has improved ductility and is used in applications where deep draw is required.

Temper and hardness are affected by the method of rolling and annealing. Steels range from "dead soft" (easily folded over) to stiff and springy. Metal is work-hardened if rolled while cold, thus producing a much stiffer steel. Double-reduced (DR) steel is rolled once, annealed and then cold-rolled again. These DR steels are used whenever maximum stiffness is required.

Steel temper and hardness are related values. Stiffer steels are harder to work and do not draw well. Steel temper must be carefully matched to the application, and a compromise must be found between stiffness and workability. Metal temper is designated by an arbitrary number, using a Rockwell 30-T hardness tester. The Rockwell gauge measures the penetration of a hardened steel ball into the sheet surface at a given force. (See Table 7.2)

Historically, tin mill product weights were specified by the base box: the weight in pounds of 112 sheets measuring 14 in. × 20 in. Plating weights were given as the weight added per base box. Differential tinplate will give the values

Table 7.2

Temper classification, Rockwell hardness and typical tinplate applications.

Temper Classification	Rockwell Hardness	Typical Application
T50	46–52	Soft and ductile steel for deep-drawn parts
T52	50–56	Shallow draw cans, closures
T57	54–63	General use can ends and bodies; crowns and closures
T65	62–68	General purpose; can bodies and ends
T70	67–73	Stiff can bodies and ends
DR-8	70–76	Maximum-stiffness ends and bodies
DR-9	73–79	Maximum-stiffness ends and bodies
DR-9M	74–80	Beer and carbonated beverage can ends

for each side. Metric practice quotes metal grammage: the mass per square metre. System International Tinplate Association (SITA) quotes tinplate in kilograms per 100 square metres.

THREE-PIECE STEEL CANS

Steel three-piece can bodies can be mechanically seamed, bonded with adhesive, weldeded or soldered. (See Figure 7.3) Aluminum cannot be soldered or welded economically. Welded sanitary three-piece can bodies are, therefore, made exclusively of steel. Mechanical seaming, or clinching, would be used only for containers intended for dry product, where a hermetic seal is not important.

Adhesive bonding, or cementing, uses a thermoplastic (or other) adhesive extruded onto a hot can blank. The blank is shaped into a cylinder on a body former, the hot thermoplastic adhesive is applied, and the seam is "bumped" and quickly chilled to set the bond.

Adhesive bonding is an attractive body-assembly method for applications where the can will not be subjected to thermal processing. Unlike welded cans, adhesive-bonded constructions can have full wraparound lithography. At one time, three-piece beverage containers were adhesive bonded. Some frozen juice concentrate and paint cans are adhesive bonded.

To solder a can, engaging hooks are bent into the can blank similar to that for a mechanical seam. Molten lead- or tin-based solder is flowed into the seam. Lead extraction by food products is always a potential problem, and the industry quickly adapted welding technology when it became available. Soldered food cans are no longer permitted in North America. Some soldering is still done for nonfood applications. Many of these solders have reduced or eliminated the lead content.

Most three-piece steel food cans are welded by a process initiated in Europe by Soudronic. The body sheet is formed into a tube with a slight overlap along the joint. In the most common process, the joint is passed between two continuous copper wire electrodes; an electrical current passing through the joint heats and fuses the metal. (See Figure 7.4) Lithographed can blanks require about 6 millimetres (mm) (0.25 in.) of undecorated strip along the weld edges to ensure good electrical contact for welding. The welded seam line is about 30% thicker than the two base metal sheets. Cans shorter than 75 mm (3 in.) are too short to be welded individually, and are made by welding a body twice the required length and cutting it into two cans.

All three-piece can bodies are pressure-tested and have the ends flanged to receive the can top and bottom ends. The can maker applies one can end and sends the other end to the user for double seaming after the can is filled.

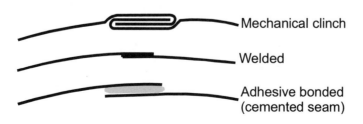

Mechanical clinch

Welded

Adhesive bonded
(cemented seam)

Figure 7.3

Mechanical, welded and adhesive-bonded side-seams for three-piece cans.

Figure 7.4

Three piece can production.

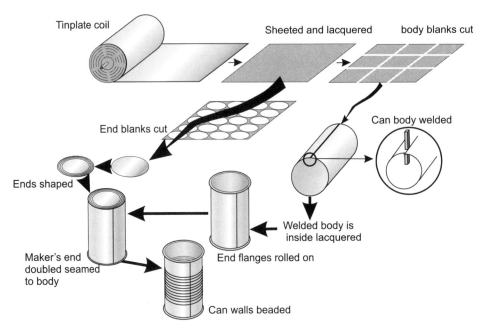

Sanitary food cans that may be thermally processed in a retort have bead patterns embossed into the can sidewalls; the patterns improve resistance to collapse because of external pressure. (See Figure 7.1) This prevents paneling during pressure differentials encountered during retorting and enables the can to withstand an internal vacuum. Sidewall beading requires more material, reduces top-to-bottom compression strength and complicates labeling. Many sidewall bead geometries are designed to maximize hoop strength while minimizing the accompanying problems.

Can ends intended for thermal processing are stamped with a series of circular expansion panels. (See Figure 7.5) This allows the ends to move so that the contents inside the can are able to expand and contract without bulging or otherwise distorting the can. The chuck panel is designed to give the proper clearance to the double-seaming chuck used to seal the can end to the body. A vital can-end component is the compound applied around the perimeter curl. This compound acts as a caulk or sealant when the end is mated and double-seamed to the can body. (See Figures 7.6 and 7.7)

Figure 7.5

Representative can-end embossing pattern.

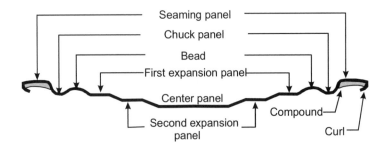

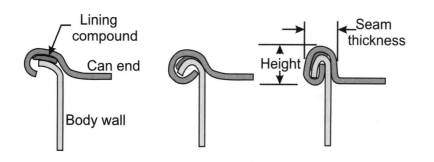

Figure 7.6

Double-seaming is the attachment of the can end to the body. It involves two curling steps.

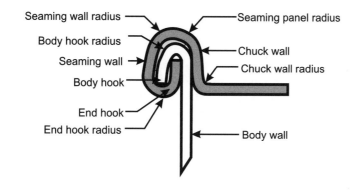

Figure 7.7

The double seam is a critical can component. Every angle, radius and dimension must be correct to ensure a hermetic seal.

TWO-PIECE DRAWN CANS

There are three methods of making steel or aluminum two-piece cans:

- Draw
- Draw and redraw (DRD)
- Draw and iron (D&I)

Table 7.3 shows the most common aluminum alloys used in packaging.

Draw Processes

A shallow-profile can—one whose height is less than its diameter—can be drawn directly from a circular metal blank. The metal blank is stamped or drawn through

Table 7.3
Most commonly used aluminum alloys for packaging.

Designation	Typical Applications
1050	Foils and collapsible tubes
3004	Draw-and-iron can bodies
5182	Beverage can pull-tab closures

Figure 7.8

Straight lines on a blank (left) become distorted in different directions when drawn into a can (right).

a die and re-formed into a new shape. The thickness of the finished can sidewall and bottom remain essentially the same as in the original blank. The process is sometimes referred to as "shallow draw."

Blanks for shallow-drawn cans may be decorated prior to drawing. Art must be distorted so that when the metal is re-formed, a correct image will develop. (See Figure 7.8) Cans that have continuous decoration across the sidewalls and bottom have been printed prior to drawing.

A single-draw operation is limited in how far the metal can be reshaped. Cans having a height equal to or greater than the can's diameter will usually require a second draw in what is called the "draw-and-redraw" process. The first draw produces a shallow cup. The second reduces the diameter as the can is deepened. Cans having a height significantly greater than the can diameter would require a third draw. If the container is to be thermally processed, sidewall beads are rolled into the walls in a separate step. Body flanges for engaging the can end are rolled on in a manner similar to that used in three-piece can manufacturing.

Draw-and-iron Process

Carbonated beverage cans are made by the draw-and-iron (D&I) process. A blank disk is first drawn into a wide cup. (See Figure 7.9, step 2) In a separate operation (see Figure 7.9, step 3), the cup is redrawn to the finished can diameter and pushed through a series of ironing rings, each minutely smaller in diameter than the previous one. (See Figure 7.10) The rings "iron," or spread, the metal into a thinner sheet than the original disk.

The bottom of a D&I can has the same thickness as the starting disk; however, the sidewalls are considerably reduced in thickness and the metal area of the final can is greater than that of the initial disk. Necking operations reduce the diameter of the can top, thereby reducing the end-piece diameter. This results in significant metal savings, since the end piece is much thicker than the sidewalls.

The thin walls of a D&I can restrict its use to applications where it will not be thermally processed and that will lend support to the walls. Carbonated beverage cans, where the internal pressure of the carbon dioxide keeps the walls from denting, is the primary application. Noncarbonated juices packed in D&I

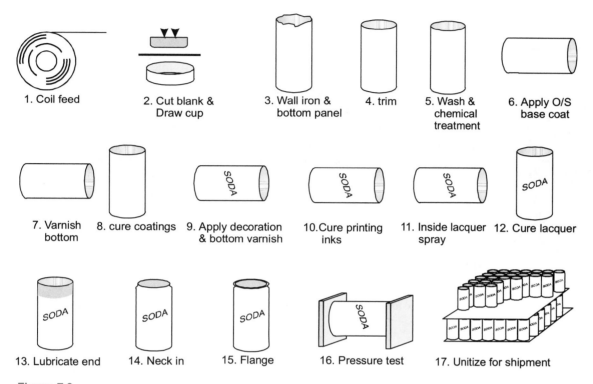

1. Coil feed
2. Cut blank & Draw cup
3. Wall iron & bottom panel
4. trim
5. Wash & chemical treatment
6. Apply O/S base coat
7. Varnish bottom
8. cure coatings
9. Apply decoration & bottom varnish
10. Cure printing inks
11. Inside lacquer spray
12. Cure lacquer
13. Lubricate end
14. Neck in
15. Flange
16. Pressure test
17. Unitize for shipment

Figure 7.9

The manufacturing sequence for a necked D&I can.

cans rely on internal pressure created by inert nitrogen gas introduced into the container.

Both steel and aluminum are used to produce D&I beverage cans. Aluminum alloys such as 3004 are used for can bodies, while the softer 5182 alloy is used for can ends. Soft drink producers can use either steel or aluminum equally well. Beer, however, is particularly sensitive to traces of dissolved iron while being relatively insensitive to aluminum.

Draw-and-iron manufacturing has been used to produce beverage cans as large as two litres.

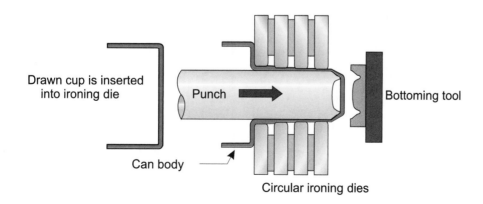

Drawn cup is inserted into ironing die

Punch

Bottoming tool

Can body

Circular ironing dies

Figure 7.10

In the D&I process, the second draw and ironing stages occur in one continuous movement. The illustration exaggerates the punch and ironing rings. The punch finishes its stroke against the bottoming tool.

Figure 7.11

An expanded-sidewall soda can.

Expanded-wall Cans

Cans produced by conventional manufacturing have straight and perpendicular sidewalls. Shaped walls can be incorporated into a can design by sliding the two- or three-piece can body over an expanding chuck, or "mandrel." When the can body is in place, moveable parts on the mandrel open outward and expand the can walls into the selected shape. At the completion of the expansion, the mandrel folds back into itself, and the shaped can body is removed from the tool. Alternately the welded can body can be placed over a heavy rubber bladder which when it is inflated, expands the can walls to conform to an enclosing mold. Figure 7.11 shows a soda can expanded to suggest the appearance of a traditional shape.

IMPACT EXTRUSION

Impact extrusion forms ductile metals such as tin, lead and aluminum into seamless tubes. Tin and lead were the first metals to be formed by this method, and until the 1960s, most collapsible tubes were either lead or tin. Tin's high cost prohibits its use except for collapsible tubes holding certain pharmaceuticals. Lead, once the mainstay of the toothpaste market, is now used only for applications where its chemical inertness is an asset. Most impact extrusions are made from aluminum.

In impact extrusion, a metal slug is located on a shaped striking surface, or anvil. A punch strikes the slug with great force. Under the enormous impact pressure, the metal flows like a liquid straight up along the outside of the striking punch, forming a round, cylindrical shape. (See Figure 7.12) Tube height can be up to seven times its diameter.

The tube's shoulders and tip are formed as part of the process. Tubes with a dispensing hole in the tip will have a hole in the slug, while tubes that need

Figure 7.12

Impact-extrusion sequence.

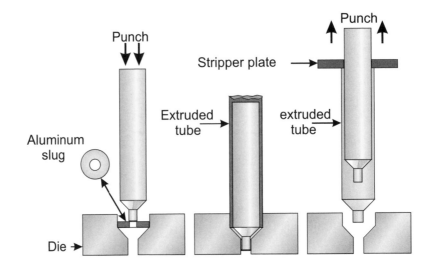

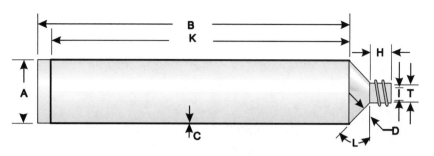

Figure 7.13

Tube dimensioning.

DIMENSION	DESCRIPTION
A	Outside diameter
B	Body length
C	Wall thickness
D	Shoulder thickness
H	Neck length
I	Orifice diameter
K	Decorated length
L	Shoulder angle
T	Finish neck diameter

a dispenser with a thin web of metal over the opening (a "blind end") will start with a solid slug. Embossed shoulders are another option.

The force of the impact work hardens aluminum and makes it stiff. Collapsible tubes are annealed to remove the stiffness. The tubes are trimmed to length, threads are turned into the neck, and the tubes are sent for finishing. Dimensions given for impact-extruded tubes always refer to the undecorated and unfilled tube. Dimensions are given as the outside diameter and the body length from the shoulder to the open end. (See Figure 7.13)

Neck designs are negotiated with the supplier and are specified by a number indicating the opening size in 64ths of an inch. Thus, a No. 12 neck has an opening of 3/16 in. Figure 7.14 shows some commonly used tips.

The round end is the most common tip, and blind-end tubes have a metal membrane across the end when a positive seal is required. Screw-eye openings are used mostly for adhesives that would bind a normal screw-cap closure. Nasal tips are used for nasal ointments and products that require local point application. Eye tips are similar, and are used for ophthalmic medications and fluids that are dispensed by the drop. Grease tips are used for dispensing greases when an applicator tip is required.

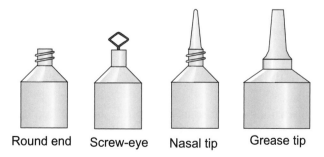

Round end   Screw-eye   Nasal tip   Grease tip

Figure 7.14

Examples of impact-extruded tube tips.

Figure 7.15

Production sequence of an impact extruded aerosol can. The slug (1) is impacted into a cylinder (2). The top end is trimmed (3), washed (4) and inside coated (5). A white base coat is applied and U.V. cured (6) and then the graphics are applied (7). The end is turned down (8) and then through a multi-step forming sequence the can end is rolled to the standard one inch opening.

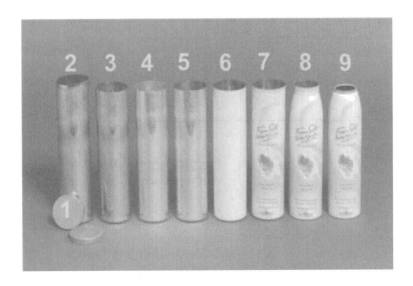

Metal tubes have a number of distinctive characteristics compared with laminate and plastic collapsible tubes:

- They are absolute barriers to all gases and flavors.

- They have the best dead-fold characteristic. (i.e., the ability to be flattened or rolled up.) This feature is particularly important for some pharmaceutical applications, where air suck-back into the partly empty tube could contaminate the contents or expose the product to oxygen.

- They can be decorated in a manner that takes advantage of their metallic character.

- They have a wide range of internal lining options because of the metal's ability to withstand high curing temperatures.

Tubes are normally coated with a white enamel base and then cured. Tubes are printed by dry offset (offset letterpress), similar to any round container. Most manufacturers offer six colors.

By starting with heavier slugs, strong cylinders can be made by impact extrusion. These cylinders hold special greases and caulks; some are used as humidor tubes for expensive cigars. A major application is for aerosol products, where the sleek, seamless appearance of these cans is an asset. When a cylinder is used as an aerosol can, a stiff sidewall is desirable and those cylinders are not annealed. The sidewall is trimmed to length, turned down and curled over to accept the spray nozzle base. (See Figure 7.15)

CAN DIMENSIONING

Nominal can dimensions are given as the overall diameter by the overall height. (See Figure 7.16) Each dimension is given in three digits. The first digit is in whole inches, and the second two digits represent 16ths of an inch. A 307-by-314 can would be 3-7/16 in diameter and 3-14/16 high.

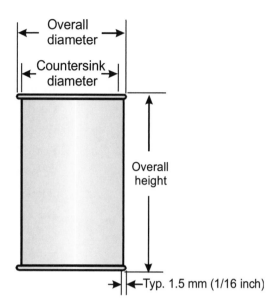

Figure 7.16

Nominal can dimensions.

Necked cans will report several dimensions indicating the neck diameters followed by a last dimension indicating the height. In metric practice the dimensions are given in millimetres.

PROTECTIVE COATINGS FOR CANS

Most cans require organic coatings to help protect the product and the container. In some instances, the tin layer helps maintain flavor and appearance.

Various coatings have been developed to solve particular canning problems. Some dark fruits bleach in direct contact with tin. In these instances, an organic coating is essential. Similarly, sulfur-containing foods (meats, corn, onions, asparagus, etc.) develop a dark stain when they come directly into contact with tin. The stain is harmless but unsightly. Special release formulations are available for products such as luncheon meats that must be easy to remove from the can. Products that contain aggressive solvents or corrosive agents would require coatings resistant to these chemicals. Table 7.4 lists typical coating characteristics.

DECORATION

Cans may be decorated either by printing directly on the metal or by applying a paper or plastic shrink label. Generally, high-volume single-product applications favor a decoration applied directly to the metal. However, some high-volume products use paper or film labels to reduce inventory. A company producing a line of twenty-five soup varieties will find it easier to inventory twenty-five labels and one can type rather than stocking twenty-five can varieties.

Lithography is used when the can blank is decorated in the flat. Metal varnishes and inks are normally baked on, or ultraviolet (UV) cured. Typical metal lithographic presses lay down two colors at a pass because of the oven-bake requirement. Designs with more than two colors must have a second printing

Table 7.4

Protective can coatings. Can coatings should not crack or chip if the can is abused.

Resin Type	Flavor	Flexibility	Color	Retortable?
Acrylic	Fair	Good	Good	Yes
Epoxy-amine	Good	Good	Good	Yes
Epoxy-ester	Fair	Good	Poor	Yes
Epoxy-phenolic	Good	Good	Poor	Yes
Oleoresin	Fair	Good	Poor	Yes
Polybutadiene	Fair	Fair	Fair	Yes
Vinyl	Good	Good	Good	No
Phenolic	Fair	Fair	Fair	Varies

pass. UV-curing inks provide an "instant" cure, and the metal can receive another ink application almost immediately. Modern printing presses will UV cure each ink immediately after application.

D&I and other round containers have no natural register point and must be printed by offset letterpress, also called dry offset. (See Chapter 4. Package Printing and Decorating, Figure 4.17) Through imaginative design and the clever use of halftones, the process produces decorations approaching the appearance of process art.

Another decorating option is the use of a preprinted, plastic shrink label. Preprinting allows for the use of any printing process for process-color art and for other special decorating effects. When applied to a two-piece can, the label shrinks and conforms readily to a can's contours.

AEROSOLS

Aerosol packaging refers to products in a pressurized container having a valve that permits controlled product release as required. Depending on the formulation, valve system and pressurization method, aerosols can be designed to release product in forms ranging from fine mists to heavy pastes.

Personal care products such as perfumes, shaving creams, deodorants and hair sprays make up the largest segment of the aerosol market, followed closely by household products such as polishes, cleaners and room air fresheners. Paints, automotive products and insect sprays have smaller market portions. Food applications are limited.

Although the principles of expelling fluids from a container by internal pressure were known earlier, the first practical application came in about 1942, when the U.S. military adapted a heavy metal tank pressurized with a fluorocarbon to disperse a fine insecticide mist. The aerosol could disperse a product into much finer particles that stayed suspended in the air for a much longer time than was available from hand pumps and other systems. This "bug bomb" was used extensively in the Pacific during World War II to reduce the incidence of insect-borne diseases among the troops. By 1946, the first civilian aerosol insecticides made from modified beer cans entered the market, followed quickly by room air fresheners and window cleaners.

Aerosol Propellants

A typical aerosol product has a liquid phase and a vapor phase. (See Figure 7.17) The liquid phase contains the product to be expelled. The vapor phase is at an increased pressure and will force the product up the dip tube and expel it through the nozzle whenever the valve is opened. The product typically occupies about 75%, but never more than 92.5%, of the available space in the aerosol. Well-designed aerosol containers will deliver 95% or better of the contained product.

A large part of aerosol design concerns the selection of a suitable propellant. In principle, product can be expelled simply by charging the container with compressed air. The problem with this method is that as product is expelled and the head-space volume increases, the container pressure will drop proportionately. Carbon dioxide and nitrous oxide gases have some solubility in water, and to that extent, the vapor-phase pressure can be maintained by gas coming out of the solution to replace lost head-space gas. These gases are used in some aerosol applications.

The ideal propellant is a gas that can be easily compressed and liquified at the desired operating pressures of an aerosol system. Hydrocarbons, dimethyl ether and chlorofluorocarbons (CFCs) exhibit this property.

Table 7.5 lists characteristics of the most common aerosol propellants. Each propellant (except for the soluble gases) will develop the vapor pressure shown in the table if sealed with an excess of liquid propellant in a closed container at room temperature. Propellant vapor pressures are used to determine which materials or blends to use in a formulation. Because of their significantly lower cost, most aerosol propellants have been based on hydrocarbons, or hydrocarbon blends. Hydrocarbons are flammable, and care needs to be exercised during packaging and use.

Hydrocarbons have low liquid density and will usually float on top of the product. Halogenated propellants are denser than water and will therefore sink to the bottom of most formulations. If the propellant is on the bottom, dip tube

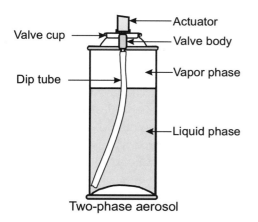

Two-phase aerosol

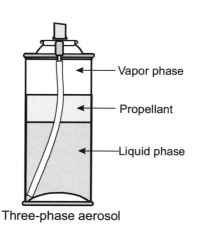

Three-phase aerosol

Figure 7.17

In a two-phase aerosol, the propellant is dissolved in the product. In a three-phase system, the propellant forms a separate layer.

Table 7.5
Characteristics of common aerosol propellant gases.

Name	Boiling Point	Vapor Pressure at 70°F	Water Solubility, volume gas/liquid	*Flammability, volume %	Flash Point
Hydrocarbons					
Propane	−44.7°F	109 psig	0.01	2.2–9.5	−156°F
Isopropane	10.9°F	31 psig	0.01	1.8–8.4	−117°F
N-propane	31.1°F	17 psig	0.01	1.8–8.5	−101°F
Compressed Gases					
Carbon dioxide	−109°F	837 psig	0.82	Not flammable	None
Nitrous oxide	−127°F	720 psig	0.6	Not flammable	None
Other					
Dimethyl ether	−12.7°F	63 psig	34	3.4–18.0	−42°F
HFC 152a	−11.2°F	62 psig	1.7	3.9–16.9	−58°F
HFC 134a	−15.1°F	71 psig	Insignificant	Not flammable	None

*Flammability, Volume, % lists the limits at which the propellant is flammable. The percentages represent the volume of propellant gas mixed with air which will support combustion.

length must be adjusted to end just at the product-propellant interface; otherwise, only the propellant will be expelled.

Chlorinated fluorocarbons (CFCs), characterized by high density and non-flammability, were among the first propellants. In the early 1970s, CFCs were implicated in depletion of the atmospheric ozone layer, and by 1979, they were banned from utility aerosols and were phased out of commercial production. A new group of halogenated hydrocarbons, based on chlorodifluoromethanes and halogenated dimethyl ethers, have a reduced impact on ozone depletion, and are marketed by DuPont under the Dymel trade name. Some of these products are referred to as HCFCs.

Product Formulations

There are many aerosol variations, depending on the product and application. Product and propellant must be matched to produce the desired result. In addition to the need to create a constant internal pressure, chemical compatibility, consumer safety and formulation requirements must also be considered.

In the simplest two-phase system, such as glass cleaners and room air fresheners, the propellant dissolves in the product. However, a solution of the propellant with the product is not always available, and in other instances, not desirable. Three-phase systems are those where propellant and product are not mutually soluble and remain separate in the can.

Products that are expelled as lathers or foams are two-phase systems produced by creating emulsions of product and propellant. Emulsified propellant leaving the can expands to form the foam. Figure 7.17 illustrates two- and three-phase systems.

Dry antiperspirants, artificial snow and paints contain solid particles. These require special consideration in formulation and nozzle selection. In some instances, the product may need to be agitated in order to remix the particulate component with the carrying fluid. A glass ball is often placed into the container to help agitation.

Products with low viscosity, or low density, will expel readily under low pressures. Paint, a viscous product loaded with heavy pigment particles, needs a great deal of pressure to expel. Other products may need a range of pressures between these two extremes. Most common aerosol containers have internal pressures of 322 to 791 kilopascals (32 to 100 psig).

Carbon dioxide, dissolved in water or solvent, is used when high delivery pressures are required such as with wasp and hornet sprays, for example, where the aerosol must be effective at a distance. Carbon dioxide is not significantly affected by freezing temperatures and is used in cold-weather car starters formulations.

Both carbon dioxide and HCFC propellants are candidates for applications where the flammability of hydrocarbon propellants may cause a problem.

Nitrous oxide has a sweet taste and is used predominantly in food products.

Spray paints are a major application for dimethyl-ether-based propellant. Dimethyl ether provides a smooth paint application with little tendency to foam.

Aerosol Valves

Aerosol valves are tailored to meet specific applications. Most valves come fitted to an industry standard 25.4 mm (1 in.) mounting cup that allows it to be seamed onto a can body. (See Figure 7.18) Small impact-extruded aluminum cans such as those for perfumes and pharmaceuticals have standard 13 or 20 mm openings. Ferrule seals are used to attach valves to glass bodies.

The aerosol valve stem (See Figure 7.18) has a small body orifice that when in a normal rest position is sealed by a rubber seating washer. When the actuator button is depressed or tilted, the valve stem moves out of the rubber seat, and the

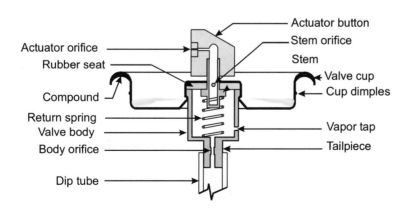

Figure 7.18

Typical aerosol valve and mounting cup.

exposed body orifice allows the pressurized contents to escape through the stem orifice and move up to the actuator orifice. When the actuator button is released, a return spring pushes the stem back into the rubber seating washer, sealing the stem orifice. As with any can, the valve cup curl is lined with a compound that will provide for a hermetic seal when the cup is mounted onto the can body.

Many aerosol characteristics are controlled by adjusting the opening dimensions of the body, stem and actuator orifice. The following describes selected aerosol products and valve systems:

Powder aerosols. Formulas try to match powder and propellant densities in order to reduce settling problems. These work best with high pressures and a valve seat close to the terminal orifice.

Fine sprays. The vapor tap is a small hole (stem orifice) in the valve body case. (See Figure 7.18) This allows a small amount of propellant to mix directly with the product as it is expelled. The rapid propellant expansion mixed with the product produces a much finer spray.

Inverted operation. Products such as food toppings packaged in aerosol cans are designed to operate in an inverted position. These valves are not fitted with a dip tube.

Multiposition dispensing. Large-diameter dip tubes can hold enough product to spray in the inverted position for short periods. For extended multiposition use, a dip tube containing a small sphere that opens a top or bottom port is used. This allows the aerosol to be used in any orientation for extended periods. This design is typically used in such products as oven and bathtub cleaners.

Foams. Foams can be produced by encapsulating some propellant into the product droplets. Propellant expansion into the gaseous state produces the foam. Foam valves usually have a long stem to increase the size of the expansion chamber. They have a minimum of restrictions in the body and actuator orifices.

Mechanical-breakup actuators. Some actuators have a swirl chamber designed to eject the product in a wide, hollow cone pattern that breaks into a fine mist as it spreads out. Mechanical-breakup chambers help reduce the chilling effect on skin from rapid propellant expansion. Sprays intended to coat a surface need larger droplets and would not use this device.

Metering valves. Metering valves are double-valve constructions in which one valve is closed when the other is open. This type of valve works best with products that can be mixed with the propellant. They are useful for pharmaceuticals where there is a need to control dosage.

Single-use valves. A single-use valve is basically a regular valve without the return spring. Products used to repair and inflate flat tires temporarily and insecticide dispensers for fumigating buildings use these valves.

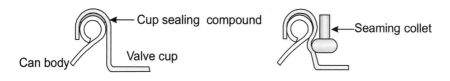

Figure 7.19

Valve-cup crimp dimensions are critical to achieving a good seal between the cup and container body.

The most common method of mounting the valve cup is shown in Figure 7.19. The valve cup is dropped into the can opening, and a seaming collet is rolled around its internal circumference. This expands the bottom portion of the cup against the base of the can body curl.

Other Pressurized Dispensers

Many products cannot be delivered using standard aerosol technology. For example, mixing most propellants with a food product would be objectionable. In other instances, even small amounts of propellant dissolved in the product could cause unwanted foaming. These and other situations are best served by a design variation wherein product and propellant are in separate chambers.

Two common systems address this issue. One uses a collapsible inner bag to hold the product. The other applies the pressure through a piston. (See Figure 7.20) The propellant charge in both instances is introduced through a port in the can bottom that is subsequently sealed with an elastomeric plug.

Most shaving creams use piston designs. The product is ejected as a solid gel, but about 2% of an isopentane and isobutane blend incorporated into the gel readily boils to a gas at about 26°C (79°F) to produce a heavy lather. The hydrocarbons rapidly rise to this temperature when in contact with skin. Products for piston-driven dispensers must be quite viscous, since the product must form a seal between the piston and can wall. The piston itself is usually made from polyethylene and does not offer a high-barrier separation between product and propellant chambers.

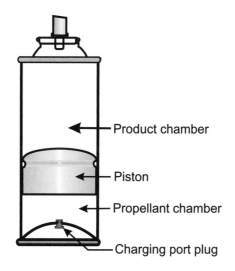

Figure 7.20

Piston type pressurized dispenser with propellant in a chamber separate from the product.

High-barrier laminate flexible bags are used where little or no permeation of propellant into the product is required. These bags are constructed of high-barrier plastics, and in most instances, are metallized.

Regulation

An aerosol container is a pressurized vessel, and therefore, has a potential explosion hazard associated with it. In Canada and the United States, aerosol containers are governed by each country's hazardous product codes—in Canada by Transport Canada (TC) and in the United States by the Department of Transportation (DOT). The construction and minimum container performance level is specified according to the contained pressure. The specifications are similar for both countries.

Briefly, systems that exhibit a pressure of less than 1,070 (kilopascals (kPa) at 54.5°C (140 psig at 130°F) are classed as nonspecification containers and need not be identified. They must pass a minimum burst test of 1,550 kilopascals (210 psig). Containers with higher internal pressures are classed as specification containers and must meet more stringent requirements. The manufacturer must have one in 25,000 tested to destruction and must mark the container with a TC (Canada) or DOT (United States) specification marking. Table 7.6 gives examples of specification values from the U.S. Code of Federal Regulations (49 CFR) and voluntary industry guidelines.

Industry voluntary guidelines for minimum burst pressure are above the legislated requirement. Specification aerosols must be marked as 2P or 2Q containers, depending on the internal pressure. They are not common. Most aerosols are propelled by flammable gases, and in Canada, regulations require cautionary markings on the container, indicating both an explosion hazard and a flammability hazard.

Table 7.6

Specifications for aerosol containers.

Measurement	Nonspecification	Specification 2P	Specification 2Q
Product pressure	1,070 kPa	1,200 kPa	1,340 kPa
at 54.5°C (130°F)	(140 psig)	(160 psig)	(180 psig)
Min. metal thickness	None	0.178 mm	0.203 mm
		(0.007 in.)	(0.008 in.)
Minimum burst	1,550 kPa	1,760 kPa	1,960 kPa
pressure (regulation)	210 psig	240 psig	270 psig
Min. burst pressure	1,650 kPa	1,860 kPa	2,070 kpa
(unofficial industry)	225 psig	255 psig	285 psig
Distortion pressure	1,140 kPa	1,270 kPa	1,450 kPa
(unofficial industry)	150 psig	170 psig	195 psig

Note: Readers should use the appropriate official publications as reference documents rather than this summary table.

REVIEW QUESTIONS

1. List the methods of creating a body seam on a three-piece steel can. What are the advantages and limitations of each?

2. What are the advantages and disadvantages of a two-piece can?

3. Where would you use type L, MR and D steels?

4. What three metals can be formed by impact extrusion?

5. What is the actual material used to make a "tin" can?

6. What is differential tinplate?

7. What is the purpose of the 2CR or DR process?

8. Which steel temper would be used for: (a) the can body for a thermal-process can, (b) a deep-draw cone top for an aerosol, (c) a shallow-draw shoe polish can?

9. Collapsible tubes can be made of metal, plastic or laminates. What advantages does a metal tube have over the other possible choices?

10. A sanitary can body is made from 1,794-gram steel. What does this mean?

11. What is the printing method for three-piece can bodies?

12. What is the purpose of "compound"?

13. What two container types are made by impact extrusion?

14. A special decorating process variation is used to decorate draw-and-iron cans. What is it called, and why is it necessary?

15. What kind of cans would have sidewall beading, and what is its purpose?

16. How can you tell the difference between a can that was drawn and one that was drawn and ironed?

17. What is the main advantage of a D&I can? What is the main limitation?

18. A typical food can might be described as being a "202 × 406." What does this mean?

19. What does Rockwell hardness measure?

20. What is an F style can?

21. What are the four processes used to make two-piece cans?

22. What propellants are the basis of most modern aerosols?

23. What are the principal requirements of an aerosol propellant?

24. What is the difference between a two-phase and a three-phase aerosol?

25. What size is the standard aerosol can cup opening?

26. Why are aerosols regulated? What is regulated, and what body is responsible for the regulation?

CONTENTS

Glass Types and General Properties

"Glassy" materials, typical soda-lime glass composition, decolorizers, colorants, general properties, advantages and limitations. Pharmaceutical glass: types 1, 2, 3 and NP.

Commercial Glass Manufacturing

Glass furnaces, glass fusion temperatures, cullet, forehearth coloring, standard furnace glass colors, amber glass, UV filtering. (Is "amber glass" associated with "UV filtering"? If yes, then restore the "and.")

Bottle Manufacturing

Stock and custom molds, general design process, furnace draw-off and gob shears, blow-and-blow manufacturing, press-and-blow manufacturing, annealing, surface coatings, inspection and packing, tolerances.

Bottle Design Features

Design protection, general design considerations, round versus nonround shapes, shape and labeling, flat bottles and spike defects, finish specifications. Neck, shoulder, sides, heel and base design. Stacking features, stability and machinability, labeling and decorating options, vials and ampoules, carbonated beverages, gas volumes.

GLASS CONTAINERS

GLASS TYPES AND GENERAL PROPERTIES

"Glass" refers to an inorganic substance fused at high temperatures and cooled quickly so that it solidifies in a vitreous or noncrystalline condition. That is, the molecular structure of the solid glass is practically the same as liquid glass, but the cooled glass is so viscous that the mass has become rigid. Glass has no distinct melting or solidifying temperatures. There is gradual softening with heat and gradual solidifying with cooling.

Many metal oxide materials can be formed into a "glassy" condition; however, all commercial glass is based on silica (quartz), the principal component of sand. Common beach sand is unsuitable for making commercial glass, since it contains impurities and varies widely in composition. Large deposits of high-purity silica sands are available in various parts of the world.

Glass production relies on many formulations. Silica sand fused with about 10% sodium compounds (usually carbonates) produces sodium silicate or "water glass," a water-soluble glasslike form. Insolubility is imparted by adding calcium compounds. Soda-lime-silica glass, or more simply soda-lime glass, is the type most commonly used for most commercial bottles and jars. Table 8.1 lists the ingredients commonly used to make soda-lime glass. The percentages of the different ingredients will vary slightly depending on the manufacturer and the exact composition of the raw materials available.

Other mineral compounds may be used to achieve improved properties. Decolorizers added to clear glass overcome the slight color imparted by mineral impurities. Other additives aid in processing. Colorants and opacifying agents change the finished appearance. Standard glass colorants are:

- Chrome oxides for emerald (green) glass
- Iron and sulfur for amber (brown) glass
- Cobalt oxides for blue glass

Besides soda-lime glasses, many other glass types are used for special applications. They are rarely—if ever—used for packaging purposes. For example,

Table 8.1

Typical soda-lime glass-making ingredients.

Ingredient	Percentage by Weight
Silica sand (silicone oxide)	68 to 73
Limestone (calcium carbonate)	10 to 13
Soda ash (sodium carbonate)	12 to 15
Alumina (aluminum oxide)	1.5 to 2

lead compounds provide a soft glass (crystal glass) with exceptional optical properties that may be used for upscale perfume bottles. Boron compounds (borax, boron oxide) give low thermal expansion and high heat-shock resistance. Borosilicate glasses also have exceptionally low extractables and are used to contain the most critical parenteral drugs, those administered by injection.

Glasses other than soda-lime can cause problems if they are included with regular container glass recycling. For example, borosilicate glasses—of which Pyrex bakeware is probably the most visible example—have a significantly higher melt temperature than soda-lime glass. Along with Pyrex items, window glass, laboratory glassware, china and household glassware should not be included in glass collected for recycling.

Glass has many advantages as a packaging material:

- It is inert to most chemicals.

- Foods do not attack glass, nor do they leach out materials that might alter taste.

- Its impermeability is important for long-term storage of products sensitive to volatile loss or oxidation by atmospheric oxygen.

- Clarity allows product visibility.

- It is generally perceived as having an upscale image.

- The rigidity of glass means that container shapes and volumes do not change under vacuum or under pressure.

- It is stable at high temperatures, making it suitable for hot-fill and retortable products.

Despite these advantages, many traditional glass markets have been eroded or displaced by plastics. The disadvantages of glass are its breakability and high density. Glass manufacturing is energy intensive and high energy costs will affect the cost of glass.

Pharmaceutical Glass

Although glass is generally classed as inert, sodium and other ions within its formulation will leach out into certain solutions. While of no consequence in most applications, some pharmaceutical preparations can be affected. Glass types 1, 2 and 3 have specific limits to titratable alkalis specified by the United States Pharmacopoeia (USP) for exacting pharmaceutical glassware. USP-specification glass is used mostly for the manufacture of ampoules and vials that typically contain injectable drugs.

Type 1 glass is a borosilicate glass and has the most stringent extractables standard. A disadvantage is the higher melting point of this glass type.

Type 2 glass is a soda-lime glass formula (type 3) that has been treated in the annealing oven with sulfur to reduce alkali solubility. The treatment produces a discolored appearance.

Type 3 glass is conventional soda-lime glass that has been tested and shown to have a specified extractives level. Soda-lime glasses not meeting type 3 qualification are classed as USP type NP.

COMMERCIAL GLASS MANUFACTURING

Commercial glass is made in gas-fired melting or fusion furnaces lined with high-temperature refractory materials. (See Figure 8.1) Premixed raw materials are continuously fed into one end of the furnace while gas-fired heating flames are directed over the glass surface from the firing ports located along the furnace sides. The raw materials fuse into glass at about 1,510°C (2,750°F) accompanied by the release of carbon dioxide gas from the decomposition of carbonate ingredients. The released gases and convection currents serve to mix the glass.

Ten volumes of air are required to burn one volume of natural gas. At the high temperatures of a glass furnace, environmentally objectionable nitrogen oxides can form. Newer furnaces are using oxygen instead of air, eliminating a possible pollution source, while also reducing the overall energy requirement by up to one-third. The hot flue gases are passed through some form of heat exchanger (see Figure 8.2) that is used to heat incoming cold air or oxygen.

Typical dedicated large-volume production furnaces may hold up to 500 tons of glass and can produce about 200 to 400 tons in twenty-four hours. Smaller furnaces in the ton or less range are used to produce special glassware for such applications as fancy cosmetic bottles or art glassware. Furnaces operate continuously for ten or more years between maintenance shutdowns.

The dry mineral ingredients are weighed and batch-mixed in a rotary mixer. A typical batch contains about a ton of sand, with appropriate amounts of soda-lime and other mineral compounds, and conditioning materials. "Cullet"

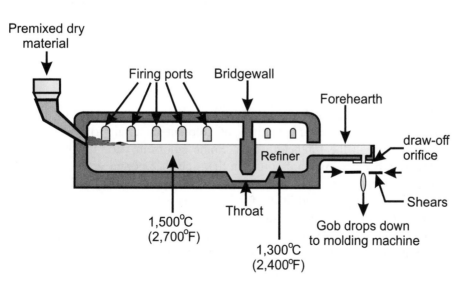

Figure 8.1

A glass furnace cross-section.

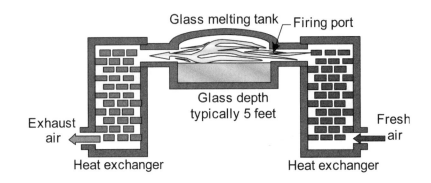

Figure 8.2

Heat exchangers recover heat before the spent gases are exhausted. In the furnace shown above, the firing direction is changed every twenty minutes, alternately heating and cooling each heat exchanger.

is broken glass recovered from plant operations and from post-consumer waste. Cullet is added to enhance the melting rate and significantly reduce the energy requirements. Cullet is used in percentages as high as 80% of the batch charge.

The surface level of the molten glass at the furnace draw-off orifice (see Figure 8.1) is about 4 meters (m) (12 to 13 ft.) above the bottle-manufacturing floor level. Molten glass is gravity-fed through spouts or chutes to bottle-forming machines.

Large production furnaces can be in the order of 20 m (60 ft.) long. Fusion occurs in the main furnace chamber, or "tank." The molten glass then passes under the bridgewall that holds back any scum or unfused material floating on the glass surface. The forehearth brings the glass temperature down to about 1,300°C (2,300°F). A furnace may be equipped with several forehearths, each feeding a separate bottle-making machine on the floor below. Molten glass has the consistency of molasses and can be cut like leather.

Coloring agents may be added either to the melt furnace along with other ingredients, or they can be added at the forehearth. Because of the large furnace size, standard furnace glasses are restricted to three colors:

Flint. Basic clear glass. Used for the majority of packaging applications.

Amber. The familiar brown glass is the only standard glass that will filter out light in the critical ultraviolet (UV) region (300 to 400 nm). It is primarily used for UV-sensitive products such as beer and some pharmaceuticals.

Emerald. A bright green glass used mostly for wines and lime or lemon flavored soft drinks.

Various blue, green and opaque glasses are also available. Most of these are produced by adding smaller quantities of colorant material (frit) to flint glass as it flows through the forehearth area. Some colors in wide use by the wine industry have become standard colors in themselves. Georgia green, champagne and dead-leaf green are popular shades. An up-charge of about 5% is typical for nonstandard colors produced in the forehearth section.

Unusual colors required for smaller orders such as might be required for the cosmetics industry would be produced in smaller specialty furnaces. Blue glass makes white products look whiter. Opaque white (opal) glass adds a prestigious appearance to toiletries and cosmetics.

A ceramic-lined draw-off orifice at the bottom end of each forehearth allows the glass to extrude downwards in a controlled manner. Just after the extrusion die, a large shear-knife cuts the glass flow into individual gobs; each gob being the exact quantity of glass needed for one bottle of the type being produced.

BOTTLE MANUFACTURING

Stock and Custom Molds

Purchasers of glassware can purchase stock glassware made on existing molds directly from a plant or through one of the many container brokers that may represent dozens of glass manufacturers from around the world. Alternately, if the required volume is large enough, the purchaser may elect to have a custom bottle designed and manufactured to their specifications.

The design of a custom bottle starts with a discussion between the producer and the customer that establishes the basic design objectives. From these parameters, concept drawings will be made for customer approval. The approved concept will then be rendered into a three-dimensional, full-sized acrylic model. The customer can use this model to verify aesthetic appearance and check for label location and fit. When the model is approved, the glass-maker will proceed to the mold-making stage.

Manufacture of a glass container requires two molds: a "blank mold" in which an initial shape is formed and a "blow mold" where the initial shape is expanded into the finished bottle or jar. (See Figure 8.3) Both molds are normally made from gray or cast iron and are air cooled. Some molds have air blown through holes drilled vertically through the blank and blow molds.

The molds are an assembly of individual components that fit closely together to form the closed chamber inside of which the container is made. The blow mold will be made up of a left and right half that fit together to form the main container body. Since glass is molded hot but shrinks when it cools, the mold

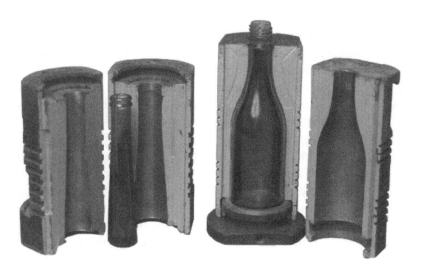

Figure 8.3

Body halves of the blank mold with parison (left) and blow mold with bottom plate and blown bottle (right).

halves and all other parts must be made larger by about 3 micrometers (um) for every millimeter of part length (0.003 in./inch.) The bottom of the mold halves, against which the container bottom will be formed, is closed by a bottom plate. The "bottom plate match" is the horizontal mold parting line running around the bottle just slightly up from the base. Mold seams are vertical parting lines running up opposite sides of the container where the mold body halves meet.

The neck ring, which forms the threaded part of the container, is incorporated into the blank mold. Precision is particularly important in the fit of the neck ring halves since any prominent mold parting lines could interfere with closure fit and sealing. The "neck match" is a horizontal line around the container neck just slightly below the neck ring or transfer bead.

A single blank or blow mold is usually made and test run to ensure that an acceptable bottle can be made before commitment to a full production set.

Blowing the Bottle or Jar

Depending on their geometry, glass containers are made by two slightly different processes, "blow-and-blow" and "press-and-blow." Both processes require two molds: a blank mold that forms an initial shape or "parison" and a blow mold in which the final shape is produced. The blank or parison mold forms the neck, the finish (the part that receives the closure) and a partially formed body known as a parison. A blank mold comes in a number of sections:

- The finish section
- The cavity section (made in two halves to allow parison removal)
- A guide or funnel for inserting the gob
- A seal for the gob opening once the gob is settled in the mold
- Blowing tubes through the gob and neck openings

Molten glass flows by gravity through draw-off orifices (See Figure 8.4) with openings ranging from 12 to 50 millimeters (mm) (1/2 to 2 in.), depending on bottle size. Mechanical shears, which are 25 mm (1 in.) below the orifice and synchronized with the draw-off flow rate and bottle-forming machine speed, snip off "gobs" of molten glass. Each gob makes one container. The falling gob is caught by a spout and directed to one of the blank molds.

A mass-production bottle-making machine is typically made up of six, eight or ten individual sections (IS), hence the term "IS machine." Each section is an independent unit holding a set of bottle-making molds. For large bottles, a set would consist of a blank mold and a blow mold. Higher production speeds are achieved for smaller bottles by the use of double or triple gobs on one machine. A mold set would then consist of a block of two or three blank molds and a similar block of blow molds. Each blow mold has a number that is imprinted on the bottles made by that mold.

Glass containers produced by two processes differ only in the way that the parison is produced. In the blow-and-blow process, the bottle is blown in the following sequence (See Figure 8.5):

Figure 8.4

Molten glass extruding from the draw-off orifice. Shears will cut will cut the extruded glass to the desired length and the gob will fall into a trough that will carry it to a section of the bottle molding machine located underneath the glass furnace.

1. The gob is dropped into the blank mold through a funnel-shaped guide. Note that the blank mold is upside down. Gob temperature at this point is about 985°C (1,800°F).

2. The guide is replaced by a parison bottomer, and air is blown into the mold (called the "settle blow") to force the glass into the finish section. At this point, the bottle finish is complete.

3. The parison bottomer is replaced by a solid bottom plate, and air is forced through the bottle finish (called the "counter–blow") to expand the glass upward and form the parison.

4. The parison is removed from the blank mold, using the neck ring (transfer bead) as a gripping fixture, and rotated to a right-side-up orientation for

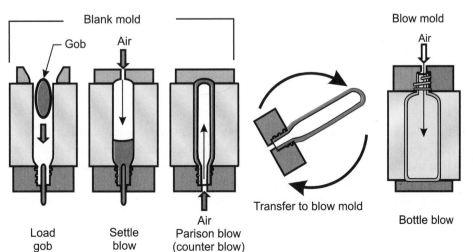

Figure 8.5

Blow-and-blow bottle manufacturing.

Figure 8.6

The press-and-blow
process forms the parison
by mechanical action.

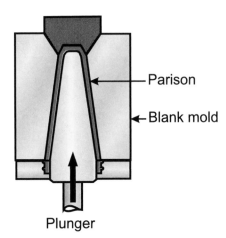

Parison

Blank mold

Plunger

placement into the blow mold. The parison is supported in the blow mold
by the neck ring.

5. Air forces the glass to conform to the shape of the blow mold. The bottle
   is cooled so that it can stand without becoming distorted and is then placed
   on conveyors that take it to the annealing oven.

In the press-and-blow process, gob delivery and settle-blow steps are similar
to those in blow-and-blow forming. However, in press-and-blow, the parison is
pressed into shape with a metal plunger rather than by being blown into shape.
(See Figure 8.6) The final blowing step in a separate blow mold is identical to
that in the blow-and-blow process.

The blow-and-blow process is used for narrow-necked bottles, while press-
and-blow is used to make wide-mouthed jars. Recent advances have allowed
press-and-blow to be used for increasingly smaller necked containers. The advantage of press-and-blow is better control of glass distribution.

Typical production rates range from sixty to 300 bottles per minute, depending on the number of sections in a machine, the number of gobs being extruded
and the container' size.

The blown bottle is removed from the blow mold with takeout tongs and
placed on a deadplate to air cool for a few moments before transfer to a conveyor
that will transport the container to the annealing oven.

Annealing

The walls of a glass bottle are comparatively thick, and the cooling of such
a cross-section will not be even. In theory, the inner and outer skins of a glass
section will become rigid long before the internal temperature has reduced enough
to produce the same degree of rigidity. The still-contracting inner portion of the
wall will build up internal stresses as it tries to contract away from the immobile
skin surfaces. Substantial stresses can develop in the glass because of this uneven
cooling. To reduce internal stresses, the bottle is passed through an annealing
oven, or "lehr," immediately after removal from the blow mold.

The lehr is a controlled-temperature oven through which the glassware is carried on a moving belt at a rate of about 200 to 300 mm/minute (9 to 12 in./minute). The glass temperature is raised to about 565°C (1,050°F), then gradually cooled until the containers exit at close to room temperature with all internal stresses reduced to safe levels. This process typically takes an hour. Improperly annealed bottles will be fragile and tend to have high breakage rates in normal transport and filling. Hot filling will also produce unacceptable breakage levels.

Surface Coatings

A glass container's inner and outer surfaces have slightly different characteristics coming from the mold. The outer surface comes in contact with the mold and takes the grain of the mold surface. However, both surfaces are pristine: monolithic, sterile and chemically inert.

Pristine glass has a comparatively high coefficient of friction, and surface scratching or "bruising" can occur when bottles rub together on high-speed filling lines. Scratched glass has significantly lower breakage resistance, and glass is typically coated to reduce the coefficient of friction. Two coatings are usually used. The hot-end coating applied at the entrance of the annealing lehr is usually tin or titanium tetrachloride. Its purpose is to strengthen the glass surface and act as a primer or bonding-agent coat for the cold-end friction-reducing coat applied at the lehr exit.

Many different cold-end coatings are available, depending on the filling process and end use. Oleic acid, monostearates, waxes, silicones and polyethylenes are typical cold-end coatings. The label adhesive will need to be compatible with the cold-end coating.

Inspection and Packing

Visual inspection has been largely replaced by mechanical and electronic means. Squeeze testers pass the containers between two rollers that subject the container walls to a compressive force. Plug gauges check height, perpendicularity, and inside and outside finish diameters. Optical devices inspect for stones, blisters, checks, spikes, bird swings, and other blemishes or irregularities by rotating the container past a bank of photocells.

Several larger physical defects are shown in Figure 8.7. In addition to these, glassware might have a number of surface or cosmetic defects:

- A blister is a bubble in the glass not greater than 1.5 mm (0.06 in.).
- A seed is a contaminating grain or grit less than 1.5 mm (0.06 in.).
- A check is a small crack on the glass surface.
- A stone is a particle of unmelted material in the glass.

Faulty containers (offware) are ejected from the line and sent for crushing into cullet.

Glass containers can be transported in reusable corrugated shippers, which are reloaded with the filled bottles. Others are shipped in tiers on pallets. Tiered

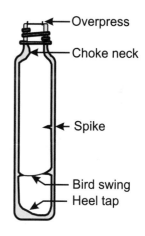

Figure 8.7

Flat bottles are prone to develop "bird swings" and "spikes." Spikes are glass projections inside the bottle; a bird swing is a glass thread joining the two walls. Heel taps and choke necks are excessive thicknesses of glass. An overpress is a ridge of glass around the bottle opening.

and palleted shipping is best for high-speed production lines where automatic equipment can be used to clear tiers off the pallet and feed them into the filling machine.

Tolerances

Variables inherent to glass container production prevent the manufacture of precisely identical containers. Tolerance for variation in any given bottle characteristic will vary depending on bottle size and design. However, Glass Packaging Institute (GPI) suggests the following ranges:

Capacity	1% for large bottles, up to 15% for small bottles.
Weight	Generally 5% of specified weight.
Height	0.5% to 0.8% of specified overall height.
Diameter	1.5% for 200 mm (8 in.) bottles to 3% for 25 mm (1 in.) bottles.

The division between what is a small and large bottle is vague. For comparison, the capacity tolerance for a typical 341 milliliter (ml) beer bottle is about 1.3%.

BOTTLE DESIGN FEATURES

Design Protection

A glass container's design or shape cannot be patented, but it can be protected by registration. Under the Trademark Act, continual protection can be maintained for a special bottle design. Decoration may be incorporated as part of a design and also protected. A functional detail, which can be considered as a new invention, may be considered for a patent, subject to the same conditions as a regular patent case.

Bottle Parts and Shapes

Figure 8.8 illustrates the terms used to describe the various parts of a bottle.

Viscous glass flows easiest into molds with smooth, round shapes. Round bottles are easiest to manufacture since they are an expansion of the circular parison, eliminating complex material-distribution problems. Round shapes run easily on filling lines and can be labeled at relatively high speeds. They can be accurately positioned in a spot-labeler via an indexing label lug on the bottle exterior. Round bottles have greater strength-to-weight ratios and better material utilization than irregular shapes. (See Table 8.2) Some round bottles, such as the "Boston round" (see Figure 8.9), have very efficient glass usage per enclosed volume and are made to standardized dimensions. This facilitates ordering small quantities from stock, at low cost.

Square shapes, angular shapes, flat shapes and sharp corners are more difficult to form properly and have many inherent problems. For example, flat flasks are

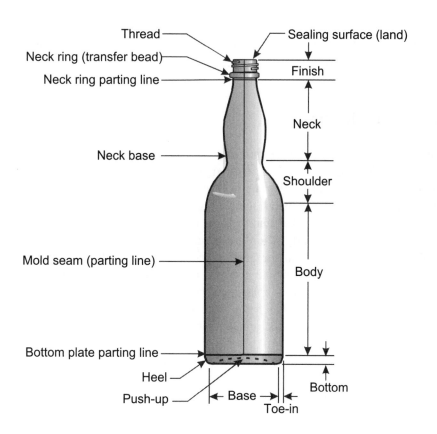

Thread — Sealing surface (land)

Neck ring (transfer bead) —

Neck ring parting line — Finish

Neck

Neck base —

Shoulder

Mold seam (parting line) —

Body

Bottom plate parting line —

Heel —

Push-up — Base — Bottom

Toe-in

Figure 8.8

Glass bottle nomenclature.

Table 8.2

Representative glass weights for round and irregular bottles.

Capacity	Round	Irregular
30 ml	45 g	55 g
340 ml	225 g	285 g
455 ml	285 g	355 g
905 ml	455 g	565 g

Figure 8.9

Examples of typical bottle shapes include the "Boston round" (left) and a bottle with a labeling panel (right).

prone to having the two sides of the parison touch momentarily during transfer from the blank to the blow mold. This results in spikes or in extreme cases a "bird swing" on the inside of the bottle. (See Figure 8.7) Rectangular bottles still have a round finish, a factor requiring careful design to avoid stress points.

Finish and Closures

A bottle finish is defined as the part that will receive the closure. Bottle finishes are broadly classified according to diameter (expressed as the nominal inside diameter in millimeters), sealing method and special features. Standards for finish sizes and tolerances have been set by the Glass Packaging Institute, and are followed by the bottle maker and closure maker. Continuous thread (CT), lug, crown, threaded crown and roll-on are common finish designs.

Closures are selected on the basis of cost, utility and decoration. Particular closure requirements will dictate specific bottle finish designs. Stock closures should be used when cost is a key criterion. While glass-bottle finish thread dimensions are similar to that for plastic bottles, the thread profile for glass has a curved or partially semicircular profile, while plastic-bottle threads have flat lands. (See Chapter Twelve "Closures"). Care should be taken to match the correct bottle and closure thread profiles.

Neck and Shoulder Areas

Neck designs have particular impact on filling, air displacement and dispensing. Differences in fill level are more visible in long, narrow necks. Headspace is sometimes needed to provide for thermal expansion and to facilitate filling.

The "upper shoulder" is the area directly below the neck. Blending of upper shoulder and neck is important to good design and efficient production. The "lower shoulder" is the integration point between upper shoulder and body. It is a vulnerable spot for abusive contact with other bottles and the origin of many handling and shipping fractures.

Sides

The sides are the most generalized area of the bottle. Labeling styles and means of preventing scuffing must be considered. Bottles are often designed with label panels that are recessed to prevent scuffing. (See Figure 8.9, right) The panel may have prominent base and shoulder ridges as part of the design.

In angular bottles, rounded corners rather than beveled ones are preferable for wraparound or three-sided labeling. Spot labeling is normally a one- or two-sided application, but four-sided labelers are available. Labeling of nonrounded shapes is typically slower than for round shapes.

Heel and Base

The heel is a high-abuse area. It should start as high from the base as possible, curving into the base to a suitable base diameter. The body-to-base curve should combine three radii. The largest radius blends body to heel, while the smallest blends heel into base.

The diameter of the base should be as large as possible within constraints of good design. The center of the base is always domed inward (the "push-up") to ensure a flat stable bottom that will not cause the bottle to rock. The circular bearing surface on which the bottle rests will usually have a stippled or knurled pattern so that scratches that inevitably occur during handling and usage do not weaken the bottle's body.

Ketchup bottles and other sauce bottles require that both heel and base be heavier and contoured to allow consumers to tap them safely and comfortably when expelling the contents.

Some wide-mouthed jar bases have designed-in stacking features. There are two types:

- Container base fits into recessed cap
- Indented container base fits over cap

Stability and Machinability

Center of gravity and the base surface area will determine a bottle's stability. Stable bottles minimize handling problems on both manufacturing and filling lines. Tall and narrow bottles present the most problems in manufacturing, packaging, line handling and labeling due to the high center of gravity. Short bottles, usually with round or oval bodies, are an efficient type for machine handling and present minimal labeling problems. Examples of this type of bottle include baby food and cold cream jars.

As much as possible, bottles designs should be all-around trouble-free to manufacture, fill, close and ship. Some designs are inherently weaker or more prone to cause trouble in their filling and distribution cycle than others.

Decorating and Labeling

Some decorative effects are molded into the bottle glass; others are added on after the bottle has been molded. Effects such as surface textures or molded-in lettering are produced by creating the "mirror" design on the blow mold's interior surface. In the same manner, a cut-glass effect can be obtained, provided the depth of the V-shaped grooves does not exceed 25% of the groove width. The cut-glass effect enhances the appearance of clear flint glass without impairing product visibility. Stippling or texturing has decorative value, but it can reduce product visibility. This can be used on the container's lower portion to mask product sediments or on the upper portion to mask uneven fill heights.

Label areas must be carefully considered prior to a design commitment. Label panels must be large enough to accept the proposed label, and in the instance of paper labels, can curve in only one axis. Round bottles label faster than flat shapes, particularly if more than one face is being labeled.

Label panels where the label is recessed enough to prevent contact and abrasion with other labels or bottle parts are an important design feature. (See

Figure 8.7) In some designs, prominent ridges encircle the bottle and are part of the overall design appearance. Other, apparently straight-walled bottles actually have a slight (0.08 mm or 0.003 in.) "hourglass" sidewall curve.

Wraparound labels use minimal amounts of adhesive, requiring only a band of adhesive to glue the label to itself at the overlap. A stripe of label pickup adhesive is applied directly to the container. Spot labels can be applied to virtually any location on a container. Adhesive can be applied to the container or to the label back. Wraparound labels are impractical for bottles with concave or convex surfaces. Paper spot labels may be used if the contour is in one axis. Plastic shrinkable labels are likely a better choice.

The shrink properties of plastic labels have the advantage of being able to conform to areas that curve in two axes. Clear labels made from materials such as polypropylene are used to create various decorative effects, including excellent imitations of screen printed decoration.

Screen printing can be used to apply decoration directly to the bottle surface. In most instances, such inks are fired on to produce an extremely durable applied ceramic label (ACL). The process has some color limitations, and process printing cannot be done. ACL labeling was common in times when glass soft drink bottles were refilled.

Pressure-sensitive labels are another decorating option. These offer the full range of printing possibilities.

A frosted appearance can be produced by etching bottles with hydrofluoric acid (a relatively costly process) or by sandblasting. These surfaces show "wet" spots when handled, due to surface moisture on the hand. Ceramic frosting is achieved by spraying the bottle exterior with a ceramic paint, or "frit," made from a ground glass-and-oil mixture, and then firing. During firing, the oil evaporates and the ground glass is fused to the bottle surface. This process is used primarily for upscale cosmetics containers.

In many designs, it is necessary to register or align a label with another design feature. Typical situations involve the need to:

- Register the application so that a label does not fall across a mold parting line

- Actuate automatic ACL or other labeling machinery

- Align labels with closure features

- Align an applied label with other labels or markings

Registration features are most often found on round containers, and are usually in the form of a projecting lug or a small recess along the base perimeter or on the bottle base itself.

Vials and Ampoules

Vials and ampoules such as those illustrated in Figure 8.10 are used mainly for pharmaceuticals and sera. They are made from preformed tubing stock rather than by the blowing methods used for glass bottles (See Figure 8.11). Ampoules

Figure 8.10
Examples of pharmaceutical vials and ampules.

are sealed glass containers with a constriction that has been treated to allow for easy fracture. This may be a controlled score, or it may be coated with a ceramic paint that causes a stress concentration in the constriction. Standard ampoule sizes are 1, 2, 5, 10 and 20 ml.

Serum vials are small bottles that are fitted with a rubber septum retained by an aluminum neck ring. The rubber septum is pierced by a needle cannula to withdraw serum. Unlike an ampoule, the vial can be accessed several times. Vials come in standard sizes of 1, 2, 3, 5, 10 and 20 ml.

Carbonated Beverages

The pressure developed by a carbonated beverage depends on, among other factors, the amount of gas dissolved in the product. Beverage producers express this as the number of volumes of gas dissolved in a unit volume of the product. For example, if a 48 oz. volume of carbon dioxide at standard conditions is dissolved in 12 oz. of beverage, then the beverage is said to yield 4 gas volumes. Table 8.3 lists common gas volume ranges.

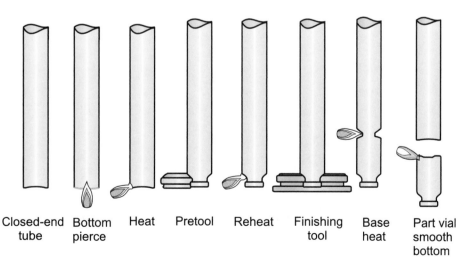

Closed-end tube | Bottom pierce | Heat | Pretool | Reheat | Finishing tool | Base heat | Part vial smooth bottom

Figure 8.11
Unlike glass bottles, ampules and vials are shaped from preformed glass tubing. Vials and ampules have no mold lines or markings.

Table 8.3
Product gas volumes of common carbonated beverages.

Product	Gas Volumes
Fruit flavors	1.5 to 2.5
Beer	2.6 to 3.0
Colas	3.5 to 4.3
Mixers	4.5 to 5.0
Sprite	3.6 to 4.2
7-Up	4.0

Carbonated beverage and beer bottles must withstand internal gas pressure and must be well capped. Internal pressure in a soft drink container may reach 0.34 millipascals (50 psi), while beer during pasteurisation may reach 0.83 millipascals (120 psi). The stress on the glass causes a loss of bottle strength over time with the greatest losses occurring within the first week after filling. Bottle designs for pressurized products are always round in cross-section and have gently curving radii in order to maximize bottle strength.

REVIEW QUESTIONS

1. What are the three principal constituents of glass?

2. What is cullet, and why is it important to glass manufacturing?

3. Glass can be colored for decoration, however, an important technical consideration dictates the use of a particular color. What is the color, and why is it used?

4. What are the two methods of molding glass containers? What type of container is most typically made by each molding method?

5. What is the difference between type 1, type 2 and type 3 glass? Where are they used?

6. Who establishes the finish tolerances for glass bottle manufacturers?

7. What is annealing, and why is it necessary?

8. What coloring agents are used to make emerald glass and amber glass.

9. Glass containers are surface-coated at the glass plant. What is the function of these coatings?

10. Like any packaging material, glass has advantages and limitations. Name three of each.

11. What problems might be encountered with a bottle that is wider at the top than at the base? What problems might be encountered with a poorly designed oval bottle?

12. Glass bottles cannot be made to have a perfectly consistent volume. What is the general capacity tolerance level for large glass bottles?

13. Define:

gob	blank mold	finish
heel tap	choke neck	push-up

14. What are the disadvantages of a bottle designed with a long neck?

15. What design feature is used to reduce label abrasion? What design feature is used to help register a label with a bottle feature?

16. What are the advantages of a round bottle design?

17. What is a "bird swing," and on what kind of bottle is it likely to be found?

18. What are the proper names for the three standard furnace glass colors?

19. What is one reason that might influence a designer to specify a blue-colored bottle?

20. What is the approximate melting point of glass?

21. Why is the bottom of a glass bottle usually stippled?

22. How are bottle surfaces made to look frosted?

23. Why is a transfer bead (neck ring) a part of every glass bottle design?

CONTENTS

Introduction to Plastics

Definition of the terms "plastic" and "polymer," molecular size, raw material sources, common packaging polymer abbreviations and trade names, commodity polymers, engineering polymers.

Polarity and Material Properties

Electron sharing, Van der Waals' forces, polarity, effect of polarity on solubility, coefficient of friction and adhesion, flame and corona treatments to increase polarity.

Hydrocarbons and Polyethylene

Polymerization, the carbon atom, monomers, addition polymerization, derivation of proper names, simple hydrocarbons, effect of increasing molecular weight. Branching, difference between HDPE, LDPE and LLDPE. Copolymers, ethylene (vinyl alcohol) as a copolymer of polyethylene.

Other Packaging Polymers

Polypropylene, poly(vinyl alcohol), poly(vinyl chloride), poly(vinylidene chloride), polystyrene, poly(vinyl acetate), polyamide, poly(ethylene terephthalate), urethane.

Molecular Structure and Properties

Crystalline and amorphous polymers, thermal history, clarity, molecular weight distribution, affect on processability, metallocene polyethylene. Viscous and elastic behavior, nature and significance of viscoelasticity.

Thermal Behavior

Phase changes, rigid, thermoelastic and thermoplastic regions. Glass transition temperature and melt temperature. Orientation, heat-shrink properties. Thermal expansion compared with metals, molds and thermal expansion.

Density and Yield

Definition of density and yield, density and yield of packaging thermoplastics.

Thermoplastic and Thermoset Polymers

Cross-linking, general properties of thermoplastics and thermosets compared, packaging applications for thermosets.

POLYMER CHEMISTRY FOR THE NONCHEMIST

INTRODUCTION TO PLASTICS

"Plastic" describes the ability of a material to be molded or formed. Historically, this referred to natural materials such as wax, clay, tar, rosin and asphalt. With advances in chemistry, the term "plastic" began to describe modified natural resins and finally a large group of synthetic materials that could be formed into useful shapes. The words "plastic" and "polymer" are used interchangeably, but plastic tends to be used to describe finished parts; polymer tends to describe the raw material and is used by the scientific community.

Polymers are very large molecules. A water molecule has only three atoms, one oxygen and two hydrogen, whereas a typical polymer molecule contains hundreds, or more typically, thousands of atoms. A polymer is created when a large number of identical repeating monomer units are joined together to make a single large polymer molecule (from the Greek "polys," meaning many, and "meros," meaning parts). The "mer" is the smallest repetitive unit in a polymer and for this discussion is based on the carbon atom.

Today, there are hundreds of identified "species" of synthetic polymers. Any of these is available in a range of molecular masses, most can be modified by the addition of other monomers and the properties of each can be dramatically influenced by processing conditions. In reality then, the choice in plastics is almost limitless.

Polymers can be grouped into two chemical classes: "thermoplastic" and "thermoset"—terms that describe how polymers behave when heated. (See section "Thermoplastic and Thermoset Polymers" below for details.) They also fall into two economic groups—"commodity polymers" (i.e., economical) and "engineering polymers" (i.e., costly). Only a small number of available polymers are of practical significance for packaging, and practically all of these are commodity thermoplastics.

With few exceptions, the essential raw materials used to make packaging plastics are derived from the petrochemical industry. The amount of petrochemicals diverted for plastics is quite small compared to that used for fuel and heating. Depending on the source, the estimated amount of petrochemicals used by all the plastics industries ranges from 5 to 7%. Packaging uses a fraction of this percentage.

Each plastic type has a unique structure and proper chemical name. However, chemical names can be lengthy and common industry usage is a mixture of trade names, common names and abbreviations. (See Table 9.1) Spellings and abbreviations developed randomly, and today, the same polymer may be spelled and abbreviated in a number of different ways.

The casual use of spellings, abbreviations and trade names can be confusing and sometimes technically incorrect. For example, "Styrofoam" is Dow Chemical's trade name for an expanded polystyrene material used primarily by the construction industry, but also used in other areas such as crafts. It is not

Table 9.1

Selected abbreviations and trade names for packaging polymers.*

Abbreviation	Generic Name	Common Trade Names, Alternatives
BOPP	Biaxially oriented polypropylene	
CTFE	Chlorotrifluoroethylene	Aclar
CPET	Crystallized PET	
EEA	Ethylene-ethyl acrylate	Frequently grouped as an acid copolymer
EPS	Expanded polystyrene	
EVA	Ethylene-vinyl acetate	Also abbreviated EVAC
EVOH	Ethylene-vinyl alcohol	EVAL
HIPS	High-impact polystyrene	
LDPE	Low-density polyethylene	
LLDPE	Linear low-density polyethylene	
OPP	Oriented polypropylene	
mPE	Metallocene polyethylene	
PA	Polyamide	Nylon, also abbreviated NY
PAN	Polyacrylonitrile	Barex, also abbreviated AN
PEN	Poly(ethylene naphthalate)	
PC	Polycarbonate	
PE	Polyethylene	
PET	Poly(ethylene terephthalate)	Polyester, Mylar, Melinex
PETG	Poly(ethylene terephthalate) glycol	
PP	Polypropylene	
PLA	Polylactide	Often referred to as poly(lactic acid)
PS	Polystyrene	
PTFE	Polytetrafluoroethylene	Teflon (DuPont trade name)
PVAC	Poly(vinyl acetate)	Also abbreviated PVA
PVC	Poly(vinyl chloride)	
PVDC	Poly(vinylidene chloride)	Saran (Dow trade name)
PVAL	Poly(vinyl alcohol)	Also abbreviated PVOH
None	Ionomer	Surlyn (DuPont trade name)

*Plastic and polymer terminology varies considerably. This text uses spellings and abbreviations recommended by ASTM International. (Reference: D 883, Standard Terminology Relating to Plastics, and D 1600, Standard Terminology for Abbreviated Terms Relating to Plastics).

correct to use the term "Styrofoam" to describe expanded polystyrene packaging materials. "Cellophane" was a trade name coined in the 1930s to market a regenerated cellulose product. It was the first clear plastic wrapping material used in quantity by the packaging industry. Up to the 1950s, if it was plastic and clear, it was quite likely cellophane. Today, the packaging use of regenerated cellulose film is negligible. It is technically incorrect to refer to a plastic bag as "cellophane" since the possibility of it actually being made of this material is remote.

Most of the polymers listed in Table 9.1 are commodity thermoplastics. Engineering plastics such as polysulfone, acetal and silicone polymers are several orders of magnitude higher in cost.

The following sections examine factors that give individual polymers their different properties, as well as establishing a number of basic concepts that apply to all polymers. In particular, the sections will show that a particular plastic can have completely different performance properties depending on factors such as thermal history and mechanical history.

A polymer's properties depend primarily on:

- The elements that make up the polymer molecule. By intuition alone, we would surmise that a polymer made up hydrogen and carbon atoms alone—polyethylene, for example—would behave differently from one such as poly(vinyl chloride) that also included chlorine atoms.

- The polymer molecule's polarity. Depending on the participating atoms, molecules exhibit varying degrees of polarity. Degree of molecular polarity will influence such factors as melting point, coefficient of friction, solubility, barrier properties and adhesiveness.

- The size or molecular weight of the molecule. Most polymers are available in a range of molecular weights. Properties such as melting point, stiffness and solubility will change as molecular weight changes.

- The molecule's shape. The shape of a molecule will determine how large numbers of them will fit together. Degree of crystallinity, clarity, barrier, melting point and other physical properties are affected by the molecule's shape.

- The polymer's thermal history. Every thermoplastic needs to be melted in order to get it into a form that can be shaped, and so every plastic part has a thermal history. Changing the thermal history changes the plastic's performance characteristics.

- Mechanical history. A plastic's final properties also depend on its mechanical history—how it flowed in the molten state and how it was stressed when cold. Sometimes mechanical forces are used alone, but in other plastic forming methods, thermal and mechanical histories are combined to give still another variation on the plastic's basic properties.

POLARITY AND MATERIAL PROPERTIES

Atoms join through various arrangements for sharing electrons to make the molecules of a new substance. Such atomic bonds can be very strong, and it takes significant energy to disrupt them and revert the molecule back to its constituent elements. Where the sharing of electrons is fairly equal between two participating atoms, the negative electrons and positive protons cancel each other. However, in many instances, electrons will spend more time at one end of the new molecule. This unequal sharing creates a molecule having polarity; that is, it has a positive and a negative pole similar to a magnet.

Molecules also develop varying degrees of attraction for one another through a group of weaker electrical attractions generally referred to as "Van der Waals' forces." Van der Waals' forces allow a molecule to develop temporary or permanent polarities that act to attract the opposite poles on nearby molecules.

Of the packaging polymers only polyethylene and polypropylene are predominantly nonpolar. All the remaining polymers have varying degrees of polarity.

Polarity influences many material properties. For example, of two molecules of similar molecular weight, the one with the higher polarity will have the higher melting point, since a greater amount of energy must be put into the substance to overcome the polar attractions between the molecules. Confirming this observation, nonpolar polyethylene has one of the lowest melting points of all the packaging polymers.

Polarity affects solubility. Alcohol, a highly polar substance, is readily soluble in another highly polar substance such as water, because the attraction between one water molecule and another is similar to the attraction of a water molecule for an alcohol molecule. However, oil, a nonpolar substance, is not soluble in water, because the attraction between water molecules is much greater than the attraction of water molecules for oil molecules. Two nonpolar substances are mutually soluble, since there are no attractive forces to be overcome. The above principles are the basis of the general observation that "like dissolves like."

"Barrier" is that material property that stops or reduces the permeation of a gas through the material. Only metal and glass are absolute barriers. All plastic materials are permeable to varying degrees depending on the nature of the plastic and the permeant gas. A prime determinant of whether a particular gas will permeate through a particular plastic is the solubility of the permeating gas in the plastic material.

For example, polyethylene is a nonpolar material. Consider the possible barrier properties of polyethylene to water vapor (a highly polar molecule) and oxygen (a nonpolar molecule.) Following our like-dissolves-like rule, we would conclude that water molecules would not be soluble in polyethylene whereas oxygen would, and therefore that polyethylene would provide a good water vapor barrier and a poor oxygen barrier. (See Figure 9.1) Polymer barrier qualities will be discussed in greater detail in Chapter 14, "Flexible Packaging Laminates."

A high coefficient of friction occurs where highly polar surfaces attract one another. (See Figure 9.2) The mechanism of adhesive bonding is mostly attributed to maximizing the polar attractions between the adhesive material and the substrate. Low polarity materials such as polyethylene or polypropylene are difficult to bond using adhesives. Similarly it is difficult to achieve a satisfactory

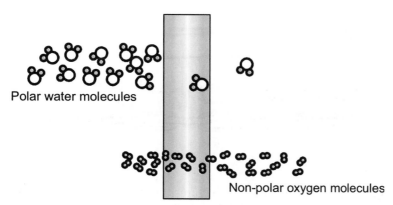

Figure 9.1

Nonpolar polyethylene provides a good barrier toward polar water molecules, but a poor barrier to nonpolar oxygen.

Polar water molecules

Non-polar oxygen molecules

Non-polar polyetheylene film

bond with a printing ink unless the substrate is treated to increase surface polarity.

The packaging industry uses either "flame treatment" or "corona discharge treatment" to impart polarity to the surface of low polarity plastics. These methods are thought to increase polarity by partially oxidizing the polymer surface. The polarity, or "dyne" level, of a plastic surface is indirectly measured by noting the contact angle of a drop of water on the surface, or by determining which solution in a set of solutions of known dyne level will be able to wet the surface. This subject is covered in more detail in Chapter 13, "Adhesives."

HYDROCARBONS AND POLYETHYLENE

Polymerization

Most polymers are based on the carbon atom. This is because carbon has these unique abilities:

- Form four bonds with other atoms
- Join to itself to form long chains and other shapes

The individual structural unit of a polymer is a "monomer" (i.e., one part). "Polymerization" describes the chemical reaction that joins monomer units to-

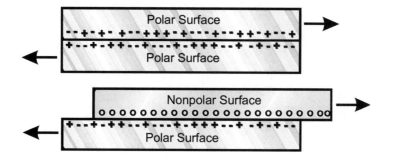

Polar Surface

Polar Surface

Nonpolar Surface

Polar Surface

Figure 9.2

The attraction of two polar surfaces can cause the surfaces to cling and drag when pulled over each other. A nonpolar surface will not have such attractions.

Figure 9.3

An addition polymerization is one where the individual monomer units simply add onto themselves to form chain-like structures. A mixture of low molecular weight prepolymer components is an oligomer.

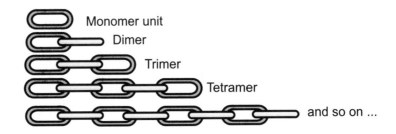

gether to form complex polymeric structures. Proper polymer names are derived from the individual structural unit. For example:

- ethylene   polymerizes to   polyethylene
- propylene   polymerizes to   polypropylene
- styrene   polymerizes to   polystyrene
- vinyl chloride polymerizes to   poly(vinyl chloride)

Depending on the particular monomers involved, several chemical reactions can be classed as polymerization. Most packaging polymers are formed by "addition polymerization," where under correct conditions of temperature and pressure, and with the aid of catalysts and promoters, the monomers simply add onto themselves like links in a chain. (See Figure 9.3)

The exceptions, poly(ethylene terephthalate) and polyamide, commonly called nylon, are made by condensation polymerization. In this reaction, two reactive monomers join together with the release (i.e., condensation) of a molecule of water. (See Figure 9.9)

Most polymer concepts can be readily illustrated by examining a family of molecules variously called olefins, polyolefins or hydrocarbons. As the name suggests, this family is composed of only hydrogen and carbon atoms.

The simplest possible combination of hydrogen and carbon is methane, with four hydrogen atoms attached to one carbon atom. However, as mentioned, carbon can link to itself to form chains, and thus create a hydrocarbon with two carbons or more. (See Figure 9.4)

Figure 9.4

The first four hydrocarbons are gases at room temperature. Pentane, next in the series, is the first to be a liquid at room temperature.

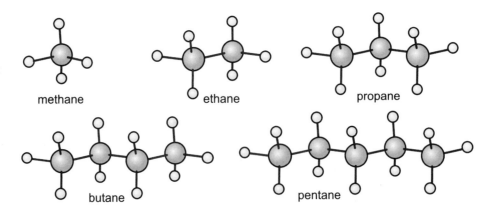

H   H
\C=C/
/   \
H   H

ethylene (ethene)

H   H
\C=C/
/   \
H   CH₃

propylene (propene)

Figure 9.5

Examples of hydrocarbons with double bonds between the carbon atoms. In older systems of chemical nomenclature, compounds based on a pair of carbons connected with a double bond were called "vinyls." The term is still used for many polymers.

Carbon can also form a double bond with itself, to form a near relative of the above series. Hydrocarbons with double bonds use the parent name, but with the suffix changed from "-ane" to "-ene." Ethyl*ene* and propyl*ene* (see Figure 9.5) are the monomers from which polyethylene and polypropylene are formed.

Low-molecular-weight molecules are small and therefore mobile. Thus, the first four members of the series just described are gases at room temperature. Methane and ethane, the smallest hydrocarbons would require very high pressures or very low temperatures to liquefy them. These extreme conditions are impractical and so these gases are usually used as fuel. The propane molecule is large enough that there is some interference to the free movement of individual molecules. Propane can be pressurized and liquefied at more reasonable conditions and so is delivered as a fuel in heavy steel tanks. Butane's boiling point is almost within ambient conditions, and therefore, it can be liquified at low pressures such as those found in a plastic butane lighter.

Table 9.2 illustrates the effect of increasing molecular weight by adding more carbon atoms, each with its accompanying two hydrogens. Pentane's boiling point is low enough that body heat will boil it away. Larger molecules are able to develop greater Van der Waals' forces to bind them together and are less free to move over each other due to entanglement of the longer molecular chains. From $C = 5$ to $C = 10$, hydrocarbons are liquids at room temperature. Increasing

Table 9.2

Some members of the hydrocarbon family.

Chain Length (Molecular Weight)	Melting Temperature	State
1 to 4		Gases at room temperature
5 to 7		Liquids boiling below 100°C (212°F)
8 to 11		Light naphtha
12 to 15	−10 to +10°C	Viscous fluids (mineral oil)
20	36°C	Semisolids (petrolatum)
30	60°C	Very soft (paraffin) wax
50	92°C	Soft (paraffin) wax
70	105°C	Hard (paraffin) wax
1,500	120°C +	Polyethylene

molecular weight increases the boiling point, moving from the realm of low-boiling-point solvents to fuels and solvents having higher boiling points.

Hydrocarbons whose carbon atoms number in the low teens have chains long enough to drag over each when the fluid is poured. This molecular drag or resistance to flow is observed as "viscosity," and these hydrocarbons are oily compounds. Viscosity continues to increase with increasing chain length, eventually resulting in semisolid substances. By carbon number 18, the substance is a definite solid, though it will melt in your hand (petrolatum or Vaseline). With increasing molecular weight, the hydrocarbons become familiar soft paraffin waxes. As the molecular weight increases further, the paraffin waxes become progressively harder. The chain at about 1,500 carbons long would be classed as a low-molecular-weight polyethylene.

Members of a chemical family share common properties. Polyethylene, like wax, its lower molecular mass relative, is relatively inert and does not wet out readily with water. It will burn, and when it does, the smoke has a slight paraffin aroma. As the molecular weight of a polyethylene goes up, so do certain other properties such as melting point, stiffness and hardness in continuation of the established trend.

This relationship between molecular weight and material properties is true for all polymer types. In summary, for any given polymer, as molecular weight goes up:

- Melting point increases
- Tensile strength, stiffness and hardness increase
- Barrier properties will be higher
- Solubility in solvents decreases

Polymer Chain Branching

The examples to this point have suggested that polyethylene is composed of long, straight chains. In fact, polyethylene chains exhibit varying degrees of side branching. Linear chains with very little side branching can be packed closely together in a dense structure, while steric hindrance prevents highly branched hydrocarbons from being closely packed.

Polyethylenes with similar molecular weights can have dramatically different properties, depending on the degree and nature of side branching. The most immediate difference is density. Highly branched molecular chains cannot pack closely together, and hence, produce a low-density polyethylene (LDPE). Highly linear polyethylene molecules can be closely packed and result in a high-density polyethylene (HDPE). A third variant, linear-low-density polyethylene (LLDPE) has short controlled side branches. (See Figure 9.6)

LDPEs are polyethylenes with densities between 0.910 and 0.925, while HDPEs are between 0.941 and 0.959. Medium-density polyethylenes fall between the LDPE and HDPE ranges. All are commonly used in packaging. The difference in properties and applications of LDPE and HDPE are great enough that they are usually treated as if they were completely different polymers rather than variations of the same family. Table 9.3 shows how selected properties are affected by side branching.

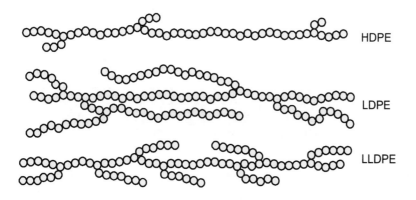

Figure 9.6

Polyethylene branching gives rise to different densities. Linear chains are representative of HDPE, while the highly branched chains are found in LDPE. LLDPE is also branched, but the branches are short.

LLDPE is actually a polyethylene copolymer. (Copolymers are discussed in the following section.) Including 10 or 20% of butene, hexene, octene or similar monomers along with the ethylene monomer, introduces deliberate branching during polymerization. The branching, length and frequency is more controlled than for LDPE and yields a product that can be made into exceptionally tough films. LLDPE also provides excellent hot tack and heat seal strength.

Branching can affect the degree of crystallinity. Higher crystallinity offers greater physical strength, better barrier properties and higher softening points. (A more detailed discussion of crystallinity appears later in this section.)

Various properties of polyethylene are related to the nonpolar nature of its molecule. For example, polyethylene's nonpolar surface can be difficult to print or bond to unless the surface is treated with an oxidizing flame or a corona discharge (a high-voltage electrical discharge that in turn generates high levels of ozone, a powerful oxidizing agent) in order to create surface polarity. Permeability depends partly on permeant solubility in the barrier material. Polyethylene is a good barrier to such highly polar substances as water vapor, but a poor barrier to nonpolar oxygen.

Table 9.3

Property trends related to polyethylene side branching.

LDPE	Property	HDPE
more branching	branching	less branching
0.910 to 0.925	density	0.941 to 0.965
lower	crystallinity	higher
higher	clarity	lower
80 to 100°C	softening point	120°C
4 to 16 mPa	tensile strength	20 to 38 mPa
500%	elongation	20%
lower	gas barrier	higher
lower	grease resistance	higher

Figure 9.7

Copolymers combine needed properties. Ethylene-vinyl alcohol can be considered to be a copolymer of the homopolymers polyethylene (top) and poly(vinyl alcohol) (middle).

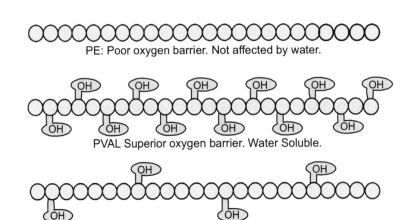

PE: Poor oxygen barrier. Not affected by water.

PVAL Superior oxygen barrier. Water Soluble.

EVAL copolymer: Excellent oxygen barrier. Reduced water solubility.

Copolymers

A polymer that is built up from one type of monomer is a "homopolymer." However, a polymer can be constructed from more than one type of monomer unit. "Copolymers" contain two different monomer types, and "terpolymers" contain three monomer types.

Copolymers bring together the favorable properties of two distinctly different polymers. For example, polyethylene has excellent water vapor barrier properties, but is a very poor oxygen barrier. Poly(vinyl alcohol) (PVOH) is almost the opposite; it has superior oxygen barrier properties, but readily dissolves in water. (It is the highly polar –OH functional group that is responsible for both high solubility and high oxygen barrier properties).

By making a copolymer of the two (see Figure 9.7), some properties of both can be incorporated into one polymer. The more –OH units copolymerized into a polyethylene chain, the more the material tends toward the properties of PVOH. Fewer –OH units in the chain will favor the properties of polyethylene. By striking a balance, (in packaging typically between 17 and 48% polyethylene in the chain) a good oxygen barrier material that won't dissolve in water can be had.

Copolymers and terpolymers can have monomers joined in different ways. An alternating copolymer has the two monomers joined in alternating order; a random copolymer has no particular order; a block copolymer has monomers in specific blocked groupings.

OTHER PACKAGING POLYMERS

Most packaging polymers are addition polymers and can be described as derivatives of ethylene. One or more of the hydrogens can be replaced by some other element or functional group to yield a plastic with completely different properties. (See Figure 9.8) Other polymers have more complex polymerization reactions. Polyamides, polyesters and urethanes, among others, are condensation polymers. Their names represent not a particular structure, but rather a large family of poly-

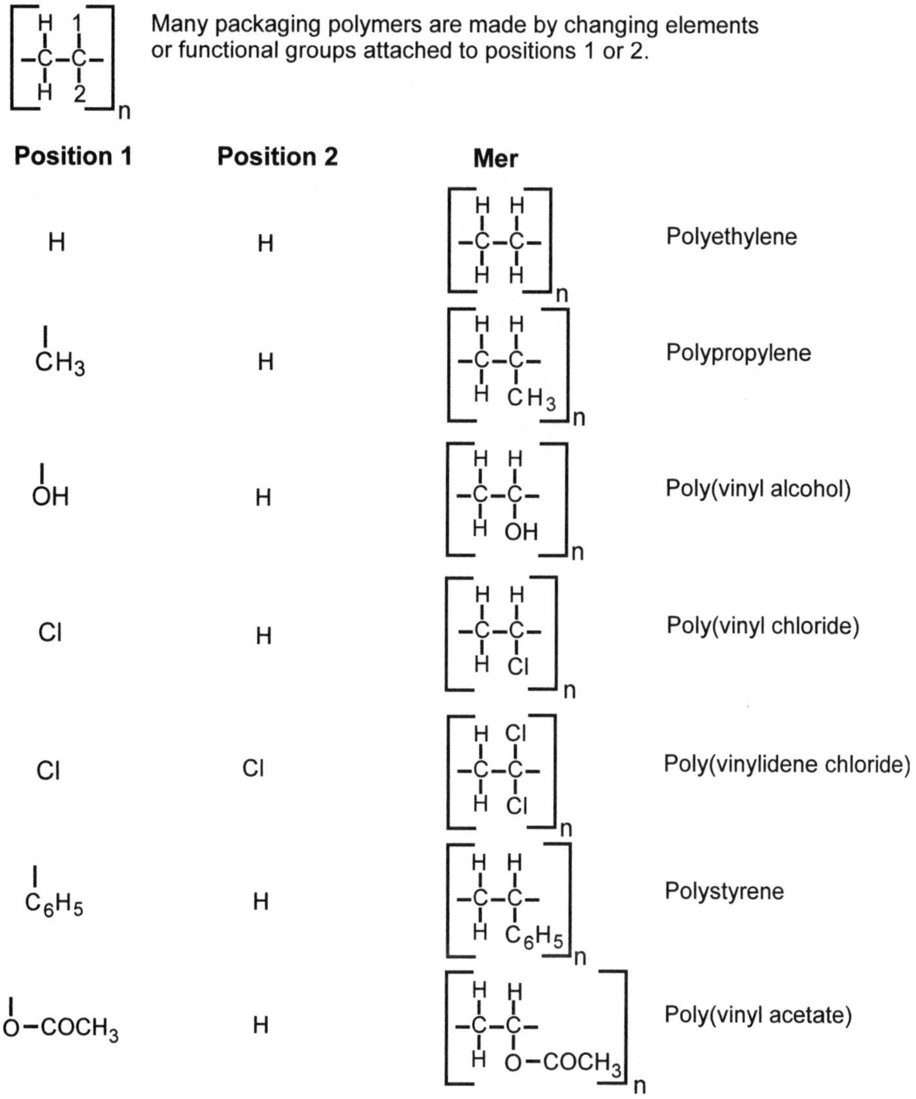

$$\begin{bmatrix} \overset{H}{\underset{H}{-C}} \overset{1}{\underset{2}{-C-}} \end{bmatrix}_n$$

Many packaging polymers are made by changing elements or functional groups attached to positions 1 or 2.

Figure 9.8

Examples of common packaging addition polymers similar in structure to polyethylene, excepting that one or more hydrogens have been replaced with other atoms or functional groups. The "n" subscript indicates that the mer unit is repeated numerous times.

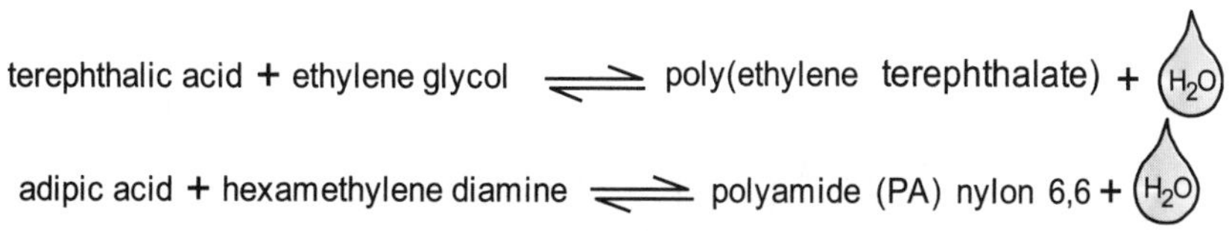

Position 1	Position 2	Mer	
H	H	$\begin{bmatrix}\overset{H}{\underset{H}{-C}}\overset{H}{\underset{H}{-C-}}\end{bmatrix}_n$	Polyethylene
$\overset{\mid}{C}H_3$	H	$\begin{bmatrix}\overset{H}{\underset{H}{-C}}\overset{H}{\underset{CH_3}{-C-}}\end{bmatrix}_n$	Polypropylene
$\overset{\mid}{O}H$	H	$\begin{bmatrix}\overset{H}{\underset{H}{-C}}\overset{H}{\underset{OH}{-C-}}\end{bmatrix}_n$	Poly(vinyl alcohol)
Cl	H	$\begin{bmatrix}\overset{H}{\underset{H}{-C}}\overset{H}{\underset{Cl}{-C-}}\end{bmatrix}_n$	Poly(vinyl chloride)
Cl	Cl	$\begin{bmatrix}\overset{H}{\underset{H}{-C}}\overset{Cl}{\underset{Cl}{-C-}}\end{bmatrix}_n$	Poly(vinylidene chloride)
$\overset{\mid}{C}_6H_5$	H	$\begin{bmatrix}\overset{H}{\underset{H}{-C}}\overset{H}{\underset{C_6H_5}{-C-}}\end{bmatrix}_n$	Polystyrene
$\overset{\mid}{O}-COCH_3$	H	$\begin{bmatrix}\overset{H}{\underset{H}{-C}}\overset{H}{\underset{O-COCH_3}{-C-}}\end{bmatrix}_n$	Poly(vinyl acetate)

terephthalic acid **+** ethylene glycol $\rightleftharpoons$ poly(ethylene terephthalate) **+** H_2O

adipic acid **+** hexamethylene diamine $\rightleftharpoons$ polyamide (PA) nylon 6,6 **+** H_2O

Figure 9.9

Production of poly(ethylene terephthalate) (top) and polyamide (bottom). One molecule of water is released for every monomer linkage. The two way arrows indicate that the polymerization reaction is reversible.

mers. Properties between these family members can vary dramatically. Polyesters, for example can be thermoplastic (melt when heated) or thermoset (do not melt when heated). Urethanes can be soft foams or rigid solids, depending on the formulation. The structure of polyesters and polyamides as used in packaging are shown in Figure 9.9.

A polyester is a reaction product of a dibasic acid and a glycol. Since there are many dibasic acids and many glycols, it follows that there are many polyester types. Terephthalic acid and ethylene glycol produce poly(ethylene terephthalate) (PET), the most common polyester used in packaging. PETG is a glycol-modified copolyester made by replacing part of the ethylene glycol in PET with another glycol.

A polyamide (nylon) polymer has a nitrogen-bearing –CONH repeating group and is produced when a dibasic acid reacts with a diamine. As with polyesters, there are many possible combinations. Polyamides are identified with numbers indicating the number of carbon atoms in the acid and amine monomers. The most common polyamides are polyamide 6 and 66.

One aspect of packaging polyamides and poly(ethylene terephthalates) is that the polymerization reaction is easily reversible. Given the right conditions of temperature and pressure, and in the presence of water, these materials will tend to revert back to their base monomers. It is essential that these polymers be dried prior to melting for further processing.

Urethanes are a reaction product of polyisocyanate (–NCO–) and polyhydroxyl (–OH–) groups.

MOLECULAR STRUCTURE AND PROPERTIES

Crystallinity

Polymer chains fit together in various ways. Highly ordered molecular arrangements are said to be "crystalline," while completely random arrangements are "amorphous." Spaghetti dumped on a plate, for example, would be amorphous, but if it was combed out into reasonably conforming bands, it would be crystalline or linear. The greater the ordering, the greater the degree of crystallinity. (See Figure 9.10)

The degree of crystallinity depends partly on the polymer chain's shape. High-density polyethylene with its long linear chains is predisposed to high levels of crystallinity, while low-density polyethylene with its many randomly arranged branches has an irregular geometry and tends to be amorphous. Similarly, the large bulky pendant benzene groups attached to the carbon backbone chain of polystyrene predisposes it to be amorphous.

Figure 9.10

Crystalline and amorphous regions in a polymer.

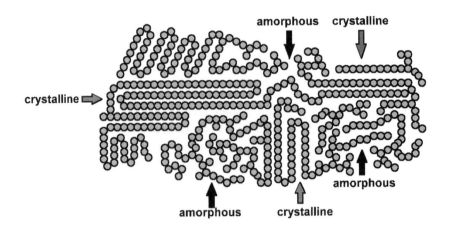

Many polymers can exist with varying degrees of crystallinity depending partly on their molecular geometry, but also depending on their thermal history. All polymers are amorphous in the molten state, since rapid molecular movement prevents the ordering of individual groups of molecules into crystalline regions. Rapid cooling will tend to freeze the polymer chains in this random state, while slow cooling allows time for the molecules to realign themselves into a more ordered crystalline state. Paraffin candle wax, which can be considered to be an ultra-low-molecular-weight polyethylene, is clear in the molten (amorphous) state, but turns a translucent white immediately on cooling because of the formation of crystalline regions.

Partially crystalline polymers such as HDPE are, as a rule, translucent or opaque, while amorphous polymers such as LDPE and polystyrene have higher clarity. Light is refracted when it passes from one medium into another of a different density. Light passing through an amorphous polymer travels through a medium having more or less the same density throughout. Little or no light is scattered by refraction, and the polymer appears clear. Light passing through a polymer with crystalline regions will be continuously passing through areas of different densities. The constant refraction of the light will cause some of it to be scattered, and therefore, not visible to the observer. Such a polymer will appear hazy or opaque. As a general rule, a polymer with lower crystallinity will have better clarity than the same polymer with higher levels of crystallinity.

An exception to the above rule is where the crystal formation sites can be kept from growing into large crystalline regions. When the crystal sites are smaller than the wavelength of visible light, light is not diffracted. Special additives (i.e., nucleating agents) can be used to deliberately induce very fine crystallinity. This technique is sometimes used to improve the clarity of some polymers, most commonly polypropylene.

Degree of crystallinity affects most plastic physical properties. For example, all else being equal, as a polymer's crystallinity increases:

- Stiffness increases

- Heat tolerance increases

- Barrier properties improve

- Likelihood of a loss of clarity

Molecular Weight Distribution

While we may speak of polymers as if they had a specific molecular weight, in reality this is not so. Molecular weights reported in specification sheets are average values, with some molecules weighing more and some less. The molecular makeup of two polymers with identical reported molecular weights can be quite different depending on the molecular weight spread. Phase changes such as melting point are spread out over a temperature range as the different molecular weights become activated by a temperature rise. The greater the molecular weight spread, the greater the transition zone over which the polymer becomes progressively softer. Polymers with a narrow molecular weight distribution will have a narrower transition zone.

Components with a lower molecular weight act as plasticizers for the longer chains. The end product is not as stiff but is easier to process. Newer metallocene catalysts are producing polymers that have very narrow molecular weight ranges not possible with the traditional catalysts. Polymers made using metallocene catalysts have many advantageous properties, but are more difficult to process. One group of polyethylenes produced using these catalysts can be made with elongations approaching that of an elastomer. This has led to the coining of the term "plastomer" to describe a highly elastic thermoplastic material.

Viscoelastic Properties

A metal spring illustrates elasticity. It elongates with the application of a load. When the load is removed, the spring will return to its original shape (providing that its elastic limit was not exceeded). The application rate and duration of the load (time) have little influence on the end result. Such behavior is said to be "elastic." Other materials behave like a highly viscous fluid. Application of force causes the material to flow and permanently deform. Unlike a spring, a material with viscous properties will not return to its original shape when the load is removed. Also, the rearrangement of molecules characterized by viscous flow is time dependent.

Viscoelastic materials combine elastic and viscous properties. Accordingly, rapid application of a load to a plastic will cause it to bend, and if that load is quickly released, the plastic will return to its original shape: It behaves like an elastic or a spring.

However, the same load applied over a long time period allows viscous flow to take place. Polymer molecules will flow and rearrange themselves in new orientations that reduce the internal stress caused by the load. When the load is released, the plastic will not go back to its original shape. This deformation of plastics under load is variously referred to as "creep" and "cold flow."

While all thermoplastics have some degree of viscoelasticity, the polyethylene family, in particular, exhibits relatively high cold-flow characteristics. Designs for parts that will be required to hold significant loads should be evaluated; where necessary, a plastic with lower cold flow should be selected or the part thickness may need to be increased. Cold flow is most commonly observed as loss of torque with plastic closures. Polyethylene bottles subjected to excessive stacking loads will slowly distort and eventually fail.

THERMAL BEHAVIOR

Properties such as melting point are sharply defined in a substance where all molecules are small and have similar molecular weight. Water, for example, goes visibly from a solid state to a liquid state at exactly 0°C (32°F) at 1 atmosphere. The physical transition points of polymers are less sharply defined

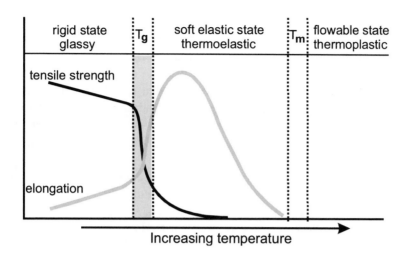

Figure 9.11

Material behavior changes at glass and melt transition points for an amorphous polymer. As temperature increases, a plastic's tensile strength goes down. Elongation will increase to a maximum value, and then also goes down as the plastic becomes more fluid.

and are not accompanied by a clearly visible phase change. This is partly because it is virtually impossible to obtain a polymer in which all molecules are of the exact same molecular weight and partly because the large molecules are entangled and are restricted in their movement.

A polymer will go through a series of transition zones as it is heated, identified as rigid, thermoelastic and thermoplastic in Figures 9.11 and 9.12, rather than going directly from a rigid solid to a melt. A polymer material will exhibit a unique set of physical properties, characteristic of each zone. The transition temperature refers to the temperature where the polymer's properties dramatically change. Figures 9.11 and 9.12 illustrate glass transition temperature (T_g) and melt transition temperature (T_m), and their relationship to tensile strength and elongation.

Glass transition temperature (T_g) is the temperature at which a polymeric material changes from a rigid solid state to a soft, rubbery or elastic state. T_g

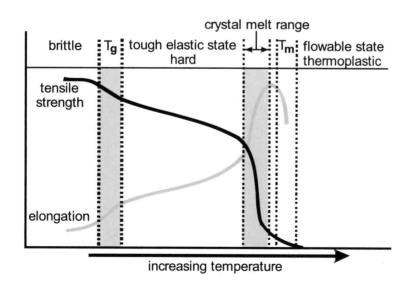

Figure 9.12

Material behavior changes at glass and melt transition points for a crystalline polymer.

is thought to be related to the point at which there is sufficient energy (i.e., temperature) for segments of the polymer molecules to move with respect to one another. As the temperature increases, the plastic will enter a melt phase at the melt transition point (T_m). These values are used to characterize polymers.

It can be seen in Figures 9.11 and 9.12 that amorphous and crystalline polymers have different transition temperature patterns. Amorphous polymers tend to have a more prominent transition at T_g, while crystalline polymers have a more prominent transition at T_m, the point at which the crystalline regions disassociate.

The transitions are accompanied by a number of other changes in physical characteristics. For example, the expansion per degree of temperature rise has a marked increase at T_g. Characteristics such as T_g and T_m are most easily determined by following some physical property as it relates to increasing temperature. Typical thermal analysis methods are differential thermal analysis (DTA), differential scanning calorimetry (DSC) and differential mechanical analysis (DMA).

The unique temperature-influenced behavior of polymers is useful when molding. A degree of elasticity or flowability can be selected as most appropriate to the molding method by governing the polymer temperature.

Orientation

Orientation refers to a marked directionality in how a particular molecule is arranged. (See Figure 9.13) When a polymer melt cools without any external forces acting on it, the orientation of molecules tends to be random. If the randomly oriented polymer is subjected to external stress, the molecules straighten out and rearrange to align generally in the direction of the stress. This orientation changes the polymer's properties remarkably.

To orient polymer molecules permanently, the material is physically stretched at a temperature below its T_g. The general effect of straightening and aligning polymer chains is to enhance many desirable properties such as tensile strength, barrier qualities and T_m. The overall advantage is it allows thinner sections of material to be used.

Orientation can be carried out in one direction (monoaxial) or in two directions (biaxial). Monoaxial orientation is used in such packaging products as plastic strapping, where a maximum of tensile strength is required in one direction.

Most plastic packaging films are biaxially oriented. Unoriented polypropylene film is soft, has high elongation and low tensile strength. Biaxially oriented film is stiff, has low elongation and its tensile strength increases three- or four-fold.

Figure 9.13

Orientation stretches and aligns molecules in the direction of the stretching action.

Heat Shrink Properties

The previous discussion on orientation described the effect of mechanical history on a plastic's final properties. This section examines the effect of combining thermal and mechanical history.

Polymer chains below T_g are rigid, and excessive stress will cause permanent deformation. Molecules will flow or slip over one another to take up new stable positions. This viscous flow is nonrecoverable.

However, at temperatures between T_g and T_m, portions of the polymer chains become more mobile and are able to both unfold and disentangle. This molecular realignment is frozen into the structure if the temperature is quickly brought below T_g; however, under the right conditions, the polymer will retain a "memory" of its former condition and will tend to return or shrink if reheated to a temperature that will allow the chains to move again.

A combination of thermal and mechanical history is used to produce shrink film. The greatest orientation and the greatest shrink strength at a given percentage of stretch are obtained at the lowest temperature above T_g. Molecular flow is kept to a minimum at this low temperature.

The stretching rate is as high as practical, again giving the highest orientation and percentage of shrink. Since realignment is faster than flow, realignment will predominate at high stretch rates. Finally, regardless of other conditions, the fastest quench, or cooling rate, will preserve the greatest orientation and stretch.

Like orientation, shrink properties can be made monoaxial or biaxial or any combination of the two. Biaxial orientation is used for most shrink-wrap applications. Tamper-evident neck bands shrink monoaxially to provide a grip on the bottle neck without any change in the vertical direction. Similarly, shrinkable label stock is usually monoaxially oriented. The degree of shrinkage is controlled by the degree of stretching.

Where plastic materials will be subjected to heat (for example, hot filling, heat sealing or oven drying), shrinkage is undesirable. The tendency to shrink can be reduced by a slow cooling process similar in principle to annealing. The stressed molecules have an opportunity to flow and relieve internal stresses.

Thermal Expansion

Plastic materials have thermal expansions coefficients ten times and more than that of metals. (See Table 9.4) Also, unlike metals whose expansion coefficients are linear, the expansion per degree for a plastic is typically different at temperatures below T_g, between T_g and T_m, and above T_m.

The high expansion coefficient of plastic creates some challenges when it comes to molding a part. A mold needs to be made larger by a dimension calculated from the unique expansion coefficient of the plastic being molded and the temperature at which the molding will take place. Using the same mold for a different plastic will produce parts with slightly different dimensions. Close attention to shrinkage coefficients is particularly important when different plastic components need to match exactly as for example a threaded polypropylene closure on a polyethylene bottle.

Table 9.4

Coefficients of thermal expansion of selected common metals and plastics given in 10^{-6}mm/mm per °C. Thermoset plastics such as phenolic have a lower coefficient than a typical thermoplastic.

Metals	*Coefficient of Expansion*
Aluminum	23.5
Brass	18.8
Copper	16.7
Steel	10.8
Plastics	
Poly(vinylidene chloride)	190–200
Polyethylene	110–250
Polystyrene	60–80
Polyamide (nylon)	90–108
Phenolic (thermoset)	30–45

DENSITY AND YIELD

Equal volumes of different polymers can vary considerably in mass. "Density" is the measure of this property, and is reported as "mass per unit volume" of the plastic. Density can be reported as kilograms per cubic metre, but more often, "relative density," the density of the plastic relative to water, is used. A plastic with the same density as water would have a relative density of 1.0. Polypropylene with a relative density of 0.88 is less dense than water (and would float), while PVC with a density of 1.23 is significantly heavier than an equal volume of water.

For practical reasons, polymer resins are priced and sold by weight. However, during manufacture, the user is interested in yield (i.e., the number of parts or the area of film that can be made from a kilogram or pound of resin). When estimating manufacturing costs for plastic parts, it is the yield that must be used in calculations, not the price per kilogram or pound. Table 9.5 lists typical polymer resin relative densities and the square inches of 0.001-in. plastic film that could be made from a pound of the material. Mineral pigments and other additives can significantly change the density of the base resin.

THERMOPLASTIC AND THERMOSET POLYMERS

A monomer can join to itself to form a complex polymer structure in a number of ways. The monomer units can simply join onto each other to form long chains as in a thermoplastic, or they can cross-link between the chains in a three-dimensional pattern resulting in a thermoset plastic. (See Figure 9.14)

Table 9.5

Relative density and expected yield of 25-micrometre-thick (0.001 in.) plastic film.

	Relative Density	*Square Metres per kg*	*Square Inches per pound*
Polypropylene	0.88	45	30,800
Oriented polypropylene	0.905	44	30,600
Low-density polyethylene	0.910	44	30,000
Linear low-density polyethylene	0.915	43	30,000
High-density polyethylene	0.941	42	29,000
Ionomer (e.g., Surlyn)	0.95	42	29,000
Polyamide (nylon)	1.13	35	23,500
Polyacrylonitrile (e.g., Barex)	1.15	34	24,000
Polycarbonate	1.2	33	23,000
Poly(vinyl chloride)	1.23	32	20,000
Poly(ethylene terephthalate)	1.36	29	20,000
Poly(vinylidene chloride)	1.64	24	16,200
Fluorocarbon (e.g., Aclar)	2.2	18	13,000

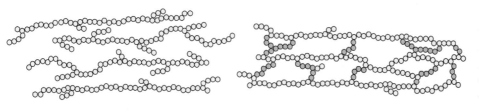

Figure 9.14

Thermoplastic polymer chains (left) are free to pass over one another at melt temperatures. Cross-linked thermoset polymer chains (right) can never come free of one another without destroying the material.

Thermoplastics are supplied to the molder in a fully polymerized state. As the name implies, thermoplastics become fluid with the application of heat. A thermoplastic can be softened, solidified and resoftened a number of times, allowing process waste and recycling of spent material.

Unlike thermoplastics, thermosets are supplied in a monomeric or prepolymer stage, and the final polymerization reaction, the building up and the cross-linking of chains, is carried on during the molding process itself. Polymerization can take place between two reactive components that are mixed just prior to molding, can be initiated by a catalyst added just prior to molding, or can be initiated by heat or by other energy sources such as UV light, electron beam or irradiation. Once a thermoset has "set," there is no possible recovery of scrap.

Thermosets can be compared to an egg: Once heat has been applied and "polymerized" the egg-white albumin, there is no means of returning the coagulated white back to its original state. Thermoplastics can be likened to candle wax, which can be repeatedly melted and cast into new shapes. Process scrap recovery makes thermoplastics the material of choice for packaging applications.

Heating a thermoplastic polymer adds energy and motion to the molecules until there is enough motion to allow the polymer chains to untangle and slide over one another. The polymer becomes fluid-like and can be made to flow. In a cross-linked (thermoset) polymer, the chains are interconnected and can never actually come free of one another and flow. Accordingly, thermosets will normally have a much higher potential use temperature and will finally degrade rather than melt.

Solubility depends on the dissolution of molecular chains from the main polymer body. Again, since the polymer chains in thermosets cannot be freed from the main mass, their resistance to solvents is very high. Only very aggressive chemicals will attack a thermoset and break apart the chain structure, but not dissolve it.

In packaging, thermoset polymers are found mostly in adhesives, coatings, inks and specialty applications where unusual heat or chemical properties are required. Thermosets such as phenol formaldehyde and melamine formaldehyde are used for some specialty closures.

Many polymers have been designed with low levels of cross-linking. These have properties intermediate between thermoset and thermoplastic polymers, depending on the degree of cross-linking. Most elastomeric materials are lightly cross-linked polymers.

1. Polymers can be divided into two general chemical classes. What are they, and which is most commonly used in packaging? What is the difference in molecular structure that characterizes the two general polymer classes?

2. Complete the following sentences:

   a. As the molecular weight increases, melting point _____.

   b. As the degree of branching increases, density _____.

   c. A plastic that has two monomers in its molecular structure is called a _.

   d. A polymer in which the chains are highly ordered is said to be _____.

   e. A polymer in which the chain arrangement is essentially random is ____.

   f. The stiffer HDPE is the one with a _____ molecular weight.

3. What is the molecular structural difference between HDPE, LDPE and LLDPE?

4. Properties of plastic film can be improved by stretching the film in one or two directions. What is this process called, and what does it actually do?

5. Identify these abbreviations:

LLDPE	PP	PS
PVC	EVOH	PA
PET	PVDC	OPP
PVAC		

6. You are given an amorphous and a crystalline version of the same polymer. How could you probably tell the difference?

7. How do the general properties of thermoplastics and thermosets differ?

8. What properties of plastic are affected by the molecule's degree of polarity?

9. How are heat-shrink properties imparted to a polymer?

10. What is cold flow? Where are cold-flow considerations most important?

11. All plastics are clear in the melt state. Why?

12. Which two common packaging plastics are predominantly nonpolar?

13. From what raw material source are most packaging plastics made?

14. What is the purpose of flame and corona treatment?

15. Which would have the higher melting point: high-molecular-weight polysulfone or low-molecular-weigh polysulfone?

16. What is the purpose and advantage of producing copolymers?

17. What is the difference between addition polymers and condensation polymers?

18. What would influence whether a particular PET would be amorphous or crystalline?

19. Why can't the same mold be used to shape all plastic materials?

20. Name four plastics that would sink in water.

21. Plastic films can be made to have uniaxial or biaxial shrink properties. Name two applications for uniaxial shrink film. Why are uniaxial shrink films used for these applications?

CONTENTS

Selecting the Material and the Process

Factors affecting process selection, most common forming methods.

Plasticating Extruders

Melting the polymer, typical extruder.

Profile Extrusion

Profile extrusion, profile applications, cast-film extrusion, blown-film extrusion, machine- and cross-direction orienting, cast and blown films, co-extrusion.

Injection Molding

Principles, injecting extruders, clamping force. Sprues, runners, gates. Two-plate, three-plate, hot runner, stack molds. Undercuts, polymer shrinkage, sink marks. Co-injection molding.

Extrusion Blow Molding

Application, principles, bottle designs, blow molds, pinch-off, machine configurations, coextruded bottles, material distribution, programmed parisons, trimming, mold identification numbers, standard bottle terminology.

Injection Blow Molding

Principles, one-step injection blow molding, machine configuration, injection-stretch blow molding, applications, extrusion blow molding and injection blow molding compared.

Bottle Design

General design principles, pastes and semisolid product, fill-level considerations, vertical and circumferential design features, machinability, label panels.

Thermoforming

General principles and applications, undercuts, draft angles, matched die molding, simple cavity and plug thermoforming, plug-assisted molding, billow forming, vacuum snap-back forming, microwavable trays and containers.

Other Forming Methods

Pressforming, compression molding, rotational molding, blow-fill-seal molding.

Recognizing Molding Methods

Recognizing methods of manufacture.

SHAPING PLASTICS

SELECTING THE MATERIAL AND THE PROCESS

The term "plastics" can be likened to the term "metals." Plastics embraces a broad spectrum of synthetic materials with the common capability of being molded or shaped by the application and removal of heat and pressure.

Thermoplastic materials are fully reacted or polymerized products that, when subjected to sufficient heat, will soften. Pressure makes them flow and assume new forms, at which point they are cooled to form a useful shape. Scrap or defective shapes can be remelted and reprocessed. The easy formability and economic recovery of recyclable material make thermoplastics the material of choice for many packaging applications.

Thermoset plastics are polymers that have not fully completed their polymerization reaction, but do so when activated, usually by heat. The resulting product is cross-linked. It will not be softened again by heat and cannot be reprocessed or reshaped. Thermosets such as phenol, urea and melamine formaldehyde are occasionally used for specialty closures, but the use of thermosets for dimensional parts in packaging is negligible. This discussion of plastic forming methods is limited to methods that shape thermoplastic materials.

The proper balance of product protection, containment and appearance qualities, relative to affordable cost, can be obtained by referring to the mechanical and chemical properties of the various polymers. Once a material is selected, the process or method for converting the selected polymer resin into a useful form must be determined.

One of most important considerations when thinking of producing a plastic dimensional part is tooling cost; the cost of molds and other devices that will be needed to shape the plastic into the desired form. The cost of tooling is directly related to the forces that will be required to create the form.

- Profile extrusion to make continuous solid profiles or tube simply requires a shaped aperture through which to push the plastic. Tooling cost is low.

- Thermoforming is done with open molds using vacuum and compressed air at moderate levels. Tooling cost is low to moderate depending on the complexity of the form to be made.

- Extrusion blow molding of bottle forms requires a water cooled mold consisting of two matched halves. Tooling costs are moderate. Almost any company with reasonable market share can afford to produce a custom designed bottle.

- Injection blow molding tooling cost is somewhat higher than extrusion blow molding in that two molds are necessary. Process savings from not having any secondary trimming and regrind steps reduces the overall cost somewhat.

- Injection molding requires massive molds capable of withstanding molding forces calculated in hundreds of tons. The cost of 32-cavity stack mold to make margarine tubs can be a half million dollars and more. It is common for companies that make injection molded closures and dairy tubs to have stock molds by which means the high mold costs are borne by a number of customers.

Other factors that need to be considered are:

- Resin type

- Geometry of the finished part

- Number of units required

- Dimensional tolerance requirements

- Container wall thickness required to meet structural and economic requisites

To relate these factors, the principal manufacturing methods must be understood. Following are the most common thermoplastic forming methods for packaging purposes will be discussed in this chapter:

- Extrusion (including profile extrusion, extrusion cast film and sheet, blown-film extrusion and co-extrusion)

- Thermoforming (a secondary forming process using extruded sheet).

- Injection molding

- Extrusion blow molding

- Injection blow molding (including injection stretch blow molding)

- A brief mention of rotational and compression molding.

In all thermoplastic shaping methods, the plastic must first be heated to a point where the material has a plasticity or fluidity appropriate to the intended molding method. A key attribute of any plastic material is its behavior at elevated temperatures.

Melt flow rate (reference test method ASTM D 1238) is a method of quantifying this behavior. (See Figure 10.1) Briefly, a charge of the polymer is heated to the test temperature in a chamber. A specified load is then placed on a piston, which forces the polymer melt through a calibrated orifice. The weight of polymer extruded in 10 minutes is reported as the Melt flow rate (sometimes referred to as the melt index). Since for a given polymer, the flow rate will decrease as molecular weight increases, and melt flow rate can be regarded as a crude indicator of molecular weight.

PLASTICATING EXTRUDERS

Polymer resins are received at a molding plant in the form of small granules or pellets, similar in appearance to rice. Regardless of the forming process, the

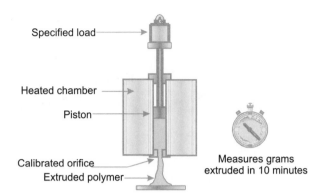

Figure 10.1

A polymer's flow characteristics at elevated temperatures is measured with an extrusion plastometer. Different test temperatures are used for different polymers.

first task is to heat and melt the polymer resin pellets into a flowable form. The plasticating extruder is a heavy barrel in which a screw rotates, driving pellets from the feed hopper at one end to the exit port at the other end. (See Figure 10.2) The work of driving polymer melt down the barrel provides most of the heat required to melt the polymer. Heater bands help maintain precise melt temperatures, and a cooling jacket keeps the feed hopper area cool.

Extruder sizes are described as the barrel diameter to screw length ratio. For example, a 20:1 extruder will have a screw length twenty times the barrel diameter. Length-to-diameter (LD) ratios and screw geometry vary widely depending on the material and the nature of the molding process.

PROFILE EXTRUSION

A shape of constant cross-section (a profile) can be extruded by forcing polymer melt through a shaped orifice in a die placed at the exit port. At its simplest, the die may be a metal plate with a round hole drilled into it, in which case the extrusion is a round rod of approximately the hole's diameter. Tooling costs are low since the process takes place at relatively low pressures, and neither the extruder nor the die need to be substantial. Placing a suitable torpedo-shaped mandrel in the die exit permits extrusion of a hollow pipe or tube. (See Figure 10.3)

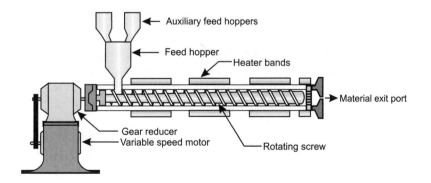

Figure 10.2

A plasticating extruder. Most plastics are colored by adding color concentrates along with polymer resin at the feed hopper. Auxiliary hoppers are used to meter in colorants, antistatic agents and other additives.

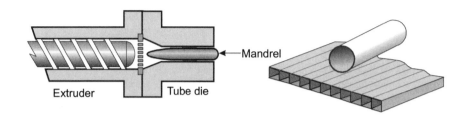

Extruded Profile Applications

Thin-walled tubes cut to length and with an applied injection-molded head (See
Figure 10.41) are made into collapsible plastic tubes such as those used for
personal care products. After the tube is filled, the lower end is flattened and
heat-sealed. Most tubes are made from polyethylene for its softness. Where flavor
barrier or oxygen barrier are required, the tube would be coextruded with a layer
of a barrier polymer such as ethylene-vinyl alcohol.

Heavy-walled extruded plastic tubes, cut to length and given an added injection-
molded nozzle, are used for caulking tubes. The bottom is sealed with a sliding
piston.

Any tubular package of constant cross-section and with no seam along its
length started out as an extruded profile. To make a enclosed package, a closure
method must be added. The most common method is friction fit plugs, although
in some instances a thread to accept a screw type closure has been rolled onto
the tube end.

For novelty markets, tubes are extruded from cellulose-based plastics such as
cellulose butyrate or cellulose propionate. These exhibit excellent stiffness and
clarity and incorporate end plugs that can be easily attached by solvent bonding.
This application is one of the few instances where a cellulose-based plastic is
still used.

Applications include glass thermometer tubes, drill bit tubes, confectionery
containers, small parts tubes and other novelty containers.

Sheet and Film Extrusion

Sheet extrusion is an application of profile extrusion, but it uses a die with a slot
orifice. (The dies are also called "coat-hanger" or "T-shape" dies.) The dies have
a narrow opening between the die lips through which the plastic melt is extruded
in a thin film. (See Figure 10.4) The film is immediately cooled and solidified on
chill rolls. (See Figure 10.5) The dies can be a metre or more wide. Depending
on thickness, the end product may be called "film" or "sheet." There is no clear
division between the two. Film product formed by this process is referred to as
"cast film."

Thicker sheet is used for thermoforming or is die-cut and folded into carton-
type constructions similar to paperboard cartons. Thinner extruded films are

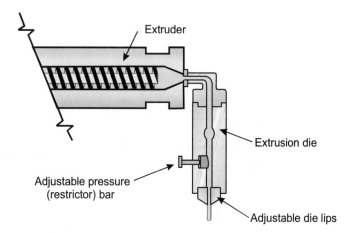

Figure 10.4

Cross-section of a slot-orifice die. This is an end view, and the die may be a metre or more wide.

used alone or laminated with other materials in a variety of flexible packaging applications.

Blown-film Extrusion

Plastic film can also be manufactured by extruding the polymer through a circular die into a closed circular bubble and expanding the bubble with air. (See Figure 10.6) The material is extruded upward, and by pulling the inflated bubble upward and continuously extruding more plastic, a continuous seamless tube of thin film is created. (See Figure 10.7) Air flow along the outside of the bubble provides cooling and an air cushion. After the film has cooled, it is flattened in a collapsing frame and wound into rolls. The bubble can be wound up as a seamless tube, or it can be cut to length and sealed at one end to make seamless plastic bags. Alternatively, it can be slit and rolled into one or several flat rolls of film as shown in Figure 10.8.

In addition to devices that control size and shape, other process units, such as those for printing and embossing, gusseting, vacuum forming, slitting and folding, can be introduced into the downstream system. This provides more integrated

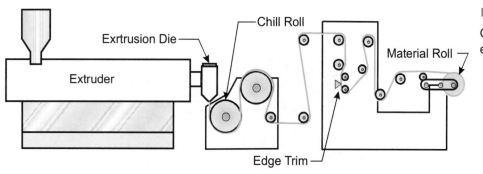

Figure 10.5

General layout of a cast-film extrusion line.

Figure 10.6

Cross-section of a
blown-film die.

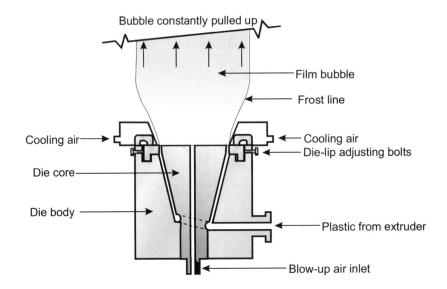

Figure 10.6

Cross-section of a
blown-film die.

product manufacturing lines. The blown-film process is used to make nearly all PE and other films.

The blown-film method can produce very wide sheets. A 2-metre (6.5-foot) diameter bubble, when slit, will open out to a sheet 6 metres (19 feet) wide. It would be impractical to make a cast-film die of this width.

The thermal histories and production mechanics of films made by cast and blown methods are completely different: The same resin made into films by the two methods will have different properties. (See Table 10.1)

In cast film production, the rapid chilling provided by the cold casting rolls favors amorphous molecular behavior, and the product tends to be limper and

Figure 10.7

A blown film extrusion die.
The point at which
significant crystallinity
appears is readily visible at
the frost line where the film
changes from being
translucent to being opaque.

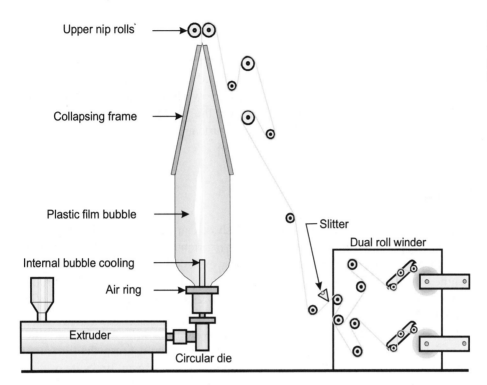

Figure 10.8

A blown-film line that produces a tubular film that is slit into two flat sheets.

have better clarity than a blown film. Casting is also able to produce thinner films.

Blown film uses slower air cooling to remove heat from the polymer extrusion. Crystalline plastics such as polyethylene or polypropylene will exit the die in a clear form, but at some point above the die, as the temperature drops and the polymer begins to crystallize, there will be a distinct change from clear to opaque. (See figure 10.7). The transition zone is quite abrupt and is known as the "frost line."

Table 10.1

Comparison of films made by the blown and cast processes.

	Blown Film	Cast Film
Required melt flow rate	lower	higher
Process temperature	lower	higher
Crystallinity	more (slower cooling)	less (rapid cooling)
Optics	hazy, less gloss	better, glossy
Gauge variation	± 5 to 10%	± 2%
Output	lower	higher
Web control	size adjustable	neck-in, more rework
Flatness	less	better

Film thickness and surface irregularities are harder to control for blown film than for cast film. Film thickness around the circumference of a blown bubble can vary by as much as 10%. If simply wound up on a roll, these thicker areas would produce a hard ring, or gauge band, around the roll. To avoid this problem, most blown-film dies rotate while the film is blown to ensure distribution of any small thickness and surface irregularities over the width of the rolled material.

Blown film production machinery is significantly lower in cost than a cast film and tenter frame orientation combination.

Orientation

The properties of cast and blown film and sheet can be improved by physically orienting the polymer molecules. Cast sheet is oriented in the machine direction by being pulled away faster than it is being extruded, thus stretching it in the machine direction. This is usually accomplished by passing the cast film through a series of rolls, each roll rotating progressively faster than the previous roll. (See Figure 10.9, top)

Cross- or transverse-direction orientation is done in a "tenter frame." (See Figure 10.9, bottom.) Clips traveling down diverging tracks grasp the film along each edge and stretch it in the cross direction up to about seven times its original cast width. Film oriented in two directions is said to have "biaxial orientation."

Both machine and cross-direction orienting is done at somewhat elevated temperatures. If the stretching and cooling processes are rapid, the film will retain some memory of its original dimensions. It will want to return to these dimensions if reheated; in effect it will be a "shrink plastic." Oriented films are heat-stabilized by keeping them at the elevated temperature (annealing) for a brief time.

Blown film is orientated by adjusting the inflation ratio and take-away speed relative to the tube-forming rate. Blown film cannot be oriented to the extent

Figure 10.9

Orienting cast film. Machine-direction orientation (top) is done by pulling the film through progressively faster rotating rolls. Cross-direction orientation is done on a tenter frame (bottom). It stretches the film in the transverse direction as illustrated in this perspective that looks down on the process.

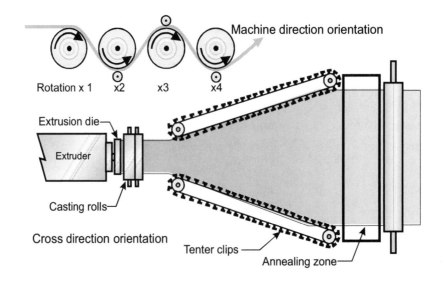

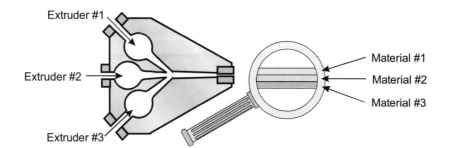

Figure 10.10

A co-extrusion, slot-orifice cast-film die. Similar multichannel dies can be made for blown-film extrusion.

that is available with cast-film extrusion, however, the biaxial orientation is well balanced.

Co-extrusion

Both cast and blown film extrusion dies can be designed to be fed from more than one extruder, thus producing a sheet composed of two or more different materials. (See Figure 10.10) Co-extrusion systems feeding as many as seven different layers through one die block have been made. High polymer viscosity limits the mixing of the extruded layers, so they exist essentially as separate layers in the finished product.

Most co-extrusion is done to combine the performance advantages of two dissimilar materials. For example, heat-sealable polyethylene is extruded onto materials that have poor heat-sealing characteristics, or a high-barrier polymer might be extruded between protective layers of a less costly low-barrier material. Co-extrusion is used to bury recycled plastics into center layers or to produce sheets with decorative colored stripes or layers.

INJECTION MOLDING

Injection molding uses a powerful extruder with the capability to inject a precise amount of resin into a fully enclosed mold. Very high hydraulic pressures drive hot, relatively viscous molten material through the chilled passages of a part mold and fill the cavity before the plastic solidifies. The process requires substantial molds that will not flex or move under extreme temperature and pressure. An eight-cavity mold for margarine tubs may weight upward of a ton. This required mold mass and the tooling's complexity makes injection molding the highest in tooling cost of the plastic forming methods.

Injection molding is the leading method of manufacturing closures, wide-mouthed thermoplastic tubs, jewel boxes and other complex dimensional shapes. Because part dimensions are completely controlled by metal mold surfaces, injection molding gives the most dimensionally accurate part. Tooling sophistication, accompanied by newly developed high melt flow rate (low melt viscosity) thermoplastics, permits the manufacture of thin-walled plastic containers with wall-thickness in the order of 180 micrometres (μm) (0.007 in.).

Figure 10.11

"Shot" size for an injection-molded part can be metered either by or by a reciprocating screw (top) or an extruder with a separate hydraulic piston (bottom).

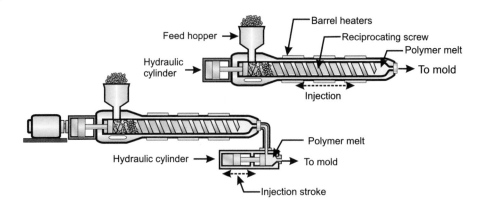

Injection Molding Machines

The extruder section of an injection molding machine must have provision for ejecting a precise amount, or "shot," of polymer melt into the mold. Ram-screw-type (reciprocating screw) machines use a melt-conveyance screw designed to provide reciprocal as well as rotary motion, combining the function of screw and piston. A disadvantage of this system is that a great deal of power is required to move the entire screw and its attendant load of plastic resin. Screw-plunger or two-stage machines have a separate chamber and piston for injecting the molten polymer, (See Figure 10.11) allowing for faster injection of the plastic into the mold.

The mold cavity is exactly in the form of the desired part. When the part has cooled, the mold opens and the part is ejected.

The injection machine's mold clamp section must be large enough to hold the mold and provide adequate space for the part to be readily removed when the mold opens. It must have sufficient clamping force to hold the mold tightly closed against the pressure of the material being injected into the mold. Inadequate clamping pressures (or excessive shot size) will force the mold open and result in prominent parting lines or unsightly flash.

An injection molding machine is rated by available clamping force tonnage. A 600-ton injection molding machine has 600 tons of clamping force to hold the mold closed. The required clamping tonnage is not related to the amount of plastic in the part, but rather to the part surface area. The greater the area over which the fluid can act, the greater the hydraulic force.

Injection Molds

A simple injection mold is comprised of a core and cavity halves. Wall thickness of the molded part is determined by the space between the mold's core and cavity. A mold assembly may be designed to have a single cavity or multiple cavities, however for packaging purposes essentially all molds are multicavity. (See Figure 10.13)

Mold temperature control must be accurate. Auxiliary cooling systems, either with water or water-glycol mixtures, provide consistent coolant temperature. Good part molding also depends on material condition. Hygroscopic plastics—

such as poly(ethylene terephthalate), nylon and polycarbonate—are continuously preconditioned and dried "on line."

Simple, open-topped tubs are easily made with a mold consisting of a cavity half that is mounted to the machine in a stationary position and a core half that is mounted on a sliding frame so the mold can open and close. The molten plastic follows various channels to fill the cavity of the closed mold:

- The "sprue" is the main channel through which molten plastic enters the mold. If the mold had only one cavity, then the sprue would lead directly to the gate.

- "Runners" are channels that distribute molten plastic to various cavities in a multicavity mold. Runner geometry must be very exacting since the distance from the sprue to any gate must be exactly the same.

- The "gate" is the small opening through which the molten plastic enters the mold cavity. (See Figure 10.12)

As the cooling plastic shrinks, the part will adhere to the plug half of the mold. Compressed air might be used to push the tubs off the cores. For more complex parts, knockout pins move forward when the mold opens to eject the part physically.

A simple, two-piece mold where the sprues or runners connect directly to the gate would produce a part with the sprue and runner still attached to the part. This is done for very low volume applications where it is important to keep mold costs down but rarely found in packaging applications. A three-plate mold (See Figure 10.13) has a third plate that automatically pulls the sprue and runners away from the molded parts. These would be cycled back into the molding feed-stream.

Figure 10.14 shows a more advanced mold having heating elements, insulated from the chilled mold, along the sprue and runners. In this mold, the cavity plate remains stationary and the cold part would pull away from the still molten plastic in the immediate gate/runner area. Such "runnerless" molds add considerably to the mold cost, but they eliminate the need for separating the sprues and runners and regrinding them to a form that could be reintroduced into the injection molding cycle.

An injection machine's productivity can be increased by stacking two mold sets in a back-to-back configuration as shown in Figure 10.15. This will double part output without need to go to a machine with double the clamp tonnage.

An "undercut" is a part feature that prevents a mold from opening in a normal back-and-forth motion unless other pieces of mold metal are first removed.

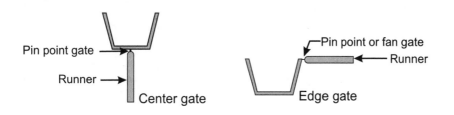

Figure 10.12

The gate is the small opening through which plastic melt enters the mold cavity. Mold makers try to hide the gate mark in the most unobtrusive location.

Figure 10.13

A three-plate mold that strips sprue and runners away from the part. Knockout pins push the parts off the cores.

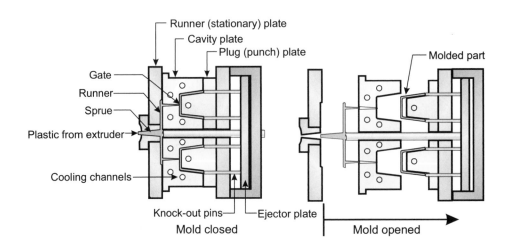

Figure 10.14

"Runnerless" or "hot runner" molds are designed with material feed runners and gate systems that are insulated from the cooled mold cavity and core. Auxiliary heaters are often incorporated into the runner system to ensure that the plastic is kept in a hot, fluid state.

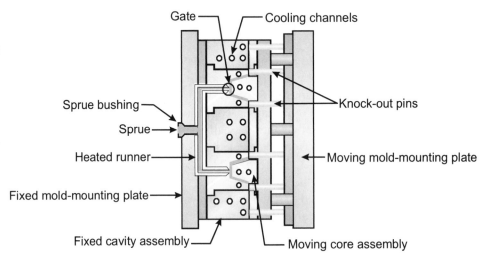

Figure 10.15

A stack mold puts two molds back to back. The runners are kept hot so that the chilled part separates at the gate.

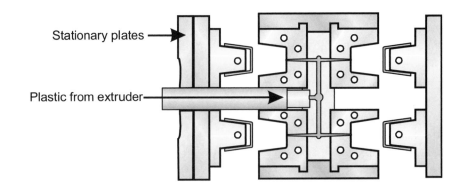

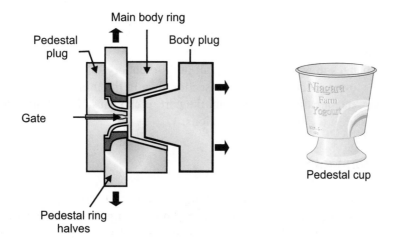

Pedestal cup

Figure 10.16

A part with undercuts, such as this pedestal cup, require a mold with components that move away from the undercut so the part can be removed from the mold.

Closure threads and designs, such as the pedestal-base yogurt cup shown in Figure 10.16, are examples of undercuts. Undercuts, or other complications, require that some mold parts be designed to move away before the part can be ejected. For example, the yogurt cup mold would need to be assembled from a number of pieces, including a pedestal ring portion in two halves. Since these halves need to open and move away at right angles to the normal mold-opening movement, power and drive mechanisms need to be incorporated into the mold.

In the instance of threaded closures, provision would need to be made for removing the closure from the core. This can be done by unscrewing the core from the closure, by collapsing the core so it can be pulled away from the threads, or in certain situations, by stripping the closure off the threaded core by momentarily stretching the plastic over the threads. (The relationship of closure thread undercuts and mold design is discussed in Chapter 12, "Closures.") Seemingly simple design variations that include undercuts can increase mold costs significantly.

Plastic shrinks as it cools and solidifies from the melt state. Each polymer has a characteristic shrinkage rate. Shrink allowance must be designed into the mold cavity and core section dimensions. Because of the varying rates of shrinkage, molds built for a specific material may not be suited for molding containers of a different material if fit and container capacity control are to be maintained.

Where a molded part has substantial and abrupt wall thickness changes, the part may develop "sink marks." (See Figure 10.17) These are mostly due to

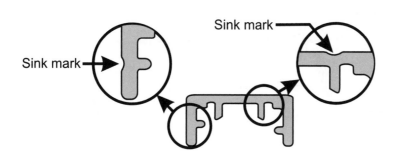

Sink mark

Sink mark

Figure 10.17

Sink marks occur where there is a substantial variation in the thickness of the plastic.

plastics' high expansion coefficients. Sink marks can usually be seen on closures opposite the thread on threaded closures and opposite the sealing ring on valve type closures.

Other changes in wall thickness result in different crystallinity, as the cooling rate will be slower in the thicker cross-section than in the thin section. When the plastic at the gate area pulls away from the part, it can cause a sucking effect on still-soft plastic in the heavy cross-sections.

Co-injection Molding

Co-injection molding is injection molding's counterpart to co-extrusion. Co-injection of multiple polymer layers can be done by injecting the first material, and then moving the mold core with the first material form on it into a second cavity. The second cavity has a clearance between it and the first material shape. The second material is then injected around the first.

Another method uses multiple runners that converge just before the gate. The materials flow into the mold cavity as concentric layers. Multilayer, injection-molded preforms for blowing into beverage bottles have been made using poly(ethylene terephthalate) (PET) and ethylene-vinyl alcohol (EVOH) in one application version and PET and nylon in another.

Injection Molding Design Example

The complexities of injection molding can be illustrated by examining some of the issues that need to be resolved when injection molding the common dairy tub and lid. (See Figure 10.18)

Most dairy tubs are injection molded from relatively stiff polypropylene. (The most significant exceptions are frozen-product tubs. Polyethylene is preferred for this application since polypropylene can become brittle at freezer temperatures.) But the lids for polypropylene tubs need to be extended easily so as to stretch slightly and then snap over the interference fit on the tub's lip. Polyethylene is the preferred material for lids because of its ability to stretch slightly.

As noted in Table 9.3, different plastics have different expansion coefficients, and in designing the mold cavities for the tub and matching lid, different

Figure 10.18

Design details for an injection-molded dairy tub and lid. The nest wall and nest ledge keep sidewalls of nested containers from touching and becoming difficult to separate on a production line.

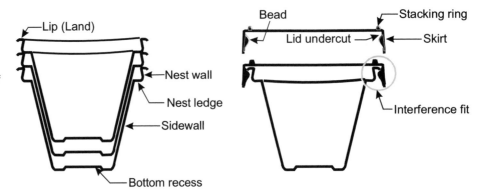

allowances need to be made in mold dimensions to ensure that the tub and lid snap together properly.

Most plastic parts need some slight body taper, or "draft," to make it easy to remove the part from the mold core. For dairy tubs, the draft angle is considerable, so the tubs can be nested into compact stacks for shipping. Tubs with a straight angle from base to lip would jam together and be difficult to de-nest on the production line. Jamming is prevented by designing a nesting wall and ledge that prop the tubs up slightly and ensures a small separation between the sidewalls on nested containers.

Lip dimensions need to be accurate if the tub has an interference-fit, snap-on lid. In some designs, small ribs are placed on the lip's underside to stiffen the tub edge. This leads to a series of sink marks on the lip's top surface that can interfere with attaching foil or laminated, adhesive-bonded lid stock material.

The gate marks for both lids and tubs are on the part's cavity side. The bottom recess on the tub provides for a more positive flat base for the tub, but it also raises the center of the tub bottom so that any gate projection does not interfere with the tub's stability. The gate mark is on the top visible surface of the lid.

Lids will usually have a small, raised stacking ring on their top surface. This prevents stacked lids from sliding over each other and allows for easier handling and machining. A slightly raised gate mark can interfere with printing in those instances or prop up an applied paper label.

EXTRUSION BLOW MOLDING

Thermoplastic bottles are made by one of two processes: extrusion blow molding (EBM) or injection blow molding (IBM). As the name implies, EBM combines extrusion with a blowing step. The majority of detergent, oil and other household chemical bottles are made by extrusion blow molding.

Most plastics can be extrusion blow molded providing they have enough strength in the melt form (i.e., a low melt flow rate) to hold together when extruded into a parison. PE, PP and PVC account for the majority of extrusion blow molded bottles.

EBM can accommodate many creative designs, including bottles with handles (handleware), two-part containers and containers with integral measuring chambers. Circumferential rings can be molded into a circular cross-section to produce a flexible trunk or an accordion-type flexible section that can be used as a pump.

All EBM processes are based on a common underlying sequence. (See Figure 10.19) First, a hollow plastic tube, or parison, is extruded. While in a soft and formable state, the parison is captured between the mating halves of a bottle mold. Air is blown into the hollow parison, stretching the deformable parison to conform to the mold walls. The newly formed bottle is held in the mold until it cools sufficiently to retain its shape.

Parison size and position are related to the container's finished configuration. The parison centerline does not necessarily coincide with the mold centerline. Off-centered designs and handleware will occasionally have the mold centerline

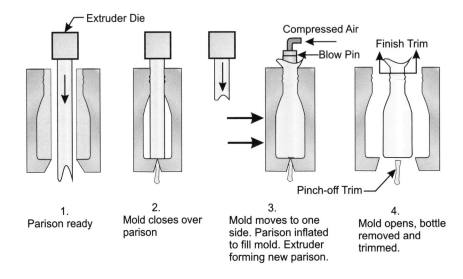

Figure 10.19

Typical extrusion blow molding sequence.

Figure 10.20

A properly designed mold will force some plastic back up into the bottle to form a uniform bead at the weld line. Poor weld lines will have a groove that significantly weakens the bottle.

on an angle to the parison centerline in order to achieve the desired material distribution. For larger bottles and for some handleware, the parison may be pre-inflated by a small puff of air prior to the mold closing and final bottle blow.

One of the more critical areas of a bottle is its base. The mechanical action of forming the molten plastic and pinching the parison off to form the weld line can introduce a great deal of stress into the plastic material. Poorly formed weld lines might occur if the plastic was too cool to fuse adequately or if the weld line was grooved because of improper tool design. (See Figure 10.20) Either condition will result in a bottle with low impact strength.

Extrusion Blow Molds

Blow molds (see Figures 10.21 and 22) are moderate in cost, allowing most users the option of using a custom-designed mold. Most high-speed bottle molds are made from aluminum or beryllium copper. The neck, finish, bottom pinch-off and pinch-off areas for blown handles are critical high-wear mold areas and are usually replaceable steel inserts. Hard, high-gloss materials such as PVC and PS with low shrink factors require polished mold surfaces. Higher shrink materials (PE, PP) use sandblasted mold surfaces for optimum container appearance. Mold clamp force must be sufficient to clamp, weld and shear the parison at pinch-off points (the neck, handle and bottom areas), and must have enough force to withstand the pressures developed during the blowing portion of the operating cycle. However, compared to injection molding, these pressures are within the range of shop air.

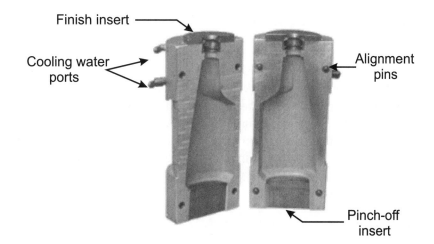

Finish insert

Cooling water ports

Alignment pins

Pinch-off insert

Figure 10.21

An aluminum extrusion blow mold with steel inserts for the finish and pinch-off. The mold has connections for water cooling.

Blow-molding cycle time is usually controlled by how quickly the blown part can be cooled and ejected. Water channels drilled into the mold body provide cooling. Trimming devices for finishing the bottle neck area and for removal of the bottom tab are preferably incorporated into the mold. Where this is not economically feasible or practical, trimming, neck finish, facing and reaming devices are used in secondary operations downstream of the blowing operation. Special trimming dies are required if large "flash" areas or the center waste area of handled bottles are to be trimmed away.

An extruder can produce parisons at a faster rate than a typical bottle blowing cycle. Multiple parison blow-molding machines allow increased productivity from an extruder. Blow-molding machines that extrude double or triple parisons are common, and a few have been made that extrude even more. In such instances, molds are grouped into blocks and several bottles are blown at a time.

A "shuttle" blow molder is the most common machine configuration. A mold or mold set is located on either side of the parison extruder. When the parison is ready, a mold slides into position, closes over the parison, cuts it off and slides off to one side for the blowing and cooling cycle. While this is happening,

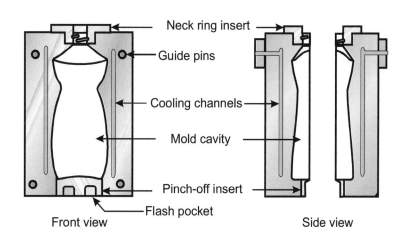

Neck ring insert

Guide pins

Cooling channels

Mold cavity

Pinch-off insert

Flash pocket

Front view

Side view

Figure 10.22

Blow molds must be cooled. Vent holes drilled into the cavity allow air to escape during the inflation cycle. The bottom pinch-off closes the parison and cuts off excess plastic.

the alternate mold set moves over the continuously extruding parison to start its cycle.

A lesser-used arrangement places a group of molds on a rotating turntable. Each mold rotates past the extruder to receive a parison, and then moves away to complete the blowing and cooling cycle while other molds are rotated under the extruder. Another method locates the molds in a Ferris-wheel-like arrangement. The parison is extruded as a continuous pipe into the closely located molds. The system is mechanically more complex, but has the advantage of minimizing trim regrind. This can be important in multilayer constructions where comingled plastic trim might cause a recycling problem.

Multilayer Bottles

Bottles having two or more material layers can be made from co-extruded parisons. A major application of co-extrusion technology is for the manufacture of plastic bottles using high oxygen-barrier polymers such as EVOH. Although an exceptionally good oxygen barrier, EVOH is detrimentally affected by moisture. This shortcoming can be eliminated by sandwiching the EVOH layer between two good moisture-barrier layers.

The choice of the outside layers depends on the final properties required. Polyethylene (PE) is satisfactory for applications such as dental pastes. However, PE's low softening temperature make it unsuitable for hot-filled sauce bottles. A common construction co-extrudes EVOH with surface layers of polypropylene (PP). (See Figure 10.23) PE or PP do not bond well to EVOH, so an additional material, the tie or adhesive layer, must be introduced to bind the laminate together. In most applications, a sixth layer composed of process regrind is introduced between the outer skin and the outer tie layer.

Where high clarity is desired, the skin layers would be PET. MXD6, a proprietary nylon with higher oxygen barrier properties than the nylon 6 and 66 usually used in packaging is being laminated with PET for high barrier bottles. An application for beer bottles uses two layers of nylon sandwiched between three layers of PET. Barrier performance is enhanced by incorporating an oxygen-scavenging material into the nylon layers.

Figure 10.23

A bottle with a coextruded translucent stripe to allow viewing of content level (left.) A typical coextruded construction used for high oxygen-barrier bottles (right.)

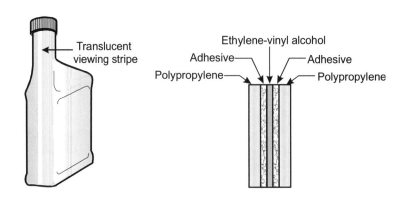

Other examples of multilayer bottle applications are:

- **Use of recycled plastic layers.** Recycled plastics are not as consistent in properties as new resin, and may contain contaminants that might interfere with the product or may simply result in undesirable colors. Two-layer co-extrusions can use an outer layer of new plastic to cover a recycle layer, or the recycle layer can be isolated completely by making it the core layer of a three-layer construction.

- **Cost reduction.** Some pigments, such as pearlescents, are costly. In some instances, savings can be had by pigmenting only the bottle's outer skin.

- **Light barrier.** Many pharmaceutical and some food products are very sensitive to ultraviolet (UV) light. A construction used to create a high UV-light barrier consists of a three-layer HDPE with the core layer heavily pigmented with carbon black.

Co-extrusions can also be made with parallel bands of material. Incorporating a clear or translucent stripe into opaque bottles to provide a viewing port for observing content level is a common application. (See Figure 10.23) Co-extrusion can be used to produce colored stripes for novel decorative effects.

Material Distribution

When a parison is extruded, the weight of the polymer melt tends to pull the parison down, thinning the upper part. This will result in containers having proportionately more material at the bottom. Container geometries can also cause problems. The simplest containers to produce are round in cross-section. In such designs, the parison expands equally in all directions. However, paneling is easily visible in round containers, and therefore, oval or oblong sections are popular.

Oblong containers require that the material flow farther to fill the corners than to the closest wall. Material will, therefore, tend to be thickest at the panel and thinnest at the corners. Narrow-waisted containers will tend to have the greatest thickness at the narrowest point. (See Figure 10.24) A programmed parison overcomes these problems. Such parisons are created by having a parison extruder die-core mandrel that moves according to a preset program. (See Figure 10.25) The mandrel position determines wall thickness at each point on the parison along the height of the bottle. Parison wall thickness is set to be greater where more material is needed to accommodate a greater expansion, and less where the bottle is narrower.

The mechanics of expanding the parison to fit the mold and then chilling the formed plastic make it difficult to maintain good wall thickness at the bottle's shoulder and base areas as illustrated in Figure 10.26. The initial blow-up of the parison expands it equally in all directions. The moment that any part of the expanding parison touches the mold, the plastic freezes and can no longer expand. Normally, the first parts of the pillow-shaped expanding parison to freeze are the central areas of the major panels. From then on, the only

Figure 10.24

Inflation of parallel-walled parisons into variable-diameter containers will give uneven wall thickness (left). The use of a programmed parison (right) results in more uniform wall thickness.

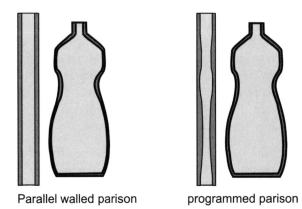

Parallel walled parison   programmed parison

Figure 10.25

The programmed parison die mandrel moves up and down to provide different clearances for parison formation.

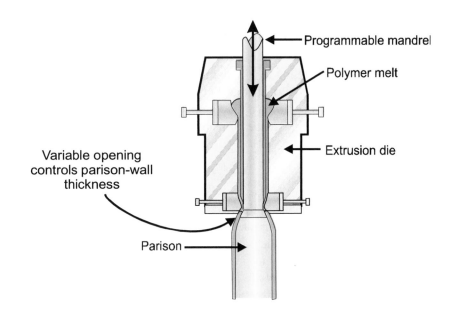

Programmable mandrel

Polymer melt

Extrusion die

Variable opening controls parison-wall thickness

Parison

Figure 10.26

The process of expanding a parison to form a bottle tends to favor producing thicker side-panel cross-sections and thinner cross-sections at the shoulder and base areas.

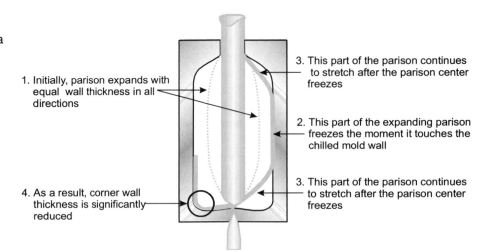

1. Initially, parison expands with equal wall thickness in all directions

3. This part of the parison continues to stretch after the parison center freezes

2. This part of the expanding parison freezes the moment it touches the chilled mold wall

4. As a result, corner wall thickness is significantly reduced

3. This part of the parison continues to stretch after the parison center freezes

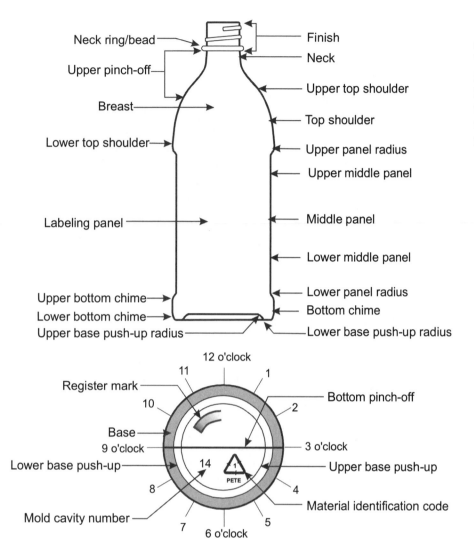

Figure 10.27

Standard bottle terminology. The 12 o'clock position is at right angles to the parting line when the container is turned so that mold numbers and other text are right side up.

stretching that can occur is in the still hot plastic in the top and bottom corners of the mold.

Bottle Terminology and Markings

Most bottles are made in multiple molds, and it is standard practice to put a mold identification number on a bottle's bottom. Investigation of any irregularity or bottle failure should start by determining whether there is a correlation between mold numbers and the observed phenomenon. The symbol identifying the bottle material for purposes of recycling will also be on the bottom of all but the smallest bottles. (See Figure 1.7 for symbols)

The Society of the Plastics Industries has developed standard terminology that should be used when discussing design features or for identifying problem areas. (See Figure 10.27)

Figure 10.28

The injection blow molding process combines preform molding and a bottle blowing cycle.

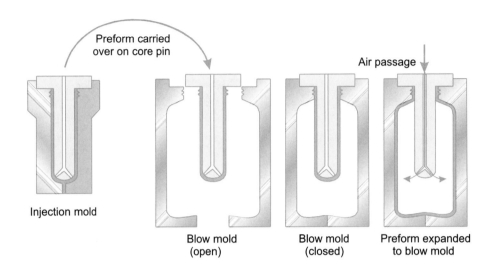

Preform carried over on core pin

Air passage

Injection mold

Blow mold (open)

Blow mold (closed)

Preform expanded to blow mold

INJECTION BLOW MOLDING

Injection blow molding (IBM) combines injection molding and blow molding. Instead of extruding a parison, as in EBM, a parison or "preform" is injection molded. Injection molding of a preform allows more exact control over material distribution than available when extruding a parison. After the preform injection cycle, the preform, still retained on the core pin, is transferred to the blow-molding station. The final blowing operation is similar to extrusion blow molding. (See Figure 10.28) When injection and blowing are done on a single machine, the process is described as "one-step." (See Figure 10.29)

Figure 10.29

Configuration of a one-step IBM machine. One core rod is shown empty for illustration purposes.

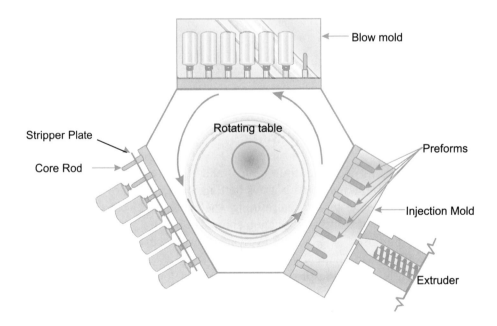

Blow mold

Stripper Plate

Core Rod

Rotating table

Preforms

Injection Mold

Extruder

Economics generally confines IBM to higher volume production, since two molds are required to make a container: the injection mold(s) to produce the preform and the companion blow mold(s) to blow the container.

Injection-Stretch Blow Molding

A variation of IBM, injection-stretch blow molding (ISBM), uses a rod to stretch the preform during blowing. (See Figure 10.30) In a typical operation, at the point that the core rod touches the bottom of the preform, a small amount of air is introduced to start the blowing process. When the core rod reaches the bottom of the mold, the full volume of inflating air is introduced. This mechanical stretching orients the polymer molecules and improves stiffness and barrier properties. For deep bottles, the core rod ensures that the inflation is evenly centered in the mold.

It is common practice for preforms to be injection-molded at a central location and for the preforms to be transported for blowing to their final bottle form at filling plants. This saves money both in the costs of injection machines and in transport. Molds may carry as many as 144 cavities.

ISBM is the favored process for making PET carbonated beverage bottles. In this application, a two-step process is used: The preforms are made on a separate injection-molded machine and accumulated in bulk bins. They are then reheated and blown in a separate operation.

The thermal history of an ISBM part is similar to the thermal history used to make a shrink plastic. (Heat the plastic to about glass transition temperature, stretch and cool quickly.) One drawback of conventional ISBM bottles is that they will shrink if they are hot filled. Several heat-setting processes have been devised to circumvent this problem. Such heat-set bottles can be hot filled at temperatures in the order of 88 to 95°C.

In a representative process, the preform is blown at about 100°C, and then held in the mold at 150°C for several seconds. Crystallization level is about 35%. Production rate is 600 to 800 bottles/hr/cavity compared to 1,100 for conventional ISBM.

Preform and core rod placed in blow mold

Core pin moves down, stretching the preform

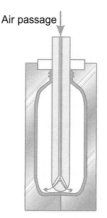

Air passage

Preform blown to mold cavity shape

Figure 10.30

A major application for injection-stretch blow molding is the manufacture of PET carbonated beverage bottles.

Table 10.2
Injection blow molding and extrusion blow molding compared.

Advantages	Disadvantages
Extrusion Blow Molding	
Requires single mold	Produces trim regrind
Handleware readily produced	Limited precision
Coextruded bottles readily produced	Limited number of cavities
Large containers possible (e.g., 200 L drums)	Cold weld is a weak area
	Wide-mouth jars awkward
Injection Blow Molding	
No secondary operations (ream, trim, regrind)	Requires two mold sets
No regrind generated	Limited size containers
High-precision neck and finish	Handleware difficult
More cavities possible for small bottles	Multilayer constructions difficult
Better material distribution	
Wide-mouth jars easy to make	

Both EBM and IBM can be used to produce narrow and wide-mouth bottle shapes. IBM, however, is able to produce bottle finishes that are more complex and with closer tolerances than could be done with EBM. Producing a close tolerance finish for a wide-mouth jar is particularly difficult for EBM. The absence of any trim and scrap with IBM is an advantage when manufacturing pharmaceutical and medical containers. Good manufacturing practice for these containers does not allow the inclusion of regrind material. Table 10.2 compares the advantages and limitations of EBM and IBM. Table 10.3 lists the general properties and applications of polymers commonly used for plastic bottles.

BOTTLE DESIGN

When designing a bottle or jar, the first considerations are the product's nature and how the consumer uses or extracts the product from its container.

If the product is a semisolid—cosmetic creams, peanut butter or jam, for example—the product is removed with a tool. This tool might be a spoon, butter knife, or in the instance of cosmetic creams, a finger. Easy access and product removal demands a wide-mouthed jar with a depth no greater than that of the tool that will be used. The jars should have minimal shoulders, and no other features that would create a dead space difficult to reach with the tool. (See Figure 10.31)

Viscous products such as syrups, sauces and salad dressings can be poured. Bottles for these products should have the largest possible opening consistent with acceptable appearance. Larger diameter openings also allow for easier and faster filling. Other desirable bottle features are smooth walls and no shoulders

Table 10.3

Common bottle plastics and their general properties.

Plastic	Clarity	Barrier Properties			Rigidity	Impact	Density	Typical Bottle Applications
		Water	Oxygen	CO$_2$				
PETG	E	G	F	F	G	G	1.27	EBM, high-clarity bottles
PET	E	G	E	G	G	F	1.33	IBM, high-clarity bottles
OPET	E	G	G	G	E	G	1.36	ISBM, carbonated beverages
PVC	G	G	F	G	G	F	1.35	solvent resistant and cosmetic bottles
LDPE	P	E	P	P	P	G	0.92	soft, squeezable bottles
HDPE	P	E	P	F	F	G	0.96	most opaque consumer bottles
PP	P	E	P	F	F	F	0.91	hot-fill applications
BOPP	P-F	F	P	F	F	G	0.91	as PP but better clarity
PS	E	F	P	P	E	P	1.05	cosmetic, hard, high gloss
PC	E	P	P	P	G	E	1.20	exceptional impact, hot fill
AN	G-E	F	E	E	E	F	1.15	high solvent-resistance barrier

P = poor, F = fair, G = good, E = excellent

or other shapes that could interrupt product flow. Rather, the bottle should slope gently like a funnel toward the opening. (See Figure 10.31)

Neck designs affect visual fill height levels. The same variation in fill volume will be much more obvious if the fill point is in a narrow neck. (See Figure 10.32) Neck bands are sometimes used to conceal the fill level. Where shipping costs are a concern, the bottle should be compact and have a minimum of neck length.

A bottle may have to accommodate internal pressures without bursting. Round, cross-section bottles provide the highest circumferential (hoop) strength. All carbonated beverage bottles, and other bottles that may have to withstand internal pressure, will be round.

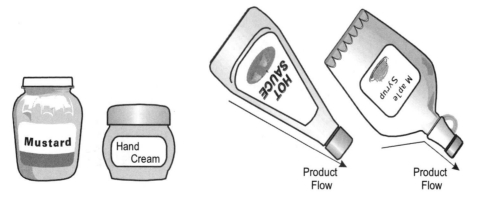

Figure 10.31

Examples of good designs for semisolid products (left) and viscous fluids (right). Embossed or textured shoulders tend to trap product and present a cleaning problem.

Figure 10.32

Expansion panels on a bottle intended for hot-filling.

A bottle may have to accommodate a partial internal vacuum without "panelling"—the deformation of the bottle wall as it "sucks in" in response to the partial vacuum. Hot-filled bottles will panel inward as the hot product cools and contracts. Where the temperature change is small, curved surfaces, thicker wall sections and carefully selected vertical and horizontal design elements may be sufficient to stop visible paneling. With larger bottles and greater temperature changes, expansion panels as shown in Figure 10.32 (usually deeply countersunk, rectangular forms placed around the bottle's circumference) move in and out to accommodate the pressure changes. Expansion panels are usually hidden by the label.

Straight-walled bottles will have less physical strength than similar bottles with added circumferential and vertical design elements. Circumferential rings increase a bottle's hoop strength, resulting in a container that will resist paneling inward or bulging outward. Vertical design elements act primarily to increase the bottle's top-to-bottom load-bearing ability. Many bottles have incorporated embossing or decorative facets that act to improve physical properties and aesthetics. (See Figure 10.33)

Sometimes a design needs both stiffened sections and flexible sections. The "squeeze" dishwashing detergent bottle illustrated in Figure 10.33 uses vertical elements to stiffen the shoulder area, but it has a large flexible center panel that can be squeezed to dispense detergent. Typically, these bottles have a narrowed waist to make the bottle easier to hold with wet, slippery hands.

While circumferential rings or grooves help stiffen the bottle in that axis, they make the bottle more flexible or springy in the top-to-bottom axis. This springiness is amplified if the rings have sharp radii and are deep. The greater the top-to-bottom flexibility, the greater the possibility of transport vibrations causing a resonance condition. Designs with unusual vertical flexibility should be tested for resonance frequency response using established preshipment testing methods.

Bottles should be designed with generous curves and radii. Sharp corners should be avoided, as they act as stress risers and can momentarily trap air between the expanding parison and a sharp corner.

Flat shoulders leading up to the finish will be easily deformed, (see Figure 10.35, left), and under prolonged loading, they will likely fracture the bottle at the finish/shoulder junction. Smoothly sloped shoulders with generous curves provide for even load distribution.

Figure 10.33

Vertical and horizontal design features.

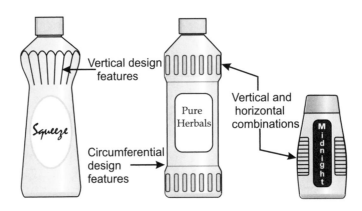

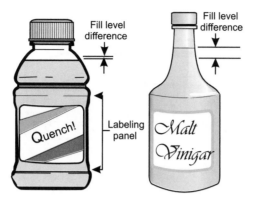

Figure 10.34

Fill-level discrepancies are more obvious in a narrow-neck bottle (left.) Vertical design lines and features add to the top-to-bottom stiffness of a bottle, while circumferential features increase hoop strength (right).

Generous radii and long curves will reduce built-in molding stresses and provide for better material distribution and strength. This is particularly important at the bottle's base where material distribution tends to be difficult to control and the bottle is most abused. Label panel breaks should have a gentle radius rather than a sharp break. (See Figure 10.35) Do not design bottles with abrupt cross-section changes. (For example, a bottle with a round upper section and a square base.)

Large jugs with built-in handles are an effective way to deliver large quantities of liquid product. Since they are heavy, top-to-bottom compression strength can become a vital issue. The most effective way of gaining top-to-bottom compression strength is to design a center-opening jug with gently sloping walls, but these can be awkward to pour in the larger sizes. Off-centered pour openings (F-style) jugs are more popular, but when stacked, can have almost the entire top-to-bottom load concentrated down one side of the bottle.

The best designs are those that raise the handle so that it is on the same level as the closure surface, (see Figure 10.36) allowing the load to be more evenly distributed across the bottle walls.

The easiest bottles to handle on a filling line are those with a low center of gravity. Bottles that are wider at the top than at the base can cause conveying problems such as the bottles tipping over when they press against each other. (See Figure 10.37) "Shingling," another possible conveying problem, occurs with narrow, oval bottles. With just a slight rotation, bottles overlap and wedge or jam between the conveyor rails. Designing small flats at the bottle ends can prevent shingling.

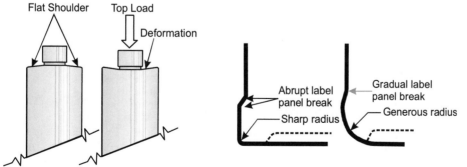

Figure 10.35

Flat panels leading up to the finish should be avoided (left). Gently sloping shoulders carry loads best. Provide for generous radii at breaks for labeling panels and in high abuse areas such as the bottle base (right.)

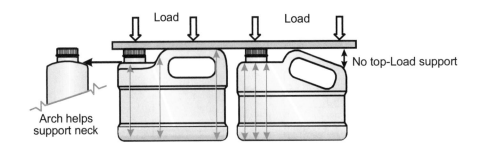

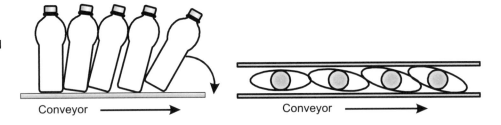

Consider labeling requirements before committing to a bottle design. Round cross-sections are preferred where high labeling speeds are important. By comparison, three-side-wrap labels on a square bottle will not be as amenable to high labeling speeds. Plastic shrink labels can conform to complex curved shapes. Paper, however, can only be curved in one axis and will not conform to surfaces curving in two axes. A shoulder label on a round bottle could be applied properly only if the shoulder was a true straight-sided cone.

Bottle design can reduce label abrasion damage. Labels on bottles with sloped shoulders and tapered bodies will not come into contact with another surface during transport and handling. Straight-walled bottle designs usually inset the labeling panel so labels do not rub against each other or against the corrugated box during shipment. Figures 10.33, 10.34 and 10.36 illustrate design features to accommodate labels. A label located where there will be point-to-point bottle or shipper contact will be prone to abrasion damage.

Sometimes, a label needs to be precisely positioned on a round bottle. The packager might not want the label to align with a mold parting line, might want one label to align with another, or might want the label to align with a directional closure. In those cases, the bottle must incorporate a device to allow precise label orientation. The most common device is a small, depressed wedge shape molded into the bottle's base. A mechanical sensor on the machine detects this register mark (wedge), and the bottle can be rotated to its appropriate orientation.

THERMOFORMING

Principle and Applications

Containers and other draw-formed packaging components can be readily manufactured from thermoplastic sheeting by a number of thermoforming variations.

All variations heat the thermoplastic sheet material to a point where it becomes soft and pliable, but below the temperature at which melt flow might occur.

Most thermoplastic materials can be thermoformed, including single-polymer materials, co-extrusions and laminated sheets. (See Table 10.4) Multilayered laminated sheet can provide specialized physical and chemical properties that are not economically attainable by other means. Thermoforms made on automated, high-performance equipment may provide a possible alternative to injection-molded containers such as tubs.

Pliable plastic sheet can be formed by mechanical means, with vacuums, with pressure or by combinations of these. In all cases, the relationship of the part surface area to the available sheet determines the average material thickness. Material distribution is governed by the part's geometry and the particular method used to form the shape. Sheet gauge and mold accuracy are important.

Since molding temperatures and pressures are very low, thermoform molds are economical. It is not unusual for prototype molds to be made of wood or epoxy/aluminum. Production molds are either aluminum or berylium/copper if exceptional thermal conductivity is required.

A sheet being formed should be heated to its optimum temperature to reduce residual stresses set up when the material is stretched. Manual operations do not lend themselves to good, consistent qualities due to the variables of time sequencing by "hand." Automatic, accurately timed, thermally controlled equipment is preferred.

Thermoformed parts cannot have undercuts. (Small lips and rims are sometimes put on during molding or as a post-molding operation. However, the tooling for these can quickly eliminate the cost and speed advantages of the basic process.) In addition, all drawn parts must have a draft angle so that the part can be removed from the mold. Draft angles are a function of part geometry— the deeper the draw, the greater the angle required. Angles from 2 degrees to 8 degrees are typical.

Table 10.4

Common thermoforming materials and their forming temperatures.

Material	Typical Forming Temperature	
	°C	(°F)
Poly(vinyl chloride)	138–176	(265–325)
Polystyrene	143–176	(290–350)
Oriented polystyrene	176–193	(350–380)
High-impact polystyrene	171–182	(340–360)
Polypropylene	148–199	(300–390)
High-density polyethylene	148–190	(300–375)
PETG	129–162	(265–325)
CPET	148–176	(300–350)

Figure 10.38

Bottles and other closed-package systems cannot be directly molded by thermoforming. However, thermoformed halves can be bonded together to make an inexpensive, bottle-like container.

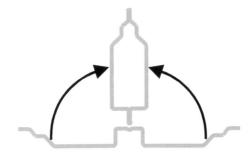

While thermoforming cannot make narrow-necked containers directly in the mold, two formed halves can be joined to create narrow-necked or other partly or completely enclosed containers. (See Figure 10.38) Ways to join the two halves include adhesive bonding, spin welding or ultrasonic bonding.

The most common application of thermoforms is for various forms of blister or clamshell display packaging. In most instances, these are formed from PVC, although PS and PET are also commonly used. Many package inserts, retaining devices and counter-top point-of-purchase displays are thermoformed from PS. Many medical and operating room supplies are arranged in easily visible and readily accessible thermoformed trays.

Some food and product tubs are thermoformed rather than injection molded. There is an obvious tooling cost advantage; however, a thermoformed part may not have the precision required for consistent fit of a snap-on lid.

Thermoforming Methods

Rotary or reciprocating matched die molding is the simplest thermoforming method. Matched dies are generally made from material with low thermal conductivity to prevent premature chilling of the heated sheet. The core part of the die simply pushes the softened plastic into the matching cavity half. Matched dies can be used only for shallow draws. Material distribution is poor.

Vacuum forming into a cavity mold or over a plug mold is the simplest form of vacuum molding. (See Figure 10.39) Vacuum holes are required in the cavity's lowest point. Vacuum forming into a cavity or over a plug has deficiencies similar to those of matched die molding—limited draw and poor control over material

Figure 10.39

Simple vacuum forming over cavity and plug molds: The material is pulled to the mold shape when a vacuum is applied between the mold and sheet interfaces.

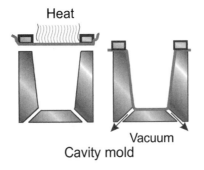

Cavity mold

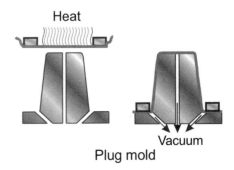

Plug mold

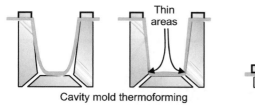

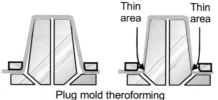

Thin areas

Cavity mold thermoforming

Thin area   Thin area

Plug mold theroforming

Figure 10.40

Although cavity or plug molds create similar shapes, material distribution differs considerably. The thinnest areas occur in the last portion of the part cooled by contact with the mold.

distribution. (See Figure 10.40) Cavity molds allow for easier part removal, since the hot plastic shrinks away from the cavity when it cools, whereas the cooled plastic will tend to tighten around a plug mold.

Material distribution problems are reduced when forming methods are combined. In plug-assist vacuum forming, the plug mold is above the sheet. (See Figure 10.37) The sheet is heated until it begins to sag, the plug moves the sheet into the mold, and a vacuum pulls it into conformity with the mold. This gives better material distribution to the corners than vacuum forming alone.

Billow forming uses air pressure to billow the sheet upward 50 to 75% of the anticipated mold draw. (See Figure 10.41) A plug pushes the billowed material into a cavity. A vacuum then pulls the intruded material to the cavity shape.

Microwavable Trays and Containers

Microwave-compatible plastic trays or containers have displaced the original aluminum TV dinner tray. Plastic trays can be thermoformed from polypropylene, polystyrene or crystallized poly(ethylene terephthalate) (CPET). The trays are formed from rolls of plastic sheet. CPET is stiff, strong and stable from −40 to 218°C (−40 to 425°F), offering dual ovenability—meaning it can be used in reheating in both conventional and microwave ovens. The material has better water- and oxygen-barrier qualities than PP or PS, good grease and oil resistance, and minimally affects food taste. CPET is, however, costly compared to other options.

PP has sufficient temperature stability to allow it to be used for most microwavable applications but not in a conventional convection oven. PP also has oxygen-barrier limitations. Where an increased oxygen barrier is required, PP can be co-extruded with a high-oxygen-barrier resin such as ethylene-vinyl alcohol.

Conventional PS has a low heat-deflection temperature, but low-density blends are available that will not deflect significantly up to about 190°C (375°F), al-

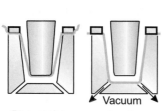

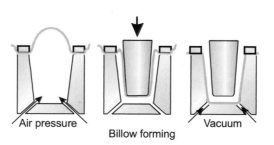

Vacuum

Plug-assist vacuum forming

Air pressure   Billow forming   Vacuum

Figure 10.41

Plug-assist vacuum forming (finish sentence with a description of this type of forming). Billow forming inflates the plastic sheet upward to produce a sheet of uniform thickness.

Figure 10.42

Configuration of a typical
rotational molding machine.

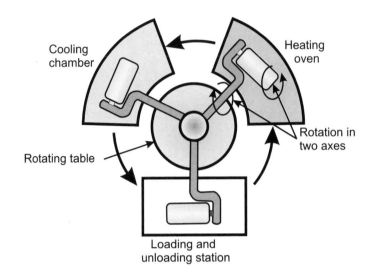

lowing for microwavable applications. The trays are sometimes made of expanded PS.

OTHER FORMING METHODS AND VARIATIONS

Rotational Molding

Rotational molding (See Figure 10.42) does not require an extruder. In this process, the polymer, usually a finely powdered polyethylene, is placed in a mold that is then heated while being rotated in two axes. The heat eventually melts the polyethylene, which flows and evenly coats the inside surfaces of the mold. While still rotating, the plastic is cooled. The mold is opened, and the part is removed. An advantage of this process is the making of a hollow object with no openings.

Since rotational molding is not a pressure process, the molds need not be massive and are usually made from welded steel plate. Rotational molding is used to make very large bins and bulk containers. It is too slow and energy intensive for small plastic containers.

Injection Molding Heads on Extruded Profiles

Occasionally a package is formed by combining two molding processes. For example profile extruded plastic collapsible tubes are inserted into an injection mold as shown in Figure 10.43. Additional plastic is injected into contact with the extruded tube and fuses to the tube walls. The sprue and gate are trimmed off in a separate operation.

Compression Molding

Compression molding is primarily used to mold thermoset plastics. A measured charge of unpolymerized thermoset plastic is placed into the hot cavity of a mold.

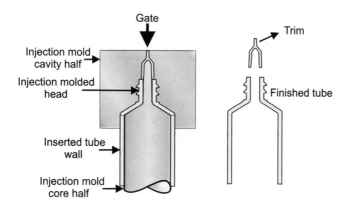

Figure 10.43

Injection molding a head onto an extruded tube body.

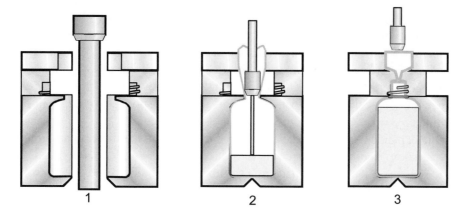

Figure 10.44

Blow-fill-seal sequence: Step 1. A parison is extruded. Step 2. The mold closes over the parison, the bottle is formed and product is introduced. Step 3. The finish is formed by moveable mold parts, and the bottle is sealed shut.

A mating core is brought down to squeeze the plastic into close conformity with the mold. The heat from the mold cures the plastic.

The compression molding technique has on occasion been used to mold thermoplastic parts. The main difference being that the thermoplastic is melted in an extruder, and a measured shot is then ejected into a chilled mold cavity. As with thermosets, the core forces the molten plastic to conform to the mold profiles. Compression molding has been used to make thermoplastic closures. One advantage of the method is that it leaves no gate mark.

Blow-fill-seal Molding

Blow-fill-seal molding is similar to extrusion blow molding in that it starts with an extruded parison. (See Figure 10.44) However, as soon as the bottle is blown, product is introduced through a tube incorporated into the blowhead. Separate mold pieces then move in to form and seal off the finish.

Blow-fill-seal is used to produce single-use bottles that are opened by breaking off the tip rather than removing a closure. It is particularly useful for sterile pharmaceutical preparations where the plastic forming temperature and the closure-less seal ensure sterility.

Expanded Plastics

Expanding a plastic into a low density cellular foam requires that a fine network of gas bubbles or cells be introduced into the plastic mass. Blowing agents, low-boiling point liquids that can be dispersed into a plastic mass, are the most common way of expanding a plastic into a cellular foam. When the mass is heated, the blowing agent in its gaseous form will expand into bubbles in the softened plastic. By controlling the kind and quantity of blowing agent, temperature and time, expanded plastics can be produced in a range of densities.

Expanded polystyrene (EPS) and expanded polyethylene represent the bulk of expanded plastic used in packaging followed by urethane.

At one time, many blowing agents were based on chlorinated fluorocarbons. Today, these have been replaced with pentane or isopentane (primarily for polystyrene) and higher hydrocarbons (primarily for polyethylene). These may be used alone or in blends. Carbon dioxide may also be used along with the blowing agent. Nucleating agents encourage the formation of very fine gas bubbles.

Smaller bubbles produce a denser foam and one in which the bubbles are all divided from each other. Such closed-cell foams will not absorb liquids. As bubbles get larger, at some point the dividing walls between bubbles collapse to produce an open-cell foam. Open-cell foams are more sponge-like and will take up liquids.

Thin expanded sheet material is extruded from an annular die similar to blown film extrusion. The blowing agent is introduced in the extruder and expands the plastic sheet as it leaves the extruder. The tube is slit, the flat sheet is then rolled up and sent for conditioning.

Loose polystyrene (PS) fill for protective packaging is made by the extrusion process.

A second method of producing EPS is to incorporate the blowing agent into a polystyrene melt and then cool the melt down, capturing the blowing agent inside the polystyrene. The solid PS beads can be transported in bulk to locations where it will be processed into an expanded form. To make a dimensional part, the beads are pre-expanded slightly and then placed into a mold. Steam heating raises the temperature to a point where the PS becomes thermoelastic and the blowing agent vaporizes, expanding the PS to the shape of the mold cavity.

To make EPS plank (beadboard) that can be fabricated into protective shapes, the beads are poured into a large block mold and expanded.

EPS foams are exceptional insulating materials.

(Styrofoam is Dow's proprietary name for a construction material and should not be used in reference to packaging materials.)

A polyurethane (PU) is produced by the polymerization of isocyanate and a glycol. PU can be expanded by gases formed during a chemical reaction between the two prepolymers. PU foams are usually open-celled and can be made into very soft resilient foams as well as stiff thermoset forms. Shaped forms can be made by mixing the liquid disocyanate and glycol in a spray-gun type of nozzle directly into a mold. A major packaging application is foam-in-place technology where the still liquid foam is directed at, and allowed to expand around the actual object to be protected.

RECOGNIZING MOLDING METHODS

The process used to make a plastic part can be recognized by the part's nature and an examination of the mold markings, or lack of them. Extruded parts have no mold markings, since they are simply pushed through a shaped opening. Thermoformed parts also have no visible markings, since they are cut from a flat sheet. The process can only make containers that can be pulled from an open cavity or off a plug. There are no undercuts.

An extrusion blow-molded bottle, by definition, must be a part that can be inflated. It will have a pinch-off across the bottom where the mold halves came together and cut off the excess parison. A faint parting line will be seen up the container sides.

Injection-molded parts will have a small bit of plastic at the gate point. Mold makers have become adept at hiding this gate mark, and sometimes it is difficult to find. Mold-parting lines on simple tubs are usually put along an edge, which makes them hard to detect. Parting lines can be seen in parts that have undercuts or other features that require the mold to come apart in segments.

Injection-blow-molded parts resemble extrusion-blown parts except that instead of a mold pinch-off, there is a circular bull's-eye pattern on the container bottom. This is the residue of the gate mark from the initial injection molding of the preform. Faint parting lines up the container sides can sometimes be seen.

REVIEW QUESTIONS

1. Name four basic ways of forming plastics into semi rigid shapes.

2. Molds for plastic manufacture are generally designed for a particular polymer. What is the problem you are likely to encounter if you switch materials?

3. What is co-extrusion, and what advantages does co-extrusions offer?

4. To mold plastic into a useful shape, it must first be heated and softened. What is the name of the machine that does this?

5. What is the principal use for thin-walled extruded tube?

6. What are: a sprue, a runner, flash, a gate, and a parison?

7. There are two ways of manufacturing plastic film. What are they?

8. How are plastic bags usually made?

9. What are combinations of vacuum, pressure and mechanical assists used in thermoforming?

10. To discuss the importance of a programmed parison

11. What is the makeup of a high-oxygen barrier multilayer bottle of the type typically used for ketchup?

12. What molding process would be used to make a 1,200-litre bulk bin?

13. What is the significance of the number they can be found on most blow molded bottles and injection-molded parts?

14. Why are carbonated beverage bottles injection stretch blow molded?

15. What designs can be made by extrusion blow molding that would be more difficult to make by injection blow molding?

16. Why isn't injection molding used to make a narrow-mouthed bottles?

17. Which extrusion blow molded ball shapes are easiest to mold, and which are the most difficult?

18. How does an extruder for injection molding differ from an extrusion profile extruder?

19. Parts made by injection molding have tighter tolerance ranges than parts made by extrusion blow molding for thermoforming. Why?

20. How is a cast film biaxially oriented?

21. What is an "undercut"? What complication is introduced women injection molded part as an undercut?

22. What are the advantages of injection blow molding, and for what specific applications and industries are these advantages particularly beneficial?

23. Molded open tubs can be made by injection molding or by thermoforming. What are the implications of choosing one method over the other? What feature can be incorporated easily into a thermoformed tub that would be difficult with injection molding? How can you tell which process was used to make the tub?

24. How can you recognize the process by which a bottle was made?

25. In thermoforming, cavity molds are preferred over plug molds. Why?

26. What is a sink mark, and what might cause it?

27. What does melt flow rate measure, in what is the significance of this value?

CONTENTS

Polyethylene (PE)

Production and variations, HDPE, LDPE, LLDPE and mPE, bimodal polyethylenes.

High-density Polyethylene (HDPE)

Applications: films, semirigid containers. North American usage.

Low-density Polyethylene (LDPE) and Linear Low-density Polyethylene (LLDPE)

Properties, applications, strengths, limitations, film applications, semirigid applications, metallocene polyethylene, North American usage.

Polystyrene (PS)

Production and properties, blown PS. Coextruded film and sheet applications, strengths and limitations, semirigid and rigid applications, North American usage.

Polypropylene (PP)

Production, properties, isotactic and atactic grades, film properties, orienting and applications. Semirigid and rigid applications, North American usage.

Poly(ethylene terephthalate) (PET)

Production, copolymer variations, properties, dual-ovenable applications, limitations. Applications, films, metallized films, bottles, North American usage, film properties, strengths and limitations, applications, injection blow-molded bottles, dual-ovenable containers.

Poly(vinyl chloride) (PVC)

Production, processing, properties, strengths and limitations, compounding, plasticizers, North American usage, applications.

Poly(vinylidene chloride) (PVDC)

Production, copolymers, barrier qualities, applications.

Poly(vinyl acetate) (PVAC) and Ethylene-vinyl Acetate (EVA)

Properties, copolymer variations, film and adhesive applications.

Polyamide (PA or nylon)

Production, types, strengths, limitations, thermoformability, applications.

Poly(vinyl alcohol) (PVAL) and Ethylene-vinyl Alcohol (EVOH)

Applications, production, copolymers, solubility, barrier qualities.

Ethylene Acid Copolymers and Ionomers

Copolymer variations, ethylene-ethyl acrylate copolymer, properties, applications. Ionomers, properties, applications.

Other Packaging Polymers

Cellulosics, epoxies, polycarbonates, acrylonitrile copolymer, polyurethanes, poly(ethylene naphthalate), styrene-butadiene, polychlorotrifluoroethylene, thermoset plastics.

Additives

Antistatics, antioxidants, heat stabilizers, plasticizers, slip agents, UV stablizers, others.

Characterizing Plastic Materials

Test procedures, ASTM. Example of test methods and typical properties. General mechanical properties, impact, heat-seal strength, coefficient of friction, haze and gloss, film permeabilities, permeability, dimensional stability, use temperatures, stress-crack resistance.

Chemical Properties

Chemical compatibility and chemical compatibility tables.

PLASTIC APPLICATIONS

POLYETHYLENE (PE)

Production and Variations

Polyethylene is produced by polymerizing ethylene gas under pressure and elevated temperature in the presence of metal catalysts. Under these conditions, ethylene molecules link up in long chains of 50 to 50,000 units, transforming ethylene gas to a white, partially crystalline solid. The product of this reaction is extruded as a hot ribbon, cooled and chopped into pellets.

Some side branching of the main polymer chain occurs during polymerization. If the branches are relatively few and short (two to four carbon atoms), the long parent chains will fold and pack neatly together in crystalline-like structures as the PE cools from a melt. With small amounts of short-chain branching, the material produced is high-density polyethylene (HDPE). HDPE is defined as a PE with a density between 0.941 and 0.959 grams per cubic centimetre (g/cu cm).

Extensive side-chain branching is encouraged by polymerizing the ethylene at higher temperatures and pressures. Long-chain branching interferes with orderly packing, resulting in low-density polyethylene (LDPE), a material that is less crystalline and less dense. LDPE is defined as having a density between 0.910 to 0.925 g/cu cm.

Linear low-density polyethylene (LLDPE) is a polyethylene in which side branching has been deliberately introduced by including monomers such as butene, hexene or octene with the ethylene. The resulting polyethylene contains sufficient copolymer short-chain branching to decrease density to the LDPE range, but unlike LDPE, the branches tend to be short, giving LLDPE properties somewhat different from LDPE.

The differences in properties between HDPE and LDPE (including LLDPE) grades are so great that their applications are completely different and they are treated as if they were different plastic families.

Many new polyethylene grades are coming into the market, and it may be expected that further developments will increase the number of polyethylene variations. These variations are usually based on new copolymer combinations or on controlling molecular geometry and molecular weight distribution. In the latter field, new metallocene, or single-site catalysts (replacing Ziegler-Natta catalysts), provide a way to produce polyethylenes with very narrow molecular weight spreads. Metallocene polyethylenes (mPE) are somewhat harder to process, but are tougher and provide stronger heat seals than conventional polyethylene.

In another development, bimodal polyethylenes are composed of molecular weights in two distinct molecular weight ranges rather than grouped about a single average molecular weight. The lower molecular weight fractions act as a lubricant, making processing of the higher molecular weight components easier.

Polyethylenes are one of the most versatile and economical polymers, and their low softening point results in low processing energy costs. These factors alone encouraged the use of PE over other resins in many applications.

HIGH-DENSITY POLYETHYLENE (HDPE)

The most significant application features of HDPE are its low cost, easy processibility and good moisture barrier. Its low oxygen-, hydrocarbon- and flavor-barrier properties, softness, low softening point, opacity and relatively high cold-flow properties may limit its use for some applications. Table 11.1 lists the most significant HDPE applications.

Some retail bags and sacks are made from extruded HDPE film, as well as some food wraps and bags. Good moisture-barrier properties encourage the use of HDPE for any application where a moisture barrier is required. Multiwall paper sacks often use an HDPE inner liner to impart water resistance. Extrusion coatings of HDPE improve water or grease hold-out for paperboard products.

Most consumer and industrial blow-molded containers are HDPE. Containers have a milky translucence, and many blow-molded containers are pigmented to improve appearance. Natural HDPE is used for many packaging applications, particularly those for food. Because it is relatively soft, PE is easily scratched and abraded. For appearance purposes, most blow-molded PE bottles have a matte surface finish.

Blow-molded bottles for food products are the largest single market for HDPE bottles, followed closely by the household and industrial chemical market. Household chemicals include such products as household cleaners, shampoos, motor oils and lawn and garden care products. Blow-molded drums and tight head pails (i.e., a pail without a removable cover) are used mostly for shipping and storing industrial chemicals and materials.

PE exhibits a relatively poor barrier to hydrocarbon solvents. Despite this, many solvent-containing compounds are packed in HDPE bottles. Solvent loss will eventually lead to bottle paneling as illustrated in Figure 11.1. Fluorination, a process where the finished bottle's interior is flooded with fluorine compounds, is sometimes used to increase barrier properties.

Injection-molded pails are open-topped containers, for which 20 litre (l) or 5 gallon (gal) are the most common, used for a broad range of consumer and

Table 11.1

HDPE packaging applications based on a total North American usage of 13,750 million pounds.

Blow-molded liquid food bottles	10%
Household and industrial chemical bottles	9%
Injection-molded pails	8%
Blown and cast film	3%
Injection-molded tubs and containers	3%
Injection-molded crates and totes	2%
Blow-molded motor oil bottles	2%
Blow-molded industrial drums	2%

Figure 11.1

Permeation of volatile
solvents through high
density polyethylene has
resulted in paneling.

industrial products. Products include prepared plasters and grouts, swimming pool chemicals, fertilizers, institutional foods, industrial chemicals, institutional paints and agricultural chemicals.

Many industrial boxes, crates, pallets, totes and other material handling and storage containers are made from injection-molded HDPE. Crates and totes include "dairy crates," a generic term used to describe all manner of crates used to handle more than just dairy products.

Almost a third of HDPE caps and closures are milk bottle caps. Covers for open-head pails and some screw-thread closures are also made from HDPE. Some yogurt, sour cream, margarine and other product tubs are injection-molded from HDPE, although polypropylene (PP) tends to be more common. (Injection molded PP, however, can become brittle at freezer temperatures. To avoid the possibility of brittle cracking, frozen products such as ice cream come in HDPE tubs.) Snap-on lids for polypropylene tubs are usually made from polyethylene to take advantage of polyethylene's higher elongation qualities.

LOW-DENSITY POLYETHYLENE (LDPE) AND LINEAR LOW-DENSITY POLYETHYLENE (LLDPE)

Properties and Applications

Like HDPE, LDPE has low cost, easy processibility and good moisture barrier. LDPE and LLDPE have good heat sealability at temperatures as low as 106 to 112°C (223 to 234°F). This is the lowest softening point of conventional packaging polymers and accounts for one of the larger applications of LDPE and LLDPE. Other significant features are clarity, high elongation and softness. Low gas-barrier properties, softness, low softening point and relatively high cold-flow properties may limit their use for some applications. Tables 11.2 and 11.3 list the most significant LDPE and LLDPE applications.

For the LDPE family of materials, properties such as tear strength, impact strength, elongation and flexibility decrease as density increases. For example, with an increase in density comes a corresponding increase in stiffness. Conversely, LDPE's poor grease-barrier properties improve as density increases.

Table 11.2

LDPE packaging applications as a percentage of the total North American usage of 6,400 million pounds.

Extruded food-packaging film	17.0%
Extruded non-food-packaging film	12.5%
Stretch and shrink films	5.2%
Injection-molded components and parts	5.0%
Blow-molded bottles	0.1%

Polyethylene film alone will not hold a vacuum because of its high gas permeability. Other LDPE limitations include poor scuff resistance, high odor transmission, dust attraction (through static) and low grease/oil resistance.

About half of all packaging uses for LDPE and LLDPE are as film made by either blown or cast extrusion. Blown film is typically used for most light- and heavy-duty consumer and industrial packaging. Cast film is used for pallet stretch wrap and overwraps. PE can also be extruded as a coating onto another substrate. Trash bags are the single largest user of LDPE.

A variety of food packaging applications such as bread bags, shipping sacks and other bagged products—where clarity and economy are required—depend on LDPE and LLDPE. Nonfood applications include light and heavy agricultural product bags, garment bags, bag liners and bags for industrial chemicals.

Stretch film for unitizing loads for shipment is a major LLDPE market. (Ethylene-vinyl acetate (EVA) is another major stretch-wrap material.) Shrink films are used to overwrap product or bundle multiple units for shipping. PE industrial liners are used for bins, boxes, drums and even the interiors of entire intermodal or bulk shipping containers to reduce water damage or contamination.

Heavy-duty bags contain products such as fertilizers, agricultural chemicals and industrial chemicals. Some products might come in a multiwall paper bag with a polyethylene liner.

A significant proportion of the LDPE family is used to produce multilayer laminated structures where the materials serve as a heat-seal medium. The LDPE/LLDPE may be incorporated in the lamination as a previously made film that is adhesive-laminated to a substrate, or it can be applied directly as an

Table 11.3

LLDPE packaging applications as a percentage of total North American usage of 7,740 million pounds.

Stretch-wrap and shrink-wrap films	15%
Non-food-packaging films	13%
Food-packaging films	6%

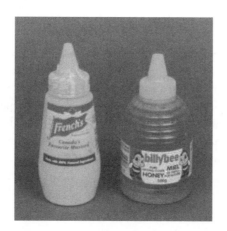

Figure 11.2

Examples of squeezable bottles made from low density polyethylene.

extrusion coating. LDPE has good heat-seal properties, and is readily sealed by various heat-sealing techniques. Medium-density polyethylene also seals well, but HDPE can present problems that are normally remedied with a LDPE heat-seal coating or by blending the polymer with LDPE or EVA. Many laminated structures also take advantage of LDPE's clarity and low water-vapor transmission rate. Other substrates are used to provide the required gas-barrier properties.

LDPE and LLDPE are used for injection- and blow-molded containers where softness, high flexibility or squeezability are required. Sauces, and other viscous fluids or semi-solids where squeezability is an advantage will be made from LDPE. (See figure 11.2).

Snap-on or interference-fit closures such as snap-on caps for margarine or sour cream tubs require some elongation for the cap to stretch over the tub's opening and snap over a slightly enlarged friction ring around the tub's opening perimeter. (See Figure 10.18). LDPE and LLDPE have suitably high elongation.

Metallocene polyethylene, the newest polyethylene family member, has up to 40% greater tensile strength, up to ten times higher dart impact strength, better hot tack and produces stronger heat seals, compared with LLDPE. Disadvantages include a high coefficient of friction, more difficult processing and higher cost than LLDPE. Current mPE applications are for tough, high-performance films and heat sealants. Another significant application is for high-oxygen/low-moisture permeable film for precut salads.

POLYSTYRENE (PS)

Production and Properties

Styrene is produced by combining ethylene with benzene to form ethyl benzene and then converting this to styrene. Styrene is polymerized with the aid of oxygen, oxidizing agents or light, as a catalyst.

PS is available as a hard, clear brittle homopolymer known as "crystal polystyrene." ("Crystal" in this context describes PS clarity, not molecular crystallinity.) Homopolymer PS has excellent clarity and high surface gloss. It can be brightly colored with opaque or transparent colorants. High-impact polystyrene

(HIPS) is a polystyrene copolymer that has been modified with elastomeric molecules such as butadiene to a form a material with significantly improved impact qualities. PS is inexpensive and easily processed.

Expanded polystyrene (EPS) is made into a variety of trays, tubs and cups. It is formed by incorporating a "blowing agent" with the PS that will expand the plastic into a low density cellular foam. Many protective packaging forms such as planks, molded forms, and loose-fill cushioning. EPS foams are exceptional insulating materials. (Styrofoam is Dow's proprietary name for a construction material and should not be used in reference to packaging materials.)

PS Applications

Table 11.4 lists the major packaging applications of polystyrene.

PS has good dimensional stability, superior opticals, good chemical resistance to food acids and alkalis, and good printing characteristics. Crystal PS film lends itself to coextruded structures, where a thin layer of PS provides high surface gloss. Typical packaging applications include windowed cartons, windowed envelopes and "breathable" wrap for fresh produce.

Unoriented polystyrene film has low tear, impact, tensile and heat-seal strengths; it has poor gas and water-vapor barrier properties. PS has poor resistance to many solvents, although this quality is used in some applications to produce solvent bonding of PS components.

Biaxially oriented crystal PS sheet possesses strength and clarity properties that are suited to thermoformed blister packs, candy and pastry trays and a variety of related food packages. Sheet PS is thermoformed into various point-of-purchase displays, product support or containment trays. Thicker sheet can be drawn into large tubs for dairy products.

Injection-molded PS closures take advantage of the material's exceptional clarity, and they have a hard, glossy surface. Polystyrenes are injection-molded into a variety of glossy, crystal clear boxes and containers used in hardware, toy, cosmetic and jewelry applications. These boxes are generically called "jewel boxes," regardless of the contents. Various interior supports and fitments to hold objects such as jewelry or wristwatches are also typically made from PS.

White opaque EPS cellular sheet material has excellent decorative qualities and can be made in a heat-shrinkable form. Cellular sheet is commonly used as label stock for glass and plastic bottles.

Table 11.4

PS packaging applications as a percentage of the total North American usage of 6,200 million pounds.*

Extruded film and sheet	22%
Injection molding	10%

*Data does not include packaging markets for expanded PS packaging forms.

Thermoformed EPS food trays of the type used to hold meat, produce and eggs are the principal products made from extruded EPS sheet. Heavier board stock can be cut to shape and fabricated for use as protective forms where volume does not justify the cost of a mold. Where volumes are significant, protective EPS forms are molded to shape. EPS loose-fill bead products are used mostly for inner packing to protect fragile products from impact and vibration.

POLYPROPYLENE (PP)

Production and Properties

Polypropylene is polymerized from propylene gas, a relatively low-cost feedstock, and processed into pellets by a method similar to that used to create PE. PP molecules differ from PE molecules only in having an extra carbon atom in the gaseous monomer. This altered monomer building block results in polymer side chains that are more uniform in length, resulting in more uniform physical and chemical properties. PP's properties can be tailored by catalyst selection, copolymerization and molecular weight control.

Homopolymer PP resin is available in two general classifications, depending on whether the location of the pendent methyl group is regular or random. Regular PP molecular structure (isotactic) gives superior properties and is used for most packaging applications. Random (atactic) PP polymerization yields a gummy PP, which has some limited applications as an adhesive base.

PP has lower crystallinity than high density polyethylene, and it is easier to produce in an amorphous state. PP clarity can be improved by incorporating nucleating agents that deliberately precipitate crystals, but limit their growth to a range that does not defract light. Copolymerizing with ethylene increases the randomness in the chain, reducing crystallinity and improving clarity; however, it also decreases the melting point and increases flexibility.

PP is a low-density material that is comparatively easy to process. Compared with PE, it has better resistance to cold flow and reduced deformation at elevated temperatures. It has good stiffness, tensile strength and surface hardness. PP has low UV light resistance and requires UV inhibitors for any application where there will be significant UV exposure. Unoriented PP becomes brittle at low temperatures. Copolymer PP has better cold performance but sacrifices other physical properties.

PP is an economical material essentially on a par with PE. It has a higher softening point, and therefore, it is used for bottles where hot filling or some other thermal exposure occurs. Medical supplies that will be steam-sterilized often use PP. Although both PP and PE blow-molded bottles are somewhat opaque, PP has contact clarity when a wet product is filled into the bottle.

PP has outstanding integral hinge (live hinge) properties and is used in many injection-molded boxes, containers and closures where an integral hinge is a part of the design. Most plastic threaded closures are injection-molded from PP.

PP film can be made by either blown or cast-extrusion methods. As a plain, unoriented, uncoated film, PP possesses superior optical properties, good water vapor barrier properties, good dimensional stability and good heat-seal strength, although in a relatively narrow temperature range. In this form, it has low tensile and impact strength, high gas permeability and poor low-temperature durability; it has only fair chemical resistance, machine performance and abrasion resistance.

Orienting PP improves its tensile strength, stiffness, moisture- and grease-barrier properties, low-temperature durability, clarity and gloss. However, oriented PP will not heat seal. This limitation is overcome by the use of heat-seal coatings (e.g., PE, PVDC, EVA or acrylic), by modifying the film resins or by coextrusion with a heat-sealable material.

PP Applications

Table 11.5 lists major North American packaging markets for polypropylene.

Polypropylene films are classified by their orientation, and by further groupings such as the following:

- Heat-stabilized (i.e., nonshrink), non-heat-sealable film is widely used in laminate structures such as snack-food packaging or combined with paper as a bag liner for cookies or dry pet food. Clear labels may use this stock.

- Heat-stabilized, heat-sealable films have been modified, coated or coextruded to make them heat sealable. Coated films (most commonly PVDC or acrylic) are grouped as gas-barrier and non-gas-barrier types. These are used as overwraps for cigarette packaging, candies and so on. Coextruded, heat-sealable films are used in form-fill-seal applications.

- White opaque films have excellent decorative qualities similar to paper, without the disadvantages of water and fat absorption. They are primarily used as a single-web wrap for candy bars and as label stock.

- Heat-shrinkable films are used as shrink-wrapping stock, and when printed, as clear or opaque shrink labels.

Biaxially oriented polypropylene (BOPP) films in various combinations are the backbone of snack-food and confection packaging. In a typical application, a thin-gauge OPP film is reverse printed and then laminated to another OPP film. The second film may have metallizing to improve gas barrier and will usually have a heat-sealable coating.

Table 11.5	
PP packaging applications as a percentage of total North American usage of 14,000 million pounds.	
Injection-molded containers and parts	10.2%
Film	9.0%
Blow-molded bottles	1.2%

Some paperboard is extrusion coated with PP to provide liquid holdout for microwavable food products. A PE would have too low of a softening point.

Most injection-molded, thin-walled containers such as those used for butter, margarine and yogurt are PP. PP ice cream tubs would risk cold fracture at freezer temperatures, and so these are usually PE or a copolymer. Snap-on lids for PP tubs are usually PE to provide the elongation needed to produce the interference fit and still be easily removable.

POLY(ETHYLENE TEREPHTHALATE) (PET)

Production and Properties

An "ester" is the reaction product of an organic acid and an organic base. Polyesters can be produced from any number of organic acids and bases, resulting in both thermoset and thermoplastic variations. Among the most widely used thermoplastic polyester materials are those formed by reacting ethylene glycol (base) and terephthalic acid to form poly(ethylene terephthalate.) The polymerization process is a condensation reaction rather than an addition reaction as with PE or PP. The 249°C (480°F) melting point of homopolymer PET is one of the highest of the common packaging plastics.

PET is made in a number of copolymer variations, each designed to enhance some desirable property of PET. Most PET copolymers are made by including an additional dibasic acid or glycol in the polymerization reaction. For example, including cyclohexanedimethanol produces a polyester (PCTA) that can be made into films having brilliant clarity, good toughness and high tear strength. Altering the copolymer proportions slightly produces a highly crystallized form with a melting point of about 285°C (545°F). This crystallized form (CPET) is used for dual-ovenable tray applications.

Another PET copolymer is made with additional glycol components (PETG). This copolymer has very little tendency to crystallize, allowing injection molding of high clarity parts. PETG's high melt strength allows it to be thermoformed or extrusion blow molded into clear bottles, unlike PET homopolymer that does not have enough melt strength to maintain an extruded parison.

All PET polymers are subject to hydrolytic breakdown if heated in the presence of water. This requires that the resins be dried to less than, 0.003% moisture content before processing. The need for a drying step and PET's high melting temperature make processing more involved than that for the PE and PP polymer families.

Careful control of processing temperatures is important to reduce thermal degradation that would release acetaldehyde (AA), which, even in small amounts, can cause off-flavors in food and beverage products.

PET Applications

PET films are manufactured by cast extrusion and are usually biaxially oriented. PET films have high tensile strength, low elongation, a high melting point, excellent grease/oil barrier properties, low gas and moisture permeability, good printing characteristics, a high use-temperature range, high impact strength, high scuff resistance and excellent dimensional stability.

Limitations of PET film include lack of heat sealability, poor machine performance, a propensity for generating static and poor package openability. Most of these plain-film shortcomings are addressed by coating or laminating with other materials. Heat-seal performance can be provided with a coating such as poly(vinylidene chloride) (PVDC), which also enhances the already good barrier properties, or by combining with a heat-sealing agent such as polyethylene. Primary end uses are as the base film for cheese and luncheon meats packages and for applications requiring high tensile strength, stiffness or high temperature resistance.

PET's heat resistance and microwave transparency makes it an ideal dual-ovenable film. Added heat-sealable layers enable the film to seal to itself, to polystyrene containers or to PET trays.

Metallized PET films are used for their barrier properties and for abrasion resistance in coffee vacuum packs. Metallized PET also has been used for pouching electronic components where it provides static-charge dissipation in addition to strength.

Almost 70% of North American PET packaging usage is for bottles. The largest single use is for injection-blow-molded carbonated beverage bottles. Conventional PET has low melt strength (very fluid at its melt temperature) and would be difficult to extrusion blow mold because of the difficulty in holding a stable parison shape in the melt form. Injection blow molding circumvents this problem by injecting a parison and subsequently blowing it to a bottle shape. Barrier and strength properties are further improved by mechanically stretching and orienting the preform during blowing; referred to as injection stretch blow molding (ISBM).

Price reductions in the early 2000s encouraged the growth of PET in markets beyond carbonated beverage bottles. Vegetable oils, alcoholic beverages and many home and personal care products now come in PET bottles. PET has also made significant inroads into thermoformed shapes.

About 7% of PET is made into film and sheet. PET's high use temperature favors it in applications such as dual-ovenable prepared food trays. By allowing the polyester to crystallize (CPET), PET's already good temperature resistance can be improved further.

PET's high tensile strength is utilized for strapping applications where high strength and relatively low elongation are needed.

The development of a depolymerizing process (methanolysis) and PET's high value make it a favorite of recyclers. Methanolysis reverts the polymer back to the original monomers, which are then repolymerized. PET has replaced PVC in a number of applications where clarity was a prime consideration.

POLY(VINYL CHLORIDE) (PVC)

Production, Processing and Properties

PVC is produced by the suspension, or emulsion, polymerization of vinyl chloride, a gas derived from an ethylene base. PVC differs from polyethylene in having a chlorine atom replace one hydrogen atom. PVC alone is hard, brittle, has low thermal stability (decomposition can start as low as 100°C or 212°F) and is essentially unusable unless compounded with a number of additives. PVC has poor thermal processing stability, and its tendency to decompose can cause processing and recycling difficulties. Decomposition is retarded by the addition of thermal-stabilizing agents.

PVC is compounded with a range of additives, making it a versatile material with properties ranging from hard and rigid to the softest of cling films.

PVC resins are dry blended with multiple additives to accomplish specified results. The mix may include any or all of the following: slip agents, plasticizers, pigments, waxes, fillers, processing aids, impact modifiers and liquid epoxy stabilizers. Among the most important additives are the plasticizers, not all of which are suitable for food-packaging applications. Plasticizers soften PVC; the more plasticizer added, the softer and more pliant the material becomes. Some plasticizers can migrate or be absorbed and can plasticize other materials such as adhesives.

PVC Applications

About 4% of the 14,320 million pounds of PVC is used in packaging.

Most PVC films have high impact strength, good scuff resistance, good dimensional stability, good opticals, and excellent grease- and oil-barrier properties. PVC has a maximum use temperature in the 93°C (200°F) range. Its moisture-barrier properties range from poor to fair. Even with thermal stabilizers added to the dry blend, PVC remains heat sensitive and inherently more difficult to produce than PE or PP films.

Varying the formulation allows production of films with tensile strengths ranging from low to medium, elongation ranging from medium to high, gas-barrier properties from poor to medium, and tear strengths from medium to good. This marked range of properties is largely influenced by the type and amount of plasticizer used. For example, less-plasticized films are stiffer and possess better barrier properties than heavily plasticized types.

Highly plasticized PVC films have excellent stretch properties and unique "cling," making them ideal for hand-wrapping fresh meats and produce. Less-plasticized films are used for a variety of product-wrapping applications, including cassettes, toys and books. They are also widely used for medical-product packaging and are considered suitable for gamma-ray sterilization. Some plastics burn readily and some burn only with difficulty. PVC and other halogen-bearing (chlorine, fluorine, bromine) plastics tend to be self-extinguishing and burn with difficulty.

PVC films can be produced with superior shrink properties. It is the preferred shrink material for many tamper-evident bands and for shrink label stock.

PVC's clarity and thermoforming properties make it the material of choice for most thermoformed shells for blister packaging as well as some condiment portion packs.

PVC's good clarity, excellent stiffness and resistance to oils and alcohols make it a good material for blow-molded bottles where one or more of these properties is important. Many coatings, adhesives and closure seal materials are based on PVC polymers.

Some environmental groups have targeted PVC on environmental and health issues and successfully restricted its use in some jurisdictions. Their contentions have not been substantiated to date, but PVC has acquired a negative image in some segments of the population. In response, some manufacturers have chosen to switch to materials such as PET for clear plastic bottles.

POLY(VINYLIDENE CHLORIDE) (PVDC)

Vinylidene chloride is a vinyl monomer with one more chlorine than a vinyl chloride monomer. It polymerizes with itself or with monomers such as vinyl chloride or acrylates to form commercially useful resins. Various types of PVDC can be produced, depending on the ratio of comonomer to vinylidene chloride in the copolymer. PVDC films can be produced by extrusion casting or by the blown-tube process. The processing temperature must be below 205°C (400°F) to prevent decomposition. Its relatively high cost limits its use to films and coatings; it is not made into dimensional parts. PVDC is often referred to as Saran, a Dow trade name.

The most notable attributes of PVDC polymers and copolymers are exceptionally low permeability to water vapor and gases in a single material. PVDC resins are used in food and pharmaceutical packaging to provide moisture, flavor and gas barriers. PVDC also has good grease, oil and chemical resistance.

PVDC can be used as monolayer and multilayer film or applied as a coating in the form of solutions and latices. Films can be coextruded, and various processes are used to combine PVDC with PP, PET, PA and other polymers into multilayer structures, with PVDC contributing barrier qualities and other substrates providing strength and stiffness. PVDC can be used as a combination barrier and heat-sealable coating in some applications.

Monolayer film is widely used as household wrap. Industrial monolayer films are used in laminating, in pharmaceutical unit-dose packaging and as liners for moisture, gas or solvent-sensitive products.

POLY(VINYL ACETATE) (PVAC) AND ETHYLENE-VINYL ACETATE (EVA)

Properties and Applications

Poly(vinyl acetate) is a highly polar, resilient thermoplastic that can be easily dispersed into water to make an emulsion. PVAC polymers and copolymers have significant uses in the manufacture of a broad range of emulsion adhesives. The familiar white glue used at home and in industry almost always contains PVAC.

Ethylene-vinyl acetate (EVA) is a poly(vinyl acetate) copolymer of polyethylene. The vinyl acetate (VA) content can be varied from 5% to 50% depending on the desired properties. Packaging films are usually made with lower vinyl acetate levels. As VA content increases, the film becomes more elastomeric.

Many EVA film applications are similar to those of the LDPE family. EVA film has high clarity and has particularly good flex crack resistance, puncture resistance and cold temperature performance. Stretch-wrap films, ice bags, bag-in-box containers and heat-sealable films or coatings are major applications. In some instances, EVA is blended with polyethylene to improve toughness, heat-seal or cling properties.

Higher vinyl-acetate content EVAs are used in adhesive production; the greatest proportion being for hot melt formulations.

POLYAMIDE (PA OR NYLON)

Production and Applications

Polyamide or nylon (formerly a DuPont trade name) is formed by condensing a diamine and a dibasic acid, or by the polymerization of certain amino acids. Polyamides are identified by a number representing the number of carbon atoms in the basic amino acid (such as nylon type 6), or by the number of carbon atoms in the reacting amine and dibasic acid, respectively (such as nylon type 66). Of the possible polyamides, only types 6 and 66 are commonly used for packaging purposes.

Types 6 and 66 have similar physical and chemical properties. The most significant difference is maximum use temperature: nylon 6 is good to 219°C (426°F) while nylon 66 is good to 266°C (510°F). Both have excellent optical properties and resist grease, oil and many chemicals. Nylons are tough, resisting abrasion, impacts, puncturing and cracking when repeatedly flexed. Polyamide is not resistant to strong inorganic acids and is not heat sealable by conventional means. It has poor slip properties. Currently, polyamide is one of the more expensive packaging films.

Polyamides provide good barriers to aromatics, oxygen, nitrogen and carbon dioxide, but have poor water-vapor barrier properties. Water-barrier properties are often improved by application of a PVDC coating.

A semi-crystalline polyamide, trade named MXD-6, (Mitsubishi) is made by condensing m-xylene and adipic acid. The presence of the aromatic ring structure gives this nylon higher heat resistance, stiffness, tensile strength and lower moisture sensitivity than the commoner nylon 6. It also offers higher oxygen barrier properties nylon 6 or 66. The polymer melts at about 240°C and is processed at 260 to 300°C. Cost limits MXD6 applications.

Applications

Most polyamide used in packaging is in film form, mostly produced by extrusion casting. Nylon can be monoaxially or biaxially oriented, enhancing strength and barrier properties. Although PA can be blow molded and injection molded, there are few packaging applications for these forms.

Unoriented nylon type 6 film is widely used in meat and cheese vacuum packaging, (See Figure 11.3) where its good oxygen barrier properties, grease resistance and ability to be easily drawn into a thermoformed shape are advantages. (Neither oriented nylon, or OPP, can be thermoformed.)

Figure 11.3

Examples of products in a drawn nylon film. The flat side of these packages is lower cost poly(ethylene terephthalate).

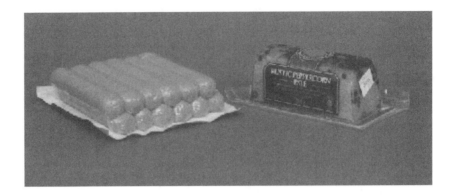

Oriented nylons are usually employed in packaging as a component in a laminated structure, usually with polyethylene. Nylon is used in laminated structures for many retail and institutional cook-in-bag foods and as an abrasion-resistant base material for coffee vacuum-brick packages. Other uses include packaging for surgical instruments. Nylon's exceptional abrasion resistance and toughness make it a material of choice for bulk bagging of frozen primal meat cuts and other applications requiring resistance to abrasion and cut-through.

MXD6's excellent combination of physical properties and excellent oxygen barrier properties has found application as the oxygen barrier layer in some PET beer bottles. A typical construction is PET/MXD6/ PET/MXD6/PET. Although ethylene(vinyl alcohol) has better oxygen barrier qualities, these are lost under conditions of high humidity. MXD6 has better oxygen barrier properties than EVAL when the humidity is higher than 80%. MXD6 is also blended with nylon 6 and nylon 66 to improve their properties.

POLY(VINYL ALCOHOL) (PVAL) AND ETHYLENE-VINYL ALCOHOL (EVOH)

Applications

Poly(vinyl alcohol) (PVAL) is water soluble, and packaging applications include water-soluble pouches. These pouches hold a premeasured amount of product; pouch and product are thrown into the blending tanks where the PVAL dissolves, releasing the product. Some dry agricultural chemicals are offered in PVAL inner bags. The approach averts a serious environmental disposal problem since the contaminated PVAL liner bag dissolves with the active ingredients. PVAL offers superior oxygen-barrier properties, but its water solubility and processing difficulty limit applications in this area.

PVAL has been surface applied to substrates such as polypropylene to improve oxygen- and flavor-barrier qualities. Because of PVAL's solubility, this material combination is strictly limited to dry-product applications.

Ethylene-vinyl alcohol is made by hydrolyzing the copolymer of ethylene and vinyl acetate. EVOH has the highest useable oxygen barrier of the packaging polymers. Though not completely soluble like PVAL, EVOH is adversely affected by water, and so in most packaging applications, other films must be used to protect it from water contact. This has led to coextrusions of five and six layers, typically using PE or PP as the outside layers and bonding these to the EVOH core with suitable adhesives. It is also coextruded into multilayer barrier bottles.

ETHYLENE ACID COPOLYMERS AND IONOMERS

Variations and Applications

Ethylene acid copolymers and ethylene-ethyl acrylate copolymers can be regarded as being polyethylene copolymers. Ethylene can be copolymerized with varying amounts of acrylic acid, methacrylic acid or ethyl acrylate. These copolymer groups reduce crystallinity, lower heat-seal temperature and add functionality that allows for good adhesion to polar substrates. By varying the amount of comonomer content and adjusting molecular weights, a range of products can be tailored to produce useful film, coating and adhesive base materials.

Ionomers (commonly known by the DuPont trade name Surlyn) are copolymers of ethylene and methacrylic acid that have been further modified by the inclusion of sodium or zinc ions. Ionomers can be made into tough, clear films that have properties particularly suitable for skin-packaging applications. Ionomers form excellent heat-seal bonds and can form a seal through fat contaminants. They have excellent adhesion to aluminum foils and are used in many laminated constructions where superior bonding to the foil is essential.

OTHER PACKAGING POLYMERS

Cellulosics

Once cellulosics were the only clear packaging film choice. Cellophane (a former DuPont trade name) is unusual in that it is based on wood cellulose rather than petrochemicals and that it is a thermoset rather than a thermoplastic. Cellophane has superior dead-fold properties and machinability. Its tendency to generate static is lower than other packaging films. However, cellulose films have a cost and performance disadvantage compared to more modern materials, and so the cellulose film market is small compared to other films.

A small amount of cellulose propionate and cellulose buterate is extruded into high-clarity tubular shapes, which, unlike other packaging plastics, can have an end cap easily attached by solvent bonding. The clear tubular containers are used to package a range of products such as drill bits, laboratory thermometers, novelty foods, confections and gift items.

Epoxies

Epoxies are thermoset polymers based primarily on epichlorohydrin and bisphenol-A (BPA). They form particularly strong bonds with many materials and are found in adhesives and protective coatings. BPA has been implicated in a number of human health issues. See entry under Polycarbonates.

Polycarbonates (PC)

Polycarbonate is made from carbonic acid and bisphenol A. It is a particularly tough plastic and has the highest impact resistance of packaging plastics as well as an unusually high use temperature. Its clarity equals that of glass, and a major application is as a replacement for glass glazing in high-risk areas.

Some packaging applications requiring toughness and environmental stability have used PC. Returnable, large water bottles and returnable milk jugs are two applications. The material is relatively high in cost.

Recent research as identified BPA as a suspected contributor to a number of human health issues including endocrine disruption, carcinogenic effects, and obesity. In packaging the two significant applications are large refillable water bottles and as the coating material for the inside liners of many food cans. In 2007 and 2008 many retailers removed polycarbonate baby bottles and refillable water bottles from their shelves. Canada listed BPA as a substance toxic to human health in and the environment in 2006 and in 2008 announced its intent to ban polycarbonate baby bottles.

Acrylonitrile Copolymer

An acrylonitrile-methyl acrylate copolymer from BP Chemicals with the trade name Barex is the only resin in this family marketed for packaging purposes. Barex has good oxygen-and gas-barrier properties but relatively poor water-vapor-barrier properties. It offers excellent resistance to many aggressive solvents not readily contained by other polymers. It is made into film and dimensional shapes.

Polyurethanes (PUR)

Polyurethanes, formed by a reaction between an isocyanate and a polyol, are used in several specialty applications. Thermoset types, frequently cured by the presence of moisture, are used as adhesive and coating base resins. PUR can be blown in foams of varying densities, and these find use as protective packaging forms. A particular application creates "foam-in-place" systems, where the two reacting chemicals are mixed just prior to being spraying around an object to be protected. The mixed components foam up within seconds to totally encapsulate the item.

Poly(ethylene naphthalate) (PEN)

PEN is a recently commercialized resin that can be used as a blend with PET or as a PET/PEN copolymer. The monomer is dimethyl 2,6 naphthalate or naphthalene dicarboxylate (NDC). The cited advantages of PEN resins are:

- Thermal properties allows it to be used for hot-fill and retort applications.

- PEN blocks out UV light entirely. Even a 2% PEN/PET copolymer will block 90% of UV. This makes it a good candidate for beer, juices, pharmaceuticals, edible oils and milk.

- Copolymers and blends show marked improvement in oxygen and water vapor barrier, and better thermal and mechanical properties. Generally, property improvement is proportional to the amount of PEN.

- It offers a high potential for replacing glass in some critical applications.

The PEN's price, about two to four times PET, limits its use as a packaging material.

Styrene-Butadiene

K-resin is Phillips 66 Company's trade name for a high-clarity, tough and easily processed styrene-butadiene copolymer. Limitations are low surface hardness, low stiffness, low resistance to organic solvents and poor performance when exposed to UV light. K-resins have relatively high gas permeation rates. Food-wrap films where barrier is not desired make use of its high clarity and softness. Some thermoforms, skin-packaging, shrink wraps, and blow-molded bottles have also used K-resin.

Polychlorotrifluoroethylene (PCTFE)

A polychlorotrifluoroethylene copolymer is marketed under the tradename Aclar. Aclar has the highest moisture-barrier properties of any packaging polymer and is a good barrier to other gases. It has excellent optical properties and is readily thermoformed. These properties in one material have made it the choice for many thermoformed blister packs for sensitive unit-dose pharmaceutical tablets. Its high cost limits most other packaging applications.
PCTFE will tolerate cryogenic temperatures and ionizing radiation.

Polylactide (PLA)

Polylactide (also referred to as poly(lactic acid)) is a polymeric material derived from corn starch rather than petrochemical feedstocks. PLA is a stiff, clear polymer that when thermoformed into a tray could easily be mistaken for polystyrene. It can be thermoformed easily at comparatively low temperatures but at the same time its low heat distortion temperature (about 40°C) will limit its use for other applications. PLA has limited barrier properties on its own. The material is biodegradable in industrial composting facilities, typically operating at 56°C. The polymer is still in its early stages of development and changes can be expected that will broaden its market applications. See also section on biodegradability in Chapter 1.

Thermoset Plastics

Thermoset plastics such as phenol-formaldehyde and urea-formaldehyde are occasionally used for applications such as specialty closures. Thermosets have superior solvent resistance making them ideal for aggressive solvent contact materials. They have a particularly hard surface and are not prone to developing sink marks when molded. These are useful features when molding massive or heavy-walled cosmetic closures. When metallized they have the feel of metal.

Thermoset polyesters and epoxies are used in conjunction with fiberglass or other fibers to produce large, highly durable shipping containers as would be used by the military.

Other Plastics

Other plastics have been used to make containers to meet some unusual performance criteria. For example, acrylonitrile-butadiene-styrene (ABS) is a tough, high impact-resistant material. It finds some packaging use to make large industrial and military shipping and storage cases. (Plastic brief cases and luggage are made from ABS.)

Some of the plastics used for special applications would fall into the engineering or exotic plastic classification. These would include such plastic materials as polyacetals, polysulfones, poly(methyl pentane), liquid crystal polymers, and others.

ADDITIVES

Most polymers are blended with additives before or during processing into their finished forms. Depending on the resin and application, some or many ingredients may be added. Although the purpose of these additives is to control or enhance specific performance characteristics, they affect other properties in some manner. Thus, an antistatic agent, while reducing static accumulation, might detrimentally affect adhesive bonding.

- Antioxidants protect the resin from deteriorating during thermal processing.

- Heat stabilizers inhibit degradation during thermal processing.

- Plasticizers impart flexibility or softness and assist in processing. PVC formulations use plasticizers heavily.

- Antiblock and slip agents such as amides and finely divided silica are used primarily in LDPE film. Antiblock agents prevent film layers in a roll from "blocking" or sticking together. Slip agents reduce frictional properties, allowing the film to slide smoothly over itself. This improves high-speed packaging and handling processes.

- UV stabilizers are used with UV-sensitive plastics such as polypropylene when they will have direct exposure to UV. PP exposed to UV cross-links and becomes brittle.

- Pigments are usually blended in as master batch color concentrates at the forming machine. Different pigment types and concentrations will affect the polymer's base properties differently. Thus, the same bottle design in different colors may not necessarily have identical performance characteristics. Some of the most brilliant and stable pigments are complexes of biologically toxic heavy metals, and their use poses serious environmental and health concerns. Their continued use is being restricted, and in some instances, banned.

- Mineral fillers improve mechanical properties and reduce cold-flow characteristics.

- Cross-linking agents improve physical and chemical attributes.

- Antistatic agents enable plastic materials to dissipate static electrical charges. High static charges can attract atmospheric dust or interfere with processing. The discharge of even small levels of static electricity can damage microcircuits.

- Lubricants improve flow and processing properties.

- Nucleating agents encourage the formation of crystallinity. The formation of minute crystalline regions (rather than large crystals that will defract light) is used as a means of improving the clarity of PP.

- Blowing agents are used to create expanded plastic foams. Polystyrene and polyethylene account for most expanded foams used in packaging. Blowing agents are low boiling point liquids such as pentane, isopentane and other low boiling point hydrocarbons. (Polyurethane foams are expanded by gases produced by the chemical reaction of diisocyanate and a glycol).

CHARACTERIZING PLASTIC MATERIALS

Test procedures help characterize materials, but they may vary, and different measurement units may be used from supplier to supplier. When discussing or comparing material test results or properties, it is imperative that the following three factors be identical:

- Same test method
- Same test conditions
- Same unit of measurement

If data sets differ in any of these criteria, comparisons will be invalid.

ASTM International (ASTM) establishes most packaging test procedures used in North America. Other technical associations may sponsor special test procedures specific to their area of interest. The majority of procedures recommended by these agencies specify the precise methodology for characterizing a property. They do not normally give pass/fail or minimum performance criteria.

The selection of a polymer, as either a stand-alone material or a component in a laminated or composite structure, is based upon a wide range of end-use, machine efficiency and cost criteria. These criteria define the properties a material must have and often the maximum and minimum performance range for each property.

Plastic properties can be classified into four general groups: physical, optical, chemical and permanence. Physical or mechanical properties relate to a polymer's various strength characteristics and its machinability. Opticals have to do with the plastic's appearance and surface and are particularly important with films. Chemical properties are the material's resistance to grease, oils, soaps, acids, solvents and other chemical agents. This classification includes gas and water-vapor permeability. Properties of permanence relate to the film's ability to retain its strength and dimensions in varying environmental conditions such as temperature and relative humidity.

Tensile Properties

Tensile strength is a material's ability to resist a direct pull. Ultimate tensile strength defines the maximum stress a material can withstand before breaking. When measured up to the point of permanent material deformation, it is reported as "yield strength" or "yield point." The force exerted at the yield, or "break point," is divided by the cross-sectional film area, and the tensile strength at the yield or break is expressed in force per unit area (pounds per square inch, psi).

For example, if the sample's cross-section area is one-thousandth of a square inch, and 30 pounds of force was recorded at the break point, tensile strength is expressed as 30,000 psi. High tensile strength is generally desirable in a packaging film. This property would be a key consideration for a suspended retail bag for a relatively heavy hardware or automotive product. The force or pull applied to a plastic during machining should nor exceed its yield point.

A material's "elongation" is the difference between the length of an unstretched tensile-strength sample and its length at the break point or the yield point. The property is expressed as a percentage of the original length. Elongation is usually observed during a tensile strength test. Low elongation is desirable in applications where the material will bear steady weight. High elongation is a positive property for applications such as stretch wraps or heavy-duty bags. However, it is difficult to hold printing register with a high elongation material. Some typical tensile property values are given in Table 11.6.

The following are standard ASTM test methods for tensile properties:

ASTM D 638, Tensile Properties of Plastics

ASTM D 882, Tensile Properties of Thin Plastic Sheeting

ASTM D 2923, Rigidity of Polyolefin Film and Sheeting

Table 11.6

General comparison of tensile and elongation properties of common packaging plastics.

	Tensile (psi)	Elongation
Best Tensile Property Materials		
Poly(ethylene terephthalate) (PET)	32,000	50%
Oriented polypropylene (OPP)	30,000	80%
Acrylonitrile copolymer (Barex)	9,500	3%
Good Tensile Property Materials		
Polyamide (nylon)	7,000	400%
Unoriented polypropylene	6,000	600%
High-density polyethylene (HDPE)	5,000	400%
Low Tensile Property Materials		
Low-density polyethylene (LDPE)	3,500	600%
Linear low-density polyethylene (LLDPE)	3,500	700%
Plasticized poly(vinyl chloride) (PVC)	2,000	500%

Tear Strength

Film "tear strength" is measured using an Elmendorf tear tester in much the same way as for paper. One end of a sample is held in a fixed clamp; the other end is attached to a pendulum. A small cut is made in the film edge, the pendulum is released, and the force required to continue the tear is recorded. Another, less common test, measures the force required to start a tear an uncut film edge. This is known as "tear initiation," as opposed to "tear propagation."

Tear strength is usually expressed as grams per mil (0.001 in.) of thickness. Films such as polypropylene are difficult to tear at a clean, unnicked edge, yet reveal relatively low tear strength in Elmendorf tests when a small cut is introduced at the film edge to initiate the tear. Tear strength must be considered in terms of protective values, as well as in terms of the strength required to open the package, if it must be torn open. Plastics such as the polyethylene and polyethylene copolymer families that have high elongation have better tear-resistant properties and have little or no notch sensitivity.

The following test methods measure tear properties:

ASTM D 1004, Initial Tear Resistance of Plastic Film and Sheeting

ASTM D 1922, Propagation Tear Resistance of Plastic Film and Thin Sheeting by Pendulum Method

ASTM D 1938, Tear-Propagation Resistance of Plastic Film and Thin Sheeting by a Single-Tear Method

ASTM D 2582, Puncture-Propagation Tear Resistance of Plastic Film and Sheeting

Impact Strength

"Impact strength" describes a material's ability to withstand direct shock. Tests measure impact strength of both films and solid plastics. To test a film for impact, a sample is stretched taut horizontally and a "dart" or weight is dropped on it. Values can be expressed as the drop height from which a given mass will puncture the film 50% of the time, or as the mass required to puncture the film 50% of the time from a given drop height.

To test solid plastics for impact, a solid bar of plastic is hit with a pendulum-mounted hammer. The force absorbed in fracturing the specimen reduces the pendulum's free swing and is used to calculate energy absorption. The following test methods measure impact properties:

ASTM D 1709, Impact Resistance of Plastic Film by the Free-Falling Dart Method

ASTM D 3420, Pendulum Impact Resistance of Plastic Film

ASTM D 4273, Total Energy Impact of Plastic Films by Dart Impact

Heat-Seal Strength

"Heat-seal strength" relates to a film's ability to make a peel-resistant seal. The property is tested by sealing samples under controlled temperature, pressure and dwell-time conditions, and then measuring the seal's resistance to peeling on a tensile tester. (The process is similar to determining tensile properties.) Heat-seal strength is usually expressed as grams per unit width of the stressed seal. The heat-seal strength of a properly made seal of most thermoplastic packaging films will approach the basic tensile strength of the film.

"Hot tack" is the ability of a heat seal to withstand stress while the seal is still hot. The higher a heat-seal material's hot-tack strength, the sooner the product can be placed into the package.

A wide heat-seal temperature range is a desirable property. The range gives the difference between a minimum acceptable seal strength and the burning or melting point of the polymer. The practical sealing range will be determined by factors such as machine speed, seal surface, product weight and product density. Lower seal temperatures use less energy and allow the package to be handled quicker; the lower temperatures will have less potential effect on the contained product. Although most plastics will heat seal given a high enough temperature, in practice, lower temperature coatings are preferred. Poly(ethylene terephthalate) and oriented polypropylene do not form practical heat seals. The following test methods measure heat-seal properties:

ASTM F 88, Seal Strength of Flexible Barrier Materials

ASTM F 1921, Hot Seal Strength of Thermoplastic Polymers and Blends

Coefficient of Friction (CoF)

"Slip" describes the degree of drag or friction a film experiences when passing over itself or over surfaces such as machine parts. Friction characteristics are an important consideration for laminating, printing and package-forming machine operations, as well as for some end-use and retailing situations. "Hot slip" relates to a film's performance when running over heated machine parts at elevated temperatures. A high degree of slip is desirable for optimum film-running performance on most wrapping and bag-making machines, but can cause problems when products are stacked on a retail shelf.

"Static slip" or "static COF" defines the force required to start the film moving (slipping) over another surface. "Kinetic" or "dynamic COF" defines the film's friction as it is moving over other surfaces. The following test measures CoF:

> ASTM D 1849, Static and Kinetic Coefficients of Friction of Plastic Film and Sheeting

Haze and Gloss

Haze and gloss are optical properties that are important primarily from a merchandizing aspect. Haze describes optical clarity and is measured on a device that meters the amount of light scattered by a film surface, compared to the amount of light transmitted. Readability of locked-in print, clarity of design colors and product visibility are some considerations. "Gloss," the brilliance of a film's surface, is measured by beaming light onto a sample at a known angle and metering the amount of light reflected back to a photosensitive receptor. The following test methods measure haze and gloss:

> ASTM D 1003, Haze and Luminous Transmittance of Transparent Plastic Films
>
> ASTM D 1746, Transparency of Plastic Sheeting
>
> ASTM D 2457, Specular Gloss of Plastic Films and Solid Plastics

Water-vapor Transmission

Several methods measure a material's resistance to the permeation of water-vapor. In simplest terms, all test methods place dry air on one side of a film and humid air on the other. The moisture passing through the film in a given time is measured, and reported as water-vapor transmission rate (WVTR) in grams per square metre per 24 hours (g/24 hr./100 sq. in.), or as grams per 100 square inches per 24 hours (g/100 sq. in./24 hrs.). In comparing films using data in published literature, care must be taken to identify the test method and units of measurement employed. Table 11.7 shows the water-vapor transmission rate for some common plastic films.

Table 11.7

Typical plastic film water-vapor permeabilities. Data are in g/24 hr/100 sq. in. at 90% R.H. Poly(vinyl alcohol) is water soluble, and ethylene-vinyl alcohol absorbs water. These polymers would require protection from water in wet or humid environments.

	Permeability	*Comments*
Best Water-vapor-barrier Materials		
Poly(chlorotrifuoroethylene) (PCTFE or Aclar)	0.04	Cost limits use
Poly(vinylidene chloride) (PVDC or Saran)	0.05	Best universal barrier
High-density polyethylene (HDPE)	0.3	Most economical barrier
Polypropylene (PP)	0.4	
Good Water-vapor-barrier Materials		
Low-density polyethylene (LDPE)	1.2	
Poly(ethylene terephthalate) (PET)	1.3	
Low Water-vapor-barrier Materials		
Poly(vinyl chloride) (PVC)	4	
Acrylonitrile copolymer (Barex)	5	
Polyamide (nylon)	25	

The water-vapor permeability of plastic film relates to the ability to retain freshness in a product, preventing the escape of moisture from moist products (e.g., fruit cake) or preventing dry products (e.g., crackers) from picking up moisture from outside.

The following test methods measure WVTR:

ASTM E 96, Water Vapor Transmission of Materials

ASTM F 372, Water Vapor Transmission Rate of Flexible Barrier Materials Using an Infrared Detection Technique

ASTM F 1249, Water Vapor Transmission Rate Through Plastic Film and Sheeting Using a Modulated Sensor

Gas Permeability

Gas transmission or permeability properties relate to gases such as oxygen, nitrogen, carbon dioxide and various volatile essential oils found in foods, confections, personal care and other products. Permeability is associated with the retention of color, flavor and odor in packaged food products. Barrier requirements range from low to high, depending on the product. Produce wraps require high oxygen permeability to permit respiration. In contrast, coffee needs a film with low oxygen and aroma permeability to preserve flavor. Similarly, specific gas-barrier properties are required for controlled-atmosphere packaging applications.

Table 11.8

Typical film oxygen-barrier qualities. Data are given in cc/0.001 in./100 sq. in./24 hr.

	Permeability	Comments
Best Oxygen-barrier Materials		
Ethylene-vinyl alcohol (EVAL)	0.02	Water sensitive
Poly(vinylidene chloride) (PVDC or saran)	0.05	Best universal barrier
Acrylonitrile copolymer (Barex)	1.0	Poor water-vapor barrier
Good Oxygen-barrier Materials		
Polyamide (PA or nylon)	3	Poor water-vapor barrier
Poly(chlorotrifuoroethylene) (PCTFE or Aclar)	4	Cost limits use
Poly(ethylene terephthalate) (PET)	5	Good universal barrier
Low Oxygen-barrier Materials		
High-density polyethylene (HDPE)	110	
Polypropylene (PP)	150	Frequently metallized
Low-density polyethylene (LDPE)	450	

In a typical gas-permeability measurement, a film sample is clamped between two chambers, one of which is filled with an inert gas. The test gas is introduced into the other chamber and remains there for a given time period, at a known temperature and at 1 atmosphere pressure. Permeability is expressed as millilitres of gas permeating 1 square metre of film in 24 hours for a specified thickness. It may be expressed as cubic centimetres of gas permeating a 100 square inches of 0.001-inch-thick film in 24 hours (cc/0.001 in./100 sq. in./24 hrs.). Table 11.8 shows oxygen transmission rates for some common plastic films.

The following tests measure gas transmission rates:

ASTM D 2684, Permeability of Thermoplastic Containers to Packaging Reagents or Proprietary Products

ASTM D 3985, Oxygen Gas Transmission Rate Through Plastic Film Using a Coulometric Sensor

ASTM F 1307, Oxygen Gas Transmission Rate Through Dry Packages Using a Coulometric Sensor

Grease and Oil Barrier

Grease and oil barrier properties describe a film's ability to resist penetration by greases and oils, with or without degradation of the film. Such migration can cause structure delamination, smearing or lifting of non-grease-resistant printing inks and package staining. A common test involves placing a film sample on a paper sheet and weighing the sample with a uniform layer of dry sand.

A measured amount of oil or grease is placed at several locations, and migration is measured by the time it takes for a stain to appear (or not appear) on the paper sheet below. The following test method measures grease and oil barrier:

ASTM F 119, Rate of Grease Penetration of Flexible Barrier Materials

Dimensional Stability

Plastics vary in their reaction to the environment, notably to changes in temperature and/or relative humidity. "Dimensional stability" is the capacity to retain original size/shape when exposed to environmental changes. Materials that shrink even slightly with the application of heat during processing, hot filling or heat sealing will produce distorted packages of unreliable volume and with puckered heat-seal areas. The following tests measure dimensional stability:

ASTM D 1204, Linear Dimension Changes of Nonrigid Thermoplastic Sheeting or Film at Elevated Temperatures (quantifies dimensional changes caused by heat)

ASTM D 648, Deflection Temperature of Plastics Under Flexural Load (identifies how material might perform at elevated temperature by measuring the temperature at which a specified cross-section bar deflects 0.25 millimetre [mm] (0.010 in.) under specified loading and temperature conditions.)

Maximum and Minimum Use Temperature

Maximum use temperature (see Table 11.9) is a vital consideration where end-use will involve exposure to elevated temperatures such as boil-in-bag packaging,

Table 11.9
Typical maximum use-temperatures. It is assumed that the materials are heat stabilized.

Material	Maximum Use Temperature (Celsius/Fahrenheit)
Poly(ethylene terephthalate) (PET)	204/400
Polyamide (PA or nylon)	177/350
Unoriented polypropylene (PP)	116/240
High-density polyethylene (HDPE)	100/212
Poly(vinyl chloride) (PVC)	93/200
Linear low-density polyethylene (LLDPE)	77/170
Low-density polyethylene (LDPE)	66/150

retortable forms, ovenable applications, heat-sterilized medical-product packaging and hot-fill packaging.

Materials vary in their ability to withstand shock-loading or vibration at low temperatures. Films that such as PE and PET that can withstand these stresses below $-18°C$ ($0°F$) are said to have good low-temperature durability. By comparison, unoriented PP and PVDC films are very brittle under these conditions.

Most plastics, except unoriented PP and PVDC, can be used at typical freezer conditions and lower. Low-temperature performance of PVC will vary depending on the plasticizer used. If a package is to go from freezer to microwave, the film used clearly must possess a wide use-temperature range.

Environmental Stress-crack Resistance (ESCR)

Molded plastic parts, particularly those made of HDPE, in addition to exhibiting creep properties when under load, are also susceptible to a phenomenon known as "environmental stress cracking" (ESC). This results in cracking of the plastic and possible loss of contents.

ESC is frequently confused with chemical compatibility, cold flow and permeability. Each of these is a different phenomenon, governed by its own physical and chemical laws. ESC is a surface-initiated physical phenomenon resulting from the operation of biaxial stresses (loads) in the presence of an external agent that produces no other discernible effect on the plastic. Chemical degradation is not involved. Stress cracks appear as small fractures or cracks and are located in areas where internal molding stress is high.

ESC tends to be accelerated by detergent-type surfactants or highly polar compounds. The effect of individual compounds should be evaluated with regard to whether they may contribute to ESC. When a known contributor to stress cracking is being packaged, the plastic container should not be expected to carry high loads relative to its actual compression strength, as this will serve to amplify an ESC problem.

A typical ESCR test method will partly fill the container with a 10% solution of nonylphenoxy poly(ethyleneoxy)ethanol (Igepal 630), a known stress-crack agent. The containers are stored at elevated temperatures and under specified load conditions. Periodic inspections will determine the approximate exposure time at which cracking starts to occur. The following tests determines ESCR:

ASTM D 1975, Environmental Stress Crack Resistance of Plastic Injection Molded Open Head Pails

ASTM D 1693, Environmental Stress-Cracking of Ethylene Plastics

ASTM D 2561, Environmental Stress Crack Resistance of Blow-molded Polyethylene Containers

ASTM D 5419, Environmental Stress Crack Resistance of Threaded Plastic Closures

Note:

Information provided in Figures 11.6 through 11.10 is compiled from a number of sources and is intended to serve only as an indicator of a particular property's general magnitude. There are a great many polymeric materials, many of them modified by copolymerization, additives and processing. The data given here should be used for general information only. Always obtain current application data from suppliers.

CHEMICAL PROPERTIES

An important material characteristic is its stability when in contact with other chemicals. In a typical test, the plastic material is placed in direct contact with the chemical in question for a given time period. Frequently the test will be "accelerated" by conducting the exposure at somewhat elevated temperatures. Chemical compatibility implies that no significant chemical activity will take place between the product and the chosen polymer. Chemical compatibility should not be confused with permeability or stress-crack resistance, both of which are governed by different chemical and physical rules.

Chemical compatibility may be observed visually, but for greater accuracy, a quantified measurement should be taken. For example, the tensile and elongation strengths of a material can be measured before and after an exposure.

Compatibility varies widely with the nature of the chemical. Aggressive solvents such as benzene, xylene and other aromatic compounds for the most part are not compatible with plastics. Carbon tetrachloride and most other chlorinated solvents are also not compatible. These solvents are packaged in metal or glass containers. Of the packaging polymers, PE and PP have the greatest range of chemical compatibilities, while PS is the most sensitive to chemical action. Food products are compatible with the six common packaging polymers (PE, PP, PVC, PET, PA and PS.) Some flavoring ingredients such as oil of wintergreen may be aggressive and need verification.

Most cosmetic and toiletry preparations are based on water emulsions, petroleum jellies, waxes, low alcohols and other chemicals having low chemical activity; most are compatible with common packaging polymers. Products with more aggressive solvents and components (such as colognes, nail polish and nail polish remover) would not likely be compatible with polystyrene or polyester. Other possibilities would need to be carefully tested.

Tables 11.10 and 11.11 have been compiled from information provided by the Society of the Plastics Industries. To be compatible, according to this information, the plastic container should show no visible change or loss of product under normal storage conditions. The tables do not address barrier qualities or stress-crack resistance.

The following test evaluates chemical resistance:

ASTM D 543, Evaluating the Resistance of Plastics to Chemical Reagents

Table 11.10
Polymer compatibility with industrial chemicals.

Chemical	LDPE	HDPE	PP	PVC	PET	PS
Acetic acid, glacial	2	1	1	X	X	X
Acetone	2	1	1	X	X	X
Alcohol, ethyl	2	1	1	1	1	2
Alcohol, methyl and N-propyl	1	1	1	1	1	2
Aliphatic hydrocarbons	X	2	2	1	1	X
Ammonia 28%	2	1	1	2	?	2
Battery electrolyte	1	1	1	2	2	2
Chloroform	X	2	X	X	?	X
Chromic acid	2	1	1	1	?	X
Creosote	X	X	1	X	?	X
Ethers, simple	X	X	X	2	?	X
Ethyl acetate and simple esters	2	2	2	X	X	X
Formaldehyde 36%	1	1	1	1	?	X
Formic acid	1	1	1	1	?	2
Hydrochloric acid 36%	1	1	1	1	2	2
Hydrofluoric acid < 52%	1	1	1	1	?	X
Hydrogen peroxide to 30%	1	1	1	1	1	2
Kerosene, naphtha	X	2	?	2	2	X
Methyl ethyl ketone (MEK)	2	2	2	X	X	X
MEK peroxide	?	1	?	X	?	X
Mineral spirits, petroleum distillates	X	2	?	2	2	X
Nitric acid	2	2	2	1	?	X
Oil of wintergreen	2	2	?	X	?	X
Oxalic acid	1	1	1	1	?	1
Phenol	?	?	1	?	X	X
Phosphoric acid	1	1	1	1	?	2
Potassium hydroxide	1	1	1	1	?	2
Sodium hydroxide 50%	1	1	1	1	2	2
Sodium hypochloride to 15% CL	1	1	2	1	2	2
Sulfuric acid to 93%	2	2	1	2	X	X
Trichlorethane	X	X	1	X	?	X
Turpentine	X	X	2	1	1	X

1 satisfactory performance
2 probably satisfactory but should be verified for specific applications
x not compatible
? information not available

Table 11.11
Polymer compatibility with household chemicals.

Household Product	LDPE	HDPE	PP	PVC	PET	PS
Ammonia	2	1	1	1	?	2
Antifreeze, ethylene glycol	1	1	1	1	2	1
Camphor oil	X	X	X	2	?	2
Charcoal starter fluid	X	2	2	2	2	X
Chlorine bleach	1	1	1	1	?	2
Detergents	2	1	1	2	2	2
Drain cleaner, dry	2	1	1	1	?	2
Drain cleaner, liquid	2	2	1	2	?	X
Fabric softener	1	1	1	1	2	2
Floor polish, naphtha base	X	2	2	1	?	X
Floor wax remover	2	2	2	1	?	X
Furniture polish	2	2	1	1	1	2
Gasoline	X	2	2	2	2	X
Glue, solvent base	2	2	?	2	?	X
Glue, vinyl acetate base	?	1	1	X	?	X
Hydraulic brake fluid	2	1	1	2	X	2
Insecticide, solvent base	2	2	1	2	?	X
Insecticide, powder	1	1	1	2	?	X
Insect repellent	2	2	1	?	?	X
Kettle cleaner	2	1	1	2	2	2
Lemon oil	X	X	2	1	2	X
Lighter fluid	X	X	2	1	2	X
Linseed oil	1	1	1	1	2	2
Lubricating oil	1	1	1	1	2	2
Moth-proofing, naphthalene	X	X	?	X	?	2
Moth-proofing, p-dichlorobenzine	X	2	2	X	?	X
Oven cleaner	?	1	1	1	?	X
Room deodorants	2	2	1	1	?	2
Shellac	X	2	1	1	?	X
Shoe polish	2	2	1	1	?	2
Silver polish	2	2	1	1	?	2
Weed killer	2	2	2	2	?	X

1 satisfactory performance
2 probably satisfactory but should be verified for specific applications
x not compatible
? information not available

REVIEW QUESTIONS

1. Name the commodity packaging plastic that:

   a. Does not burn (self-extinguishes).

   b. Is used mostly for thermoforming.

   c. Is an exceptionally high all-around gas barrier.

   d. Is strongest and stiffest.

   e. Has the lowest melting point.

   f. Has the highest melting point.

   g. Most closures are made from.

   h. Most detergent and oil bottles use.

   i. Forms the best "live hinge."

   j. Is used for thermoformed film for packaging luncheon meat.

   k. Is lowest in cost.

   l. Is made into soda bottles.

   m. Is an exceptionally high oxygen barrier but is water soluble.

   n. Is an exceptionally high oxygen barrier.

   o. Is used for most hot-filled bottles.

   p. Would be used to make a squeezable bottle.

2. Define stress.

3. Define yield point. What is its practical significance?

4. Define elongation and ultimate tensile strength.

5. What is static coefficient of friction (CoF), and how does it differ from dynamic CoF?

6. What are we testing when we test the "dimensional change" in a plastic film, and where would it be important to know this value?

7. Which plastic would you use to make a clear presentation box for a gold watch?

8. Name two materials used for heat sealing, and state where each would be used.

9. Why are many medical bottles are molded from polypropylene rather than polyethylene?

10. Which two plastics would you most likely use for a microwave application?

11. Which two materials are the best moisture barriers, and which two are the poorest?

12. What is the difference between chemical compatibility and stress-crack resistance?

13. Describe how an expanded polystyrene is made.

14. Most dairy tubs are injection molded from polypropylene except for ice cream. What material are ice cream tubs made of and why?

CONTENTS

Selection Considerations

Product compatibility, container compatibility, ease of handling, contain and protect functions, hermetic seal, reclosability, user friendliness, economy, convenience, safety, demographic considerations, decorative appeal.

Container and Closure Dimensioning

Finish specifications, dimension terminology, thread styles, closure naming conventions, L and M threads, thread mismatch, finish defects.

Metal Closures

Threaded, lug, roll-on, press-on/twist-off, crowns, friction fit.

Closure Seals

Seal types, inserted liners, plastisol liners, induction innerseals, induction seal technology.

Plastic Closures

Thermosetting and thermoplastic applications, polypropylene, polyethylene, plastic closure advantages, press-fit designs.

Injection Molds and Closure Design

Unscrewing cores, collapsing cores, stripped closures.

Closure Application

Typical application method, closure torque, stripping torque, removal torque, product effects on torque, loss of torque, suggested application torques.

Tamper-Evident Closures

FDA definition, TE closure limitations, recognized TE systems.

Child-Resistant Closures

Jurisdiction, design basis, effectiveness, testing protocol.

Special Closures and Functions

Corks, decorative functions, dispensers and pumps, example of special technical functions.

CHAPTER TWELVE
CLOSURES

SELECTION CONSIDERATIONS

A closure is a mechanical device that seals the contents within a container and can be removed to allow the contents to be dispensed. This takes in corks, stoppers, lids, tops and caps, made primarily from metal or plastic. Closures are applied to the "finish" of a glass, metal or plastic container. The finish is that part of a container that will receive the closure.

The closure is a part of the container and shares the basic packaging functions of containing, preserving and protecting the contents. Closure specifications require the same up-front thinking as the container design itself: the designer must consider the contents and the end-use situations.

- Closure materials must be chemically compatible with the contents. Particular attention must be paid to any liner materials or surfaces in direct product contact.

- Closure materials must be compatible with, and appropriate to, the container material.

- The closure must be easily handled on the filling line. This is especially important in high-speed production, where the closure must be located, correctly oriented, aligned with the container, placed on the container finish and sealed in a fraction of a second.

- The closure is a possible path by which gases, contaminants and organisms can enter the package. Alternately gases, moisture or essential oils can leave the package. The closure must have adequate barrier qualities if these are factors.

- The method of creating a seal between closure and container surfaces must be carefully considered. (e.g., inserted liner, flowed-in compound, molded-in seals, induction inner seals etc.).

- The need for reclosability affects closure choice. Some packages are opened once, the product is used and the container discarded. Other products may be used a little at a time over a long period. Reclosability should not be offered with a product that quickly becomes unfit for human consumption once the initial seal is breached.

- The closure must be "user friendly," with easy opening and, where applicable, easy and secure resealability. It is increasingly unacceptable to have a closure that requires a tool for opening.

- Economics are an ever-present aspect of any packaging design choice. Economics includes not just closure cost, but also the cost of application and production losses.

- Closure convenience features such as applicators, measurement devices and dispensers are sure to catch the eye of the convenience minded consumer.

- As well as protecting the product, the closure is sometimes required to protect the consumer. Tamper-evident closures and child-resistant closures are obvious examples. Closures must not have sharp edges or corners and should not create debris that might be hazardous.

- Is the product aimed at a specific market segment? Products for seniors, for example, must accommodate weaker, possibly arthritic fingers. Closures designed for hospital use are designed to maximum sterility confidence.

- Is the product dangerous or hazardous? Special closures have been designed that allow the safe measurement and dispensing of dangerous chemicals. Venting closures are used where internal pressure build-up is a factor.

- Is there a particular persona that will provide a marketing advantage? Stock containers are used in many packaging applications, and the only way to create a unique appearance may lie in the label graphics or in the choice of the closure system.

CONTAINER AND CLOSURE DIMENSIONING

Industry-wide standards for finish specifications have been established. Finish dimensions are described by specified letters. (See Figure 12.1) The letters used to specify closure dimensions correspond to the related dimension on the finish.

Originally, the Glass Packaging Institute (GPI) kept closure and finish standards. As plastic closures came on stream, it became evident that the rounded contour of glass threads was not suitable for plastic closures. The Society of the Plastics Industries (SPI) developed two profiles to be used with plastic bottles. M-style thread-engaging surfaces are angled at 10°, and L-style threads are angled at 30°. (See Figure 12.2) The responsibility for maintaining both glass and plastic closure standards and tolerances was assumed by Closure Manufacturers Association (CMA). ASTM D 2911, Standard Dimensions and Tolerances for Plastic Bottles, provides detailed dimensional descriptions of types L and M thread profiles for plastic bottles.

L style threads are general-purpose symmetrical threads and are used for both metal and plastic closures. The M or modified buttress thread is the preferred style for plastic containers and is used almost exclusively for this purpose.

Closure and bottle finish dimensions must match closely to effect a proper seal. A mismatch (See Figure 12.3) invariably results in leaking bottles or other closure problems. If the bottle's T or E dimensions are too large, or if the closure T or E dimensions are too small, there will be resistance to turning the closure. This can potentially lead to torque problems. With the opposite problem, in which the bottle's T or E dimensions are too small, or the closure's T or E dimensions are too large, the threads will not engage the full thread land area. This will cause

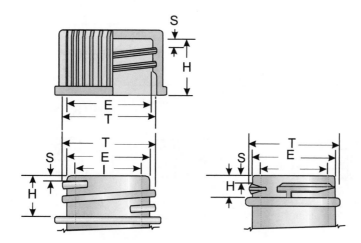

Figure 12.1

Standard finish dimension nomenclature for a continuous thread closure (left) and for a lug type closure (right). Closure dimension nomenclature mirrors container finish nomenclature.

E   Thread root diameter.
I   Diameter at smallest opening inside finish.
H   Top of finish to top of bead or to intersection with bottle shoulder on beadless designs.
T   Thread diameter measured across the threads.
S   The vertical distance from the top of the finish to the start of the thread.

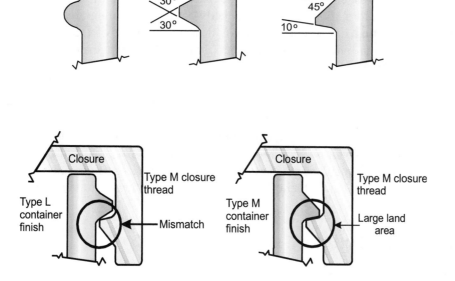

Figure 12.2

A rounded thread profile typical of older glass finishes (left). L style (center) and M-style (right) thread contours are used mostly with plastic containers.

Figure 12.3

Mismatched threads on the finish and closure will not engage properly.

torque retention problems. Stripping torque will be low, or in extreme cases, the threads will not engage. A plastic bottle's finish is often slightly oval. This can lead to a combination of problems having the characteristics of both of the above situations.

If the bottle's H dimension is small, the cap will bottom out on the bottle neck bead or shoulder before a tight seal can be achieved at the closure land (See left side of Figure 12.4) If the bottle's H dimension is too large, the closure skirt may be too high above the bottle bead or shoulder. (See right side Figure 12.4)

Figure 12.4

Conditions where closure and finish S or H dimensions are mismatched.

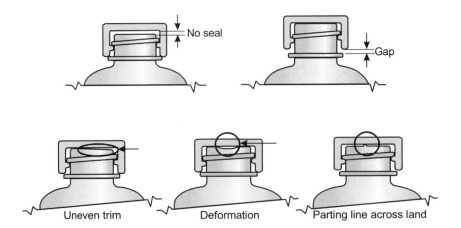

Figure 12.5

Uneven trim or other finish land area deformation can result in product leakage.

This could be a serious problem in instances where the skirt is intended to enclose the bead, as in tamper-evident closures. If bottle's S dimension is too short the closure could wind down past the bottle thread, resulting in partially unengaged threads. Similarly, if the bottle's S dimension is too long, not all of the closure threads may completely engage the finish threads.

Bottle finish defects can also cause leakage. Pitted, rough, deformed or scored land surfaces, uneven trim or cupped trims are difficult to overcome even with properly specified closures. (See Figure 12.5) Extrusion-blow molded bottles may have a mold parting line going directly across the sealing area. An overly prominent parting line could interfere with proper seating of the closure liner system. Injection-blow molded containers have the advantage of not having a parting line in this critical area.

Closures are designated by their inside diameter in millimetres followed by a CMA designation number. (See Table 12.1.) For example, a 22-400 closure identifies a closure that has an inside diameter of 22 millimetres and will fit a #400 finish. A #400 finish is identified by CMA as a shallow continuous-thread (CT) finish. Designations 120, 140, and 160 identify 2-, 4-, and 6-lug closures. The 1600 series describes roll-on-type closures. The designation numbers have been arbitrarily assigned; there is no dimensional significance to the digits.

METAL CLOSURES

Threaded Metal Closures

Threaded closures engage a thread on the container finish, and rotation draws the closure against the container finish. The amount of rotation required to effect a seal will vary depending on the container and closure, but 360° or more is typical.

Threaded metal closures are classified as either CT (continuous thread, 40 mm or more) or CTB (up to 38 mm continuous thread). The types are similar, but the larger CT styles will have a strength or stacking reinforcement designed into the top or crown panel, often in the form of an embossed ring.

Table 12.1

Selected common closure code groups. The abbreviation "CT" indicates a continuous thread closure.

Designations	Description
120, 140 and 160	2-lug, 4-lug and 6-lug Amerseal quarter turn finish
400	series shallow CT finish
	401 - with wide sealing surface
	410 - medium CT concealed-bead finish
	415 - tall CT concealed bead-finish
	425 - 8 to 15 mm shallow CT
	430 - pour-out CT
	445 - deep S CT
	460 - home canning jar finish
600	beverage crown finish
1240	vacuum lug-style finish
1600	roll-on finish
1620	roll-on tamper-evident finish
1751	twist-off vacuum seal
SP 100	T for plastic SP 100 finish
SP 103	CT for plastic SP 103 finish
SP 200	CT for plastic SP 200 finish
SP 444	CT for plastic SP 444 finish

Threaded closures are generally made from tinplate, with some smaller types being formed from aluminum. Sheeted metal receives various protective and decorative coatings and lacquers on the closure's interior and exterior faces before being formed. This allows the closure's top panel and side to be fully decorated. The prepared metal is cut into strips and then proceeds through a multistage forming process.

The forming process involves cutting a blank and forming a shell of the overall shape and dimension of the finished cap. The threads are formed, the top panel is configured and the wire edge or sharp shell edge is rolled over. The final step forms the knurled "finger grip" around the closure sides. The fully formed closure is now ready to be lined with an inserted piece or a flowed-in plastisol.

Lug-style Metal Closures

Production methods for twist or lug closures (Refer back to Figure 12.1.) are similar to those for threaded closures. Lug closures are under more stress than screw closures and therefore are normally a heavier gauge of metal. They are available in 27 millimetre to 110 millimetre sizes, with either smooth or fluted side walls.

Lug closures are designed to engage the interrupted thread of the container finish. The interlocking of the cap's lug and the container's thread creates a camming action, drawing the closure down until the soft liner forms a hermetic seal. The lug closure's advantage is that the seal is accomplished with fewer degrees of rotation (typically less than 90°) than a standard screw thread. This allows for a faster and more positive application.

Glass jar lug threads are easier to make than continuous threads. Lug cap stresses in the thread area are too high to allow them to be used on plastic containers.

Roll-on Metal Caps

The roll-on metal cap is punched from coated and decorated aluminum sheet and formed into a cap shell with a liner added to suit the end use. There are no threads at this point. The packager drops the preformed shell over the container finish and the capping machine rolls the cap's sidewalls into the bottle's finish, duplicating the threads. (See Figure 12.6) A top pressure block ensures that the liner material contours properly to the top surface of the finish.

Roll-on closures can be made tamper evident by folding an extension of the closure skirt around the bottle's neck ring or bead. Circumferential perforations around the skirt, break away to leave a portion of the skirt caught beneath the neck ring.

Press-on/Twist-off Metal Closures

The press-on/twist-off or PT metal cap has a flowed-in plastisol gasket. (See Figure 12.7) This gasket expands and conforms to a glass container's finish threads when heated during steam-vapor vacuum sealing. At this point the closure

Figure 12.6

Roll-on closure threads are formed by forcing the aluminum shell to conform to bottle finish threads.

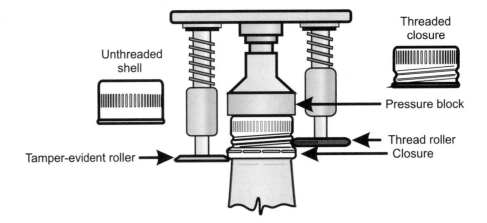

Unthreaded shell

Threaded closure

Pressure block

Thread roller
Closure

Tamper-evident roller

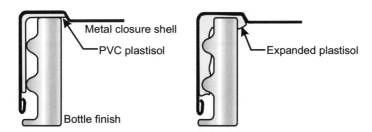

Figure 12.7

A press-on/twist-off closure utilizes a plastisol which expands during steam vapor vacuum sealing to, in effect, become a threaded closure.

becomes, in effect, a threaded closure. The end user simply twists the cap off. It is ideally suited for high-speed vacuum packaging lines, since the metal shell is simply pressed onto the bottle finish. Originally designed for baby food, this closure is now the world standard for these and other products in sizes from 27 millimetres through 77 millimetres.

A tamper-evident feature can be added if the closure top is embossed with a ring in the center of the closure to provide an "oil canning" or flexing movement. The internal vacuum draws the ring section down. When the seal is broken, the depressed ring portion pops upward with an audible sound.

Other vacuum closure variations hold a flat metal panel against the bottle finish by external air pressure; there are no threads. A plastic tear-away ring bonded to the metal panel wraps over a bead on the container finish to provide a "snap-on" lid and tamper evidence.

Crown Closures

Crown closures are the familiar crimped-on metal caps for beers, carbonated drinks and ciders. Regardless of the product, all crowns are a 26 millimetre size and are made to one North American standard. The crowns are cut and formed from predecorated tinplate. Linings are either preformed and bonded into position or formed from a flowed-in plastisol or other polymeric material. An oxygen scavenger is sometimes incorporated into the liner material for oxygen sensitive products such as beer.

The twist-off crown is a variation. These crowns are of slightly lighter gauge, reduced temper tinplate than regular crowns. This allows the material to form into the bottle thread. Removal is aided by the inclusion of liner and interior lacquer lubricants.

Both pry-off and twist-off crowns are applied by a hollow metal mandrel that comes down over the crown and bends the crown skirt down to conform with the bottle finish. If the finish has a thread configuration, the crown skirt takes on this shape.

Friction-fit Pry-off Metal Closures

Friction fit metal can ends require a sealing collar or lever ring to be double seamed to the can body. The ring is cut from a flat sheet and formed to the proper geometry in order to avoid having a seam along the ring's circumference.

Figure 12.8

A simple friction-fit metal can lid (top) and a double tight metal can lid such as would be used on a paint can. Friction fit metal can ends are also known as lever lids.

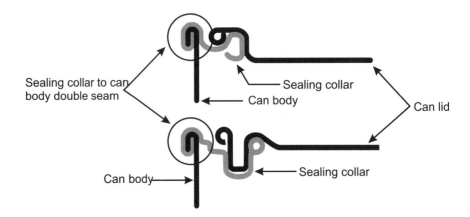

For dry products, a single point of friction as shown in Figure 12.8 (top) is adequate. Paint cans must seal in solvent vapors and prevent product oxidation or drying. An extra fold in the closure provides for an additional sealing surface. The sealing collar and can lid geometries provide for two points at which a seal is made; hence the term double tight or doubletite. See Figure 12.xx bottom).

CLOSURE SEALS

Lined Closures

In order to make a hermetic seal, a closure must have a means of drawing the inner face of the closure snugly against the container and a means of sealing tightly against the bottle finish. The latter requirement can be achieved through the use of resilient liners inside the closure that conform to the minute irregularities of the finish surface to effect a seal.

Early liners were thin cork sheets or pulpboard. Currently most liners are composed of soft resilient material such as expanded plastic that conform to the container's finish. Often the resilient backing is combined with appropriate other materials to create the actual barrier and seal. (See Table 12.2) Expanded polyethylene in various densities is the most common resilient material for general purpose closures. Lower densities would be used where a high degree of conformity or compressibility is required. However lower densities tend to have poorer torque retention. Where hot fills or induction heat seals are going to be used, expanded polypropylene is a better choice. Sometimes solid ethylene-vinyl acetate or solid synthetic rubber inserts can serve both conformability and sealing functions.

High barrier liners are made with laminations that include aluminum foils faced with a high strength material such as PET. Where metal cannot be used, a laminate incorporating EVOH will provide good gas barrier. Ethylene-vinyl acetate, nylon and poly(vinylidene chloride) are common facing layers.

Plastisol liners, usually a poly(vinyl chloride), are flowed in and then oven-cured and expanded to a soft, rubbery state.

Table 12.2

Examples of common closure liner constructions and applications. (Source: Tri-Seal International, Inc.)

Construction	Characteristics and Applications
PE/expanded PE/PE	General purpose applicationsyt
PP/expanded PP/PP	Hot fill applications
PP/expanded EVA/PP	Hot fill applications
Ethylene-vinyl acetate	Warm fills, beverages, motor oil
EVA/expanded EVA/EVA	Resilient, highly compressible
PE/isobutylene blend	Inert, fair gas and moisture barrier
PET/LDPE/expanded LDPE/LDPE	Good gas barrier
EVA/EVOH/LDPE/expanded LDPE/LDPE	Good gas barrier
EVA/PA/LDPE/expanded LDPE/LDPE	Good gas barrier
PVDC/LDPE/expanded LDPE/LDPE	Good gas barrier
PET/LDPE/foil/expanded LDPE/LDPE	Superior gas barrier

Many plastic closure designs have internally molded sealing structures so that the closure is linerless. The seal may be accomplished by bearing down on a molded-in projecting ridge or vane or by designing a plug-like form or valve that will be forced into the container opening. (See Figure 12.9) Polypropylene linerless closures do not have significant barrier properties for gases other than water vapor. Good barrier properties can be had by applying an aluminum containing innerseal to the bottle finish. In most instances the innerseal would be applied by induction heat sealing.

Liners must be physically and chemically compatible with active ingredients they will contact. An adequate barrier to gas and moisture transmission into or out of the container may be needed for some products.

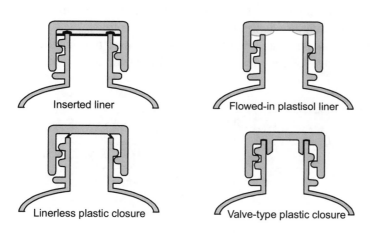

Figure 12.9

Four approaches to creating a seal: Inserted friction-fit liner (top left), flowed-in plastisol liner(top right), and two plastic linerless closures (bottom).

Figure 12.10

Two types of liner system
used for induction
heat-sealed innerseals.

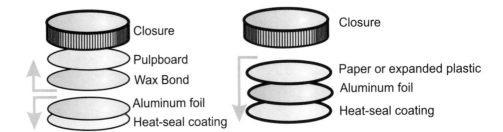

Closure

Pulpboard

Wax Bond

Aluminum foil

Heat-seal coating

Closure

Paper or expanded plastic

Aluminum foil

Heat-seal coating

Some products require that it be possible to vent any internal pressure build-up. This is usually accomplished by special treatments of the closure liner material.

Induction Innerseals

Induction inner seals across the container opening provide a hermetic seal as well as barrier and tamper evidence. These liners are inserted by the closure manufacturer as part of the cap-lining operation.

Induction heat-sealing heads have sealing coils powered by generators running at 50 to 500 kilohertz; they produce energy that couples with the aluminum foil that is part of the innerseal. The foil's temperature rises and transfers heat to the heat-seal coating which then bonds with the container's land area. Low-frequency generators provide a broad heated band around the seal perimeter, while high-frequency generators concentrate the heat more in the perimeter zone. There is no contact between the sealing coils and the closure. Low-frequency systems tend to be used where a wax bond must be released and also for larger closures.

The most common induction seal liner has an aluminum foil disk temporarily adhered to a pulpboard liner with wax. (See Figure 12.10, left). The container side of the aluminum disk is coated with a hot-melt adhesive. The entire liner assembly is inserted into the closure like a regular liner. When the cap is screwed down onto the container, the foil liner presses against the finish sealing surface (land.) The container passes under an induction sealing head where the high-intensity alternating magnetic field induces eddy currents in the foil disk. (See Figure 12.11) This results in resistance-type heating effects. The heat melts the wax, which then blots back into the pulp liner, while at the same time the molten heat sealable coating bonds the foil to the container finish.

Soaking the molten wax into the backing pulpboard has the effect of reducing the overall thickness of the liner material, resulting in an immediate loss of closure

Figure 12.11

Induction sealing coils can
be designed to generate
different field shapes.
Ferrite "energy directors"
are used to direct most of
the field to the sealing zone.

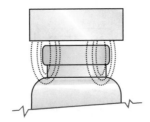
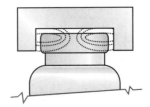

torque. In critical situations, a second application or adjustment of closure torque may be necessary.

A dispensing closure needs to have clear access to the dispensing opening and in such instances a pulpboard liner is undesirable since it remains inside the closure. For these applications the foil is permanently bonded to a paper or plastic backing piece (See Figure 12.10, right.) The liner is held in place by friction. Both liner and foil stay attached to the container finish.

Innerseals can also be adhered to the top of the container finish with an adhesive. With glassine liners, adhesive is applied to the container finish before the cap is put on. Another type uses a pressure-sensitive wax-adhesive combination.

A sufficiently wide land-area bonding surface is necessary whatever methodology is used to create an innerseal.

PLASTIC CLOSURES

Thermoset Closures

Plastic closure materials can be classified as thermosets and thermoplastics.

Once the traditional choice of the chemical, pharmaceutical and cosmetics industry, thermosets have now largely been replaced by thermoplastics. Thermoset closures are compression molded to close dimensional tolerances from resins such as phenol formaldehyde (which produces black and dark colors) or from amino resins such as urea (which give brighter colors). As a polymer class, thermosets have higher use temperatures than thermoplastics, offer better solvent resistance and are not subject to "creep" (viscoelastic deformation) problems.

Thermosets can be formed into heavy cross sections without the "sink" marks common to thermoplastic shapes. Thermoset materials are ideal surfaces for vacuum metallizing. Lastly, thermosets are stiff and have a hard, substantial feel about them. These latter qualities are often used to advantage in the cosmetics industry.

Thermoplastic Closures

Thermoplastic closures can be injection molded from many polymers, but polypropylene is the most widely used. Polypropylene is easily formed, colors well and is economical. It is less subject to viscoelastic deformation than polyethylene and has a higher use temperature. Polypropylene has the best integral hinge (live hinge) properties of any plastic. This is important for closures that have hinged flip-top components in their design.

Polyethylene is used where elongation or some deformation is needed. For example, some threaded closures designs are pressed (rather than rotated) onto the bottle finish and rely on the closure material's resiliency to allow the closure threads to over-ride the finish threads. Plastic corks for wine bottles need to deform under the interference fit. Snap-on tub lids must have some "give" to be stretched over the slightly larger container rim. Polyethylene also has better cold resistance than polypropylene.

Figure 12.12

A press-fit closure assembly where the closure engaging threads are on a separate piece that snaps over interference fit rings on the container finish. The dotted line shows where a tamper evident seal with a pull ring could be located.

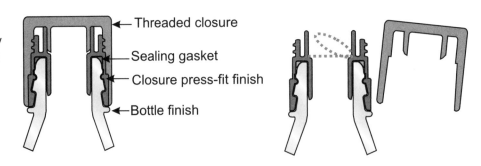

- Threaded closure
- Sealing gasket
- Closure press-fit finish
- Bottle finish

Cosmetic closures are often made of polystyrene for its hard, glossy surface. Polystyrene's exceptional clarity is also an advantage for some applications.

The ease with which thermoplastic can be formed into complex aesthetic and utility features allows closure designs not available with other materials. The resilient nature of plastic has been taken advantage of to make press-fit closure bases that snap over an interference ridge on the container. (See Figure 12.12) In effect, the threaded finish and closure screw-cap become a single system or assembly. The capping operation is very fast since there is no cap threading or torqueing required on the production line.

An advantage of press-fit type closures is that a tamper-evident seal with an attached pull ring can be molded across the finish fitment. (See the dotted line in Figure 12.12) Similarly, a comb-like device can be molded into the bore of the fitment to provide a more controllable pouring of liquids. The closure skirt can also be extended with a perforated ring that snaps over the bottle's neck ring to provide a break-away tamper-evident feature.

INJECTION MOLDS AND CLOSURE DESIGN

All threaded closures have the problem of how to remove them from the injection mold core. How this problem is resolved affects the closure's cost and performance. Removal of the closure from the mold can be done by:

Unscrewing the cores. For a mold core to unscrew from the molded closure, the thread must continue all the way into the closure until it meets the top of the closure. An inserted liner cannot have a diameter significantly greater than the thread diameter (the closure's E dimension). This means that adhesive must be

Figure 12.13

Threads go all the way to the top in the unscrewed-core closure whereas they can stop some distance away from the top of a stripped core closure.

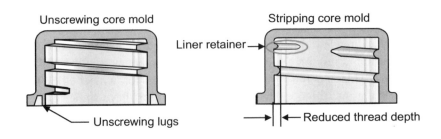

Unscrewing core mold — Stripping core mold

Liner retainer

Unscrewing lugs — Reduced thread depth

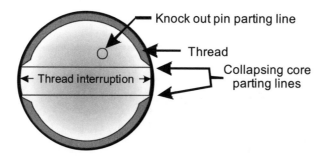

Figure 12.14

Inside view of a collapsed core closure showing thread interruption and parting lines left by the retractable central mold component.

used to hold the liner in place. On the advantage side, the closure threads can be made quite deep, giving an unscrewed-core closure the best holding power. Of the three mold types, unscrewing core molds are the most expensive. Most unscrewing core closures can be recognized by a series of serrations or lugs around the perimeter of the skirt base. These permit holding the closure from rotating as the core is unscrewed. The difference can be seen in Figure 12.13.

Stripping the closure off the core. This requires that the plastic material itself have some recoverable elongation so that the closure can be stretched enough to override the mold threads. Secondly, the threads of stripped core closures are typically 25 to 30% shallower than for a similar closure made by the unscrewing core method. On the advantage side, stripping allows the placement of a number of liner retaining ridges inside the closure. Liners are cut close to the closure's T diameter and are held in place by the retainers. Unlike an adhesive bonded liner, a retained liner is free to rotate within the closure. This can have significant implications on closure application and removal. The mechanism for pushing closures off the mold is simpler and more economical than unscrewing cores.

Collapsing core. This requires that the mold core be made of two halves that are able to collapse to a smaller diameter around a retractable center component, and thus be pulled straight out of the molded closure. To achieve this, the closure threads must be interrupted on opposite sides of the closure (so that the central component can be retraced); the interruptions is for about 12 mm (1/2 in.) (See Figure 12.14) A knock out pin helps to push the closure off the cores. Collapsing cores have a cost advantage and are able to mold liner retainers similar to strippable core systems. A disadvantage is that there is some holding power reduction since a thread portion is missing. Collapsing core systems tend to be used for large diameter closures.

CLOSURE APPLICATION

Compared to filling operations, capping operations are fairly straightforward. Closures are typically loaded into an unscrambler, which selects individual caps and feeds them in the correct orientation to a delivery chute. The selected closure slides down a ramp to meet the container. In most moderate-speed machines, the closure is presented at an angle to the moving container. (See Figure 12.14) The

Figure 12.15

Typical arrangement for mating cap and bottle finish.

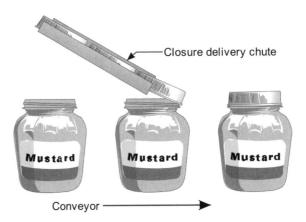

Closure delivery chute

Mustard Mustard Mustard

Conveyor ⟶

leading edge of the finish engages the closure lip (See Figure 12.15) and pulls it out of the delivery chute.

The container, with the closure resting on the finish, is indexed to a sealing or chucking station, where the appropriate mechanical action seals the closure to the container. This may be as simple as passing the closure between rotating resilient wheels that spin the closure on.

Most child-resistant (CR) closures require a positive gripping chuck. On slower machines this is done at one station while the container remains stationary throughout the closing motion. On faster machines, the containers enter into a rotary sealing head having 4, 6, 8 or sometimes more chucks or spindles. Container and chuck move together on rotary machines during the closing motion. An infeed timing screw and starwheel will be required at each end of the rotary machine to ensure proper entry and exit.

Decorative or tamper-evident shrink neck-bands are usually pre-prepared sleeves that arrive in a magazine ready to be placed over the finish. After placement, the band is briefly exposed to heat to securely shrink it in place.

Closure Torque

"Torque" is the resistance to application or removal of a threaded or lugged closure.

Thermoplastic closures on thermoplastic containers can suffer from considerable torque loss after closure application because of the viscoelastic flow (cold flow or creep) properties associated with these materials. (See Figure 12.16) This means that over time, the removal torque could be significantly less than the application torque. A general rule is that the closure will lose about half of its torque in 24 hours. Torque loss is unique to every application and should be established for each closure system, with appropriate adjustments made to the application torque to compensate for loss.

- "Application torque" is a measure of the tightness to which the capping machine turns the closure. (See Table 12.3) Since application torque

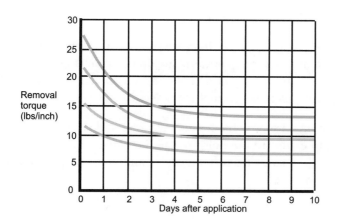

Figure 12.16

Loss of torque and removal time. Data courtesy MAC Closures.

Table 12.3

Suggested application torques. A rule of thumb is that the application torque in inch-pounds should be about half the closure's diameter in millimetres.

Cap Size (mm)	Application Torque	
	Inch-pounds	Newton-Metre
15	06–09	0.678–1.017
20	08–12	0.904–1.356
24	10–18	1.130–2.034
28	12–21	1.356–2.373
33	15–25	1.695–2.825
48	19–30	2.147–3.390
38	17–25	1.921–2.825
43	17–27	1.921–3.051
53	21–36	2.373–4.068
58	23–40	2.599–4.520
63	25–43	2.825–4.859
70	28–50	3.164–5.650
89	40–65	4.520–7.345
83	32–58	3.616–6.554
120	55–75	6.215–8.475

normally drops off, sometimes quite rapidly after application, removal torque for purposes of machine adjustment should be measured within 5 minutes of the application.

- "Removal torque" is the force necessary to loosen and remove the closure. Removal torque is normally lower than application torque. The degree of "back-off" is a function of application torque, closure and container materials, geometries, tolerances and time.

- "Stripping torque" is the torque level that will cause the closure or bottle finish to distort to the point where the closure threads will override the matching closure or finish threads, resulting in component damage, loose caps or no seal.

Product on the finish threads can significantly increase or decrease application or removal torques. In some instances the product may have a lubricating action; in others the product may literally bond the closure to the finish.

Rigid glass containers and metal closures do not change or deform under normal stress. However, liner materials used in these systems will deform and set to new shapes. In extreme cases, pulp liners applied at high humidity will shrink upon drying, causing loose caps. Induction innerseal liners also undergo significant dimensional change after sealing. While the product itself will not leak as long as the seal is intact, the closure itself can become quite loose.

TAMPER EVIDENCE

There is no officially recognized definition of what constitutes a tamper-evident (TE) closure. The Food and Drug Administration published 21 CFR 211.132, *Tamper-resistant Packaging Requirements for Over-the-counter Human Drug Products*. The FDA definition reads:

"Having an indicator or barrier to entry which, if breached or missing, can reasonably be expected to provide visible evidence to consumers that tampering has occurred."

Over-the-counter (OTC) drug products, products accessible to the public at point of sale, as well as contact lens solutions and some cosmetic products are the products mostly affected. There must be a clear statement prominently placed so that the consumer's attention is drawn to the tamper evident feature.

The main approach to preventing tampering involves the closure's design. This fixation on the closure as a defense against tampering is common to both consumers and legislators. It is not something that bothers the tamperer. Package types that are not normally considered vulnerable have been violated at points other than the closure. Professional packagers should never use the term "tamper proof," since no practical package can thwart a determined tamperer.

A case in point was the Illinois person who laced 25 or so packages, including aseptic fruit drink packs, with arsenic, apparently using a syringe. In another incident a tamperer managed to get a dose of cyanide into a conventional single-serving yogurt tub. In the final analysis it is an often-ignored truth that we cannot protect ourselves entirely from the determined tamperer. It is also an ugly truth that the "urban terrorists" will always be there.

Understanding the nature of the problem, we realize that many legislated measures will not stop a determined tamperer. TE packaging may make it more difficult, or even very difficult for the would-be urban terrorist, but it rarely makes it impossible. This is not to say that such efforts should be abandoned. We should simply be aware that a tamper-evident closure does not guarantee our product against the determined tamperer.

Most tampering fortunately is simpler and is a nuisance rather than life-threatening. The casual extraction of a cookie while the parents are in another aisle, the insertion of a dead insect or exchanging salt or sugar are examples of this kind of activity. Properly sealed packages discourage this kind of impulse or nuisance tampering. In some instances a tamper evident designs are a theft deterrent.

TAMPER-EVIDENT CLOSURE SYSTEMS

Tamper-evident closures are important for those products prone to attracting would-be tamperers. Consumers need closures that demonstrate that the package contents have not been altered or interfered with. Some packages, such as aerosols, are inherently tamper evident or difficult to deliberately violate. Other packages must have features added that provide tamper evidence. These can be grouped into 12 recognized categories:

- Film wrappers. A transparent film with a distinctive design is wrapped securely around a product or product container. The film must be cut or torn to open the container and remove the product.

- Blister or strip packs. Dosage units such as pharmaceutical capsules or tablets are individually sealed in clear plastic or in foil. The individual compartment must be torn or broken to obtain the product.

- Bubble packs. The product and container are sealed in plastic and mounted in or on a display card. The plastic or paper must be torn or broken to remove the product.

- Shrink seals and bands. Bands or wrappers with a distinctive design are shrunk by heat to seal the closure and container union. The seal must be cut or torn to open the container and remove the product.

- Foil, paper or plastic pouches. The product is enclosed in an individual pouch that must be torn or broken to obtain the product.

- Bottle inner seals. Paper or foil with a distinctive design is sealed to the mouth of a container under the closure. The seal must be torn or broken to open the container and remove the product.

- Tape seals. Paper or foil with a distinctive design is sealed over all carton flaps or a bottle cap. The seal must be torn or broken to open the container and remove the product.

- Break-away closures. The container is sealed by a plastic or metal cap that breaks away when removed from the container but leaves part of the closure attached to the container. The cap must be broken to open the container and remove the product.

- Sealed collapsible tubes. The mouth of a tube is sealed, and the seal must be punctured to obtain the product.

- Sealed carton. All flaps of a carton are securely sealed and the carton must be visibly damaged when opened to remove the product.

- Aerosol containers. Aerosol containers are inherently tamper resistant.

- Miscellaneous other systems.

CHILD-RESISTANT (CR) CLOSURES

As with tamper-evident closures, reality demands that child-resistant packages never be referred to as "child proof." Any closure that is devised for reasonable adult use, will be openable by some children, either by accident and or consistently. Hence, the correct term: "child resistant."

CR closures are under the jurisdiction of the Consumer Product Safety Commission. A list of substances covering drugs, household cleaning agents, pesticides and other products defines which substances are regulated. CR closures serve the safety concerns of the marketplace. Although CR closures can certainly be a nuisance, their effectiveness is readily apparent.

Since 1972 when CR closures were introduced, the incidence of accidental deaths has dropped 84% for all substances and 98% for aspirin alone.

Stringent test protocols define which closures can be classified as CR. These are described in 16 CFR 1700.20 in the United States. In Canada, the Canadian Standards Association administers such a program. The protocols are similar but not identical.

Briefly, the test is conducted using 200 children between the ages of 42 and 51 months. The children, working in pairs, are allowed 5 minutes to open the package. For those who are not able to open the package, a single nonverbal demonstration is given, and the children are allowed a further 5 minutes. The demonstration's purpose is to ensure that the package cannot be opened by the child once the "trick" has been observed. True child-resistant packages depend on the limited manual dexterity of a child. Typically, this involves two dissimilar simultaneous motions or actions. The CR effectiveness must be at least 85% without a demonstration and 80% after the demonstration.

The tests also incorporate a "senior friendly" phase. A separate adult test using 100 adults between the ages of 50 and 70, should have a 90% or better success rate of opening the package. Opening instructions are generally designed into the closure's crown or skirt, detailing a series of actions. Examples are: "line up the arrows and lift," or "lift and squeeze while twisting."

SPECIAL CLOSURES AND FUNCTIONS

Corks

Cork was the original closure material, and until the early 1900s it was the principal method of closing a bottle. Cork is the outer bark layer of the cork oak tree, grown principally in Spain, Portugal and North Africa. A tree produces usable cork every 8 to 10 years, and supplies have become increasingly difficult to obtain in recent years. Cork provides an old-fashioned or nostalgic product appearance, but being a natural material it has wide variability in properties and is often the source of off-tastes. Many winemaking authorities concede that screw caps make a superior closure, but the oenophile tradition keeps the cork closure alive.

Nonetheless there is a growing trend away from cork. In some instances synthetic materials imitating cork, and still requiring a cork-screw to extract, are being used. Others are adopting conventional threaded closures and it may be expected that in some time in the near future, most wines will be sold in screw-caped bottles.

Decorative Applications and Styles

The package closure is a major element in developing a package persona. There are many closure design variations and persona treatments. Some closures used to develop these personas are old closure designs that, from a practical sense, are not very effective and usually quite costly.

Sugar candy can be put in a stock jar with a stock screw-cap closure. As a presentation, it is not very inspiring. A circle of gingham cloth held over the screw cap with a string makes a tremendous difference. That touch adds visions of country cottages, and kindly, aproned grannies fixing a special treat for kids according to a secret recipe. This simple treatment increases the perceived value of the product.

The "lightning-style" closure (Figure 12.17) was patented nearly a century ago. Its ceramic plug, wire bail and rubber gasket are hopelessly complex, yet the closure is still commonly used on upscale products such as maple syrups and gourmet beers. A plastic version is available for those who can't afford the ceramic plug.

The ground glass stopper is another traditional format that now sees limited use—mostly for perfumes, specialty cosmetic containers such as bath salts and other upscale products.

Plug orifice closures will often have an extended skirt around the bottle fitment component. (See Figure 12.20) The skirt normally is dimensioned to match the bottle profile. When fitted to an oval bottle, the closure will be a snap-fit rather than a threaded attachment. A means of ensuring that the closure skirt aligns with the oval bottle shape is part of the design.

Wax seals are used both on the fronts of bottles and over the closure itself. As with lightning stoppers, plastic applied imitations are available. They are primarily there for decoration.

Figure 12.17

A lightning closure sealed
(left) and opened (right).

Multi-Lead Bottle Threads

A typical bottle thread might circle the finish until there is some overlap, and where a good seal is critical might continue till the thread has overlapped itself for a full 720 degrees. In such a design there is a considerable amount of rotation required before the closure is sufficiently tight.

Multiple lead threading (also called multiple pitch) uses short thread segments—for example a thread may only be 45° of the finish circumference— but there may be five or six such segments around the finish. The result is that there will be three or four thread overlaps at any given point on the circumference. This provides a very secure seal that requires a small rotation of the closure.

The dairy product bottle in Figure 12.18 has seven thread starts. The threads are very shallow, allowing for the LDPE closure to override the threads when it

Figure 12.18

An example of a seven-lead
finish.

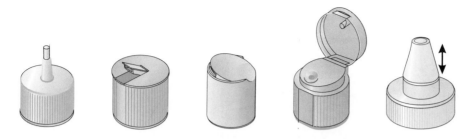

Figure 12.19

Snip-top, flip-spout, disk top, plug orifice and push-pull liquid dispensers.

is pressed onto the bottle finish. Final rotation to produce a tight seal is less than 15°. A high degree of engagement makes up for the shallow thread profile.

Multiple thread finishes help prevent the closure from "cocking" during the application of the closure to the bottle finish, providing more trouble free running at the closure applicator.

Dispensers and Pumps

A great variety of closures incorporate a dispensing feature (See Figures 12.19 and 12.20) or a pump (See Figure 12.21). There are far too many variations to describe here, and a visit to a retail establishment is a good way to become acquainted with the many options available.

Dry product dispensers usually incorporate a rotating or sliding plate that can be indexed over holes in the closure's top surface. Large pour openings and smaller sifter openings are frequently provided on the same closure.

Among the earliest liquid dispensing formats was the snip-top with a spout or "nozzle" on its crown that was cut off. (See Figure 12.19, far left) This evolved into nozzle designs with captive caps, allowing consumers to use the container in one hand, opening the spout with their thumb. The push-pull dispenser, commonly used for kitchen detergents, has a movable device on the spout that opens to the container when in an up position and closes when pushed down. Flip-spout dispensers have a spout that opens and closes as the spout is rotated into an up position. The disk-top variant is similar excepting that the dispensing passage is in a flat disk that is fitted into the top surface of the closure.

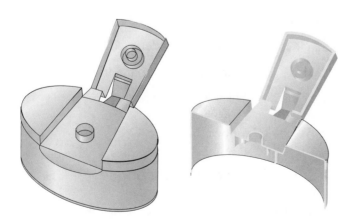

Figure 12.20

A skirted dispensing closure and a cut-away view to show finish fitment component.

Figure 12.21

A representative pump
dispensing system.
Geometries will vary but the
basic action is similar for
most pumps.

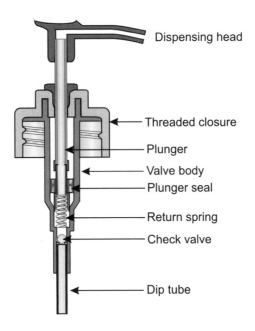

Dispensing head

Threaded closure

Plunger

Valve body

Plunger seal

Return spring

Check valve

Dip tube

None of these dispensers is suitable for food product since the action of all of them would leave a small amount of product at the dispenser tip exposed to the atmosphere. The preferred plug-orifice dispenser has a fully topped flip-up action closure with a small plug that enters the container opening and returns most product back into the container. (Figure 12.20) Other dispensers operate by turning motions.

Plastic closures also form part of pump and spray dispensing systems for a wide variety of food, garden, automotive, household, pharmaceutical and cosmetic products. Pumps are selected using the same criteria as are used for dispensers.

- What is the product's viscosity?

- What volume needs to be dispensed with every activation?

- What has to come out: a fine mist, a patterned spray, a directed spray, an extruded bead?

- What is the desired dispensing direction?

- Are material compatibility issues anticipated?

- Should activation be with a finger button, a trigger or a palm?

- What is the size and shape of the container?

A representative pump is shown in Figure 12.21.

Examples of Special Technical Functions

A number of product categories require special functions in the closure:

- Dispensers for fluids such as cooking oils will often have a comb-like piece inserted into the pouring orifice to even out the flow. A more recent development is the inclusion of a thick silicone rubber insert across the closure opening. The silicone insert has an x-shaped slit across its face that will stayed closed and retain product even when the container is inverted. Slight pressure on a plastic bottle will open the slit to dispense product.

- Champagnes and highly-pressurized cork closed bottles have a wire basket or cage over the cork. Its function is twofold: it ensures that the cork will not eject prematurely, and it adds an element of heritage and authenticity.

- A jug containing a corrosive cleaning compound used in industrial washers has a closure that is not meant to come off. The jug is installed into the machine in an inverted position, and a water jet dissolves away a soluble disk that sits just behind a closure grating. The compound empties into the machine without ever being exposed.

- Sterility is of paramount importance when dealing with injectable solutions. Saline solution bottles are filled on the molding machine while still hot, and the top is pinched over, ensuring absolute sterility. What appears to be a closure has no sealing function. The purpose of the threaded cap is to break away the bottle finish at a deliberately weakened spot when the fluid is about to be used.

- Closures that must face a specific direction are most often designed with a projection on the inside of the skirt that will stop closure rotation when this projection comes against a mating projection on the container finish. Closure and container H and S dimensions become particularly critical. The closure liner or sealing system must be fully effective at a very specific degree of closure rotation.

- The versatility of plastics allows for an almost endless parade of convenience and aesthetic designs. Virtually all plastic closures can be designed with tamper-evident features. Measuring devices, spoons, daubers, brushes, sifters, pourers and flexible spouts have all been developed. Closures having shapes ranging to automotive gears to zebras have been marketed to fascinate, entertain and, not incidentally, to inspire a purchase decision.

These are only a few examples of the ingenuity and multifunctional properties that can be built into a closure. Each of them offers important benefits to the consumer, and that is what good packaging design is all about.

REVIEW QUESTIONS

1. List 10 considerations critical to the design or selection of an effective closure system.

2. What bodies have jurisdiction over industry finish and closure standards?

3. On a bottle finish, what are the I, T, E, H, and S dimensions. What are the corresponding dimensions on a closure?

4. Which thread style is preferred for plastic closures?

5. How are closures designated?

6. What is the advantage of a metal lug closure over a metal threaded closure?

7. What are the disadvantages of a flip-spout type of dispensing closures?

8. What are the advantages of press-on/twist-off type closures?

9. Why are liners necessary in metal closures? What is the purpose of the backing material in a lined closure?

10. Explain how an induction innerseal works. What container or closure body materials would interfere with the creation of a seal?

11. For what applications might you specify a closure made from a thermoset plastic?

12. What material are the majority of plastic closures made from? By what process are they made?

13. Where might we specify polyethylene as a closure material? Where might we specify polystyrene?

14. What features and designs are available in plastic closures that cannot be made easily in metal?

15. Define application torque, removal torque and stripping torque.

16. Explain what might happen if a bottle's S dimension is too short or too long.

17. Explain what will happen if the bottle's H dimension is too small.

18. Why should the common term "tamper proof" not be used?

19. List eight packaging systems that are considered to be tamper evident.

20. What is the design principle of a good child-resistant closure?

21. What is the relationship between tamper-evident closures and child-resistant closures?

22. What causes loss of torque in a plastic closure application?

23. Where would a double tight lid be used?

24. Loss of torque would be higher when a polypropylene closure is applied to a polyethylene bottle than if a polypropylene closure is applied to a polypropylene bottle. Explain why.

25. List three conditions or situations that contribute to loss of torque.

26. What advantages are had with multiple lead closures?

CHAPTER THIRTEEN
ADHESIVES

....

CONTENTS

Introduction to Adhesives

Definitions, "adhesive" and "glue," adhesion, cohesion, general adhesive properties.

Theories of Adhesion

Mechanical adhesion theory, surface strength and bond failure, fiber tear, clay coatings. Specific adhesion theory, polarity, excessive adhesive and failure, viscosity relationship to tensile, shear strength.

Surface Treatment

Creating intimate contact, wetting out, nonpolar surfaces, treating low-polarity surfaces, flame treatment, corona discharge treatment, measuring dyne levels, interference layers, release coatings.

Solidification

Water loss, solvent loss, heat removal and polymerization methods of adhesive solidification.

Common Classes of Packaging Adhesives

Starch-based adhesives, solids content, major applications. Dextrin adhesives, solids content, applications. Casein adhesives, formulation, application. Synthetic emulsions, emulsion micelles, critical water content, breaking the emulsion, green bond formation, solids content, emulsion and starch setting times compared, upsetting the colloidal balance, advantages of water-borne adhesives. Hotmelt formulations, advantages and limitations, application options, forms. Lacquer adhesives, formulation. Pressure-sensitive adhesives, formulation, applications. Cold-seal adhesive, formulation, applications.

Adhesive Application

Roll, gravure, extrusion, spray application.

Viscosity

Definition, molecular friction, viscosity and temperature, Newtonian fluids, other shear behaviors, thixotropy, viscosity units, measuring viscosity, viscosities of common materials.

Adhesive Selection and Considerations

Physical and chemical nature of substrates, application method, machine speed, pot life, assembly rate, open time, closed time, application and end-use temperatures, moisture resistance, chemical resistance, food applications, color, density, pH level, non-volatile content, storage life, diluting.

Inspecting Bond Failures

Adhesive, cohesive, substrate failure modes.

ADHESIVES

TERMINOLOGY

There is no universal method of categorizing adhesives. Adhesives are variously classified by solidification method, polymer base type, solvent type or application category.

Strictly speaking the term, "glue" refers to a protein-based bonding substance obtained from animal hooves, bones and skins. Modern formulations, with few exceptions, are derived from natural polymers such as starch or are based on synthetic polymer classes. The term "glue," should not be used to refer to the natural and synthetic polymers used to join materials in packaging. Terms such as "gluing," "glue-line" and "glue-bond" do not specifically identify a material and are acceptable, although "adhesive bonding" might be more technically correct.

Adhesion refers to the attraction or bond of one material to another. Cohesion refers to the internal attraction or bond of a material's molecules. Adhesives with low cohesive strengths will tend to flow (creep) under stress and thus not resist peeling and shearing stresses to which the bond may be subjected. Adhesive formulation must, in many instances, balance adhesive and cohesive properties. The distinction is also important when discussing bonding failure.

An adhesive's properties determine how quickly a surface wets out and the final bond quality. The dyne level of an adhesive is related to its molecular polarity and determines how well it is attracted to a substrate surface. Viscosity will affect machinability, how the adhesive flows out over the substrate and, and in the instance of porous substrates, the level of adhesive penetration into the substrate. Solids content or nonvolatile content, expressed as a percentage, refers to the actual amount of material left to form a bond after all solvents and carrier liquids have been removed.

This discussion concerns itself primarily with adhesives used to bond two surfaces together. However, the same principles govern the adhesion of printing inks to a substrate. An ink can be regarded as a pigmented adhesive.

THEORIES OF ADHESION

A number of theories explain why one substance bonds to another. Suffice to say that all theories relate to the nature and chemistry of the bonding surfaces.

Mechanical Adhesion Theory

Mechanical adhesion theory proposes that fluid adhesive flows into tiny surface irregularities. When the adhesive solidifies, it mechanically locks into the surface cavities and can no longer be pulled away without destroying the surface. (See Figure 13.1) Mechanical bonds can never be stronger than the surface strength of the material that is bonded. For example, adhesive may flow around cellulose fibers on a paper surface, but the bond cannot be stronger than the bond of those fibers to the paper mass.

Figure 13.1

A mechanical adhesive bond occurs when adhesive flows into tiny surface irregularities in two surfaces.

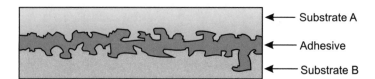

When troubleshooting a bond failure between two paper surfaces, adhesive chemists will examine the failure surface under magnification for evidence of fiber tear. If there is no fiber tear, the adhesive has not penetrated the surface sufficiently to establish a mechanical bond. If adhesive is present on both substrate surfaces, then a good adhesive bond was formed to the paper surfaces and the failure is due to the low internal strength (cohesiveness) of the adhesive.

If there is significant fiber tear, the problem lies in the paper surface. One solution is deeper penetration to provide a more substantial bond. This can be done by using a more fluid adhesive, or an adhesive that sets more slowly or by making glue-assist incisions in the paper surface.

Poorly bonded clay-coatings are frequent causes of paper glue-line failures. In such failures, close examination reveals flecks of white clay on the adhesive failure surface. Incising is the usual way of penetrating past the coated surface.

Specific Adhesion Theory

Mechanical adhesion adequately explains paper or wood bonding. However, glass, metal and plastic are relatively smooth compared to paper. The specific adhesion theory proposes that bonding takes place when minute regions of positive and negative charge are brought into intimate enough contact that they mutually attract one another, much as two magnets attract each other. The surface charges are primarily a result of dipole interaction, hydrogen bonding and Van der Waals' forces. Their range of attraction is essentially in the molecular distance order.

Two perfectly polished flat surfaces having surface polarities bond slightly simply by being brought together. Two new glass microscope slides are difficult to separate in tension because of this effect. The tensile bond between two dry microscope slides increases by wetting the surfaces with a trace of water. (See Figure 13.2) The mobile polar water molecules move to form bonds across places where the glass molecules are not quite aligned with their opposite charge as well as filling in minute surface irregularities. The number of polar bonds between the two plates increases significantly compared to dry glass. The union's tensile strength is substantially higher. This brings up several important observations:

Figure 13.2

Specific adhesion depends on the attractions of minute surface polarities.

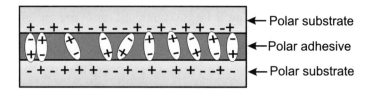

- The adhesive bond of a water molecule to glass is stronger than the cohesive bond of water molecules to each other. Increasing the water layer's thickness from a trace to a few millimetres reduces tensile strength, because now the bond separates by parting water molecules from each other (weak cohesive bonds) rather than by parting water molecules from the substrate (strong adhesive bonds). Some adhesives work the same way. Tensile strength may decrease with added adhesive, just as tensile strength decreases with added water in this example.

- Maximum bond strength occurs when the surfaces are perfectly covered with the amount of adhesive needed to contact and bridge the two surfaces. Less adhesive does not make use of the available bonding area. If the adhesive has low cohesive strength, excess adhesive will reduce the union's tensile strength. If the adhesive has high cohesive strength, added adhesive merely increases the union thickness. In either case more adhesive means higher costs.

- Tensile strength in the microscope slide/water example is high because—in trying to pull the slides apart—we are trying to simultaneously break millions of minute polar attractions. However, the shear strength of the same bond is quite weak, (that is, you can easily shift the slides sideways against each other) because here bonds are being formed and reformed. Shear strength can be increased by increasing adhesive viscosity. For example, corn syrup would give higher shear strength than water. The ultimate in viscosity is to have a material that won't flow, such as a solid.

SURFACE TREATMENT

To make a good adhesive bond, it is necessary for the adhesive molecules to intimately contact the surface of the material to be bonded. The best contact is made by a material that will flow and conform to the substrate surface. In practice, this means that an adhesive must be a liquid at the point of application and bond formation.

Furthermore, the liquid and the surface must have characteristics conducive to the formation of a chemical union. That is, the adhesive must be able to "wet out" the substrate. This means that the substrate surface should be polar and that the adhesive should be able to make contact with these polarities. Even microscopic layers of contaminating material prevents optimum bonding.

Many plastics, particularly polyethylene and polypropylene, have low polarity surfaces, more properly described as having low surface energies or surface tensions. (See Table 13.1) This makes it difficult to apply and adhere printing inks, adhesives or functional coatings. Surface tension of such materials can be increased by chemically altering the surface using flame treatments, corona discharge or chemical treatment. Flame treatment and corona discharge treatment are the two most commonly used in packaging.

Flame treatment passes the substrate through a gas flame that has been adjusted to have excess air. The hot oxygen in the flame is very reactive and is able to react with the otherwise chemically inert surface. Corona discharge

Table 13.1

Surface tension (measured in dynes) for selected untreated polymers. Higher dyne levels indicate higher polarity. Metal and glass approach 100. The dyne level of water is 72.

Material	Surface Tension (dynes)
Teflon	19
Polypropylene	29
polyethylene	31
polystyrene	33
ionomers	33–37
poly(vinyl chloride)	39
poly(vinylidene chloride)	40
poly(ethylene terephthalate)	43
polyamide	46

creates a similar highly reactive atmosphere (ozone) using a high-frequency, high-voltage charge to ionize the air in contact with the plastic. Plastic films are usually treated with corona discharge since the application of direct flame would harm most films.

These treatments alter a material's surface so that it has a higher surface tension, therefore improving its ability to attract (be wetted out by) water or solvent based inks, adhesives and coatings.

Flame and corona treatment are transitory ,although flame treatment is somewhat more durable. (See Figure 13.3) Plastic materials slowly revert back to their original condition unless printed, bonded or coated shortly after treatment. The reversion rate is highly variable depending on many factors, and it is not possible to assign a general "use before" rule for adhesive bonding.

Figure 13.3

Rates for polypropylene. (Source: Sherman Treaters.)

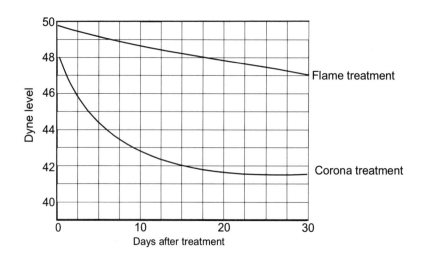

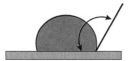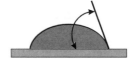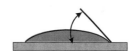

Figure 13.4

As a fluid becomes more attracted to the surface of a material, a drop of that fluid will move from having a large contact angle to a smaller contact angle. (Reference test method ASTM D 5946.)

Surface tension is measured in dynes (the force required to accelerate one gram by one centimetre per second^2). To achieve good bonding, the dyne level of a surface should be about 10 dynes/cm higher than the surface tension of the wetting liquid. It has been generally found that the dyne level of a surface should be 37 dynes/cm or higher to ensure adequate bonding of the adhesive material. However each application should be independently evaluated. To assure spreading and wetting, the fluid adhesive should have a surface tension no higher than the substrate's surface tension.

Surface tension can be measured by measuring the contact angle of a drop of distilled water with the test surface (See Figure 13.4) Water will flow out in an even film (contact angle equals zero) over a perfectly wettable surface. At the other extreme, a small water drop will bead up into a sphere. Contact angle goniometers measure the angle formed between a liquid drop and the substrate surface.

Another, simpler method is to use a series of solutions made up to have known dyne levels. These are applied to the test surface in increasing dyne increments until the solution at which an even film that will not bead up for at least two seconds is found. This is taken as the dyne level of that material.

American Society for Testing and Materials (ASTM), Standard Test Method for Wetting Tension of Polyethylene and Polypropylene Films, D 2578, describes the preparation of dyne solutions using mixtures of formamide and ethylene monoethyl ether. (Union Carbide's Cellosolve product.) DuPont's Victoria Pure Blue BO dye at about 0.03% is added to make the liquid film clearly visible. A partial listing of ethyl Cellosolve and formamide mixtures and their respective surface tensions is given in Table 13.2.

Minute quantities of surface contaminants can interfere with bond formation by preventing the adhesive from making intimate contact with the substrate. If the interfering layer is nonpolar, the adhesive releases from the interference layer. Conversely the adhesive may make a strong bond with the interference layer, but the bond between interference layer and the substrate may be weak. Interference layers can serve a useful purpose. A release paper such as used to support pressure-sensitive labels is a paper that has been coated with an interference layer (release coating) to minimize adhesion.

SOLIDIFICATION

It has been established that an adhesive must be

- polar to form chemical bonds with the substrate.

- fluid so it can flow out and make intimate contact with (wet out) the substrate.

Table 13.2
Solutions with known dyne levels.

Formamide Volume %	Ethyl Cellosolve Volume %	Surface Tension dynes/cm
0	100	30
2.5	97.5	31
10.5	89.5	32
19.0	81.0	33
26.5	73.5	34
35.0	65.0	35
42.5	57.5	36
48.5	51.5	37
54.0	46.0	38
59.0	41.0	39
63.5	36.5	40
67.5	32.5	41
71.5	28.5	42
74.7	25.3	43
78.0	22.0	44
80.3	19.7	45
83.0	17.0	46

The final requisite of all adhesives is that the applied fluid be able to solidify to make the bond permanent. Table 13.3 lists the ways that adhesives solidify.

COMMON CLASSES OF PACKAGING ADHESIVE

Starch and Starch-Based Adhesives

Starch is a naturally occurring vegetable polymer usually extracted from corn, grains or potatoes. It forms a high-viscosity paste when 20 to 30% starch is mixed with water. The high water content means that the adhesive requires a long drying time. On the plus side, starches are very economical.

Corrugated board manufacture is the largest single starch-based adhesive application. A starch/borax formula quickly gels by the application of heat.

Starch has limited solubility because of its high molecular weight. Starch molecular weight can be reduced and solubility increased by roasting in the presence of acids. The conversion can be stopped at any point, and generally, as

Table 13.3

Adhesive solidification methods.

Type	Solidification Method
Water borne	Loss of water. Starch, dextrin and casein adhesives are common examples. A special category of water-borne adhesives are the emulsion types typified by "white glue," usually a poly(vinyl acetate) emulsion.
Solvent based	Loss of solvent. Solid resins can be dissolved in various solvent combinations. Since solvents are volatile organic compounds (VOCs), their use is discouraged by many environmental, health and safety regulations. VOCs should be avoided if possible; however, certain resins can be dissolved only in solvents, and some substrates will bond well only with solvent-based adhesives.
Hot melts	Loss of heat. Unlike the previous two categories, hot melts do not need a diluent or solvent that is removed during solidification. They are 100% solids. These adhesives are favored for high-speed production applications because of their fast setting time.
Thermosets	Thermosets are usually 100% solids systems based on liquid prepolymers that can be polymerized to a solid after application. There are various ways of initiating the chemical reactions leading to solidification. Some epoxies and polyesters require the mixing of two components or a component and a catalyst. Others are initiated by atmospheric oxygen, by atmospheric moisture or by heat.

conversion advances, adhesion qualities go down and possible solids content and tack properties go up. Glucose is totally depolymerized starch. Dextrin is a partly depolymerized starch with intermediate molecular weight. Dextrin dissolves more readily in water than starch and provides solids contents of 40 or 50%.

Dextrins are economical and set faster than starches but are still relatively slow setting compared to synthetic systems. They are used where a long assembly time is an advantage or of no consequence (set-up boxes, bag making, tube winding). Starch-based adhesives have good adhesion to glass and metal but not to plastics. Mixing dextrins with borax (borated) improves tack and provides stable viscosities at moderate concentrations.

Alkaline treatment of starch produces jelly gums. These have exceptionally high tack and internal cohesion. At one time jelly gum was a key labeling adhesive but has been largely replaced by synthetics.

Starch and dextrin adhesives are thermoset polymers and have more heat resistance than most synthetic thermoplastic polymer-based adhesives.

Water-based adhesives are commonly used for various paper-bonding applications. The measure of a good bond is that it should tear the fiber when it is separated. However, care should be taken that this evaluation be done when the paper is thoroughly dried. Paper still wet from the adhesives moisture will always produce a fiber-tearing bond.

Casein Adhesives

Casein adhesives are derived from the phosphoprotein in acidified milk. Properly formulated caseins have the unique property of having good cold-water resistance but of being rapidly hydrolyzed in aqueous caustic solutions. Refillable beverage bottles use casein-based adhesives so that the bottle will retain its label when immersed in ice water, but the label can be easily removed at the filling location. Some casein is used for foil laminating.

Animal Glue

Animal glue, a collagen derivative, is a very tacky, protein-based glue used occasionally for setup boxes and tube winding. Animal glue can be supplied as solid cakes, which are run at about 60°C (140°F). Once common, animal glues are rarely used now for packaging. However, their ready repulpability in warm water may make them an attractive choice for environmental reasons.

Synthetic Emulsions

Large molecules give very strong bonds, but their solubility goes down as molecular weight goes up. The problem of having strong adhesive materials and high solids content is resolved by making an emulsion. Synthetic emulsion adhesives are based on polymers such as poly(vinyl acetates), acrylates and maleates, which in themselves are not water soluble. However, when fine particles of the polymer are surrounded by a protective colloid such as poly(vinyl alcohol), the resulting product can be suspended in water.

A single emulsion micelle consists of a polymer unit surrounded by a protective colloid and the whole surrounded by water. (See Figure 13.5) If the water is reduced beyond a critical point, the micelles can no longer be completely encapsulated, and the suspension "breaks." When this occurs, individual polymer units combine with others to form an adhesive film.

Emulsions are in the 50 to 70% solids content range, and this alone would provide a faster drying time than a starch or dextrin. When an emulsion breaks, a partial or green bond forms almost immediately. (See Figure 13.6) Emulsions can break in a few seconds, and the green bond is able to hold labels in place or carton glue flaps together. Bond strength increases slowly as the water evaporates.

Figure 13.5

An emulsion micelle.

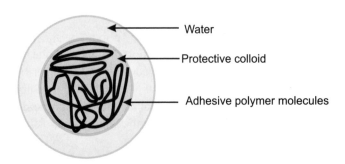

Water

Protective colloid

Adhesive polymer molecules

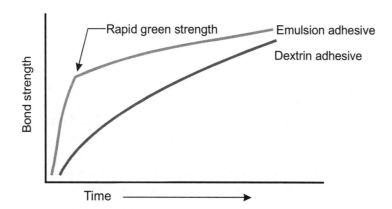

Figure 13.6

Bond development for emulsion and starch-type adhesives.

The polymers used in emulsion adhesives can be of relatively high molecular weight, providing for bonds having good performance under high stress and good heat resistance. Since the polymer molecule is encapsulated in the micelle, there are no problems with achieving a high solids content while maintaining reasonable viscosity. Emulsion adhesives have exceptionally broad formulation possibilities. For example, they can be made water resistant or remoistenable.

Freezing, pH shifts and chemical interference with the emulsifier (poly(vinyl alcohol) is typical) can upset the emulsion balance, resulting in a coagulated lump of the bonding resin.

Water-based adhesives are easy to use and clean up. They are economical and are used extensively in all forms of paper packaging applications, from cartoning to label gluing. Water-based adhesives do not perform well on most plastic substrates.

Hot Melts

A hot melt by convention describes a lower molecular weight material than "thermoplastic." Hot-melt adhesives are 100% solids and are applied in hot, molten form. Ethylene-vinyl acetate is the most common base resin used formulating hot melt adhesives. The main polymer is usually diluted, or "let down," with a material such as wax to improve melt flow properties and reduce cost. Tackifiers improve hot tack and viscosity. Other materials influence melt temperature. Added colorants make the application more visible.

Like many organic materials, hot-melt adhesives can degrade with extended heating. Prolonged heating initiates self perpetuating free radical degradation processes. Initiation is encouraged by the presences of external foreign material and char from the degradation process itself. The process initiates the joining and growth of lower molecular weight entities into higher molecular weight species that eventually become insoluble in the melt. This eventually leads to charring. Char can clog delivery systems and plug dispensing orifices. Antioxidants and heat stabilizers are important hot melt components.

Most general purpose hot melts are applied at about 177°C (350°F.) Formulations applying as low as 121°C (250°F) are available. The defined melting point of hot melts can limit their application. Few packaging hot melts are reliable above 70°C (158°F), although formulations based on polyamides and polyurethanes have fairly good performance at elevated temperatures, but at a higher cost.

The substrate must be able to tolerate the application temperature without warping or shrinking. Hot melts may not be suitable for items coming out of or going into thermal processing. Conversely, an economical hot melt may have a significant amount of wax diluent. Such an adhesive could become quite brittle at freezer conditions.

Since removal of heat can be done much faster than removal of water, hot melts have a much faster set than aqueous adhesives. This feature, along with their 100% solids content, has made them the adhesive of choice for many high-speed packaging applications. Hot melts can be extruded as a fairly substantial bead, thus enabling them to bridge gaps. Hot melts are sometimes preapplied and then reactivated later by applying heat. Conventional hot melts are, by nature, water resistant and can be formulated for many speciality applications, including thermosetting and pressure-sensitive formulas.

Hot melt adhesive bonds are best tested the next day or several days after forming. Adhesive polymer resins sometimes crystallize with time and this can seriously affect bond strengths.

Ring and ball (R&B) softening points are often used to characterize hot melts. The "R&B softening point" is the temperature at which the hot melt softens enough for a metal ball of a specified size and mass to drop through it.

Hot melts come in a variety of solid shapes. Slats, pillows, wafers and chips are the most common forms. Pellets are used in automated feeding system and extruders. They eliminate "bridging" (forming solid masses above the melt pool) in premelters and can feed into small hot-melt pot openings.

Hot melt adhesives are a paper recycling concern. At the paper mill, current hot-melt formulations cannot be readily removed or dispersed and can cause major problems when bits of hot-melt run through the paper-drying rolls. Industry is working on formulating hot melts that are compatible with recycling, but an economical product with suitable performance characteristics has yet to be produced.

Lacquer Adhesives

The term "lacquer adhesives" generally applies to any solvent-based adhesive. These adhesives are used most often by converters in coating and laminating operations, particularly with plastic substrates. They dry much faster than water-borne systems. In addition, there is considerable formulation latitude. Environmental, health and safety concerns are slowly eliminating the use of solvent-based adhesive systems.

Laminating lacquers are applied and immediately oven-dried to leave a pressure-sensitive surface to which the next laminate component is nipped. If both laminate components are impermeable, it is particularly important to drive off all solvents. Residue solvents will evaporate, and since they have no place to go, will blister the laminate structure.

Pressure-Sensitive Adhesives

Pressure-sensitive adhesives (PSA) are mostly based on one of two elastomeric polymer classes: acrylics and rubber/resin blends.

The surface of a PSA is classed as a very high viscosity liquid, and it is this feature that provides the instant bonding characteristic. Extremely soft PSAs will bond to virtually any surface; however, their cohesive strength will likely be too low for most practical uses.

Acrylic formulations are typically based on acrylic acid ester monomers with appropriate comonomers. The balance of cohesive strength (internal strength, resistance to creep) and adhesive ability (rapid wetting of a second substrate) is achieved by monomer selection and ratios and degree of polymerization. The more highly polymerized grades have higher cohesion but lower adhesion. Acrylic-based systems usually perform better at low temperatures than rubber/resin blends do.

Rubber/resin blends balance adhesion and cohesion properties by the choice of base rubber/resin combinations, their molecular weights and the type and amount of added tackifiers. Low cohesive strength formulations are sometimes used in peelable and resealable packages.

In addition to the base formulation, a curing or cross-linking step can be used to increase molecular weight after the coating step. This step can be self-initiated after the solvent is removed or activated by direct heat or another energy source.

PSAs are frequently used in conjunction with a release paper to manufacture pressure-sensitive label stock. The base is a heavily calendered paper that has been coated with a silicone or fluoropolymer release (antiadhesive) coating. A PSA is applied to the release surface, and a paper label stock is nipped against the adhesive. When peeled away, the adhesive binds to the facing paper and comes away from the release coating.

Though more expensive than regular labels, pressure-sensitive labels eliminate the need for glue stations at the labeling point. Furthermore, roll-formed labels are easier to count and track than loose labels. These features are of special importance to the pharmaceutical trades. PS labels, made in roll or fanfold form, also offer faster changeovers between product lines.

Cold-seal Adhesives

Co-adhesives or cold seal adhesives are similar to pressure-sensitive adhesives. "Co-adhesive" simply means that the adhesive has a greater tendency to stick to itself rather than other surfaces. In household use, this is referred to as a contact cement. Cold-seal adhesives, a type of co-adhesive, are usually based on natural rubber latex.

The adhesive formulation is preapplied, typically to a flexible wrapping material, by the printer or laminator. When the wrapping material is wound into rolls, the adhesive face contacts only the front side of the wrap. When a wrap or pouch is produced, two adhesive coated surfaces are brought together and a bond is immediately formed. Cold seals were originally developed for bonding plastic-based chocolate bar wraps, where chocolate's low melting point precludes heat sealing. The applications for cold seal adhesives have expanded to other flexible packaging applications where the instant bond-on-contact feature allows for faster machine speeds.

ADHESIVE APPLICATION

The following are the principal ways of applying adhesives:

Roll applicators. Roll or wheel applicators use a wheel rotating in a reservoir of adhesive. (See Figure 13.7) The adhesive can be metered in a number of ways including removing excess with a doctor blade or passing between metering rolls. Shaped rubber plates or engraved rolls can be used to apply adhesives in patterns. At high speeds, roll applicators have a tendency to throw off adhesive. Cleanliness is hard to maintain with open reservoirs.

Gravure roll. This application method is common in laminating operations. Gravure application is the most accurate application method but it can only be used with relatively low viscosity adhesives.

Extrusion applicators. In this technique, pumps move adhesive from the reservoir to a valved dispensing head. The valves are triggered with timing devices which control the flow of adhesive to the dispensing head. The dispensing head can have a number of orifices depending on the adhesive pattern. In some designs the valves are opened by actual contact with the substrate. More sophisticated designs can be programmed electronically to produce various lay-down patterns.

Extrusion applicators are the most common method of applying hot melt adhesives. Piston pump types are simple but have a slight flow interruption (wink) with each pump cycle. Gear pumps are more complex but provide a steady flow. Hot melt extrusion systems can be programmed to provide a wide range of patterned applications

Spray Applicators. Unlike extrusion applicators, spray applicators do not make contact with the substrate. As the adhesive leaves the glue-head it is dispersed into minute particles and carried by air to the substrate. Spraying requires a lower viscosity adhesive.

Figure 13.7

Typical roller type adhesive applicators for applying a continuous line of adhesive. A second roll bearing a flexible plate configured to the desired design, much as in flexographic printing, would be added for placing an adhesive pattern.

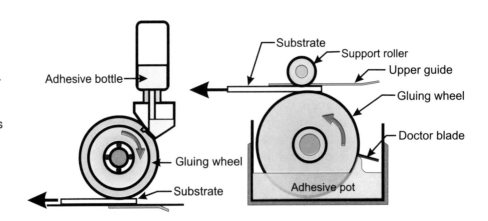

VISCOSITY

"Rheology," the science of the flow of matter, is commonly described as viscosity when referring to fluids. Viscosity is a measurable product dimension just like length, density or mass. In its simplest sense, a fluid can be called thick (such as molasses) or thin (such as water). A fluid's thickness or viscosity is that quality that makes a fluid resist changing shape or flowing. The viscosity of some common fluids is shown in Table 13.4.

When a liquid moves across a surface, the part of the fluid that is in contact with the stationary surface tends to "drag." The degree of drag depends on the energy characteristics of the surface and the fluid. The molecules farther above the stationary surface want to move faster but are held back by the slower-moving molecules closer to the surface. Finally, farthest from the stationary surface, the only hindrance to flow is the internal friction between molecules that are trying to move at different speeds relative to one another.

The degree of molecular friction that opposes fluid movement depends on the nature of the molecules. For example, when molecules are large, long or highly concentrated, they cannot readily move from one place to another.

Molecules in liquids interact more slowly at lower temperatures; therefore, liquids are more viscous at lower temperatures.

The slower the molecules interact, the more the fluid will resist changing shape (flowing), and the more viscous it is. The energy needed to overcome internal friction and keep a fluid moving is the coefficient of viscosity. Flow, or movement of different parts of the fluid, causes the stress or shear that creates molecular friction or strain. For many fluids the shear stress (resistance to movement) is directly proportional to the shear rate (the rate at which we stir or try to move the fluid.) Such fluids are called Newtonian fluids. For a Newtonian fluid, shear stress = viscosity × shear rate.

For Newtonian fluids, the amount of shear and the stress (the resistance to flow) change at constant rates relative to each other. With non-Newtonian fluids, the proportion between shear stress and shear strain is not a constant. Water,

---

Table 13.4
Typical viscosities at 20°C (68°F) in mPa × s*.

Fluid	Viscosity
Gasoline	0.65
Water	1.00
Cream	10
Olive oil	100
Honey	100,000
Pitch	10,000,000

*mPa × s = millipascal seconds (see explanation below under "Measuring Viscosity."

Figure 13.8

Viscosity behavior and shear for various non-Newtonian fluids.

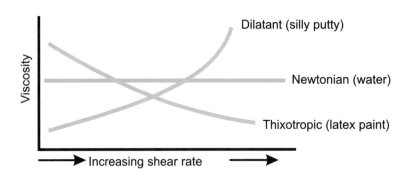

simple organic liquids, gases, and dilute suspensions are Newtonian fluids. More concentrated suspensions and emulsions are non-Newtonian.

Non-Newtonian behavior can be of several types (See Figure 13.8.) Dilatant liquids show an increase in viscosity with increased shear. Silly Putty, sold as an amusement, exhibits dilatancy. If the shear rate is low, the material flows gradually just like a thick syrup. However if the putty is impacted (high shear), it shatters with sharp, angular edges reminiscent of a brittle fracture. At the moment of impact it is, for all practical purposes, a solid. Dilatant behavior is not common and exists mostly in highly filled dispersions.

Pseudoplasticity and thixotropy are the opposite of dilatant behavoiur. The viscosity of a Pseudoplastic will decrease as the rate of shear increases. Thixotropes also start as viscous fluids or semi-solids, but the change in viscosity when stirred is time dependent. Even at a constant low-level shear, their viscosity will decrease.

Many adhesives, paints and inks become thinner as they are stirred. They revert back to their undisturbed viscosity when the shear is removed.

The viscosities of adhesives, inks, coatings and other fluids used in packaging are important. Few are Newtonian; many exhibit varying degrees of pseudoplasticity or thixotropy. Since the fluids experience shear as they are pumped, rolled and applied, it is important to know their viscosity under use conditions.

Each machine condition has an ideal viscosity associated with it. Changing conditions may make a fluid unsuitable for an application; an adhesive that applies well at one application speed may apply poorly at another because of a shift in viscosity.

Measuring Viscosity

The common viscosity unit is the poise (P) and centipoise (cps), named after Poiseulle, a pioneer in rheology. The correct SI unit is the pascal second (Pa × s). For conversion,

10 poise = 1 Pa × s
1 centipoise (cps) = 1 mPa × s

There are many ways of assigning a value to viscosity. Some are empirical while others are more exacting. Some industries have specific methods.

Rotating-cylinder instruments are based on the principle that a cylinder rotated in a liquid will experience a drag proportional to the liquid viscosity. By connecting the spindle through a spring and a pointer, the fluids viscosity can be measured. (See Figure 13.9)

The most common rotating-cylinder instrument is the Brookfield viscometer. Brookfield viscometers are supplied with numbered spindles ranging from a straight rod through rods with a disk or a cylinder. A second series of spindles is used for awkward materials such as pastes and consists of a rod with a crossbar.

A typical Brookfield viscometer has eight speeds or shear rates; coupled with the spindle selection, it is able to measure virtually the entire common viscosity range and to easily characterize non-Newtonian behavior. Temperature-controlled sample cups permit the Brookfield to be used for measuring hot-melt viscosities at use temperature.

Most adhesives are rated with a Brookfield viscometer. Always check that the model, temperature, spindle and revolutions per minute (rpm) are the same when comparing viscosity.

Cone-and-plate viscometers (e.g., the Haake viscometer) consist of a stationary plate and a cone with a small angle. The fluid is sheared between the two, and the resulting resistance to rotation is measured. Cone-and-plate viscometers have the advantage of requiring a small sample and being capable of high absolute shear rates.

Flow-cup or efflux methods are one of the simplest techniques for measuring viscosity and are based on measuring the time for a standard fluid volume to flow through a standard orifice diameter. There are many flow-cup geometries, usually named after the originator (Ford cup, Zahn cup, BS cup, etc.). Since the practical viscosity range available for any orifice size is narrow, the cups usually come in sets, with larger orifices for more viscous liquids. Flow-cup viscosity measurements are easy and convenient to make but are restricted to low-viscosity fluids and are not accurate.

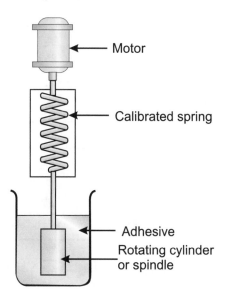

Motor

Calibrated spring

Adhesive
Rotating cylinder
or spindle

Figure 13.9

Operating principle of a rotating-spindle viscometer.

ADHESIVE SELECTION AND CONSIDERATIONS

Adhesive selection should always be done in close consultation with the adhesive supplier. Figure 13.10 shows a general model for selecting adhesives.

Chemistry of Materials to Be Bonded

The chemical nature of the two materials to be joined is the single most important factor when selecting an adhesive. Do not be swayed by similar appearances or similar materials. Every adhesive application must be verified by testing. Special treatments or primers may be needed to achieve good adhesion.

Physical Nature of the Surfaces to Be Bonded

The physical nature of the surfaces to be bonded may dictate certain adhesive choices. For example, recycled paper will have short, closely matted fibers and a surface that is not very porous. A low-solids, low-viscosity adhesive could be used, since it will not readily be "lost" in the board. A kraft stock, on the other hand, will have a long-fiber, open structure with a porous but nonabsorbent surface. The low-solids, low-viscosity adhesive would be "lost" in such an application. A high-solids, high-viscosity adhesive might be a better choice.

Flexible and extensible substrates need flexible and extensible adhesives; otherwise, the adhesive will break loose when the substrate is flexed or stretched.

Figure 13.10

The adhesive selection process.

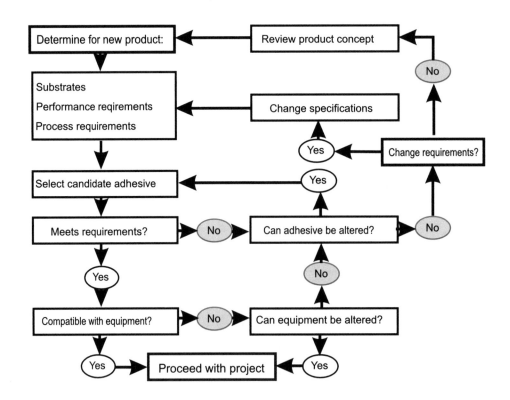

Application Method, Machine Speed, Pot Life

Application method, machine speed and pot life are interrelated and basically describe the manufacturing method. The adhesive's viscosity characteristics must suit the application method and the substrate. "Pot life" refers to the stability of the adhesive in the machine. Reactive thermosets in particular must have a pot life that will preclude them setting up in the machine during normal operations.

Drying time, as opposed to setting speed, may be important in applications where there are frequent machine stoppages. Slower-drying adhesives will not be as likely to foul the machine.

Rate of Assembly

"Open time" describes the time between adhesive application and the time at which the adhesive has set or dried to the point where it has lost tack or the ability to form a bond at the mating surface. An emulsion adhesive that breaks in 7 seconds may not be suitable for an application where there are 10 seconds between adhesive application and part assembly. Similarly, for hot melts, the parts must be joined before the hot melt has cooled to the point where it is incapable of properly wetting the mating surface.

For wet adhesives, the development of tack and the period over which a successful bond can be made is sometimes referred to as the "tack and range." In Figure 13.11, neither the PVA emulsion nor the dextrin has much tack at the beginning. The PVA emulsion rapidly develops tack when the emulsion breaks. The dextrin takes longer to develop tack, and has a longer tack period in which assembly can be done. It is also slower drying. Open time for each adhesive would be the time to peak tack level.

In situations where bonding is performed at such high speeds that the adhesive does not have time to set completely, the adhesive must often restrain other forces (such as spring-back on a folding carton) when the assembled piece leaves the machine. This requires high wet tack or rapid green strength development.

In any application there is *always* an optimum adhesive film thickness. Adhesives that are particularly sensitive to variations in application rate should have more precise methods of metering and application.

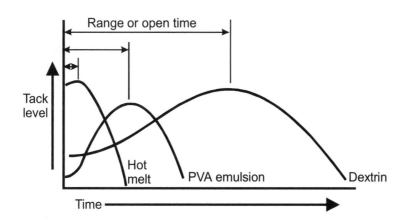

Figure 13.11

"Open time" or "tack and range" for three adhesive types.

Application and End-use Temperatures

Both application and end-use temperature requirements must be taken into account. Some products may still contain process heat, while others may be subjected to thermal processing or freezing. End-use temperatures may be environmental, or they may involve use conditions such as boil-in-bag or microwavable applications.

Humidity and Water Resistance

Water resistance is described in terms like good, poor, fair, waterproof and iceproof. There are varying degrees of water resistance, ranging from merely resisting high humidities to being totally waterproof when immersed.

Poor water resistance generally means easier clean-up. Good water resistance is necessary when the item being packed is wet or the package will be exposed to weather or freezer conditions. Iceproof adhesives (adhesives that remain adhered when immersed in cold water) are needed for brewery and soft drink labeling.

Chemical Resistance

Adhesives can be softened or plasticized by oils or plasticizer compounds that migrate from other materials. Poly(vinyl chloride) plasticizers are especially notorious. Products may also contain volatile ingredients that will deteriorate bond strength. Some flavoring ingredients, such as oil of wintergreen, are particularly aggressive. An adhesive's chemical resistance should be verified in applications involving solvents or other aggressive chemicals.

Food Applications

All food applications must use adhesives approved for that use. The food use status is provided in the U.S. by the Food and Drug Administration or in Canada by the Canadian Health Protection Branch. Some adhesives are capable of imparting off flavors or odors to some foodstuffs.

Color

Dark-colored adhesives may show through substrates with poor opacity. In other applications, color may be added to provide visual evidence of spray or wheel patterns on white board. Hot melts that have been degraded are darker than the color stated on data sheets, indicating aging or degradation.

Specific Density (Weight/Gal. or Kg/Litre)

Specific density is the ratio of product density to that of water at the same temperature. Most adhesives are sold by weight. If they were always used by weight, usage calculations would be simple, but most adhesives and coatings are used by volume (for example, 1 drum/100,000 cases); therefore the lower-density product will provide better yield if all other characteristics are equal.

Some adhesives are extended with fillers and appear less costly when comparing per kilogram price, but when density is taken into account, they are in fact more expensive. If density figures are not available, look at the invoice cost per drum. Compare drums that are the same *volume*. For example:

Product A — $1.35/kg (density 1.1 kg/l)
Product B — $1.45/kg (density 1.01 kg/l)

Product A — cost per litre $1.35 × 1.1 = $1.48/l
Product B — cost per litre $1.45 × 1.01 = $1.47/l

Product B costs more per kilogram, but is the better buy by volume. This assumes that it will be used by volume (extrusion, smooth roll, wheel).

pH (Water-based Adhesives Only)

Following are pH ranges: acidic (2 to 6), neutral (7), alkaline (8–12).

Adhesives at pH extremes, either acid or base (alkaline), should be run with stainless steel equipment. Acidic and alkaline pH systems are not generally compatible and will coagulate when mixed. Resin emulsions are generally acidic. Most latexes and borated dextrins are alkaline. Some substrates can be affected by extreme pH values. Aluminum foil, for example, corrodes quickly in the presence of alkali.

Solids or Nonvolatiles Content

Solids content refers to the solid material that is left behind to do the actual binding of the substrates. Hot melts are 100% solids. Water and solvent-based adhesives can be compared on a dry-weight basis when comparing relative cost.

Product A: 40% solids at $1.25/kg wet, or $\frac{\$1.25}{0.40} = \$3.125$/kg dry

Product B: 60% solids at $1.25/kg wet, or $\frac{\$1.25}{0.60} = \$2.083$/kg dry

If applying 5 grams of coating per square metre, product B is the better buy, since its dry weight is about $1.04/kg less per kilogram.

Storage Life and Storage Conditions

Most liquid adhesives have a storage life over which they will give optimum performance. Oldest stock should always be used first. Adhesives will become thicker in cold temperatures and thinner when it is hot. Adhesives are generally formulated to work at about room temperatures. Accordingly, some attention

Figure 13.12

The result of mixing a water based dextrin adhesive with a water dispersed poly(vinyl acetate) emulsion.

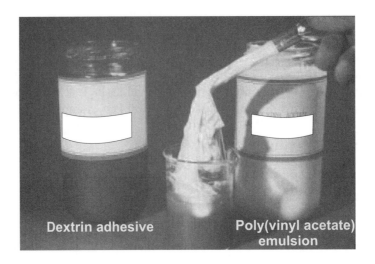

Dextrin adhesive

Poly(vinyl acetate) emulsion

must be given to storing adhesives at reasonable temperatures. (15 to 32°C/60 to 90°F.) If necessary, bring adhesives into the production area to bring them up to plant temperature. Some adhesives (e.g. emulsions) will coagulate if frozen.

Diluting Adhesives

Dilution of adhesives should be discussed with the supplier. Where it is necessary to add water to an adhesive reservoir to make up for evaporation losses, always use an adhesive liquor mixture of half adhesive and half water. Bear in mind that a thixotropic adhesive may appear to be semi-solid after standing for a period of time. Always stir an adhesive and measure viscosity before making any decision about adding diluents.

Adhesives should never be mixed without the express direction of the supplier, even though they may share the same resin or solvent base. For example, a borated dextrin adhesive and an emulsion based adhesive are both water dispersible. However the dextrin is alkaline (pH 9) while the emulsion is acidic. Mixing the two upsets the pH balance and breaks the emulsion. The emulsion resin coagulates into a large insoluble lump. See Figure 13.12.

INSPECTING BOND FAILURES

Identifying what actually came apart is the first step in tracking down a failure's cause, and close inspection of the failed surfaces is usually the first step. This inspection is best done with a good magnifying glass. Figure 13.13 shows three possible outcomes of such an inspection:

* all the adhesive is attached to one of the substrates
* some adhesive is visible on both substrates
* separation has occurred in the substrate.

A fourth possibility is that adhesive has not covered the complete bonding area.

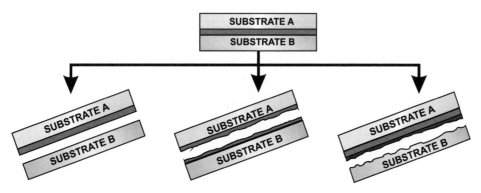

Figure 13.13

When analyzing a bonding failure, it is important to identify exactly where the separation took place—and adhesive failure, a cohesive failure or a substrate failure.

An adhesive failure indicates that the applied adhesive was unable to form a bond to the substrate. This narrows the search down to that interface. Questions to ask:

- Were the surfaces brought together past the adhesive's effective open time?

- Is the dyne level of substrate without adhesive too low?

- Are surface interference layers such as processing oils, anti-static agents, release agents or other materials present?

A cohesive failure suggests that the adhesive does not have enough cohesive strength for the application or that the adhesive application was too heavy. In analyzing this kind of failure, bear in mind that certain volatiles (such as flavoring ingredients) and material additives (such as plasticizers) can migrate into some adhesives and substantially reduce the adhesives cohesiveness.

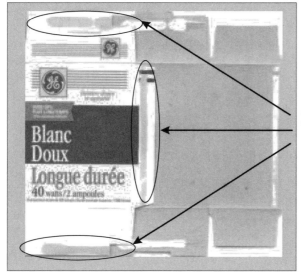

Areas where clay was lifted from the board

Figure 13.14

A clay-lift failure. Dried poly(vinyl acetate) adhesives are translucent, not white. The adhesive has pulled lifted the clay and even some ink off the paperboard. Note that inks and other surface coatings should not extend over gluing areas.

If the inspection reveals that there is material attached to the open failed surface, then the adhesive has bonded well to that surface, but the surfacing material has not bonded well to the mass of the substrate. Common examples of this kind of failure are

- Surface fibers of a paperboard have been torn away (fiber tear failure).

- Clay coating has lifted off the paper. See figure 13.14

- Printing ink or a varnish coating has separated from the substrate.

- A laminate layer has separated from the body of the laminate.

Areas devoid of adhesive on either substrate surface suggest incomplete adhesive coverage. This kind of failure will be accompanied by one of the other symptoms. The adhesive should be reapplied at the proper rate and the bond re-evaluated to see if it meets performance requirements.

REVIEW QUESTIONS

1. Explain the two theories of adhesion.

2. Of the four adhesive types—starch, dextrin, hot melt, and PVA emulsion—which will have the highest solids content and which will have the lowest?

3. Name three features that might make hot melts a favored choice.

4. Name two places where you would not use a hot melt.

5. What are the major applications of the following adhesive classes and why are they chosen for these applications? Starch adhesive, casein adhesive, cold-seal adhesives?

6. A production engineer is not happy with the strength of an adhesive bond, so he increases the amount of adhesive. To his surprise, the bond is even weaker. What has happened?

7. You are examining the bond failure between a plastic film and a carton board. What might be your conclusions if you observed:

   a. All the adhesive was on the carton board.

   b. The adhesive is evenly distributed between the carton board and the plastic film.

   c. The adhesive was all on the plastic film, and the failure surface had a powdery whitish, appearance.

   d. The adhesive was all on the film, and the failure surface had a lot of paper fibre stuck to it.

8. What is the difference between a cohesive failure and an adhesive failure?

9. What are the four basic solidification methods for adhesives?

10. What is meant by the term "wettability," what does it indicate, and why is it important?

11. List five factors you would take into account when selecting an adhesive for an application.

12. A PVA emulsion adhesive will form an initial adhesive bond much faster than a dextrin adhesive with the same solids content. Why?

13. True or false:

   a. Viscosity is a good indicator of solids content.

    b. Two different adhesives can be mixed, providing they are both water-based systems.

    c. A cold-seal adhesive is one that has a tendency to stick to itself.

14. Describe the flow characteristics of a thixotropic fluid.

15. Why might it be important to know the viscosity of an adhesive at several shear rates?

16. What does corona treatment do?

CONTENTS

Laminates

Why make laminated packaging materials, desired properties.

Aluminum Foil

Production, characteristics, flexible packaging applications, coatings, decorating, pin-holing and flex cracking.

Vacuum Metallizing

Process, metallized paper advantages and applications, metallized film advantages and applications, microwave applications, optical density.

Other Non-Organic Coatings and Barrier Teatments

Silicone oxide and carbon coating, nanocomposites

Laminate Structural and Physical Properties

Tensile strength, elongation, toughness, processing stresses, stiffness, obtaining bulk. Coefficient of friction, body and deadfold, tear, thermoformability, use environments.

Flexible Bags, Pouches and Sachets

Vertical form-fill-seal, horizontal form-fill-seal, multi-lane form-fill seal, basic pouch styles, advantages and disadvantages.

Sealability

Heat seal materials and applications, cold seals, typical-seal temperatures.

Barrier Properties

General barrier qualities for oxygen and moisture, aroma constituents, metal foil as a barrier, oxygen permeability units, oxygen and moisture, high barrier-plastics, permeability test methods, general proportionality of barrier material properties, low barrier requirements, light barrier.

Aesthetics and Other Properties

Clarity, reverse printing, metallizing, tie layers, primers, reflecting radiant heat, static dissipation.

Laminating Processes

Wet bonding, dry bonding, hot-melt bonding, extrusion and co-extrusion. General configuration of a laminating machine, gravure coating, extrusion laminating process, wet-bond laminator configuration, dry-bond laminator configuration.

Specifying Laminates

Listing plies, caliper measurement conventions, standard roll orientation descriptions.

Examples of Laminates

Retort pouch, aseptic juice box, infant formula pouch, lidding stock, ketchup portion pack, snack-food bag, luncheon meat web, collapsible-tube web, high- oxygen-barrier EVAL web, dry-food pouch, candy bar wrap, tobacco overwrap, shampoo pouch.

FLEXIBLE PACKAGING LAMINATES

LAMINATES

The purpose of a laminate is to combine the best of all properties—protection, aesthetics, machinability, and cost—into a single packaging structure. Laminates are made for the simple reason that there is no "super-substrate" possessing all desired properties for all applications. For example, polyethylene is economical and a good water vapor barrier, but it is a poor oxygen barrier and may elongate if used to contain a heavy product. Poly(ethylene terephthalate) is a better barrier to oxygen, but it does not heat-seal well and is more expensive.

Flexible packaging based on laminates has been a major packaging growth areas in recent decades. Despite questions concerning the environmental status of multimaterial laminates, it is certain that these materials will continue to be a healthy part of the packaging mix simply because they are typically designed to replace a more material- or energy-intensive option.

A multi-layered construction can be made by bonding together two or more selected material plies. The plies may be assembled by joining roll-fed materials using coater-laminating machines, by coextrusion of multiple layers of plastic, or by some combination of these. Companies engaged in the production of laminated structures are generally classed as being "converters". Most converters will also print the flexible materials they produce.

Usually, but not always, these plies will be in roll-fed form. The problem of creating an optimum flexible packaging material for an application is resolved by selecting materials that have the individual desired properties and combining them into a single laminated structure featuring the most desirable attributes of the individual plies.

Individual laminate materials can best be examined by the quality or property they contribute to the final product.

- Compatibility with the product.

- Structural properties such as physical strength, elongation, puncture resistance, abrasion resistance and dead-fold.

- Performance properties such as machinability, sealability, environmental tolerance (i.e. Freezing, boil-in-bag, microwaving).

- Barrier properties against water vapor, gas, odor, ultraviolet light.

- Aesthetic properties such as clarity, opacity, feel, metallic appearance.

These and other required performance characteristics must be delivered at minimum cost. Laminates are assembled from various combinations of paper, adhesives, plastic films, surface coatings, aluminum foils and aluminum metallized paper and foil. With exception of aluminum, all of these materials have been discussed in previous chapters.

ALUMINUM FOIL

Aluminum is made from bauxite, a clay-like deposit containing aluminum oxides and silicates. Pure aluminum is a soft, silvery white, comparatively light metal (about one-third the weight of steel). The metal is ductile and malleable at normal temperatures and is a good conductor of heat and electricity.

Aluminum alloys containing small amounts of copper, zinc, magnesium, manganese and/or chromium have excellent strength properties. Alloys 1100, 1145 and 1235 are most commonly used for reroll stock. Alloy 3003, containing manganese, is used in applications such as pie plates, where good draw and greater stiffness are required. Aluminum and its alloys can be reclaimed readily at about 5% of the energy consumption required to refine the original ore.

Aluminum Foil Production

By definition, rolled aluminum less than 152.4 micrometres (0.006 inch) is called foil. Foil is produced by being rolled from ingots or by continuous casting in-line with the furnace. All foil is supplied in 0 temper, the softest, most workable form.

A typical continuous-casting foil production line runs in-line from the melting furnace at the start to a winding reel at the end. The system continuously feeds, casts, chills and coils the foil, eliminating an intermediate ingot-making step. Continuous-cast foil stock does not need to be re-annealed when being converted to foil. It is in an annealed condition as fabricated. Ingot-rolled stock must be re-annealed between mill passes to eliminate work hardening and restore workability.

Rolling is a form of extrusion. Aluminum entering the roll nip encounters a squeezing force exerted downwards and in the machine direction. The displaced metal is moved or extruded through the nip, always in the web travel direction because this offers the least resistance to metal flow. Each pass through a rolling mill reduces metal thickness and at the same time increases its length, while the width remains essentially the same.

The work-rolls that come into contact with the metal have finely ground and polished surfaces to ensure flatness and a bright finish. The work rolls are paired with heavier backup rolls, which bear against the work rolls, exerting pressure to help prevent deflection of the work rolls. This ensures gauge uniformity across the web.

The foil faces in contact with the work-rolls are polished to a bright finish. When a single web is run, both sides are bright. Foil gauges under 25 micrometres (0.001 inch) usually pass through the nip back-to-back, two at a time. The foil-to-foil face of each web has a satin-like matte finish. Other finishes can be produced with special patterns on work rolls or, more commonly by using separate or in-line mechanical finishing machines. (See Table 14.1)

Chemical Characteristics

When exposed to air, an aluminum surface acquires a natural, hard transparent oxide layer that resists further oxidation. Aluminum foil's resistance to chemical

Table 14.1
Standard aluminum foil finishes and treatments used in packaging.

Type of Finish	Description
Bright two sides (B2S)	Uniform bright specular finish, two sides.
Extra-bright two sides (EB2S)	Uniform extra-bright specular finish, two sides.
Matte one side (M1S)	Diffuse reflecting finish, one side.
Matte two sides (M2S)	Diffuse reflecting finish, two sides.
Embossed	Pattern impressed by engraved roll or plate.
Annealed	Completely softened by thermal treatment.
Chemically cleaned	Chemically washed to remove lubricants.
Hard	Foil fully work-hardened by rolling.
Intermediate temper	Foil temper between annealed and hard.

attack depends on the specific compound or agent which it contacts. Aluminum resists mildly acidic products better than mildly alkaline compounds such as soaps or detergents. Strong mineral acids will corrode bare foil. The mild organic acids generally found in food have little or no effect on aluminum.

Aluminum has high resistance to most fats, petroleum-based greases and organic solvents. Generally, food products such as candies, milk, unsalted meats, butter and margarine are compatible with bare aluminum, as are many drug and cosmetic products.

Intermittent contact with clean water has no visible effect on aluminum foil. However, in the presence of some salts and caustics, standing water can be corrosive. Hygroscopic products may cause corrosion if packaged in bare aluminum foil, particularly where a product contains salt or some mild organic acid. Applications that may subject aluminum to mild attack use coated, or laminated stock on the next-to-product surface. The decision as to whether to use a bare, coated or laminated surface in contact with a product must be based on reliable information and suitable testing.

Aluminum Foil in Flexible Packaging

Aluminum foil has many unique qualities that account for its widespread use in packaging.

Appearance   Aluminum foil has a bright, reflective metallic gloss that projects an exceptionally attractive and upscale appearance. In packaging, all reflective gloss surfaces are either solid aluminum foil or an aluminum metallized surface.

Barrier Properties	Heavier foil gauges (> 17 μm/0.0007 inch) are 100% barrier to all gases. As thickness is reduced, pinholing becomes more common. Typical water-vapor transmission rate (WVTR) for 0.00035-inch foil is 0.02 grams or less per 100 square inches per 24 hours. Many foil applications make use of foil's excellent gas and light barrier properties. Food and nonfood products that are ultraviolet degradable are protected by foil's opacity
Dead-fold	Foil has superior dead-fold properties. Dead fold is the ability of a material to hold the geometry of a fold. Wraps that must stay in place without adhesive assistance and roll-up collapsible tubes require this property.
Friability	Unsupported foil is easily punctured and torn, key properties when designing unit-dose and dispensing-tablet packages as well as various tear-away seals. An added benefit is the inherent tamper evidence.
Hygienic	Aluminum foil can be easily sterilized. The smooth, metallic surface does not absorb contaminants. It is inert to or forms no harmful compounds with most food, cosmetic or other chemical products.
Conductivity	Microwave susceptor films, electrostatic shielding and induction heat sealing are examples of applications that depend on aluminum's abilty to conduct electricity and heat.
Formability	Aluminum is a ductile metal. Heavier foils can be molded into trays and cups. Sheet stock is drawn into a variety of beverage and other can types. Solid aluminum slugs are impact-extruded into collapsible tubes, cigar humidor tubes and aerosol cans.

Foils are available in thicknesses of as little as 4 micrometres (0.00017 inch). The selection of foil alloys, gauges and tempers for bare conversion or for combining with other materials will be determined by the end use and by conversion process requirements.

Foil Coatings

Packaging applications for plain foil are relatively limited and largely decorative. In most applications, aluminum foil is coated, and such coating may:

* render the foil surface heat sealable

* increase foil's scratch or scuff resistance

- increase tensile or burst strength

- produce a specific surface (e.g., slip, nonslip, release, decorative)

- improve adhesion of other coatings or printing inks

- enhance the water-vapor/gas-barrier properties of light-gauge foils

- increase foil's resistance to corrosive agents or products

- impart high gloss and three-dimensional depth to foil decoration or printing

- lubricate during converting or processing operations

Coatings are employed to protect the package, the product or both. Coatings generally can be classified as decorative, protective or heat sealing. In most instances a coating is selected for one characteristic, but one coating may embody all three, as in a tinted, heat-sealable coating with high food-product compatibility.

Transparent lacquers and varnishes allow the brilliant reflective metallic sheen to show through. A transparent yellow lacquer would give the appearance of gold, while a transparent reddish orange would look like a copper alloy. Foil printed with an opaque ink has a particularly smooth, hard appearance.

The inherent heat sealability of many protective coatings is an added bonus. Effective heat-seal coatings provide strong, usually airtight seams and closures. Poly(vinyl chloride) heat-seal coatings are widely used with aluminum foil, but other formulations are also available. It is essential that the coating be compatible with all materials it contacts to protect and seal the contents.

Heat-seal coatings do not appreciably add to a foil's bursting or tear strength in thicknesses under 25 micrometres (0.001 in.).

Various polymeric coatings are applied by extrusion or co-extrusion. More typically, such coatings are used in combination with foil and other substrates such as papers, paperboards and plastic films to produce a multipropertied laminated material. Potential coating applications should be developed as individual cases. Selected materials and application weights should satisfy production criteria for coating and converting. Table 14.2 lists common coating materials and their chemical resistance properties.

Decorating and Printing

Foil offers graphic designers a unique surface capable of producing a kaleidoscope of attractive effects unattainable with other materials. Unlike paper, foil is fluid in its play of light and shadow and will tend to pick up surrounding tones and light values. Thus, it can shine bright white, recede into rich black or reflect colors from adjacent objects. While this mirror-like quality provides the essential excitement in foil design, it should be exploited or muted with intelligence and discretion.

Type on foil, unless fairly large, tends to be overpowered by the surrounding brilliance and may prove difficult to read. Reverse type on bare foil should be avoided unless it is display sized. Opaque white is often put down first to avoid

Table 14.2

Chemical resistance of coating materials. (Source: Aluminum Association, Aluminum Standards and Data).

Coating Type	Acid	Alkali	Water	Solvent
Acrylics	fair	fair	fair	good
Alkyd	fair	fair	good	good
Butadiene-styrene	excellent	excellent	excellent	good
Butyrate	fair	fair	fair	fair
Cellulose acetate	fair	fair	fair	fair
Chlorinated rubber	excellent	excellent	excellent	fair
Epoxies	excellent	excellent	excellent	excel
Ethyl cellulose	fair	excellent	good	fair
Melamine	excellent	excellent	good	good
Nitrocellulose	good	fair	excellent	good
Polyamide-epoxy	fair	excellent	excellent	good
Polyester	good	fair	good	good
Polystyrene	excellent	excellent	excellent	fair
Poly(vinyl acetate)	fair	fair	good	poor
Poly(vinylidene chloride)	excellent	excellent	excellent	fair
PVA chloride copolymer	excellent	excellent	excellent	fair
Urea	excellent	excellent	excellent	good

reflectivity in a given design element and to provide a base for fine-screen process work. Foil can be used to design advantage within the printed design, shining through appropriate areas of the process halftones.

Foil that is to be printed is usually given a primer or wash coat to anchor the ink. A further function is to provide a barrier keep undesirable materials from coming into contact with the foil surface prior to printing or coating. Wash coating is frequently done in conjunction with a laminating operation. Shellacs and vinyls are common primers for rotogravure and flexo printing. Heavier coatings, generally vinyl copolymer or nitrocellulose, are applied for lithographic printing. A second coating is sometimes applied over the printing to give scuff resistance or to reduce surface friction.

Thin, annealed foil is readily embossed in web form by passing the web between an engraved steel roll and a soft matrix roll. Laminated foils or heavier-gauge foils may be embossed with two engraved steel rolls. The design positive is engraved on one roll, the design negative is engraved on the other. Embossed copy can be used in applications where plain or coated foil is allowed, but printing inks or lacquer cannot be used.

The multiple "pre-creasing" effect achieved with an overall embossed pattern generally improves dead-fold properties. This is an advantage in packaging where nonadhered overlaps and end folds are employed (e.g., butter and margarine wraps).

Foil Pinholing and Flex Cracking

Most foils used for packaging applications are in gauges below 13 micrometres (0.0005 inch.) Household foil is about 18 micrometres (0.0007 inch.) Although solid aluminum foils theoretically offer a total barrier to all gases, minute holes occur at thinner gauges because of metallurgical impurities and variations. "Pinholing" increases as foil gauge decreases and obviously is a major pathway for gas penetration. Gas penetration through pinholes is reduced somewhat when a foil is coated or laminated with polymeric materials.

Aluminum foils are also subject to "flex cracking," the splitting of the foil when worked. A flex crack can provide a significant entry point for gases. Heavy laminates tend to reduce the tendency to flex-crack.

Foil laminates intended for barrier applications should be evaluated for barrier properties on the finished package after all machining is complete and preferably after a real or simulated shipping cycle. It is not uncommon for a prospective barrier laminate to have no measurable permeability in the flat but to have significant permeability when formed, folded and creased into a package.

VACUUM METALLIZING

The Metallizing Process

"Vacuum metallizing" refers to the depositing of a metal layer onto a substrate, carried out in a vacuum. Although many metals can be vacuum-deposited, only aluminum is used in packaging. The process, developed in the late 1940s, emerged as an important option for flexible packaging in the 1970s. Currently, packaging is the largest consumer of metallized papers and plastic films.

The initial role of metallized materials was for their decorative and aesthetic values. Recognition of the materials' functional properties has greatly extended packaging applications. Metallizing plastics improves gas- and light-barrier properties, provides heat and light reflectance and electrical conductivity. The barrier properties achieved are a product of the thickness of the metal deposit and the properties of the substrate being metallized.

Most metallizing is done as a batch processes. A typical system employs a horizontal tubular chamber, up to 2.1 metres (84 inches) in diameter and 2.8 metres (110 inches) long. Paper or film rolls are loaded onto unwind stations on one side of the chamber. The web is led down through tension rolls, under a large chilled roller, and through tension rollers to a rewind roll. (See Figure 14.1) A vacuum is needed within the chamber to help aluminum vaporize at a lower temperature and to minimize oxidation of the metal vapor as it rises to the web.

Pure aluminum wire, approximately 3.2 millimetres (1/8 inch) thick, is fed into machined metal "boats" located below the chilled drum. These are electrically heated to aluminum vaporizing temperatures. The boats rest in water-cooled troughs to extract radiant heat and minimize stray vaporization. Vaporized

Figure 14.1

Cross section of a representative batch metallizing chamber.

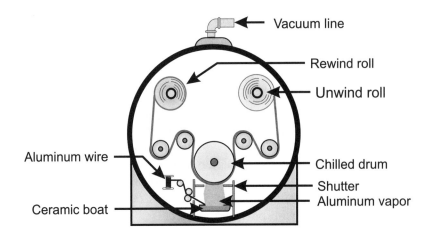

aluminum rises up and then condenses on the underside of the film or paper web as it passes over the chill roll. The thickness of the metal deposited is controlled by a combination of web speed, wire feed rate and boat temperature.

Pattern metallizing is not possible with current technology; however metallized pattern effects can be achieved by metallizing a preprinted film. Another process uses caustic solutions to selectively remove the metallized layer to create clear windows in a metallized film.

Vacuum Metallizing Paper

Most metallized papers are quality virgin stocks clay coated on one or two sides, depending on end-use criteria. The clay coating's weight varies, but, generally, higher coating weights provide a smoother surface and higher reflective values in the metallized surface. All paper stock must be lacquer coated before being metallized. The gravure-applied lacquer seals the surface, enhances surface smoothness and promotes consistent metal adhesion.

Since the high vacuum within the chamber will boil away moisture, the paper's moisture content is normally reduced to below 5%. Remoisturizing is an essential production step after metallizing paper; this step reestablishes correct moisture content in the paper to improve its resistance to curling. Gravure coaters apply the primer coating for post-metallizing printing.

Vacuum metallized paper gains the aesthetic appeal of a reflective aluminum surface but does not gain barrier properties. A major market for metallized papers is for label stock.

Vacuum Metallizing Films

Plastic film being metallized does not need to be sealed, smoothed or dried as a paper substrate does. In addition to adding decorative appeal, metallizing a plastic film significantly improves barrier properties to all gases. Although most plastic films can be metallized, oriented polypropylene (OPP), poly(ethylene terephthalate) (PET) and nylon (PA) are the most commonly metallized films.

OPP is the most widely metallized film. Snack-food packaging is its single largest application with potato chip bags being a major consumer. Metallization compliments OPP's properties. OPP:

- is excellent moisture barrier.
- offers use temperatures up to 150°C (300°F)
- is a limited oxygen barrier (significantly improved by metallizing)
- is economical
- produces a fair metal-to-film bond

Desirable properties also encourage PET's use. This material:

- produces the best metal to film bond

- offers the best combination of oxygen-, moisture- and UV light-barrier properties

- offers high use temperatures (Up to 205°C/400°F)

Metallized biaxially oriented nylon (BON) films first gained market share in retail and institutional flexible packaging of ground coffee because of nylon's barrier qualities and resistance to abrasive coffee granules. Metallized PET is also used in this market niche because of current cost advantages. BON film:

- is a good oxygen barrier
- has excellent tear, abrasion, flex crack and puncture resistance
- is hygroscopic (modest moisture barrier)
- is more costly than OPP or PET

Metallized films are used alone in some applications but are usually a component in a laminated structure.

Microwave Applications

Metallizing is used in "susceptor" packaging where the metallized component serves to create a local microwave energy "hot spot" (the aluminum converts microwave energy to radiant heat). Microwave popcorn and frozen pizza are two applications where metallized susceptors are used. Since susceptors are exposed to high temperatures, PET is the base material of choice. The metal deposition level is low.

Measuring Metal Deposition

Metal deposition thickness is one factor determining a metallized substrate's barrier properties. Aluminum deposition is on the order of 1 millionth of an inch, and so thickness measurement must be done indirectly.

Electrical resistance and optical density are two methods used to measure the deposited layer's thickness. The industry prefers the optical density method

Table 14.3

Conversion table for aluminum deposition. Typical applications call for about 2% light transmission.

Angstroms	Optical Density	Percent Transmission	Ohms/sq. Resistance
50.8	1.10	7.94	5.35
63.5	1.20	6.31	4.55
71.1	1.30	5.01	3.98
81.3	1.40	3.98	3.50
84.0	1.50	3.16	3.32
98.5	1.60	2.51	3.06
101.6	1.70	2.00	2.86
106.7	1.80	1.59	2.68
114.3	1.90	1.26	2.50
121.9	2.00	1.00	2.35
127.0	2.10	0.79	2.20

when measuring deposition on clear plastic films. A densitometer measures the amount of light that penetrates through a metallized material, providing data that is expressed as percentage of light transmission. Electrical resistance is expressed in terms of ohms per square. The expressions are readily converted. (See Table 14.3)

OTHER NON-ORGANIC COATINGS AND BARRIER TREATMENTS

An advantage of aluminum vacuum metallizing of plastic films is the significant increase in barrier properties. However, by its nature, the aluminum deposit makes the package opaque. This is a benefit in some applications since it eliminates UV light degradation. However, in many instances there is a desire to have both high gas barrier and high clarity as well.

There has been ongoing work to develop other inorganic treatments to improve barrier and retain clarity at the same time. Significant advances have been made in depositing silicone oxides (SiO_x) and carbon (DLC or diamond-like coating). Both methods use plasma deposition technology rather than vacuum metallizing.

Silicone oxide. Like aluminum, SiO_x (or glass coatings) significantly improves gas barrier. Oxygen permeation values of 0.046 cc/m^2/24 hr (0.003 cc/100 in^2/24 hr) have been reported. A significant advantage is that these coated films are clear and unlike aluminum metallized films, glass-coated films can be micro-waved. The glass coating is clear and tolerates folding and flexing of the film without significant loss of barrier.

The coating is applied using plasma technology. Plasma is a gas that has been activated using electro-magnetic energy sources to the point at which portions of the gas separate into electrons, free radicals, ions and other excited state species. Fluorescent and neon lights are examples of this process.

The highly reactive species present in plasma interact with the first few atomic layers of a surface, breaking some chemical bonds and forming others. These reactions change material surface properties without changing bulk properties. The deposition of thin films of silicone oxides (in the order of 500 angstroms) onto PET, PP, PA or other film surfaces is of interest to the packaging industry.

The cost of producing SiO_x coated films is still high, but a number of commercial applications, notably in the medical supply sector, are making use of the technology.

Carbon coatings. A number of companies have developed methods for depositing thin films of carbon over plastic substrates. The coatings are clear and claim to offer substantial barrier improvement over untreated plastic.

"Nanocomposite" technology describes a technique wherein extraordinarily fine particles of plate-like minerals such as clay are incorporated into the plastic. The mineral platelets themselves are not permeable to gases and so a permeating molecule has to go around each platelet. The overall effect is that a permeating molecule has to work its way through a circuitous path that is several orders of magnitude greater than the actual thickness of the film. Nanocomposite films are said to be relatively clear.

LAMINATE STRUCTURAL AND PHYSICAL PROPERTIES

Structural properties are related to physical strength and performance. Physical strength is needed to hold the product. Relatively little strength is required to hold packaged dry soup, coffee or confectionery products; more is needed when designing a 20-kilogram bag for industrial or bulk products.

For large bags, one might suppose that a material with high tensile strength such as PET would be a good choice. However, material in a large bulk bag must be resistant to tear propagation. It should be reasonably flexible in the heavy gauges that would be used, and the large bag size puts a premium on material economy. Medium-density, low-density and linear low-density polyethylene better meet these requirements. The bags may be monolayer or could be coextruded with LLDPE, Surlyn or EVA as a heat sealing layer. Additional layers might be incorporated if high barrier is required.

A material with low elongation is desirable for heavy products; otherwise the weight would distort or stretch the package. Materials such as PET provide high tensile strength and low elongation. However, even though polyethylene has high elongation compared to polyester, the thick film gauges used for heavy products usually minimize this problem. Heavy-gauge polyethylene combinations provide the performance needed at a lower cost.

The property of "toughness"—the ability to resist puncture and abrasion—is needed for products that are abrasive or that have sharp edges. Nylon provides this, and frozen primal meat cuts are packed in nylon-based laminates for this reason. Some coffee brick pack laminates have a nylon layer to resist the abrasiveness of coffee grounds.

Product weight or physical characteristics are not the only structural criteria. Retort pouches, for example, must undergo commercial sterilization that subjects the pouch to extreme temperatures and pressure. End use and consumer preference may also dictate structural elements. Both a paperboard box and a polyethylene bag will hold fluid, but the paperboard box stands by itself. Stiffer materials must be used where pouches must stand by themselves. A gusseted pouch bottom provides the required geometry to stiffen a flexible pouch.

Coefficient of Friction

Machinability is a composite of many properties, one of the most important being coefficient of friction (CoF). "CoF" refers to the material's ability to slide over itself, the product or a machine part during conveying, filling, collating and casing operations. CoF can be reported as static CoF (the force needed to start an object moving from a standstill) and kinetic or dynamic CoF (the force required to maintain motion once it has been initiated.) Static and kinetic CoF are almost identical for some materials, while in others static CoF can be significantly higher than kinetic CoF. Kinetic CoF is never higher than static CoF.

CoF can vary dramatically, depending on the surfaces being compared and the speed and temperatures at which the material is running. There are numerous CoF test procedures; always ensure that identical methods are being compared and that the appropriate test is being used. CoF is critical for vertical form/fill/seal (VFFS) equipment and somewhat less critical on horizontal form/fill/seal (HFFS) equipment.

Generally, a low CoF allows for easy running of the web over stationary parts. However, low CoF can detrimentally affect material feeds where a traction device is used to pull film through the operation; (for example in a vertical form-fill-seal machine) low COF can make for a slippery, unstable package. A low CoF, in the range of 0.12 to 0.2, would be considered slippery. A CoF range of 0.25 to 0.35 would be considered high.

ASTM D 1894 Coefficient of Static and Kinetic Friction of Plastic Film and Sheet describes one method of determining friction values.

Body and Dead-Fold Properties

Stiffness and "bulk" are usually obtained by incorporating economical paper layers into the laminate. Heavier aluminum foils, thicker-gauge plastics and cellular plastics are also used to impart stiffness, depending on other properties that may be desired.

Laminated collapsible tubes must have some "body" or substance as well as the ability to dead fold, so that they can be rolled up as the contents are ejected. Both paper and foil are used in the laminate layers of this construction.

Some laminate constructions are used as simple wraps where the material's ability to conform to the wrapped object, and to stay permanently in position without a sealing medium, is vital. Aluminum foils have the best dead-fold properties, followed by paper. Most plastic films have relatively poor dead fold. However some polypropylene, high-density polyethylene an poly(vinyl chloride) films have been designed to have reasonably good dead-fold.

Tear Properties

Films such as PET and polypropylene tend to propagate tears; that is, once a small cut or puncture has been made in the film, a tear readily propagates from this point. Other films, such as the polyethylenes, do not propagate a tear.

While a package should not tear open in transit, easy opening is a user benefit. Most plastic laminates have awkward tear properties. Tear properties can be enhanced by paper or aluminum foil layers. In instances where a notch-sensitive material is being used, a small nick at the laminate's edge can help initiate the tearing action.

Thermoformability

Meat or cheese packs that have one part of the web drawn to a product-conforming tray require easy formability of the web stock. The web stock also needs to have clarity to show off the product, and must have good oxygen-barrier properties. This combination of properties is best found in nylon-based laminates. (OPP does not thermoform and does not heat seal.) The laminate would be coated, usually with poly(vinylidene chloride) (PVDC) to improve barrier qualities, and with an ionomer (Surlyn) heat-seal coating to seal through any fats on the seal line.

Laminated materials are also used to thermoform rigid high-barrier cups and tubs for shelf-stable microwavable products. The material for these applications is in the order of 380 micrometres (0.015 inch) thick compared to the 10 to 50 micrometres (0.0004 to 0.002 inch) typical of flexible constructions.

Use Environments

Laminate materials must be selected on the basis of the environment the package will experience. Adhesives and components with low melting point adhesives and components can't be used for boil-in-bag, ovenable or microwaveable applications. The package would come apart. Unoriented polypropylenes and some vinyls become brittle at low temperatures. Poly(ethylene terephthalate) (PET) and polycarbonate have the highest use temperature. For this reason, most dual ovenable applications use PET as the base plies.

FLEXIBLE BAGS, POUCHES AND SACHESTS

Vertical and Horizontal Form-Fill-Seal Machines

Every machine has its own characteristics and material requirements for optimum running. Since most webs are pulled through a machine, the material's yield point, the force at which permanent deformation takes place, is critical. Where eye-mark or other register points must be observed, recoverable elongation is also important. Other performance requirements will vary depending on the laminate purpose and application.

A significant proportion of flexible packaging is produced and filled on vertical form-fill-seal (VFFS) machines or horizontal form-fill-seal (HFFS) machines. (See Figures 14.2 and 14.3) In a typical VFFS machine, the package material is unwound at the back of the machine and follows a vertical path over a forming collar where the flat material is shaped into a tube. A longitudinal seal is put into the tube, and product is introduced from the top. After product filling, horizontal sealing bars place a heat seal across the bag width, at the same time cutting across the center of the horizontal seal to separate one package, while leaving the tube sealed at the bottom ready to receive the next product dump.

HFFS machines operate with the package-material roll stock being fed horizontally over a forming collar. Heat-seal bars seal-off the appropriate-sized pouch and, after filling, seal the completed package. Depending on machine design, the formed pouch may be cut away from the parent web before or after filling. In some designs, laminate material may be formed directly around the product.

Both machine types can be used to fill liquid, powder, granular materials or small multiple products. VFFS equipment typically occupies a smaller footprint but is more restricted in the number of filling or functional stations that can be grouped over the pouch. Horizontal machines can have a great number of operating stations grouped along the horizontal travel path of the pouch. This allows for multiple filling heads, steam purges, and other activities.

Figure 14.2

Material and product flow in a vertical form-fill-seal (VFFS) machine.

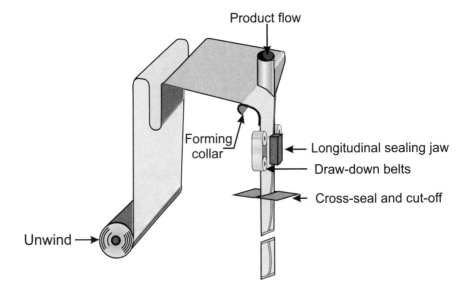

Product flow

Forming collar

Longitudinal sealing jaw

Draw-down belts

Cross-seal and cut-off

Unwind

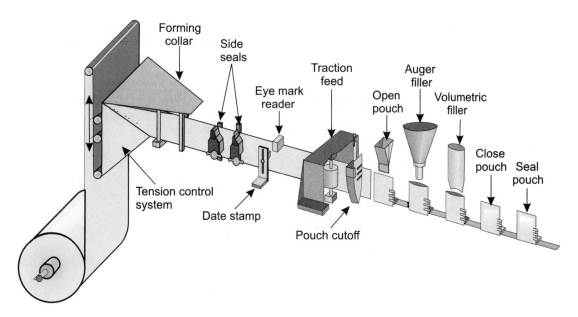

Figure 14.3

Material and product flow in a horizontal form-fill-seal (HFFS) machine.

Multiple lane VFFS machines (See Figure 14.4) mostly fill smaller pouches such as single-service condiments (mustard, ketchup, etc.) and sample sachets. Some high-volume larger pouches are also filled on multiple lane machines. Since the machine is fed from two separate material rolls, there is the opportunity to use two different materials; an opaque back and a clear front, for example.

Pouches made on a VFFS machine are characterized by a seal across the pouch top and bottom and a vertical seal across the center of the back. A fin style vertical seal is easier to make since it brings together two inside heat seal coated surfaces. However it uses slightly more material and the flattened seal is

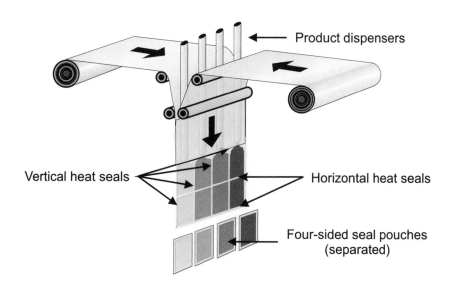

Figure 14.4

A multiple lane VFFS machine.

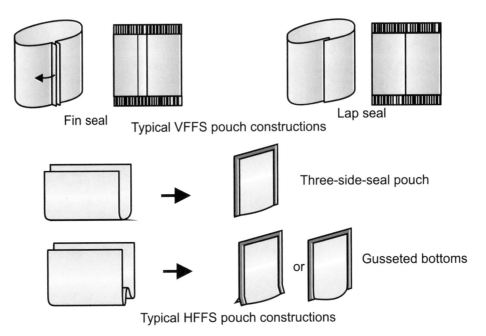

Fin seal   Typical VFFS pouch constructions   Lap seal

Three-side-seal pouch

or   Gusseted bottoms

Typical HFFS pouch constructions

arguably not as aesthetically pleasing as a lap seal. A lap seal looks better and uses less material, however it requires that an inside surface be able to bond to the package outside surface. (See Fig 14.5)

Pouches made on HFFS machines are characterized by a three-sided edge seal. A graphics advantage is that both front and back panels are free of seals. HFFS pouches can be easily accommodated to produce gusseted stand-up pouches.

Multiple lane FFS pouches will have four sealed edges.

SEALABILITY

The majority of flexible packages are closed by heat sealing. The layer that provides this capacity is important, since seal integrity is absolutely essential, particularly for pharmaceuticals, foods, liquids and fine powders. Heat-seal materials must be closely matched to the machine and the operating parameters being used to create the seal.

Heat sealing temperature, dwell time, and sealing jaw pressure are the machine variables. However, a machine is set to run at a designed speed, so dwell time is a given within narrow limits. Jaw pressure is also fixed within narrow limits by the machine and is difficult to measure. In practice most heat seal control involves manipulating the temperature.

Waxes and wax blends are the most economical heat seal materials, but they are not strong and have limited low- and high-temperature tolerance. They can be used only in noncritical applications.

Low-density polyethylenes are the most common heat-sealing mediums, although performance properties and cost varies widely depending on the specific type of polyethylene. These may be formulated with other additives or copolymers to improve selected adhesive qualities. Polyethylenes can be applied by

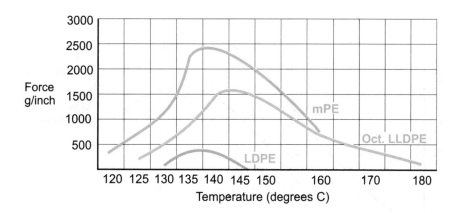

Figure 14.6

Hot tack strength of LDPE, LDPE (octene), LLDPE and (metallocene) PE compared. (Source: M. Lutteroti, DuPont).

extrusion, or a previously formed film can be bonded onto the laminate with an adhesive. In both instances, the film forms a layer over the entire laminate and contributes other properties as well as heat sealability.

Where the seal requirements are more challenging, LDPE is replaced by more aggressive heat seal mediums. Figure 14.6 shows hot tack strength of different polyethylene grades, and Table 14.4 indicates general performance and cost of common heat-sealing materials.

Poly(vinyl chloride) formulations are used where the heat seal is to a PVC cup or portion pack. Ionomers (e.g. DuPont's Surlyn) are used where high melt strength is needed. Ionomers tolerate contaminants and create adequate heat seals across contaminants such as bacon fat or fine powders. They also have superior adhesion to metal surfaces. Acrylic polymers (e.g. DuPont's Nucrel) are sometimes used alone or blended with other materials to increase adhesion to metals.

Hot melts formulated to seal at temperatures as low as 60°C (140°F) can be used when LDPE's higher seal temperature (120°C/250°F) is not acceptable. Hot melts are easier to pattern-print and have easier seal initiation at lower

Table 14.4

The most common heat-sealing materials in the general order of performance and cost.

Material	Comments
Ionomer	highest cost, highest performance, seals through contaminants
Acid copolymers	good foil bond, good chemical resistance
Metallocene PE	low initiation temperature, fast strong seal
LLDPE	good hot tack, tough, wide seal temperature range
PE/EVA blend	low seal temperature, very soft film, good hot tack
Medium-density PE	stiffer and better barrier than LDPE
Cast polypropylene	higher use temperature than LDPE
LDPE	most economical, lowest performance, adequate for many uses

Figure 14.7

The optimum condition for creating a strong heat seal should be determined. Considerations include seal bar pressure and seal-bar temperature.

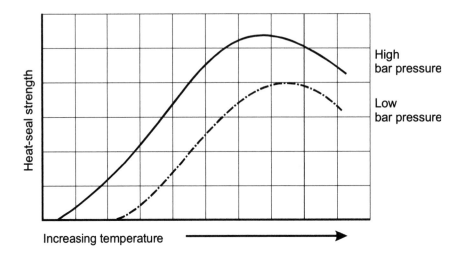

Figure 14.7

The optimum condition for creating a strong heat seal should be determined. Considerations include seal bar pressure and seal-bar temperature.

temperatures and pressures. Ethylene-vinyl acetate is a common base resin used to make hot-melt heat-seal coatings.

Time/temperature/pressure data should be developed for all heat-sealing systems. (See Figure 14.7.) Excessive combinations of time, temperature and pressure tend to force melt from the seal area and create a weaker seal.

Hot tack is an important sealing material characteristic, particularly on VFFS machines, where heavy product might be resting on a seal immediately after formation. A good hot-tack seal will be able to resist peeling apart, even though it is still hot.

Cold seals are based on elastomeric materials that have a great tendency to adhere to themselves but not to other materials. Cold-seal adhesives are pattern-applied by the converter to the appropriate matching sealing surfaces on the web. In the package filling operation, machinery simply brings the two surfaces together and applies a slight pressure. Since time and temperature needs have been eliminated, sealing speed is very fast. Cold seals are useful in applications such as sealing chocolate wrappers, where the product is sensitive to elevated temperatures.

Laminate materials must be compatible with the product, and a laminate's internal plies must be adequately protected against aggressive product constituents. Aluminum foils are attacked by some chemicals, particularly caustics. Layers between the aluminum foil and the product must stop the penetration of any such ingredient to the foil interface. Aggressive flavor and perfume components can plasticize adhesive bonding layers as well as detrimentally affecting other structural properties.

BARRIER PROPERTIES

Almost every food or pharmaceutical application requires some form of barrier property. "Barrier" is a nonspecific word that describes a material's ability to prevent gases from permeating through the volume of the material. As can be seen in Table 14.5 the barrier qualities of a given material vary depending on the

Table 14.5

General oxygen- and moisture-barrier properties.

Material	Moisture Barrier	Oxygen Barrier
LDPE	fair	poor
HDPE	excellent	poor
EVOH	poor	excellent
PVDC	excellent	excellent
PA (nylon)	poor	good
PS	poor	poor
PET	fair	good
OPP	good	poor

gas being permeated. It is not enough to say "we need a high- barrier material." The gas to which a barrier is required must be specified.

Oxygen and water vapor are the most common barrier concerns, being the gases most responsible for product degradation. Another class of permeants against which barrier properties are vital are the volatile or essential oils associated with aroma and flavor. These are usually present in minute concentrations, and their presence is often critical to product quality.

Flavor and aroma constituents can be delicate or very aggressive, and retaining them is a packager's challenge. Fresh coffee aroma is a complex essential oil that can evaporate quickly or oxidize readily to leave a bland, flat-tasting beverage. Coffee packaging laminates must hold essential oils in and keep moisture and oxygen out. Additionally, the vacuum pack will pull the web tight against an abrasive granular material. This places a premium on toughness and abrasion resistance.

Of the flexible packaging materials, only intact aluminum foil is potentially a 100% barrier to all gases. In the thinner gauges used for most packaging, (as low as 7 micrometres/0.000285 inch) foils suffer from pinholing—minute holes through the foil. Furthermore, foil is not durable to repeated flexing and can develop flex-cracks during machining and shipping.

Barrier properties are usually reported as the rate at which a permeant passes through a given thickness and area over 24 hours at atmospheric pressure. However, there are many ways of expressing this data, and care must be taken to ensure that identical methods and units are being compared. One standard, ASTM D 1434, Method for Determining Gas Permeability Characteristics of Plastic Film and Sheeting, provides an appendix with conversion factors for the various gas-transmission units in use.

Oxygen permeability has traditionally been expressed in mixed inch/pound and metric units:

$$\frac{\text{mL (STP) mil}}{100 \text{ in}^2 \times \text{d} \times \text{atm}}$$

In metric, this would be expressed as

$$\frac{\text{mL (STP) mil}}{\text{m}^2 \times \text{d} \times \text{atm}}$$

Where

STP = standard temperature and pressure

d = day

atm = atmospheric pressure

Oxygen permeability is usually measured using instrumentation developed by Mocon (ASTM D 3985). The method uses a cell that is divided into two chambers by the film being evaluated. (See Figure 14.8) Nitrogen flows through one cell while oxygen flows through the other. Any oxygen that permeates through the film being evaluated is caught up in the nitrogen flow and taken to a coulometric sensor that quantifies the amount of oxygen permeated.

The permeability of plastic films can increase dramatically with increases in temperature and relative humidity. The temperature in a transport truck on a hot summer day can increase permeability by three or four times. Moisture absorbtion by plastics such as nylon or ethylene-vinyl alcohol will also increase permeation substantially.

Water-vapor transmission rate (WVTR) is expressed as grams of water permeated rather than millilitres. The reference test method, ASTM E 96, is a gravimetric determination and describes a desiccant and water method of determining WVTR. ASTM D 1294 describes an instrumental method for determining the water vapor permeability of plastic film.

Water and oxygen permeation do not correlate, other permeabilities do. In general, a good oxygen barrier will also be a good carbon dioxide barrier and a good barrier to many (but not all) organic vapors.

Metallizing plastic films significantly increases barrier to all gases. Poly(vinylidene chloride) (Saran) and poly(chlorotrifuoroethylene) (Aclar) are also good all-around barrier materials.

Figure 14.8

A dynamic permeation cell for measuring oxygen permeation.

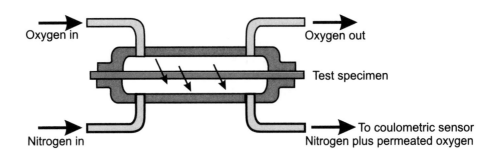

Oxygen in — Oxygen out

Test specimen

Nitrogen in — To coulometric sensor
Nitrogen plus permeated oxygen

Ethylene-vinyl alcohol (EVOH) is used as a high oxygen barrier. However, EVOH absorbs water and must be sandwiched between materials that will keep moisture away from it. One common construction places the EVOH between two layers of polypropylene. Since EVOH and PP do not bond, PP films must be bonded to the EVOH with an adhesive or "tie" layer.

Barrier properties, as a general rule, are inversely proportional to film thickness on a fairly linear basis. Doubling the thickness of a given barrier layer will halve the permeation rate of the gas in question. Obviously, the required barrier property can be achieved with any material, provided it is thick enough. However, the oxygen barrier provided by 25 micrometres (0.001 inch) PVDC would need about 25 millimetres (1 inch) of polyethylene to equal it—1,000 times thicker. Even though the cost of PVDC is two or three times that of polyethylene, it is a thousand times more effective as a barrier. For both practical and economic reasons, the choice is PP coated with PVDC.

In designing a barrier, the options must be evaluated and the best construction selected. Usually, the final analysis concerns the amount of barrier per dollar, tempered with machinability and other use properties.

Not all packages require a high barrier. In fact, some packages must have low barrier qualities. Red meats, for example, retain bright red coloration only when there is ready access to oxygen. Fruits and vegetables need to respire, ridding themselves of water and carbon dioxide while taking in oxygen. Products with high water activities would establish high humidities ideal for the propagation of microorganisms if they were packed in a high moisture-barrier package. Packaging films for these products must have permeabilities tailored to meet their individual respiratory requirements.

A light barrier may be needed by products that can be harmed by light, usually the ultra violet component. Fluorescent lighting in retail dairy cabinets degrades butter, and a paper/foil combination is frequently used, as it provides both 100% dead fold and a light barrier.

AESTHETICS AND OTHER PROPERTIES

A final concern in selecting a laminate is achieving the desired shelf or decorative appearance. The laminate must take into account whether the presentation should be in a sparkling clear package or an opaque package. Usually, where the product is attractive and is not adversely affected by light, a clear package is specified. The sales appeal of stewed clams, on the other hand, would not likely be enhanced by a clear package.

Oriented polypropylene's (OPP) combination of excellent base properties at an economical cost make it one of the most popular materials for wraps and laminates having sparkling clarity. Coatings and treatments readily improve such properties as machinability, oxygen barrier, and flavor barrier. Where additional strength or temperature tolerance is needed, OPP can be replaced by PET, though at somewhat higher cost. Both OPP and PET are dimensionally stable films and can be printed well with good register. Maintaining tight register on extensible films such as polyethylene is much more difficult.

In some instances, shelf appeal rests in providing a brilliant metallic appearance for all or parts of the package. Metallizing or aluminum foil are the only ways of creating large brilliant metallic surfaces. (Local metallic decorations can be made by hot-stamp printing). OPP and PET are the most often metallized films.

Aesthetics often means providing a suitable printing surface. Clear plastic laminates are typically reverse-printed to lock in the printing inks and provide a smooth, high-gloss surface finish. An underlayer of white film provides the bright white background for high-quality graphics. A metallized underlayer provides a brilliant metallic background.

Laminate webs are usually printed by gravure or flexography, depending on the run size and the graphic quality desired. Clear surface coats or over-lacquers can be applied at the last printing station. Surface coatings for plastics are frequently treated with antistatic compounds to eliminate problems of dust attraction.

Other functional properties may need to be provided for that do not fall into the above categories. For example, an adhesive or "tie' layer that might be needed to bond two portions of a laminate together. Sometimes primers and surface sealers are necessary to enhance adhesion. Nitrocellulose lacquers or shellacs are commonly used on aluminum.

An aluminum layer is commonly used for ice cream wrapper laminates intended for sale at outdoor events, for its ability to reflect radiant heat. Both foiled and metallized substrates are used for packages where dissipation of static electricity is important.

Often a single material serves several functional purpose. For example, polyethylene is both a good-heat seal medium and a good moisture barrier. Metallizing improves gas barrier and provides a decorative surface.

CONVERTING PROCESSES

"Converting" is the term that describes the production of multi-layered materials used in packaging.

Almost without exception, converting is done as a web-fed rather than a sheet-fed process. Regardless of the machine, certain stations are common to all converting machines.

A coating/laminating machine has an unwind stand for each of the raw web-fed materials that will be used in the process and a rewind stand to gather up the finished product. The unwind stands have tension-controlling devices so that materials are fed into the operating stations at a constant tension. A rewind-stand tension-controlling device ensures that the finished product is pulled out of the machine and laid up on the roll at a constant tension. Depending on the machine, there may be additional tension-control zones within the machine.

Tracking devices keep the material aligned with operational stations in the machine direction. Special rolls such as bowed rolls and herringbone rolls keep the material spread out flat while it is being processed.

Most converting machines that will combine or print plastic materials will have a corona discharge station through which the plastic film will pass in order to increase surface polarity (dyne level). Adhesives, coatings and inks will have higher bond strengths with the treated substrate.

Coating/laminating machines have one or several coating stations at which additional material in a liquid state is applied to the base substrates. These may range from simple glue applicators to large extrusion dies attached to plasticating extruders. Depending on the coating process, the machine may have drying ovens either before or after the material-combining nip.

The laminating process starts with a base web to which further layers are added until the desired construction is built up. Additional layers can be applied as fluid coatings, by bonding additional webs, by extruding and co-extruding, or by any combination of these. Base webs may be plain or may already have been printed, metallized, or otherwise treated.

Coating Stations

Coating stations apply fluid materials such as varnishes, waxes, PVDC emulsions, and adhesives. There are literally hundreds of ways of putting a coating onto a web. The essential differences in the methods concern the way in which the coating is physically applied and the way the coating is metered. These factors in turn are related to the substrate type, its texture, and the coating's nature and purpose. Each method has its features and limitations. Gravure and extrusion coating predominate in flexible packaging.

Gravure coating (see Figure 14.9) applies and meters the coating from the cells of the gravure roll. Gravure rolls apply a precise coating thickness, regardless of variations in substrate thickness. Gravure does not work well with rough surfaces where the small gravure cells may lose contact with the substrate surface. The coating must be of fairly low viscosity.

Extrusion coating applies polymer melt to a substrate. In a typical application, polyethylene pellets are forced through an extruder barrel, where they are heated

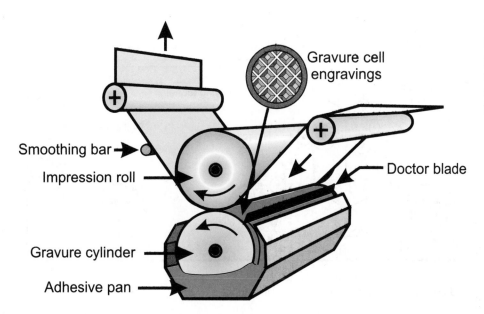

Figure 14.9

Gravure coating applies a predetermined amount of wet coating from engraved cells, shown enlarged at top.

Figure 14.10

Extrusion laminating uses an extruded melt to bond two materials.

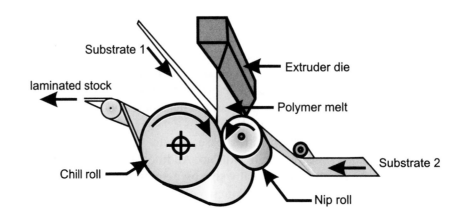

and softened to a syrup-like consistency. The viscous polyethylene is fed through a die with a long, narrow slot, forming a thin curtain, which falls onto the substrate. At this point it can be cooled to form a surface layer (extrusion coating) on the substrate, or a third material can be pressed against the still-molten polyethylene (extrusion laminating) and bonded to the base substrate. (See Figure 14.10.)

Wax lamination is an economical method of joining a paper or tissue support to aluminum foil. It is not a structurally and environmentally stable bond and so has few other applications. The base material goes from the unwind roll to the heated-wax coating station. The second material is pinched against the hot wax at the combining nip and immediately chilled. After chilling, the finished laminate is rewound.

Wet bonding (see Figure 14.11) requires that at least one substrate be porous enough to allow adhesive solvent or water to escape. Almost invariably this substrate is paper. Adhesive is applied to one substrate, the two substrates are nipped together and the whole sent through an oven to set the adhesive.

Figure 14.11

A representative wet-bond laminator.

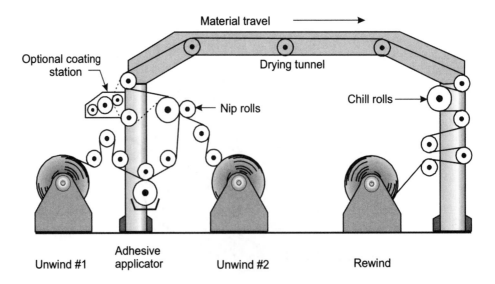

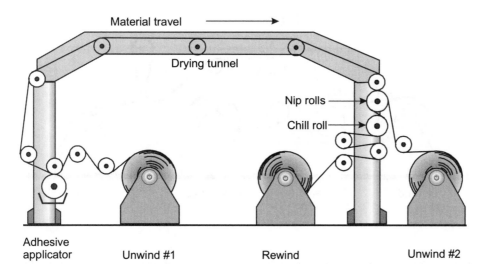

Figure 14.12

A representative dry-bond laminator. If both substrates are relatively impermeable, they cannot be nipped together until all adhesive solvents have been removed.

In dry bonding, adhesive is applied to the substrate and then dried of solvents. (See Figure 14.12) The resinous adhesive is either tacky or can be activated and set by heat. The second substrate is joined by a heated nip against the first to effect the bond.

With both wet and dry bonding, particular care must be taken to ensure that all traces of solvent are driven out. Since laminators prefer o run their machines at top production speeds, there is always the danger that the envelope will be pushed too far and some volatiles will remain in the laminate. These can give off-flavors to packaged food products. Trapped solvents can cause later bubbling or blistering of the laminate. Quality laminators constantly check their production for volatiles using gas chromatography techniques.

Solventless Laminating

Many adhesives used in wet and dry bond laminating are solvent based and require driers to remove the solvents. Releasing solvents into the atmosphere is no longer a tolerated practice.

Solventless laminating machines (see Figure 14.13) use bonding agents that have no volatile ingredients in their formulation. They may be fluid prepolymers where hardening or curing is initiated by the addition of a catalyst or by chemical reaction of two prepolymer components. Curing may also be initiated or accelerated by heat or ultraviolet light. Using a hot melt adhesive is another way of eliminating solvent release.

Solventless laminators require significantly less floor space than conventional laminators with drying ovens.

Coextrusion

Co-extrusion dies combine the outputs of two or more extruders so that the curtain of material exiting the extruder is actually several materials fused together. As

Figure 14.13

A solventless laminator is a
fraction of the size of wet or
dry bond systems.

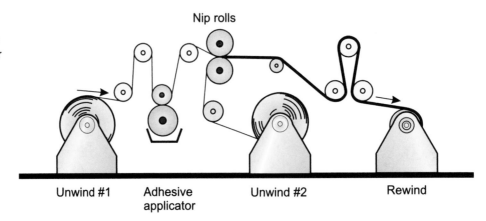

Nip rolls

Unwind #1   Adhesive   Unwind #2   Rewind
applicator

with solventless laminating, there is no release of objectionable solvents. The
principles of coextrusion have been described in Chapter 10, Shaping Plastics.

Technological advances in die-making have allowed for coextrusions of 11
and more layers. Table 14.6 illustrates the construction of a high barrier, thermo-
formable nine-layer coextrusion. Splitting the PA into two layers increases flex
crack resistance. Locating the EVOH layer between the two PA layers improves
thermoformability.

SPECIFYING LAMINATES

Material plies are properly listed from the outside of the package to the inside.
In metric, a laminate's weight is given in grams per square metre (grammage)
and in micrometres of thickness. Microns used to describe micrometres, is not a
recognized SI unit.

Table 14.6
Construction of a nine layer laminate.

Material	Function
1. PP	reverse printed surface film
2. Tie	adhesion
3. LLDPE	bulk
4. Tie	adhesion
5. PA*	barrier & formability
6. EVOH	oxygen barrier
7. PA*	barrier & formability
8. Tie	adhesion
9. EVA	sealant

(Micrometre is properly abbreviated to "μm." The "μ" symbol is awkward to insert and so um is commonly substituted for μm. In the vernacular some have taken to calling the micrometre an "oom.")

In inch/pound units, caliper may be quoted in thousandths of an inch, in mils or in gauge. 1/1000 inch = 1 mil = 100 gauge (Note that in the paperboard industry 1/1000 inch is a "point," therefore 1 point = 1 mil).

$$0.0005 \text{ inch} = 50 \text{ gauge} = 1/2 \text{ mil} = 12.7\mu m$$
$$0.001 \text{ inch} = 100 \text{ gauge} = 1 \text{ mil} = 25.4\mu m$$

A laminate's orientation on a roll must be specified exactly (See Figure 14.14) so that it will unwind in the desired direction and the eye-spot register marks are located correctly for the machine it will be used on. Printed laminates in particular can be confusing. A converter will need this information before starting the job.

There are few ordering conventions for laminates. Web materials are described in pounds per 1,000 square feet (basis weight), pounds per roll, linear feet, square inches per pound (yield), number of repeats or impressions, and by a variety of other methods particular to the purchaser's needs.

There is no simple formula for designing a laminate, and there are almost as many constructions as there are product types. Similar effects can be achieved in many different ways, and the bottom line is the price paid to get a certain amount of a particular property. First and foremost, understand which properties are needed and how much of each property is needed.

While many laminating machines exist in the basic configurations illustrated in this text, most producers will have multi-purpose lines that might for example combine both wet laminating and dry laminating capabilities in one line. An even more complete line would include some extrusion laminating capability, or even co-extrusion.

Coating and laminating machines are built to accomplish specific operations. While there is some flexibility, no machine can be configured to do all possible

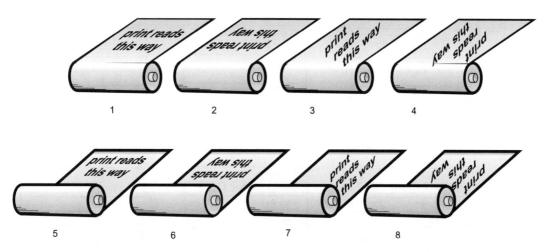

Figure 14.14

Standard roll unwind direction.

laminating procedures. In some instances, the web material will need to be passed through the machine or several machines two, three, and even more times to build up the specified construction. Process waste can be as high as 15 or 20%. Fewer machine passes generally means less process waste.

Different suppliers might put together similar laminates in completely different ways, depending on their available machinery. Talk to several suppliers and get several opinions on how a particular combination or result can be achieved and at what price.

EXAMPLES OF LAMINATES

Figure 14.15 shows examples of nine typical laminates containing aluminum foil as one of the components. The purpose of the foil component in all the examples is to provide barrier to atmospheric gases and aroma constituents.

The identification "LDPE" in this figure includes LLDPE and various copolymers and blends based primarily on LDPE. In some instances, the seal material is proprietary or varies with application or converter. These are identified as "sealing medium." LDPE and other heat-seal layers (For example, ethylene-acrylic acid, and ionomer) can be extruded onto a substrate, or a previously manufactured film can be bonded on. Adhesive bonded LDPE is somewhat stiffer than extrusion applied LDPE. Bonded on films are also used to build up thickness and provide better caliper control in thicker cross sections. A thick heat-sealing layer is desirable in such products as instant soup pouches where the thick polyethylene

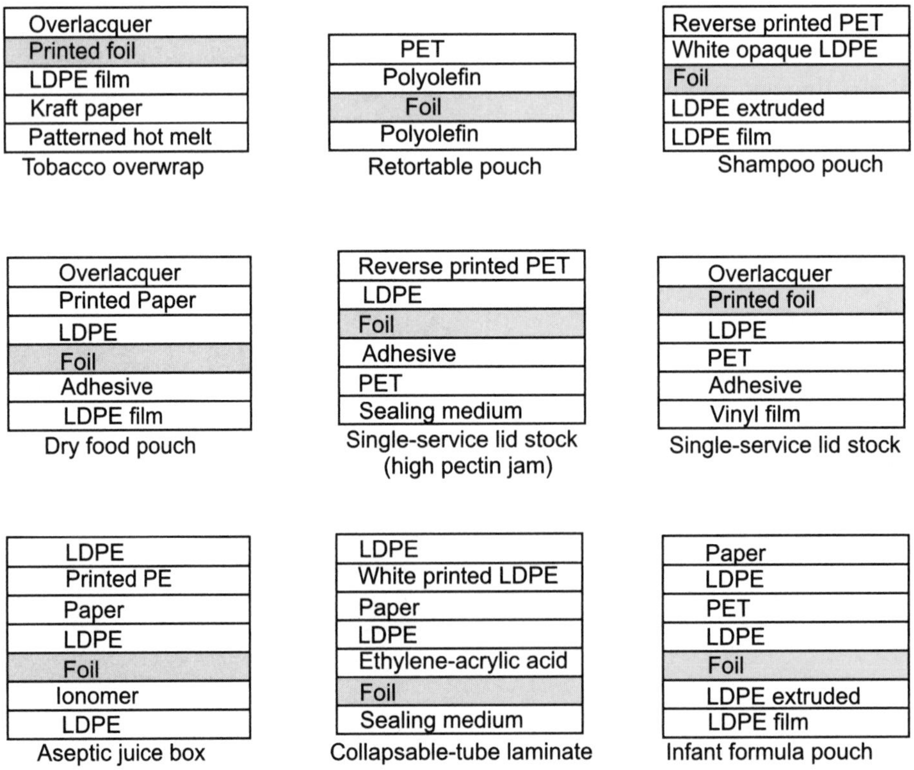

Figure 14.15

Examples of laminate constructions containing aluminum foil.

| Overlacquer |
| Printed foil |
| LDPE film |
| Kraft paper |
| Patterned hot melt |

Tobacco overwrap

| PET |
| Polyolefin |
| Foil |
| Polyolefin |

Retortable pouch

| Reverse printed PET |
| White opaque LDPE |
| Foil |
| LDPE extruded |
| LDPE film |

Shampoo pouch

| Overlacquer |
| Printed Paper |
| LDPE |
| Foil |
| Adhesive |
| LDPE film |

Dry food pouch

| Reverse printed PET |
| LDPE |
| Foil |
| Adhesive |
| PET |
| Sealing medium |

Single-service lid stock
(high pectin jam)

| Overlacquer |
| Printed foil |
| LDPE |
| PET |
| Adhesive |
| Vinyl film |

Single-service lid stock

| LDPE |
| Printed PE |
| Paper |
| LDPE |
| Foil |
| Ionomer |
| LDPE |

Aseptic juice box

| LDPE |
| White printed LDPE |
| Paper |
| LDPE |
| Ethylene-acrylic acid |
| Foil |
| Sealing medium |

Collapsable-tube laminate

| Paper |
| LDPE |
| PET |
| LDPE |
| Foil |
| LDPE extruded |
| LDPE film |

Infant formula pouch

serves also to stop the dry hard noodles from cutting into the pouch stock. A vinyl heat sealing film is used for lidding stock that will be applied to PVC single service containers.

Retort pouch laminates must withstand thermal process stresses, and therefore the laminate's main structural component is PET, a material with low elongation, high tensile strength, and a high softening point. Aluminum foil provides the 100% barrier required for a shelf-stable package. The adhesive and a polypropylene-based heat seal-layer can withstand retort temperatures and pressures.

Laminates for aseptic juice packages usually consist of seven material layers. Paper provides body, while aluminum foil provides a barrier. The ionomer provides a superior bond to the aluminum metal.

The heat seal on the tobacco overwrap is a hot melt adhesive applied in a pattern. This allows for heat sealing the overwrap and eliminates the need for a wet gluepot at the point of manufacture.

Pectin, a very aggressive component of some jams, will permeate LDPE and attack aluminum foil. The lidding stock for this product has a layer of PET to either side of the aluminum.

Figure 14.16 shows examples of six laminates that do not contain aluminum foil. The snack food laminate is typical of potato chip packaging. Barrier to moisture and oxygen is substantially increased by the metallized BOPP component. Laminates containing EVAL are used where good oxygen barrier and clarity are desired. Although the figures shows outside LDPE and PP layers, these could also be nylon or PET, depending on what other laminate performance characteristics are needed.

Heat sealing cannot be use near chocolate confections. A typical construction applies a pattern of cold-seal adhesive on the inside of the wrap. Two coated simply need to be brought together to form a seal. White opaque PP provides and excellent base for high quality graphics.

Luncheon and cheese laminates often use nylon as one of the layers. Nylon has good oxygen barrier properties (needed high-fat luncheon meats and cheeses), and can be easily drawn by thermoforming into a product conforming shape. The ionomer heat-seal layer is capable of sealing through any fatty contamination that might be over the seal area.

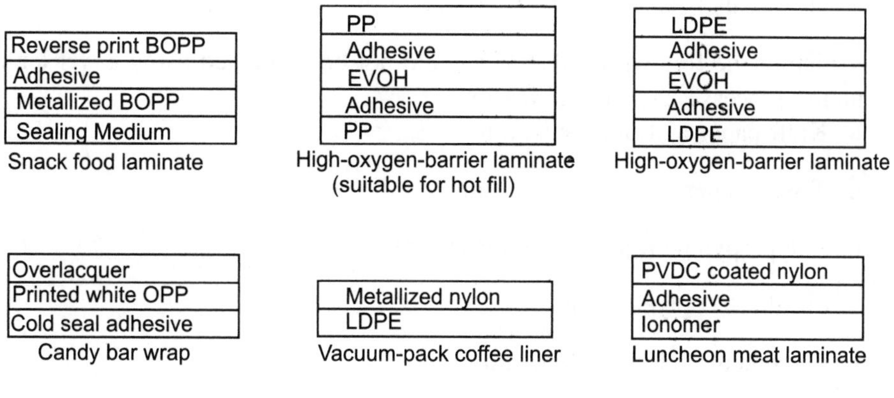

| Reverse print BOPP |
| Adhesive |
| Metallized BOPP |
| Sealing Medium |

Snack food laminate

| PP |
| Adhesive |
| EVOH |
| Adhesive |
| PP |

High-oxygen-barrier laminate (suitable for hot fill)

| LDPE |
| Adhesive |
| EVOH |
| Adhesive |
| LDPE |

High-oxygen-barrier laminate

| Overlacquer |
| Printed white OPP |
| Cold seal adhesive |

Candy bar wrap

| Metallized nylon |
| LDPE |

Vacuum-pack coffee liner

| PVDC coated nylon |
| Adhesive |
| Ionomer |

Luncheon meat laminate

Figure 14.16

Examples of laminate constructions without aluminum foil.

1. What is the objective of combining various materials into a laminated packaging material?

2. Describe the co-extrusion process and explain its advantages over alternate systems.

3. Describe the laminate structure of a juice box container and explain the purpose of each layer.

4. You want a transparent package with a high oxygen barrier. What two polymeric materials are candidates for adding barrier properties to the laminate structure? If the package did not need transparency, what other options might you consider?

5. Describe the difference between dry-bond laminating and wet-bond laminating.

6. How might you recognize whether a pouch was made on a VFFS machine or a HFFS machine?

7. A 25-micrometre thick plastic film has a moisture permeability that is 840 mg/100 square inches/24 hours. What is the likely permeability if we go to a 12.5 micrometre film of the same material?

8. When designing a laminate, what material
   a. Tolerates the highest use temperature?

   b. Is an economical way of adding stiffness or bulk?

   c. Is a good oxygen barrier and can be thermoformed?

   d. Heat-seals through grease and bonds well to aluminum?

9. Which of the following substrates could not be laminated using a wet laminating process? Explain the reason.
   a. Kraft paper and polyester film

   b. Tissue paper and aluminum foil

   c. Polypropylene film and cellulose film

   d. on film to polyethylene

   e. Parchment and cylinder board

10. In what order are the components of a laminate specified?

11. How thick is a 150-gauge film in thousandths of an inch? How many mils is that?

12. Why is it always necessary to specify the permeant(s) when discussing barrier properties?

13. Raising the temperature or increasing the pressure of heat-sealing jaws in some instances can decrease bond strength. Why?

14. What three material characteristics might be key to good machinabilty on a VFFS machine?

15. What is the advantage of a HFFS machine over a VFFS machine?

16. Why might a heat seal's poor hot-tack performance slow down a filling operation?

17. What provision would I need to make if I were designing a EVAL-based barrier laminate for an organic soup product?

18. Which is easier to make: a fin seal or a lap seal? Why?

19. From an appearance and marketing point of view, what might be the advantages of a pouch made on an HFFS machine?

20. Why is aluminum foil used in packaging usually shiny on one side and matte on the other?

21. List six unique foil properties that are taken advantage of by packagers, and give an example of a package that uses each property.

22. Foils are almost always coated. What are some reasons that foil might be coated?

23. Below what gauge does pinholing become a major concern? What is the concern?

24. Why should all barrier measurements be conducted on the finished package, preferably after a real or simulated shipping test?

25. How is a reflective gold surface developed on a plastic film using metallizing technology?

26. What is the advantage gained by metallizing paper?

27. Why must paper be dried prior to being metallized?

28. Which are the two most commonly metallized plastic films?

29. What advantage is gained by metallizing films?

30. What is a susceptor film?

31. What graphic advantage does a HFFS pouch have over a VFFS pouch?

CONTENTS

Historical Perspective

Railroads and corrugated board, carrier rules, Mullen burst, edge crush tests

Corrugated Board

Construction, fiberboard grades, basis weight and grammage, methods of specifying board, common medium weights. Natural kraft, white-lined, solid bleached, recycled linerboards, adhesives. Standard flutes, take up factors, board descriptions. Board manufacture, finger and fingerless machines, scoring wheel geometry, balanced and unbalanced boards, wax treatments, tape inserts. Dimensioning flat pads.

Properties and Tests

Viscoelasticity, hygroscopicity, hygroexpansiveness, Mullen test, edge crush test, flat crush test, combined weight of facings, thickness, porosity, stiffness, water takeup, puncture tests, pin adhesion, ply separation, coefficient of friction.

Carrier Rules and Regulations

Application, rule summary, box maker's certificates.

Corrugated Boxes

Flute selection, relative flute flat crush values, general flute application guidelines. Box styles, regular slotted, die-cut, Bliss box styles, manufacturer's joints. Box design variations, common box abbreviations, "design" styles. Box production process, nominal dimensioning of a box, score allowances, determining a box size.

Corrugated Box Printing

Flexographic printing, post printing and limitations, preprinting, litho labeling, litho laminating, screen printing.

Special Board Treatments

Wet-strength boards, wax curtain coating, wax cascading

Corrugated Container Quality Assurance

Hand samples, industry gap tolerances, out-of-square, fishtailing, overlap, glue tab and width, score and slotted sheet tolerances

CORRUGATED FIBERBOARD

HISTORICAL PERSPECTIVE

The railroads were the first continental mass movers of goods. Since common carriers are liable for loss or damage of goods in their care, they had an early interest in shipping container quality. The first rules for constructing corrugated containers were established in the United States by the railroad's Freight Classification Committee in 1906. These rules, updated many times, continue today as rule 41 of the Uniform Freight Classification (UFC). A similar set of rulings was later adopted by the trucking industry as National Motor Freight Classification (MNFC) item 222.

The Canadian counterpart, RAC-6000, is similar but not identical to rule 41. The Canadian trucking industry has no counterpart to NMFC item 222.

Broadly speaking, the classification systems require that boxes shipped by rail or truck meet certain construction requirements. Briefly, the rules provide that specified board grades are used to construct corrugated boxes, depending on the weight and dimensions of the intended box. The box construction was to be described on a box maker's certificate on the bottom of the box. Figure 15.8, later in this chapter, shows examples of these stamps.

A key aspect of earlier rules was the sole use of the Mullen burst test for designating corrugated board grades. This led to the establishment of essentially five linerboard basis weights from which corrugated board could be constructed. Until recently, these rules guided corrugated container design.

Over time, however, transport and materials handling methods changed. Box compression strength became an overriding consideration. Yet, the burst test measured a board's resistance to rupture and related to the board's tensile properties; it has no direct correlation to a container's ability to hold a load stacked upon it. Paper manufacturing advances can produce stiffer papers, but these would not necessarily meet existing burst-test standards.

The edge crush test (ECT) was proposed as a more suitable test for grading corrugated board, the advantage being that an ECT value could be used to calculate a container's anticipated compression strength. After much debate, a dual grading system went into effect in 1991, by which a corrugated box could be designed to meet the original criteria based on the Mullen burst test or meet new criteria based on ECT values.

CORRUGATED BOARD

Terminology

The Fibre Box Association refers to their products as "boxes" and that they are produced in box plants. The Uniform Freight Classification rules speak of boxes and the box maker's certificates. However, when the most common box design is produced it suddenly becomes a regular slotted container (an RSC)—though it may receive an International Box Code number. The packaging machinery industry makes case packers and the captain of a cargo ship will call them cartons.

In this text, "box" will be used as the most correct term. "Cartons" is reserved for lightweight paperboard folding cartons. "Container" is a generic term that can apply to any containment form, or more specifically to large intermodal cargo containers. "Case" as a reference to a package type will be avoided entirely.

Furthermore, it is a corrugated box (or fiberboard box) not a corrugate box and certainly never a cardboard box.

Construction

Corrugated fiberboard is the most common distribution container material, and the regular slotted container (RSC) is the workhorse corrugated box style. Corrugated board, in its most common form, is made up of two facings, or linerboards, bonded to a fluted or corrugated medium; it is called "singlewall" board. "Doublewall" board (two fluted medium plies and three linerboard plies) is made into boxes for heavier or more bulky products such as machinery, appliances or furniture. (See Figure 15.1) Triplewall (three fluted medium plies and four linerboard plies) is mostly used as a substitute for wood when constructing large bulk bins and boxes.

Facings are typically kraft linerboard manufactured on a fourdrinier paper machine with two headboxes. Corrugating medium is a one-ply sheet and frequently contains hardwood and recycled fiber. The corrugating machine forms the medium into a fluted pattern and bonds it to the linerboard facings, usually with a starch-based adhesive. A material with only one facing sheet, called "single face," is flexible in one axis and is sometimes used for a protective wrapping.

The fluted medium, similar in form to the arches used in bridges and buildings, is the basis of corrugated board's significant stiffness using three layers of paper. Crushing or flattening the flutes even slightly reduces the board's stiffness.

Even the normal process of producing corrugated board and boxes—stacking flat sheets, printing, feeding through box-making machinery, bundling for shipment—inadvertently causes some flute damage as measured by a loss of thickness. The manufacture and handling of corrugated material should be done

Figure 15.1

Singlewall (left) and doublewall (right) board components.

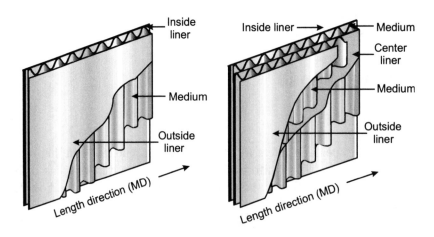

Table 15.1

The most commonly used linerboard grades, based on Mullen test grading. These have been essentially phased out in favor of the ECT system.

North American Grades		European Grades
Grammage	Basis Weight	Grammage
127 g	26 lb	125 g
161 g	33 lb	150 g
186 g	38 lb	—
205 g	42 lb	200 g
—	—	225 g
—	—	250 g
337 g	69 lb	300 g
Other grades	—	400 g
—	—	440 g

in a manner that maintains flute integrity if maximum stiffness and stacking strength is to be preserved.

Fiberboard Grades

Facings and corrugated medium material can be made to virtually any paperboard weight or thickness; however, historical North American freight rule requirements led to the standardization of certain traditional grades. (See Table 15.1) Linerboard and medium are specified in metric by their grammage: the mass in grams per square metre. "Basis weight" refers to the weight in pounds per 1,000 square feet. This is sometimes abbreviated to lb/MSF. The most common medium weights are shown in Table 15.2.

A generation of newer linerboards, referred to as high-performance boards, is being made to meet ECT rather than Mullen burst test and basis weight requirements. Since the alternate carrier rules call for these boards to meet

Table 15.2

The most commonly used corrugating medium weights.

Grammage	Basis Weight
127 g	26 lb
147 g	30 lb
161 g	33 lb
195 g	40 lb

stiffness values measured by an edge crush test, there are no standard basis weights of the kind found in the older Mullen and basis weight system. Users have found—to their advantage—that in many situations they get satisfactory performance using lighter grades of high-performance boards.

Linerboard is made in several material constructions, natural kraft being the most common. A linerboard with a whiter surface to provide better graphics is made by using bleached fiber in the second headbox of the paper making machine. Because the bleached fiber layer is thin, some of the background kraft shows through, giving it a somewhat mottled appearance. "Mottled white" and "oysterboard" are common commercial names used to describe this board. Solid bleached white kraft is used where top quality graphics are needed, but at a significant cost markup. It is typically used in preprint applications.

Varying amounts of recycled or secondary fiber are used to produce both linerboard and medium, a practice that has grown as recycling increased. Recycled board is made to the same specifications as virgin containerboard, so that ECT stiffness or burst values are met. Other properties will depend on the source and quality of the fiber.

Recycled board typically has a smoother surface finish and a lower coefficient of friction than virgin kraft. A good recycled board has an excellent printing surface. Some recycled board is not as stiff as virgin kraft and performs better on equipment such as wraparound casers—machines that wrap a sheet of corrugated board around the product rather than putting it in a previously manufactured box.

Corrugating Adhesives

Standard corrugated board is made with a starch-based adhesive applied at about 10 to 14 grams per square metre. Starch does not tolerate high moisture levels and loses strength quickly. Since corrugated board itself loses about 50% of its compression strength between 50% relative humidity (R.H.) and 90% R.H., this does not pose a limitation. Where higher resistance is needed, starches can be modified or supplemented by the addition of various polymeric materials. A weather-resistant adhesive would maintain box properties at a somewhat higher level for a longer period.

Water-resistant adhesive would be required for applications where the finished container will be in actual contact with water for periods of time. These are more expensive than weather-resistant adhesives and would be used only with corrugated board that is waxed or otherwise treated.

Flute Standards and Corrugated Board Grades

The four standard flute sizes established by UFC are designated as A-, B-, C- and E-flute. Sizes do not go in logical alphabetical progression. A is the largest flute and C is the second largest, followed by B- and E-flutes. Finer flutes, such as F-flute, or microflute and others, being produced by a few board manufacturers, are not described in the UFC rules. "Take-up factor" is the length of medium per length of finished corrugated board; for example it takes 1.54 metres of medium to make 1 metre of A-flute. (See Table 15.3)

Table 15.3

Standard flute configurations. (Source: ASTM D5639, Selection of Corrugated Fiberboard Materials and Box Construction based on Performance Requirements)

Flute	Flutes/Metre	Flutes/Foot	Thickness*	Take-up Factor
A	100 to 120	30 to 36	4.67 (0.184 in.)	1.54
B	145 to 165	44 to 50	2.46 (0.097 in.)	1.32
C	120 to 140	36 to 42	3.63 (0.142 in.)	1.42
E	280 to 310	86 to 94	1.19 (0.047 in.)	1.27

*Not including facings

Finished board is described by component grammage or basis weight, starting from the outside. The outside sheet has the smoother finish. Embossed lines from the corrugating rolls are usually visible on the inside. Corrugated board described as 205/127C/161 would have the following components:

Outside liner = 205 grams
Medium = 127 grams, C-flute
Inside liner = 161 grams

Board Manufacture

A corrugating machine has a number of operating stations (see Figure 15.2) that take the appropriate linerboards and mediums, shape the flutes and join the fluted medium to the linerboards.

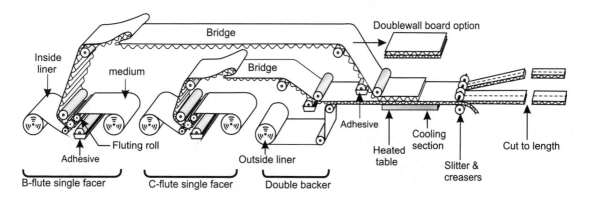

Figure 15.2

A corrugating machine. Machines are commonly equipped to run both B- and C-flute and sometimes E-flute as well. Doublewall boards are produced by combining the output of two single-facers.

At the single-facer station, medium is preconditioned with heat and steam to make it pliable and capable of being formed into a fluted configuration. (See Figure 15.3) Linerboard is also pretreated to bring it to the same temperature and moisture conditions as the medium. The medium is fluted by being passed between large rolls with a geared surface pattern matching the desired flute geometry. A vacuum system holds the medium to the forming rolls.

Adhesive is applied to the flute tips and preconditioned linerboard is pressed against the medium, where heat and pressure gel the starch adhesive. This liner frequently has visible lines embossed into the surface and boxes are usually constructed with this liner to the inside; hence the term "inside liner."

The single-faced material is flexible in one axis and is sent to a "bridge" where it is draped in an overlapping wave pattern as it travels to the double-backer station. The purpose of the bridge is to isolate the two ends of the corrugating machine. This allows either end of the machine to change speeds momentarily without having to slow the entire machine down.

At the double backer, adhesive is applied to the flute tips on the other side of the medium, and the outer linerboard is matched to the single-faced board. (See Figure 15.3)

Control of the individual board's moisture content during assembly into corrugated board is critical. Too large a difference in moisture content of the linerboards will result in warpage of the completed corrugated board. A board lacking "layflat" will cause feeding and printing problems in subsequent box-making operations and at the erecting station in a customers case packer.

The assembled corrugated board is no longer flexible in any axis, and the final heat setting and cooling is done between two long, flat belts. The edges are trimmed and the finished board is slit to widths and cut to lengths corresponding to required orders. Finished sheets are stacked ready for further operations.

If the board is destined for a regular slotted container (RSC) style, scores along the top and bottom flaps (the reverse scores) are rolled in at the same station that slits the board to the correct width. Different score geometries might be used, depending on the supplier and intended use. Three-point or point-to-point scores are used where the box flaps will be folded in one direction to close the container. On filling operations that require that the flaps first be bent outward,

Figure 15.3

The single-facer station of a corrugating machine is where the flutes are formed and bonded to the inside liner.

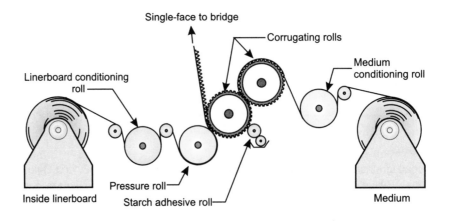

three-point scores will produce and uneven break. In such instances a five-point score is preferred. (See Figure 15.4)

Most corrugated board is manufactured in a balanced construction: the outer and inner liners have identical grammage. For some purposes an unbalanced construction may be specified. For example, going from a board with 205-gram (42-pound) liners to one with 337 gram (69-pound) liners, the next available balanced construction, is a substantial step up. A customer looking for a small performance gain may elect to upgrade one liner only.

Unbalanced constructions tend to have more problems with board warpage, but this should not preclude their use where the economics justify it. For better printing, the heavier liner is placed on the outside of the finished box. For better compression strength, the heavier liner is put on the inside.

A number of other features can be built in at the corrugator. These include light wax treatments of the medium to impart some moisture resistance and the inclusion of various tape materials. Tapes can be selected to reinforce critical box areas, such as handholds, or to provide easy-opening tear features. Inserted tapes must always run in the machine direction as the board is manufactured.

Flat corrugated sheets are dimensioned by specifying the width, the dimension parallel to the flutes, first. (See Figure 15.5). In manufacture this is the cross direction, or width, of the sheet as it comes off the corrugator. The direction perpendicular to the flutes is the length or machine direction.

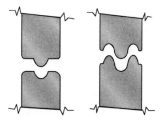

Figure 15.4

Profiles of three-point (left) and five-point (right) scoring wheels.

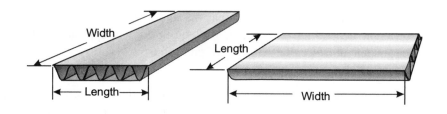

Figure 15.5

Dimensioning flat corrugated sheet. The order in which the dimensions are given will determine the relative flute direction. The width of a sheet is always the dimension parallel with the flutes.

PROPERTIES AND TESTS

Paper Properties

Viscoelasticity. Paper's physical properties depend on the rate at which load is applied. Simply put, the faster a load is applied, the greater the apparent strength. Over long periods of loading, paper fibers move and distort, or "creep," and long-term static compression strength is much less than dynamic compression strength. Boxes tested at 500-kilogram load (1,100-pound load) compression strength in the laboratory (a fast loading rate) can be expected to fail in about a year when loaded to 250 kilograms (550 pounds) in the warehouse.

Hygroscopicity. The percentage of water retained by paper is a function of temperature and relative humidity. Paper moisture content affects all mechanical properties, and for properties such as compression strength, there is degradation with increasing moisture content. Since paper's physical properties depend on

Figure 15.6

Equilibrium moisture content for paper and fiberboard.

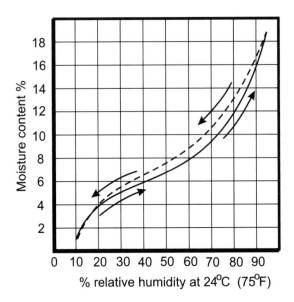

the moisture content, paper characterization tests must always be done at the same temperature and humidity. The internationally accepted standard is 50% R.H. and 23°C (Reference test method ASTM D 685, Conditioning of Paper and Paperboard Products for Testing).

Paper exhibits hysteresis, meaning that the equilibrium moisture content is slightly different depending on whether the equilibrium is approached from a lesser or a greater moisture content. (See Figure 15.6)

Hygroexpansiveness. When paper absorbs moisture, it expands, when it dries it shrinks. Between 0 and 90% R.H., dimensions can change by 0.8% in the MD and 1.6% in the CD.

A 1% shrinkage on a 1-metre (39-inch) corner post designed for tight insertion would be 12 millimetres (0.4 inch), hardly an accurate fit. A 1% shrinkage of and RSC blank in the flat can create register and fit problems for all subsequent production steps.

Uneven moisture contents in the two liners as board comes off the corrugator can lead to board warpage when the liners come to equilibrium. Warpage should not exceed 12 millimetres over a 610-millimetre span (1/2 inch over a 24-inch span) when measured in accordance with ASTM D 4727, Corrugated and Fiberboard Sheet Stock (Container Grade and Cut Shapes).

Fiberboard Characterization Tests

A number of paper characterization tests describe certain basic properties in the corrugating plant and, to varying degrees, in subsequent operations for purposes of design input and quality control. Only the most common are noted here. Most board tests are described in methods provided by the Technical Association of the Pulp and Paper Industry (TAPPI).

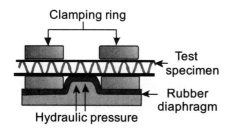

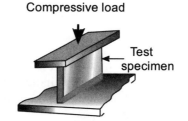

Figure 15.7

Standard corrugated Mullen board burst and edge crush tests.

Mullen Burst Test (TAPPI T810). Briefly, the Mullen burst test involves forcing a rubber diaphragm against a facing of the fiberboard (see Figure 15.7, left) until the facing bursts. The burst test or bursting strength values are reported as pounds per square inch (p.s.i.) or kilopascals, (kPa) (p.s.i. × 6.895 = kPa). Burst values are not significantly affected by the medium.

The burst test has limited use as a design value, since it is not related to the most critical properties of corrugated board from a box user's point of view. Burst tests are related to paper tensile strength, while the box user is often interested in stiffness and compression. Cloth will have a high Mullen burst value but has no compression strength.

Edge Crush Compression Test (TAPPI T 811). In an edge crush compression test (ECT), a small specimen (2 in. × 2 in.) is placed between the platens of a compression tester and loaded until failure occurs. (See Figure 15.7) Edgewise compression values are a function of the stiffness contributed by the facings and the medium. ECT values have a direct relationship to projected stacking strength.

A number of formulas have been devised that related ECT values to expected box compression strength. The most common calculations for a RSC use the simplified McKee formula:

$$\text{Box compression strength} = 5.87 \times \text{ECT} \times \text{BP} \times \text{T}$$

Where:

RSC top-to-bottom box compression strength is expressed in kilonewtons (kN) or pounds-force per square inch (lbf/in^2 or p.s.i.)

ECT = edge crush test, kN/m (lbf/in^2)

BP = inside box perimeter, m (in)

T = combined board thickness, m (in.)

Carrier rule changes allow either Mullen values or ECT values to specify the boards used to construct a corrugated container. The majority of shippers have elected to use ECT values.

Combined Weight of Facings. This value is required on the box maker's class stamp when the box is constructed to Mullen test rules. This measurement describes the combined linerboard weight (the weight of the inner and outer liners on a singlewall board) per 1,000 square feet of corrugated board. This information is not required on the class stamp when using the ECT system.

Thickness of Corrugated Board (TAPPI T 411). Reduced board thickness (caliper) is an excellent indicator of reduced compression strength. Caliper can be reduced by improper manufacture, excessive printing pressure and improper handling and storage.

Gurley Porosity (TAPPI T 460 and T 536). Gurley porosity measures the time it takes for a given volume of air to pass through a paper. The lower the number, the more porous the paper. Porosity can vary from 2 seconds to 200 seconds, but averages between 10 and 20 seconds. The paper's porosity is sometimes the culprit when problems occur at vacuum-cup transfer points.

Flexural Stiffness (TAPPI T820). Flexural stiffness is related to box compression strength. Reduced stiffness is a good indicator of damage during fabrication.

Water Take-up Tests (TAPPI T 441). Gluing problems are not common with corrugated board. When they occur, the Cobb size test, which measures the amount of water absorbed by the facing in a given time, is frequently asked for. This "how-much" value is not a good test for gluing problems. What is really needed is a "how-fast" value, and the time to absorb a single drop of water or ink would be a better comparative test.

The Cobb test is used to measure water absorption for materials specified to be used for hazardous product containers.

Puncture Test (TAPPI T 803). The puncture test measures the energy required to puncture a board with a triangular pyramidal point affixed to a pendulum arm. Beach puncture (also knows as the G.E. puncture test) is used mostly to quantify the puncture resistance and stiffness of triplewall corrugated.

A triangular pyramidal point with 25-millimetre (1-inch) sides, mounted on a weighted swinging pendulum, is forced through the board under test. The energy absorbed in forcing the tip completely through the board is reported in "puncture test units."

Pin Adhesion (TAPPI T 821). Pin adhesion quantifies the strength of the bond between the medium's flute tips and the linerboard facings.

Ply Separation (TAPPI T 812). Ply separation evaluates the board's resistance to ply separation when exposed to water. It is used to differentiate boards made with conventional adhesives from those made with weather-resistant adhesives.

Coefficient of Friction (TAPPI T 815 and ASTM D 4521). Coefficient of friction (CoF) can affect machinability and load stability. One method of determining

CoF consists of placing a weighted sled of the test material onto a plane surface faced with the material. The angle is gently increased, and the plane angle at which slippage is first observed is noted. The tangent of the average slide angle is reported as the static CoF. A stress/strain machine such as an Instron can be used to directly measure the force required to pull a sled along a flat surface. A stress/strain machine method will give both static and dynamic CoF values.

A CoF of less than 0.30 is considered to be unacceptable and values between 0.30 and 0.40 are marginal. Boxes with a CoF of between 0.40 and 0.50 are fairly stable; normal untreated boxes fall within this range. Boxes with values below 0.30 usually need to be treated in some way. This may be as simple as brushing them with water after sealing and stacking or as complex as special antiskid surface treatments and coatings.

Cautionary Note:
UFC rule 41 and NMFC item 222 are similar but not identical. This discussion is meant to be a general overview; readers are advised to consult the original documents.

CARRIER RULES AND REGULATIONS

Application

The Uniform Freight Classification (UFC) and National Motor Freight Classifications (NMFC) were established to categorize articles for shipment via common carrier with respect to value, density, fragility and potential for damage to other freight. Rail and motor carriers publish the classifications which specify conditions under which specific articles can be shipped and at what rates.

- When shipping by rail, refer to UFC. Pertinent rules include 5, 6, 19, 21, 39, 40, 41 and 49.

- When shipping by truck, refer to NMFC. The items (rules) to consult include 110, 205, 220, 222, 540, 580, 680, 687, 689 and 780.

- UFC rule 41 and NMFC item 222 are the most frequently used in describing corrugated packaging.

There are four basic steps for determining authorized packaging:

1. Fully identify the product. The product must be identified by its transportation description, not by trade or popular names. The bill of lading description is often the best reference.

2. Select the proper governing classification. If you know that the product will be shipped exclusively by rail or truck, use that classification. If there is some question consult both and follow the more demanding requirement.

3. Use the "Index to Articles" to find the applicable item number.

4. Consult the proper article to find the required packaging.

Failure to comply with regulations can subject the shipper to penalties such as higher freight rates, refusal of acceptance by the carrier or nonpayment of damage claims.

Summary of Rules for Corrugated Box Construction

Carrier rules for corrugated box construction can be summarized as follows: Specified boards (using either Mullen burst test or ECT values) shall be used for a given product weight, providing the box does not exceed a specified dimensional limit. The dimensional size limit for a box is determined by adding an outside length, width and depth.

Table 15.4 summarizes the construction requirements for singlewall and doublewall boxes. Additional tables are available for triplewall and solid fiberboard constructions. The rules also require that the maker place a box maker's certificate stamp on the bottom of the box. (See Figure 15.8)

If the user elects to use Mullen values to specify box construction, the board must meet the minimum burst requirements in Table 15.4, Part A. If the user elects to use ECT values to specify box construction, the board must meet the minimum ECT values in Table 15.4, Part B. Note that although the two parts are

Table 15.4

Summary of carrier rules for singlewall and doublewall boxes.

Max. Weight, Box and Contents (lbs.)	Max. Outside Dimension (length + width + depth, in.)	Part A*		Part B*
		Min. Burst Test (lb./sq. in.)	Min. Combined Weight of Facings, Including Center Facing on Doublewall	Min. Edge Crush Test (ECT) (lb./in. width)
		Singlewall Corrugated Fiberboard Boxes		
20	40	125	52	23
35	50	150	66	26
50	60	175	75	29
65	75	200	84	32
80	85	250	111	40
95	95	275	138	44
120	105	350	180	55
		Doublewall Corrugated Fiberboard Boxes		
80	85	200	92	42
100	95	275	110	48
120	105	350	126	51
140	110	400	180	61
160	115	500	222	71
180	120	600	270	82

*Mullen (Part A) and ECT values (Part B) are presented side-by-side, but there is no correlation between the values.

side by side, Mullen and ECT values have no correlation; the boards that have the values listed in parts A and B of the table are not equivalent.

Using the freight classifications as a design specification has a number of disadvantages. For example,

- No reference is made to duration of warehouse storage
- No reference is made to flute type (Mullen system)
- No reference is made to distribution hazards
- The tables essentially apply only to regular slotted boxes. (RSC) designs.
- The contribution of different medium weights is not taken into account.

Freight classifications therefore do not necessarily form the most effective basis for a design.

CORRUGATED BOXES

Selecting the Correct Flute

Consult closely with your corrugated supplier to select the correct flute and board weight. Although there are apparently many choices, in practice a corrugated supplier stocks few. Barring any established technical reason to do otherwise, use a carrier classification and C-flute as good starting points.

E- and F-flutes are not associated with shipping containers: rather they are most commonly used to replace thicker grades of solid paperboards for heavier or special protective primary packages. The general rule of thumb says that E- or F-flute should be considered if a folding carton design calls for boards thicker than 750 micrometres (30 point). They are an excellent choice where the primary container may become a distribution container for some part of its travels. Small tools, hardware, small appliances and housewares often fall into this category.

A-flute, one of the originally specified flutes, is not in common use today. A-flute's almost 5-millimetre (1/4-inch) thickness occupies more space that C-flute and has significantly greater deflection before bearing a load when compressed.

In theory, A-flute's thicker section should give it the highest top-to-bottom compression strength of the three flutes. This is true under laboratory conditions. However, A-flute has the lowest flat crush resistance. (See Table 15.5) This makes A-flute with 127-gram (26-pound) medium almost impossible to machine

Table 15.5
Relative flute flat crush values.

Medium Grammage	A-flute	C-flute	B-flute
127 g	0.70	1.00	1.15
161 g	0.90	1.25	1.45
196 g	1.10	1.50	N.A.

and transport without damaging the flute structure. Engineering studies suggest that A-flute is most efficient when constructed with a 195-gram medium. Some authorities regard 127-gram medium C-flute to have the minimum acceptable flat crush for shipping applications. Heavy mediums cannot be made into the small B-flute.

A-flute is useful for cushion pads and the construction of triplewall board grades where the added thickness is an advantage. With heavy mediums, A-flute makes a strong, rigid box. B-flute is used for canned goods or other products where box stacking strength is not required. B-flute's high flat crush strength is an advantage when supporting heavy goods such as bottles or cans. It can also be used to advantage for lighter load applications where a high stack strength is not needed, or where the distribution environment is very short.

C-flute has about 10% better stacking strength than the same linerboard weights in B-flute. It is best for applications where the corrugated container must bear some or all of the warehouse load. C-flute is sometimes chosen over B-flute for boxes that will hold glass bottles, despite C-flute's lower flat crush strength. It is felt that the thicker flute will provide more protection for the glass. Table 15.6 summarizes the differences among the various types of flutes.

Table 15.6
Comparison of corrugated board characteristics.

Characteristic	A-flute*	B-flute	C-flute	E-flute
Stack strength	best*	fair	good	poor
Printing	poor	good	fair	best
Die cutting	poor	good	fair	best
Puncture	good	fair	best	poor
Storage space	most	good	fair	least
Score/bend	poor	good	fair	best
Cushioning	best	fair	good	poor
Flat crush	poor	good	fair	good

*A-flute is subject to the limitations of flat crush when light mediums are used.

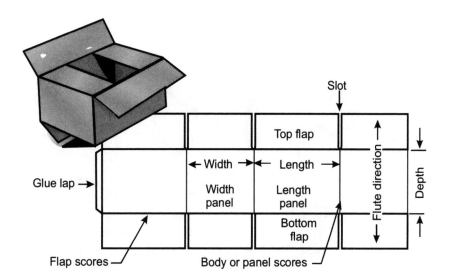

Figure 15.9
Parts of a regular slotted
container (RSC) blank.

Box Styles

Corrugated board is an extraordinarily versatile material and can be fabricated
to a variety of shapes. Generally, these fall into one of three manufacturing
categories.

"Regular slotted containers" (RSC) are boxes in which all scores and cuts
are in straight lines, in machine and cross directions only. (See Figure 15.9)
These boxes require no special tooling. The manufacturer simply resets slitters
and folder-gluers to the required dimensions.

"Die-cut designs" require the manufacture of a steel-rule cutting and creasing
die. Die-cut designs usually have a longer delivery time and are somewhat more
expensive. The added expense can be justified by the many useful features that
can be created on die-cut designs. Die cutting can be done on flatbed presses
(more accurate) or rotary presses (faster).

Die-cutting is used on any design that has angles, cuts and creases, curves
or internal cutouts. (See Figure 15.10) As well as being available in complex de-

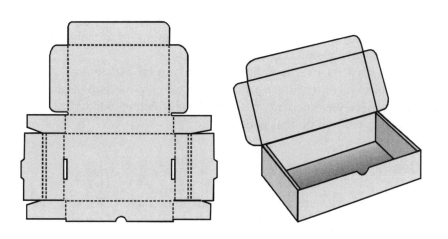

Figure 15.10
Typical die-cut box.

Figure 15.11

Bliss-style box design
variations.

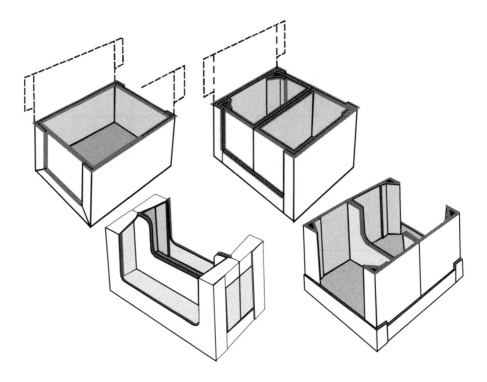

signs, die-cut boxes are dimensionally more accurate than those made by slitting and scoring methods. However, the mechanics of die-cutting flatten corrugated flutes somewhat, resulting in a loss of compression strength.

The "Bliss box" is a third design category. (See Figure 15.11) Bliss-style boxes are assembled from a number of cut pieces, usually a body panel and two end panels, rather than from a single sheet. They have the advantage of providing maximum board utilization and compression strength for a given board area. The basic box can be made with or without top flaps. Other design variations include the incorporation of H partitions, triangular corner posts, and double-glued corners, and tray versions. Disadvantages of Bliss designs are that the packer must have a special erecting machine and inventory is increased.

The manufacturer's joint is that corner of a box where materials overlap and the manufacturer has joined the materials with glue, tape or staples.

Gluing, the most common joining method, offers a strong joint, capable of being produced at high speed. Taping and stapling or stitching are usually semiautomatic and are slower operations.

Taping is used for oversized boxes not able to be put through a gluer and for applications where the overlap of the normal glue tab is undesirable. Wire stitching is most commonly used on triplewall constructions and where treatments such as waxing prohibit normal gluing.

Box Design Variations

Beyond the basic styles are a number of variations. Table 15.7 lists some abbreviations commonly used to describe boxes.

Table 15.7

Common box abbreviations.

RSC	Regular Slotted Container	DCB	die-cut container
CSSC	Center Special slotted container	5PF	five-panel folder
FOSB	Full-overlap slotted container	1PDF	one-piece display folder
SPSB	Special slotted container	DCS	die-cut sheet
TEL	telescope	PTN	partition

Figure 15.12 shows examples of boxes similar to RSC's but with different closure treatments. A normal RSC's inner flaps do not meet in the center of the box. The "center special" design increases the length of the inner flaps to be about equal to half the box length so that when the box is closed the inner flaps meet. This provides more even product support as well as providing more strength and cushioning thickness. This design must be die-cut because of the irregularity of the flap lengths.

A "full overlap" slotted box extends the width of the major flaps to close to the box's width so that when closed, the major flaps overlap. This doubling up of board produces an exceptionally strong end as well as providing significant cushioning effect. Overlapped major flaps are also used where the ends will be sealed by stitching or stapling. If all flaps are of the same depth, then the box can be made by the RSC process.

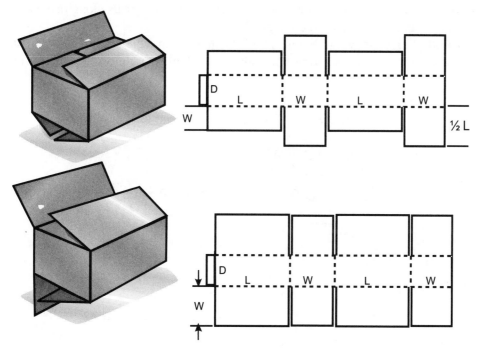

Figure 15.12

"Center special" (top) and "full overlap" slotted box (bottom) are similar to the RSC, but the closure treatment differs.

Figure 15.13

A full telescope design style
(left) and a design style with
cover (right.) Unlike RSCs,
design style boxes have a
solid bottom sheet.

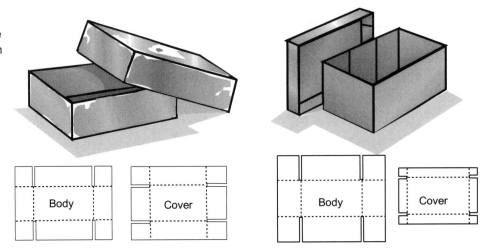

"Design style" boxes such as those shown in Figure 15.13 have glue joints
at the four corners and a solid sheet bottom. They are economical in board usage
since the absence of the usual end-seals reduces doubling up of the board in
non-critical areas. The cover can be partial or full telescope.

Design style boxes are common for shipping some produce products. Depending on the application, the body may be made of a heavy board to act as the
main load carrier and the cover of a lighter grade of board. Bulk office papers
use design style boxes with a cover. A similar effect can be had by making two
half-slotted RSCs (an RSC with flaps at one end only.) This would use more
board, but would provide a stronger bottom.

One piece and five-panel folders (Figure 15.14) are used for products ranging
from books to food. The one-piece folder's wrap-around flaps meet on the center
of one side and are sealed with tape. The five-panel folder seals along one edge,
leaving both major panels free for graphics.

Both designs shown in Figure 15.14 illustrate simple die cutting, but current
practice allows the corrugating box industry to duplicate almost any design of

Figure 15.14

A one-piece folder (left) and
a five-panel folder (right.)

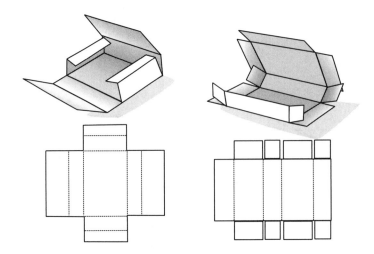

reasonable size that can be made with folding solid paperboard. This includes more complex forms such as self-erecting Himes bottoms and various designs featuring internal partitions and other supports.

The Box Production Process

The manufacturing sequence can follow many different paths depending on the nature of a box design and how it is decorated. Board leaving the corrugating machine might be natural kraft or any one of the several white surfaced or solid white krafts. The top linerboard may be unprinted or the linerboard may have been pre-printed. The sheets cut to the correct width and length will then follow one of the paths shown in Figure 15.15.

For a regular RSC, a flat sheet cut to the box overall dimensions and with the flap scores in place, is sent through single machine that prints, panel-scores and slots, folds and glues the box in one operation. An RSC that has a preprinted liner already in place as it leaves the corrugating machine needs to be panel scored and slotted, folded and glued. Preprinted blanks intended for complex box designs other than RSC styles are sent for rotary or flat-bed die-cutting and then folding and gluing.

Die-cut boxes leave the corrugating machine as flat unscored sheets. They can be decorated by direct printing or by applying preprinted lithographed labels (litho labeling). After the appropriate decorating, the blank is sent for die-cutting, folding and gluing.

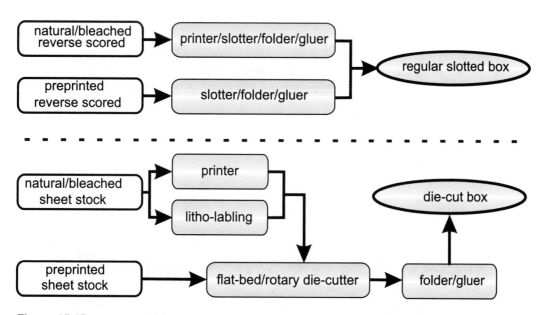

Figure 15.15

The production of a corrugated box can follow many different paths through a corrugating plant's various machines. The upper paths are for RSC designs, the lower paths are for die-cut designs.

Litho-laminating is a less common process that laminates a lithographically printed label paper (not kraft) to a single faced board, most often using a specialized small corrugating machine. The process is most usually done with E-, B-, or smaller flutes.

Dimensioning

A box's length is always the greater of the flap opening dimensions. (See Figure 15.16) Depth is the inside dimension between the top and bottom inner flaps. The order in which dimensions are reported records where the opening will be. Top-loading boxes present the largest opening for ease of loading but use the greatest board area to enclose a given volume. End-opening boxes use the least board for the same volume but have the smallest opening. Side openers are intermediate. An end-opening box is thus the most economical if it can be used in a system.

When laying out a box, allowance must be made for the material that will form the scores.

Corrugated board folds by collapsing in on itself, and the lines drawn on a flat sheet will not be equal to the finished box dimensions. (See Figure 15.17) Scoring allowances (K) are added, based on the box design, flute, material and on the type of scoring wheels used. When discussing box sizes with a supplier, it is always best to send the product or a sample box. In the event that you must size a box accurately, follow these directions:

1. Tear or cut the box open at the manufacturer's joint and lay it face down. (Refer back to Figure 15.9)

2. Determine box style, board and flute.

3. Mark the exact center line of the panel and flap scores.

4. Measure between the center marks of the second and third panels (the width and length dimensions in Figure 15.9) Do not measure the first or fourth panels.

Figure 15.16

Box size is expressed in the inside dimensions in the order of length, width and depth.

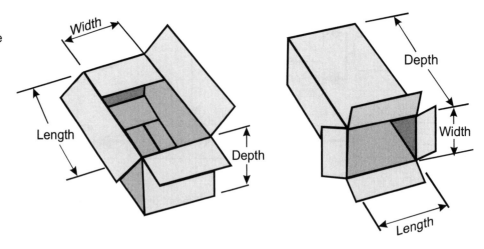

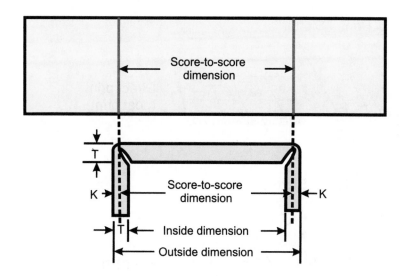

Figure 15.17
A flat-sheet layout and the resulting folded dimensions.

5. Subtract scoring allowances as dictated by step 2 (See Table 15.8) The result is the box length and width.

6. Repeat steps 4 and 5, measuring between the end scores (the Depth dimension in Figure 15.9). The result is the box depth.

CORRUGATED BOX PRINTING

The four methods used to print corrugate board are shown in Figure 15.18.

Plain corrugated boxes are direct printed by flexography, using water-dispersible inks. Natural kraft board does not make a good decorating medium:

- It has poor color

- The kraft fibers make for a rough printing surface

- Fluting makes the printing surface uneven. A typical result is a "washboard" appearance.

Table 15.8

Scoring allowances for boards of varying thicknesses. Scoring wheel geometries and individual company practice will affect allowances.

Flute	Typical Thickness	Typical Score Allowance
A	4.8 mm (3/16-in.)	6.4 mm (1/4-in.)
C	4.0 mm (5/32-in.)	4.8 mm (3/16-in.)
B	3.2 mm (1/8-in.)	3.2 mm (1/8-in.)
BC	6.4 mm (1/4-in.)	7.9 mm (5/16-in.)

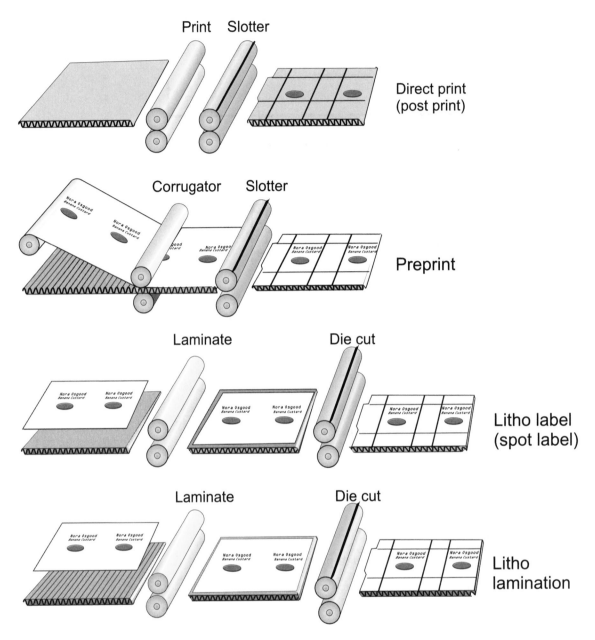

Figure 15.18
Different ways of applying a graphic to a corrugated board.

These limitations are not a problem for a general shipping box. However, where some decorative value is needed, other printing methods must be used.

Natural linerboard can be replaced with a white-lined kraft. This provides a better color for the printing surface, and the box graphics will look brighter. The white is usually not solid but rather somewhat mottled in appearance.

Solid bleached kraft linerboard can be preprinted and then converted to corrugated board. Preprinting eliminates the problems of trying to print an assembled corrugated board. The usual minimum amount for preprinting is 2 mill rolls, several tons of paper. This limits the process to fairly large production runs.

The box can be spot-labeled with a label, usually printed by lithography. Litho label printing can produce a full range of colors on wide selection of label paper stock. The label can be big enough to cover the entire box surface; it can be a spot label over a kraft or white-lined box or a spot label over a box surface that has some other graphics applied to it.

Litho-laminating refers to process wherein a sheet of lithographically printed label stock is applied to a single faced corrugated board (unlike spot labeling that applies a lithographically printed label to a single-wall board.) The product does not meet normal carrier rules since the outer liner is label stock rather than kraft linerboard.

The heavy ink lay-down inherent to screen printing can effectively hide poor substrate color for small-volume applications. Screen printing does not need the contact pressure of flexography and the surface undulations due to the corrugated medium are of no consequence.

Normal flexographic printing applies pressure to the corrugated board to transfer ink. This pressure can cause partial compression of the flute structure, with a corresponding loss in potential compression strength. Heavy and multiple-color ink coverage should be avoided where top-to-bottom compression strength needs to be maximized. Typical allowable crush per color is about 0.1 millimetre (0.004 inch).

SPECIAL BOARD TREATMENTS

Most corrugated board treatments improve performance for board exposed to high humidity or direct water contact. The treatments can be added to the paper furnish or put on the liner or medium as it goes into the corrugator; the finished box also could be treated.

Thermoset resins can be added at the paper mill to provide board with wet strength. Usually these resins are melamine based and are added at levels up to 2%. Higher resin levels would tend to make the board too brittle. Wet-strength boards have marginal performance improvement at normal conditions, but retain tear, puncture and compression values to a much higher degree in humid atmospheres. Wet-strength board is sometimes further treated with waxes to increase wet performance.

Waxing is done in several ways. One is to add the wax to the liner or medium in-line with the corrugator. About 12 to 18% wax based on paperboard weight can be added this way; higher levels would interfere with the manufacturing process and adhesive bonding. The wax soaks into the fiber and can't be seen on the exterior. This treatment is often referred to as dry waxing.

The wax forms a matrix around, but does not seal off, connecting fibers. One immediate positive effect is that the added wax matrix significantly improves the box's compression strength. The box still absorbs moisture at high humidity, but at a slower rate, and when equilibrated at high humidity, the wax provides for significant retention of compression strength.

In curtain coating, the finished blank passes through a curtain of molten wax which then sets by quick chilling. This "wet waxing" develops a wax surface film that effectively seals off the board surface and makes it resistant to direct water contact. Humidity will still penetrate the board through the flutes, reducing compression strength. Curtain-coated boards are useful where temporary or short-term surface water resistance is desirable.

Cascading passes the finished box through a number of hot wax curtains so that the wax can run down inside liners and medium as well as the outside surface. Wax add-on typically ranges from 45 to 60% of paperboard weight. Cascading effectively seals the surface and most of the fibers and affords the highest level of moisture and water protection. The ultimate wax treatment is to cascade a dry-waxed or wet-strength board. Barring any other difference, it can be said that generally the more wax added, the better the final effect. An aesthetic disadvantage is that the heavy wax treatment turns the kraft paper a dark brown.

As Table 15.9 shows, compression strength increases as the treatment level goes up. The compression tests for the chilled, high-humidity condition were conducted at 4.4°C. Even higher values could be obtained if the boxes were wet-strength grade to start with, or if the cascaded box had been dry-waxed by the corrugator first.

One of the largest volume applications for waxed boxes is for produce and fresh and frozen meat products. The level of wax treatment depends on the product's nature. For example, some vegetables that are not wet, but that have high respiration rates that result in high local humidity, require boxes able to tolerate this condition without undue loss of strength. Dry-waxed medium and liners or a wet-strength board might be sufficient. Often such boxes have ventilation holes to provide air circulation to remove moisture and provide fresh air. These boxes are invariably die-cut designs. (See Figure 15.19)

If the produce item is a little damp when packed, the inner liner might be curtain-coated with wax to shed water droplets. Fresh or frozen meat parts might use a similar design. If there is the possibility that water droplets will touch both the inside and outside of the box, then both sides would be curtain-coated. In the

Table 15.9

Compression strength (in pounds) of wax-treated boxes after environmental exposure. (Source: M.B.I.)

Type of Treatment	23°C, 50% R.H.	4.4°C, 8 Days High Humidity	Water Spray, 1 hour
No treatment	680	399	—
Waxed medium and curtain coated	798	854	835
Waxed medium and liner	829	574	350
Waxed medium and liner, and curtain coated	872	915	835
Cascaded	1,146	929	1,049

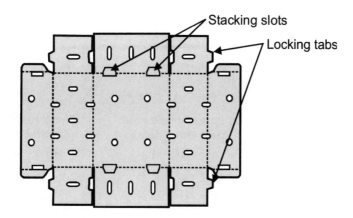
Stacking slots
Locking tabs

Figure 15.19
Layout of a typical die-cut produce box. Produce boxes are commonly waxed.

most severe conditions, crushed ice is poured over the contents of the box, or the box may be taken out to the harvesting fields where it will be expected to survive the occasional rainfall. These boxes require heavy wax treatments, such as cascading.

Although the term "waxing" has been used throughout this discussion, the materials used are usually proprietary blends of waxes, low-molecular-weight polyethylenes, rosins, ethylene-vinyl acetates and other polymers. Wax blends, while economical, have very poor scuff resistance. Polyethylene extrusion coatings are used when better scuff resistance is required.

Other corrugated board treatments are available that reduce abrasion, increase coefficient of friction, improve grease resistance and provide a release surface.

CORRUGATED BOX QUALITY ASSURANCE

Corrugated boards specifications sometimes disregard the fact that paper is a natural product. A given paperboard characteristic can easily vary by 8% or more, and tolerance levels must take this into account.

A corrugated box manufacturer normally supplies the box purchaser with one or several hand samples for evaluation prior to full production. These are sometimes tested for compression strength, and the data become part of the decision process. It should be clearly understood that hand samples are cut from pristine board on a sample cutting table. This method of producing a box is very gentle and has no relationship to what will happen in production, where board will be palletized in high stacks, fed through machines with pickup cups and pressure belts, compressed during printing and die-cutting, and otherwise abused. A production box with high ink coverage can lose 25% or more of its compression strength compared with the hand sample. Furthermore, compression testing of a single hand sample is statistically irrelevant, because of natural variation in the board. (See Table 15.10)

Figures 15.20 through 15.23 provide typical scored-sheet and manufacturer's glue-joint tolerances for B- and C-flute singlewall boxes, as jointly published by the Packaging Machinery Manufacturers Industry and the Fibre Box Association.

Table 15.10

Box compression strength comparison of identical hand samples and production boxes. Printing ink coverage was about 25% in two colors.

Production stage	Compression Strength (new kraft liners)	Compression Strength (recycled kraft liners)
Unprinted hand sample	1030 psi ± 61 lb	1073 psi ± 73 lb
Unprinted production box	852 psi ± 35 lb	858 psi ± 39 lb
Printed production box	839 psi ± 44 lb	843 psi ± 42 lb

Figure 15.20

Typical scored and slotted sheet tolerances.

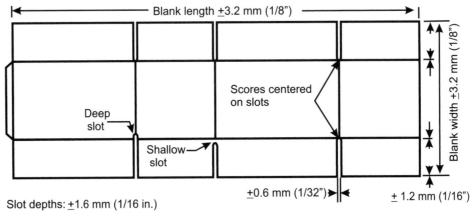

Slot depths: ±1.6 mm (1/16 in.)

Body panels center of score to center of score ±1.6 mm (1/16')

Scores not to vary more than ±1.6 mm (1/16 in.) from vertical

Figure 15.21

Gap tolerances and overlap.

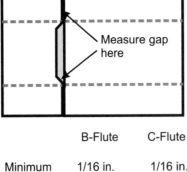

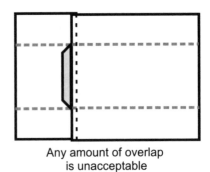

Any amount of overlap is unacceptable

	B-Flute	C-Flute
Minimum	1/16 in.	1/16 in.
Ideal	3/16 in.	7/32 in.
Maximum	5/16 in.	3/8 in.

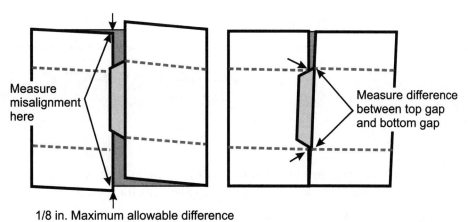

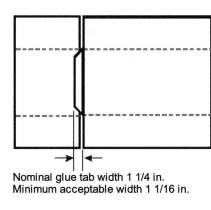

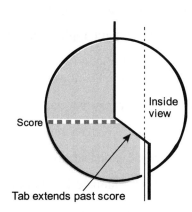

Figure 15.22
Out of square (left) and fishtailing ('V' joint).

Figure 15.23
Length and width of glue tab. Tabs extending more than 1/16 in. beyond horizontal scores, and tabs that hinder proper flap folding are unacceptable. The condition causes out-of-square boxes.

1. What are the five corrugated board flutes called in order from largest to smallest? Give examples of the typical applications for each flute.

2. Your corrugated box supplier informs you that he will use 205/127B/186/ 127C/205. What is he talking about? What problem will likely occur if the corrugated board producer does not control the moisture content of the two linerboards used to make a corrugated board?

3. What are the main applications for F-flute and other microflutes.

4. The opening for a corrugated box can be put in the top, end or side. Discuss the principal implications of these choices.

5. What is the correct way of dimensioning a corrugated box?

6. What are the practical implications of paper's viscoelasticity?

7. What are the practical implications of paper's hygroscopic nature?

8. What does "combined weight of facings" describe? Where is this value used?

9. What is the McKee formula and what is it used for?

10. What is the printing method used for corrugated board? What are the inherent limitations in printing natural kraft formed corrugated board?

11. What is "preprint"? What are the advantages and limitations of preprint?

12. What are the advantages and disadvantages of a die-cut box compared with an RSC?

13. A loaded box weighs 47.6 pounds and is 19x16x6 inches. What must the construction of this box be to comply with rule 41 of the UFC?

14. Calculate the estimated ECT value required for the box in question 13. The box will use a C-flute 0.460 inches thick and the required stacking strength is 700 lbs force. How does this compare with the UFC value? Why is their a difference?

15. Why is a regular slotted box one of the most popular box styles?

16. What is the difference between wax curtain coating and wax cascading? Where might each be used?

17. What is the major application for triple-wall board?

18. What is a score allowance and why must it be used?

19. Where might you need to specify a five-point score?

20. What do carrier rules basically specify?

21. How are flat corrugated pads dimensioned?

22. What are the international conditioning standards for testing paper? Why are these needed?

23. Define a box's size limit as described by carrier rules.

24. A-flute is rarely used for constructing corrugated boxes. Explain why.

25. What is a Bliss box? What are the advantages and disadvantages of this design?

26. What are the advantages of a center special slotted container (CSSC)?

CONTENTS

Distribution Packaging: A Systems Approach

Definition of distribution packaging, sequential approaches and system approaches, product design, fragility factors, distribution environments, unplanned shipping containers, complementary primary and shipping containers, efficient dimensioning, ease of assembly and disassembly, multiple use, compliance, material disposal, efficient materials handling. Typical distribution environment hazards, example of a distribution environment.

Tracking Distribution Losses

Tracking losses, damage reaction costs, true cost of loss, damage reporting, summer and winter loss levels, warehouse damage levels, damage in rail shipment.

The Warehouse

The warehouse environment, stock-picking, product identification, assembly into mixed loads, odd shapes.

Unit Loads

Pallets, slip sheets, clampable loads, wood pallets, wood types, standard dimensions, block pallets, stringer pallets, reversible and nonreversible pallets, winged pallets, pallet overhang, losses attributed to pallet issues. Unit load efficiency, area and cube utilization, palletizing efficiency programs, example of typical utilizations for consumer oil bottles, implications of poor utilization. Stabilizing unit loads, strapping, shrink-wrapping, stretch-wrapping, high-friction inks and coatings, stabilizing with adhesives, fiberboard caps and trays.

Good Distribution Practice

Industry guidelines for grocery products, maximum and minimum container dimensions, pallet footprint, storage capability, pallet stability, bagged product, shrink-wrapped trays.

Evaluating Distribution Packaging

Preshipment testing, agencies sponsoring preshipment test procedures or requiring pretested packages, typical preshipment testing equipment and test methods, recommended standard atmospheres, ISTA and ASTM comprehensive test protocols and example sequences, comparison of ASTM and ISTA methods, examples of ASTM elements.

DISTRIBUTION PACKAGING

DISTRIBUTION PACKAGING: A SYSTEMS APPROACH

Designing for Distribution

Distribution packaging describes technical packaging functions that provide product protection and that facilitate safe and cost-effective product distribution. We may further observe that distribution packaging does not *add value* so much as it *conserves value*.

The designer of a CD player might logically consider the environment in which the product will be used. However, the household environment is gentle compared to the transport environment required to get the CD player there. Such a product, designed only with its end use in mind, is quite likely to cost the manufacturer extra dollars in protective packaging. More costs will be incurred if the product cannot be efficiently fitted into a standard distribution system.

The time to start considering distribution packaging is at the inception of a product's design. Unfortunately, there is a marked tendency to concentrate time and resources on product promotion and the consumer package, and then add the distribution package—an afterthought when all other design aspects have been committed. (See Figure 16.1.)

A systems approach (see Figure 16.2) treats distribution packaging as an integrated activity. During product design, it considers all inputs and all events that the product and package will experience on the way to the final consumer.

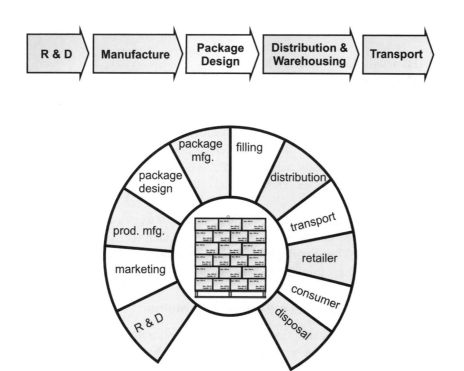

Figure 16.1

A sequential approach considers each step at the completion of a preceding step.

Figure 16.2

A systems approach to distribution package designed considers all inputs.

System Considerations

Product Design

Whether a product will survive a particular journey depends partly on its susceptibility to damage from hazards it will experience. In considering a packaging system for a product, the packaging engineer must start with the product itself.

"Fragility" describes a product's susceptibility to damage. Sound package design must consider quantified fragility factors, not general statements. The design process needs to assess potential damage from many sources including:

Compression	What is the safe working load?
Shock	What is the critical drop and "G" level?
Vibration	What are the resonance frequencies?
Heat or cold	What are the critical temperatures?
Moisture	What is the critical humidity?
Time	What is the projected shelf life?
Electrostatics	What is the critical discharge voltage?

Product fragility factors must be evaluated and compared against likely distribution occurrences. Providing protective packaging for an unreasonably fragile product can be very costly. It is often more cost-effective to improve the product design. Protective package design should be considered only after one understands the product's unavoidable fragilities.

The Distribution Environment

You must thoroughly understand the nature of the distribution environment through which the product must travel:

- How will the product be handled?
- How will it be stored?
- How will it be transported?
- How high will it be stacked?
- What will the temperature and humidity range be?
- How many times will it be transferred and handled?
- What kind of pallets will be used?
- Will it be unitized or containerized?

The distribution package must be able to survive the environment. A container for local shipment need not be as sturdy as one that will be warehoused and shipped nationally. The distribution package or shipper must suit the handling methods used and must provide appropriate protection for the contents.

The Primary Container as a Shipping Container

Make no unwarranted assumptions as to what the shipping container will be for different stages of the journey. A household toaster may be packed in a primary paperboard carton, and then six of these may be packed into a corrugated box.

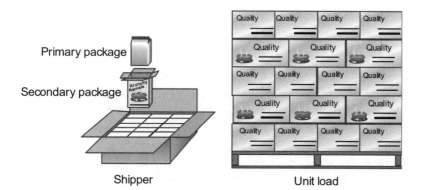

Figure 16.3
A packaging system may consist of many subsystems.

However, the sturdy corrugated box may go only as far as the local distribution warehouse. From that point, the actual distribution container may become the flimsy carton that houses each toaster.

Complementary Primary and Shipping Containers

The distribution system may require several "layers" or levels of packaging. (See Figure 16.3.) Optimal distribution packaging builds the correct protective and handling qualities into each packaging subunit and ensures that all the qualities are mutually complementary. This requires that we understand which package will be used for different stages of distribution and the best compromise for such factors as load sharing and sizing.

Dimensions for Maximum Efficiency

An "arrangement" is a way of orienting a number of primary packages in a shipper. Each potential arrangement needs a different size shipping container, each requiring different corrugated board and divider material areas. Carrying the problem further, each shipping box size will have various possible palletizing patterns. Some patterns will give better cube utilization, while others may provide more stable loads. Still others may give maximum stack strength. Small adjustments to primary container dimensions can have major impacts on total shipping efficiencies and costs through better cube utilization. (See the section "Unit Load Efficiency" on page 449.)

The final objective is system efficiency: a shipping container that is cost-effective to produce and that is efficient to palletize, transport and warehouse.

Ease of Assembly and Disassembly

Every shipping container must be erected for packing and, when the container has served its purpose, must be opened or dismantled. Ease of disassembly, particularly for consumer products at the retail level and for components that will be used for further manufacture in an industrial package, can be a significant design feature.

A major problem at retail locations is knife cuts to package or product when stock persons cut open corrugated containers. Easy-opening features or specific indicators for opening will reduce this damage.

Multiple Use and Reuse

Henry Ford is said to have designed a wood engine-packing crate to exacting tolerances. When the engine was removed, the crate boards were reassembled as the automobile floor. There are many examples of packaging components having continued or useful value beyond the obvious. The use of distribution packaging as part of the sales display is perhaps the most common. Component protective packaging has been used as part of finished product packaging. Protective expanded polystyrene forms have been used as assembly jigs and fixtures. For high-volume products or products with a fixed or controllable distribution cycle, multiple-trip and bulk containers should be considered.

Compliance with Legal and/or Carrier Requirements

Commodities classed as dangerous must, by law, be packed in containers that meet specified construction, performance, labeling and identification specifications. Packaging practices recommended by carriers and the trade are not all mandatory, but they are based on experience and should not be bypassed without thorough analysis.

Disposal of Packaging Waste Material

Source reduction, waste management and recycling is playing a significant role in design decisions in a world that is increasingly conscious of global sustainability.

Efficient Materials Handling

Thoughtful product and package design frequently yields savings during the distribution cycle. Many export automobiles, for example, have tie-down eyes as part of their construction. For mechanical handling, keep load centers of gravity low. Provide clearance for forklift tines. Select stable pallet patterns, and further increase load stability with stretch-wrapping, banding, caps, slip sheets or friction coatings.

Consider ergonomics where manual handling is expected. Simple features such as handholds better control orientation, reduce the chance of dropping and—in the event of a drop—reduce the probable drop height. Avoid boxes heavier than 20 kilograms (44 pounds) for general consumer goods.

The Physical Distribution Environment

The physical distribution environment consists of all the handling, storage, transport and other events that a product is subjected to between the end of a production line and the final consumer. Think of the physical distribution environment as an area that is hazardous to the product. (See Table 16.1.) Distribution packaging protects the product and ensures a safe, cost-effective journey.

Typical distribution systems have a surprising number of individual events, each with its own characteristic potential for damaging the product. It is said that a breakfast cereal carton will be picked up, moved, stacked, transported and otherwise handled 17 (or more) times before the final consumer selects it at a

Table 16.1

Typical distribution environment hazards.

Basic Hazard	Typical Circumstances
Shock	Drops during manual handling; package thrown, rolled or tipped over; mechanical shocks (chutes, conveyors, palletizers); vehicle shocks (rail shunting, potholes, curbs).
Vibration	Roadbed patterns (rail joints, tar strips), suspension-generated vibration, out-of-balance wheels, drive-train vibrations.
Static compression	Warehouse stacking, bracing and other restraints.
Dynamic compression	Rail shunting, clamp trucks, arrests on conveyors and chutes.
Piercing, puncturing	Equipment misuse, projections, hooks, shifting cargo, damaged pallets.
Racking, deformation	Uneven support, uneven lifting.
Elevated temperature	High ambient temperatures, direct sun exposure, proximity to boilers.
Reduced temperature	Cold climate, unheated transport vehicles.
Low pressure	Unpressurized aircraft holds, high elevations. (See Figure 16.4)
Light	Direct exposure to sunlight.
Moisture, water	High ambient humidity, rain on unprotected cargo, condensation, bilge water and seawater.
Biological hazards	Microorganisms, fungi, mold, insects, rodents.
Time	Long storage.
Contamination	Dust, dirt, rust, adjacent product leakage, other external materials.

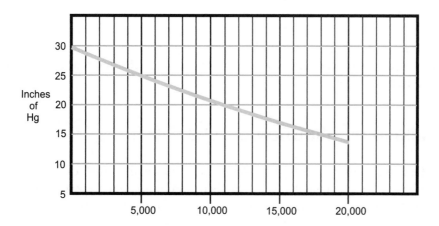

Figure 16.4

Air pressure and altitude. Most commercial aircraft maintain cabin pressure at about 8,000 ft.

retail outlet. Consider the distribution environment for a nationally shipped 8.5-litre plastic bottle of agricultural chemical manufactured in the east and used in the mid-west:

- Two 8.5-litre plastic bottles packed in a corrugated box
- Palletized manually
- Pallet moved by forklift
- Warehouse storage, 3 pallets high
- Pallet moved by forklift
- Road transport by truck
- Rail transit, trailer on flatcar
- Road transport by truck
- Pallet moved by forklift
- Warehouse storage, 3 pallets high
- Pallet moved by forklift
- Road transport by truck
- Pallet moved by hand truck
- Warehouse, retail outlet, 1 pallet high
- Manual handling of individual corrugated boxes, load into truck
- Manual handling of corrugated boxes, unload from truck
- Consumption

By far the greatest damage is caused by the "physical" events: damage during warehousing, transport and handling and damage caused by compression, shock and vibration.

To protect against the dangers listed in Table 16.1, their nature and magnitude must be thoroughly understood. It is not possible to exactly identify the hazards encountered for any particular journey; however, statistical descriptions of what typically happens are available.

For example, there is no way to predict exactly what will happen on a transcontinental train trip, but it can be determined that the typical railcar shunt speed (the speed at which one railcar runs into another during coupling) is about 9.3 kilometres per hour (5.6 miles per hour). (See Table 17.3 in Chapter 17 for a detailed distribution of speeds.)

It can also be determined that if a boxcar in shunted three times during its journey, there is a 33 percent chance that at least one of the shunts will exceed 9.7 km/hr (6 mph). The wise packaging engineer will ensure that the container and the product are capable of withstanding these shocks and that the boxcar is loaded in a way that will minimize movement.

TRACKING DISTRIBUTION LOSSES

The Insurance Company of North America estimates that 75% of international cargo losses are preventable, much of them through better packaging systems. In less developed countries, food loss between producer and consumer can be as high as 45%; unfortunately, in some instances this represents the difference between self sufficiency and starvation

It is vital to good distribution packaging development that the cause and nature of any loss be examined and understood. It is not enough to say, "The boxes fell over." The exact events leading up to the loss must be analyzed and the loss quantified. Only careful attention to detail forms a logical basis for new packaging systems or reducing losses with existing systems. Detailed loss data can also reveal over- or underpackaging.

Consider the impact of a loss on net profit. After all the materials, salaries and overhead had been paid, product loss is subtracted from net profit. How much more product is going to have to be sold to make of this loss? If net profit is five percent, a $500 claim means that an additional $10,000 in sales will have to be generated to bring the profit line back up. North American Van Lines estimated that hidden damage reaction costs are typically five times higher than the cost of cargo repair or replacement.

Since money is invested in distribution packaging to avoid loss, it is logical that product lost from inadequate packaging should be accounted as a packaging cost. Generally, increasing packaging will reduce damage. (See Figure 16.5) However, there is an optimum balance between packaging costs and damage losses. To find the minimum system costs, total distribution costs—including packaging cost and damage cost—must be established.

The relationship reflected in total cost helps to determine the optimum investment in distribution packaging. Keeping packaging costs down can be a false economy if the result is a higher damage rate.

The total cost can be the same for over- or underpackaging. In one instance the principal expense is package costs; and the other is the cost of product loss.

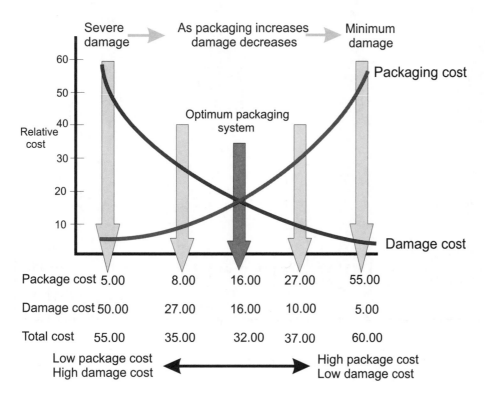

Figure 16.5

The optimum packaging system balances costs from excessive damage with the costs of overpackaging.

Increasing packaging will reduce damage rates until at some point the additional packaging costs are greater than the damage being prevented. Additional packaging would be overpackaging. Some overpackaging can be justified if it provides additional value such as goodwill or an impression of quality.

An International Safe Transit Association study determined that product losses were higher in summer than in winter. (See Figure 16.6) The difference is attributed mostly to higher humidity.

The extent to which inadequate packaging contributes to losses can be debated. Table 16.2 and Figure 16.7 certainly indicate that significant damage is caused by faulty transport equipment and improper handling and loading procedures. On the other hand, it must also be accepted that this is the real world and that packages must survive this test. Damaged product has your name on it. That the fault can be put on someone else is minimal consolation.

Many organizations have a poor or nonexistent system for tracking losses, assessing the financial and business impact and taking corrective action. No historical background supports investigations when apparently serious damage arise. For example: Is this a recent problem? Have we seen this problem before? Is it happening at particular locations or during specific seasons? Has something changed in the way we package or distribute? What is the loss value? Is it affecting our business beyond actual dollar amounts? Who reported the problem, and is it a reliable assessment?

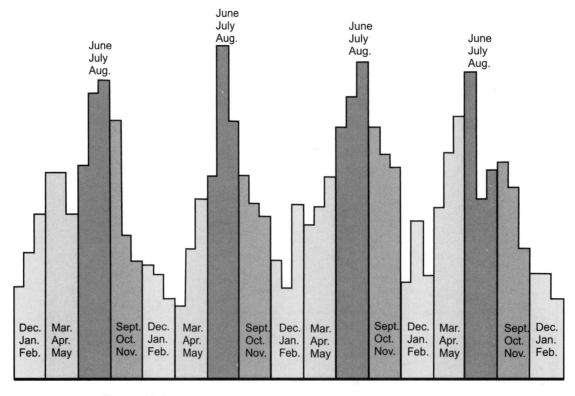

Figure 16.6

Seasonal trends of product shipping damage on all major products. (Source: International Safe Transit Association.)

Table 16.2

Warehouse damage rate by cause per 100,000 containers. (Source: U.S. Department of Agriculture.)

Cause	Number
Hitting bars at back of racks	24.5
Boxes dropped in aisles	16.1
Protruding nails in pallets	15.8
Fork tine damage	14.4
Unidentified storage damage	14.4
Pallet wings	13.0
Damaged while filling racks	12.8
Damaged while removing from second-level slot	8.6
Hitting merchandise on pallet below	7.8
Ramming by hand truck	5.1
Crushed during stacking	5.0
Leaning stacks	4.8
Corner cases hit by truck or tractor	4.6
53 other identified causes	39.0
Total damaged boxes in warehousing per 100,000	185.9

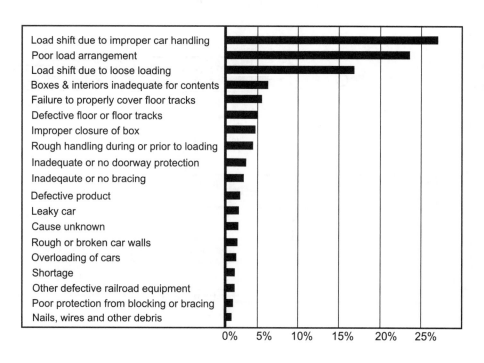

Figure 16.7

Causes of rail shipping damage. (Source: Fiber Box Association)

Furthermore, when suspecting that there may be a problem, there is sometimes no formal mechanism for investigating and implementing remedial action.

Figure 16.8 illustrates an organized method for reporting, tracking and taking action on distribution losses.

Reliable field observations are a key part of damage investigation. Reports by warehouse staff, retailers and others not familiar with the technical aspects of packaging is notoriously spotty. Field observations are often the key to identifying the problem and are best done by experienced staff. Where local observation cannot be avoided, standard reporting forms will direct the attention of the inexperienced observer to the critical issues. These should encourage hand sketches and photography.

When excessive damage is being experienced, the first step is to identify the damage mechanism; the time and place where the event (or series of events) results in the damage. The mechanism can be considered to be established when damage identical in scope and appearance can be consistently replicated in the laboratory. With the damage mechanism established, remedial actions can be considered. Product distribution can be considered as being a balance of three components:

$$Product + Package = Distribution\ Environment$$

Where the product and package are not equal to the rigors of distribution, there will be damage. Where the robustness of product and package is greater than what will be experienced in distribution then there is over-packaging.

When considering a remedy for excessive damage, all three distribution components need to be considered in order to determine the most cost-effective solution. In some instances it may be determined that correcting a product fragility is the most cost effective course. In other situations it may be possible

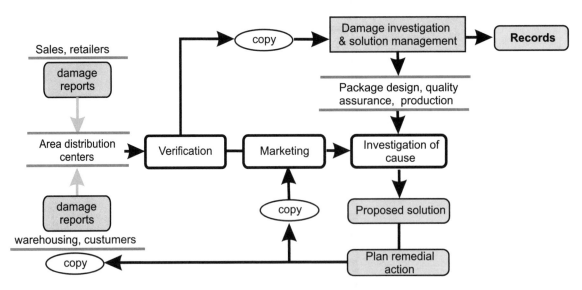

Figure 16.8

A formalized procedure for tracking damage is essential to reducing shipping losses. Depending on the product and organization, the procedure may take different forms.

to change the distribution environment. The final course of action would be to add more protective packaging.

THE WAREHOUSE

The distribution warehouse is a central collecting point for a particular good or a particular merchandising chain. Finished goods are forwarded to and held at the warehouse until selected and assembled into a customer order. The warehouse environment is not well understood by many shippers.

A typical dry groceries warehouse may contain 80,000 individual stock items. A hardware chain warehouse holds upwards of 100,000 stock items. Product arrives at the central warehouse in bulk or unitized, is broken down or reunitized according to the warehouse's needs, and then is arranged for stock-picking. Stock-picking means selecting individual items to fill an order for a particular store or destination. Central warehouses serve large customer areas; in some instances one or two warehouses may essentially serve the entire nation.

Product may be routed through more than one warehouse. For example, an export product may be moved from a local warehouse to dockside storage, to the cargo ship and back to a receiving warehouse.

A product must fit a warehouse's material handling system. This often means palleting loose loads or repalleting loads from nonstandard pallets. Depending on the operation, anywhere from 33 to 70% of product received at a warehouse must be handled manually before an order is placed in stock. Manual handling, in addition to being costly, is also a primary source of damage from dropping.

In the picking aisles, stock must be clearly identifiable from every side. Multicolor graphic displays serve only to obscure vital information from the picker. A box labeled "Golden Triangle Farms" does not inform the stock-picker of the contents. Containers should be strong enough to be dragged off the pallet by one end, and stiff enough that they don't distort and release their contents when handled in less than ideal fashion. Glue flaps must have enough adhesive to resist abusive handling.

An assembled order may contain items as disparate as eight mirrors, six assorted clocks, 10 boxes of motor oil, four shock absorbers, a stepladder and a box of Mepps #4 fishing lures. These and other items are assembled on a mixed pallet for transport to a small retail outlet. Containers must be easily handled by the picker and should be readily packed onto a mixed-order pallet. Box orientation on mixed-load pallets will tend to be on a "best fit" basis, regardless of "This side up" and "Do not stack" labels. It may be possible to pack a trapezoidal container efficiently on your pallet, but odd shapes do not pack well in a mixed-product pallet load. Use boxes with a rectangular cross section wherever possible.

UNIT LOADS

Pallets

It is simpler to move one 1,000-kilogram load than it is to more a thousand 1-kilogram loads. Product is most commonly unitized on pallets, a platform that can be picked up by the tines of a forklift truck. Another technique uses slip sheets, tough fiberboard or plastic sheets on which the load is stacked. The truck used with slip sheets has a clamp mechanism that grasps a protruding edge of the sheet and pulls the sheet and load onto a platform attached to the truck. A third method of handling a large group of assembled objects is with a clamp truck, a mechanism that picks up loads by exerting pressure from both sides of the load.

Each method has its advantages and disadvantages. Slip sheets are economical, take up little space and are light. However, the equipment is not universally available, is more expensive and is slower to operate. Pallets are universally adaptable to a variety of handling situations and locations. However, they are costly, take up space and can be difficult to dispose of. Clamp trucks use no added materials, but the geometry and character of the load must be such that it can be squeezed between the truck's clamps.

Most pallets are made of wood, and choice of wood species has a great impact on cost and durability. The denser and stiffer the wood, the greater the pallet's durability and usually the greater its cost. Well-made hardwood pallets are the most durable and cost-effective option of the many material choice available.

Other materials are usually selected for considerations other than durability. Metal pallets are often used in the pharmaceutical industry for their non-absorptive qualities and the ability to steam clean them when necessary. The many variations of plastic pallets share similar cleanability and splinter proof properties. On the down side, neither is as easy to repair as a wood pallet and both are more costly options. Where they are used, they are usually for in-house handling. Both metal and plastic pallets come at a higher price than good quality wood pallets.

There is some market for pallets made of heavy paperboard and corrugated board stock. These are light, inexpensive and easily recyclable in the normal paper recycling stream. However they are not suitable for some types of heavy loads, are not as durable as other options and there is the ever present danger of pallet failure if they inadvertently get wet.

There are many possible pallet sizes and designs; however, for standardized distribution, certain sizes and designs predominate. By convention, a pallet's size is stated length first, with length defined as the top dimension along the stringer or in the instance of a block pallet, the stringer board. (See Figure 16.9) About a third of all pallets are nominally 40 by 48 inches, the standard set by the Grocery Manufacturers of America. This size is also very close to the international 1,000 by 1,200 millimetre size.

The next most common size is 48 × 48 as might be used for carrying four 200 litre (55 gallon) steel drums.

The two broad categories of pallet design are stringer and block types. (See Figure 16.9) A range of variations is available within each design type:

- Reversible pallets have similar top and bottom decks. Nonreversible designs have different top and bottom decks, with only the top deck designed to be a load-carrying platform.

- Wing pallets have the stringers inset so that the deck boards overhang. This allows the pallets to be handled by slings. Pallets can be single wing

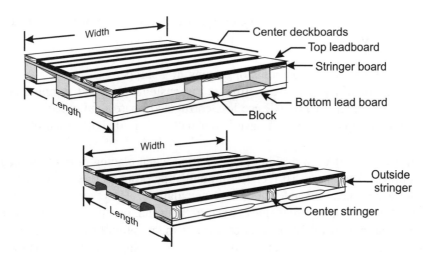

Figure 16.9

A block pallet (left) and a stringer-type pallet (right).

or double wing, depending on whether one or both decks overhang the stringers.

- Two-way entry pallets have solid stringers and can be entered only from the two ends.

- Block-type pallets are four-way entry, since any equipment can enter the pallet from all four directions. A partial four-way has notches cut into the stringer bottoms. A forklift's tines can enter from any direction, but a hand truck can only enter from two directions.

In addition to providing a product platform, the pallet is a buffer against the handling environment. A forklift driver placing a pallet into position cannot see the exact placement location: he stops when he hits something.

Viewed in this context, practices such as deliberate pallet perimeter overhang can only lead to problems, and warehouse operators condemn this habit. The Food Marketing Institute holds pallet issues responsible for about half of all observed damage and cites poor pallet footprint as the single largest cause of shipping damage. Of this damage, 50% is attributed to poor pallet stability and 35% is attributed to pallet overhang.

Pallet maintenance programs are essential. A common and easily remedied problem is fasteners working their way out of the wood.

Unit Load Efficiency

Warehouse floor space is rented by area, and the more product that can be put into that area, the better. Trucks loaded with light product should have the available volume completely filled to carry the maximum amount of product per trip. Area and cube utilization should be every packager's concern.

Optimum area and cube utilization begins with the primary package's design. Every packaging design activity is part of a larger packaging system and the primary package's design and dimensioning is a critical component of a cost-effective distribution system. When a designer commits to the primary package's configuration, the designer also commits to other system parameters:

- The possible arrangements of cartons in a shipper.
- Each of which will use a different dimension corrugated shipping box
- Some arrangements will use less corrugated board than others
- Some shipper sizes will have better pallet-area efficiency than others

Arrangement refers to packing patterns used when placing primary packages into a shipper. (See Figure 16.10.) Traditionally, the problem was solved through intuition, experience and a few nominal calculations. However, small cartons, packed 24 to a shipper, may have over a thousand possible orientation and palleting solutions. Available computer "arrangement" programs can calculate all the implications of size decisions in minutes. Typical input data for a palleting-efficiency computer program are:

- The dimensions, mass and geometry of the primary container

- Allowable orientations in the shipper

- Allowed primary design changes, if required (Small dimensional changes can have a dramatic impact on the final solution)

- Data pertaining to the proposed shipping container (for example required stacking strength, compatibility with mechanical handling systems, compatibility with modular unit loads)

- Data pertaining to palleting requirements (for example clampable patterns, stacking levels, etc.)

Typical output data for such a program might provide the following information:

- Optimum dimensions for the primary container
- Optimum packing orientations for selected primary containers
- Inside and outside box dimensions for each selected box type
- Number of units per pallet for each primary/box option
- Area and cube utilization for each primary/box option

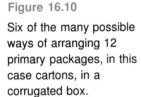

Figure 16.10

Six of the many possible ways of arranging 12 primary packages, in this case cartons, in a corrugated box.

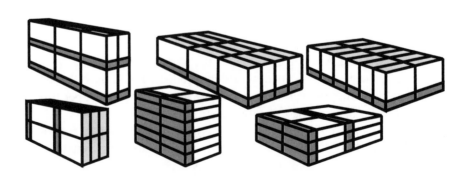

- Recommended pallet patterns, including "walk-around" views
- Dimensional details of the pallet pattern
- Material areas used in primary, divider and box construction
- Relative cost factors for each construction
- Relative compression values for corrugated board constructions
- Proposed maximum warehouse stacking heights
- Proposed selection of possible board combinations
- Proposed loading patterns in carrier vehicals

The impact of cube and area utilization can be critical. Table 16.3 compares 8 competitive motor oil bottles packed 12 to a box. F(mod) is the theoretical outcome of changing one bottle dimension by 3 millimetres (1/8 inch). It is obvious that some bottles are more competitive than others.

Figures such as 80% area utilization are difficult to visualize in concrete terms. Consider a product that is palletized in such a manner that 50 millimetres (2 inches) of space exists on all sides. This amounts to a pallet utilization of 82.5%. When compared on a large scale with a fully utilized (100%) pallet,

- 1,175 pallets are needed instead of 1,000
- Stretch-wrapping is needed for 175 extra pallets
- Forklift trucks operate 17.5% longer
- 175 more places are needed in the warehouse
- The additional pallets make up 6 additional tractor-trailer loads

A thorough system analysis (including losses) can lead to substantial savings. A major business equipment manufacturer found that it had poor shipping experience because of the hundreds of different package sizes in the product line. The company designed a modular system, and all products were designed to fit one

Table 16.3

Distribution efficiencies of motor oils.

Bottle Type	Box Blank Area (sq.in.)	Box Cost	Bottles per Pallet	Bottle Weight (grams)
A	920	56	576	69
B	1,020	62	576	65
C	1,003	61	480	61
D	995	58	600	64
E	1,069	65	576	63
F	1,210	74	384	56
F(mod)	1,066	65	432	56
G	844	52	947	60
H	1,090	67	432	73

of 17 standard box sizes. Besides significant inventory reduction, the company gained substantial transport savings, since larger, more stable pallet loads could be built with the modular system. More-secure pallet loads resulted in further savings through reduced product damage.

Stabilizing Unit Loads

Unit loads often need to be stabilized to retain load geometry and order during shipping and handling. Strapping, usually polypropylene, is used mostly for heavier goods. Care must be taken that strapping does not cut into the corrugated container, impairing strength qualities. Corner guards should be used to prevent cut-in where strapping or cord is used.

Shrink-wrapping is rarely used for load unitizing due to high installation and energy costs. Today's material of choice is stretch-wrapping. A good stretch-wrap application consists of two overlapped wraps extending 50 millimetres (2 inches) down the pallet to bind the load to the pallet. The wraps should overlap about 40% up the pallet side. Three overlapping wraps extending 50 millimetres (2 inches) past the top of the load finish the pallet. The added top wraps provide extra securement at the point in the load most likely to move.

While hand-wrapping a pallet with stretch material may save capital investment, machine-wrapping provides better material control and typically reduces material cost. Machines with prestretch features reduce material cost still further. More costly open netting is used where air circulation is essential.

Load stability can be increased through the use of high-friction printing inks and coatings or by the application of adhesive-like compounds; designed to produce a high-tack local bond. One variation is the use of a bead of hot-melt adhesive formulated to have relatively poor cohesive strength. The bead forms a readily sheared bond between two box surfaces. However, systems that bond boxes together have caused handling problems and are not a popular load-stabilizing method with some warehouses.

Caps and trays made of fiberboard or corrugated board are used to provide shape to unstable loads, to provide bottom protection against rough pallet surfaces, and, when used on top of a load, to increase the platform quality for the next pallet. Tier sheets improve available compression strength and increase stability by distributing weight and encouraging layers to act as a unit.

GOOD DISTRIBUTION PRACTICE

Industry Guidelines

Many studies have been conducted on the problems of packaging for distribution. One of these was a study conducted jointly by the Food Marketing Institute, Grocery Manufacturers of America and National American Wholesale Grocers' Association. One study recommendation was that shippers use ASTM or ISTA preshipment testing procedures to determine container performance level. Other pertinent suggestions are as follows:

Figure 16.11

A pallet without any stabilizing material should be able to hold an angle of 5 degrees.

Container dimensions. Containers should not be a perfect square in any two dimensions. The recommended maximum and minimum dimensions for shipping containers are:

Minimum container dimension	102 mm (4 in.)
Maximum width	610 mm (24 in.)
Maximum height	457 mm (18 in.)
Maximum length	762 mm (30 in.)
Maximum length: heavy products	610 mm (24 in.)
Maximum weight	20.5 kg (45 lb)

Pallets. Pallet loads should have a footprint of 40 by 48 inches (+0 in., −1 in.), *measured at the first customer receiving point.* Optimum pallet heights may be 45 or 59 inches, depending on rack sizes and how stock is picked. Unracked pallets should not exceed 83 inches. The targeted minimum storage capability of a pallet load is 30 days at 32°C (90°F) and 80% R.H., stacked two loads high. Pallet load-stabilizing materials such as stretch-wrapping are often removed at the warehouse receiving dock. The load is then moved to its storage location. For this reason, loads must have reasonable stability even without the stabilizing material. (See Figure 16.11.)

Bagged Product. Products in bags are more frequently damaged than products in any other type of packaging. Some recommended ways to avoid damage are:

- Place a slip sheet between the pallet and the first bag layer.
- If the product will be double-stacked, use a cap or another slip sheet.
- Use bag material having a slip angle of at least 30°.
- Stabilize bag pallet loads, preferably with stretch-wrap.
- Use square-ended bag designs; they give more stable configurations.
- Bag closures strong enough that the bag can be picked up by one "ear."

Shrink-Wrapped Trays. Shrink-wrapped trays are an alternative to corrugated boxes for distribution. The following considerations apply to this type of packaging:

- Choose shrink-wrap that retains tension up to 65°C (150°F).
- Place seams at the sides or top to avoid fouling in conveyor systems.

- Use nesting designs or tray covers if primary containers are irregular, to make them stackable.

- Make the tray at least 75 mm (3 in. high)

- If there is more than one layer of product in the package, use a separate tray for each layer.

EVALUATING DISTRIBUTION PACKAGING

Preshipment Testing

Knowledgeable packaging engineers have recognized for some time that preshipment testing reveals inadequate product design or packaging long before it starts costing money through damages and customer dissatisfaction. Many procedures and devices have been developed for use in evaluating distribution packaging. Some of these are material characterization tests (such as the ECT or gas permeability of a flexible laminate), but the packaging engineer usually wishes to evaluate not a single material property, but the suitability of a system.

First, the product itself should be studied to ensure that it has no inherent design faults that will make distribution difficult. These should be remedied before considering packaging. Once the product is as durable as practically possible, determine and quantify the product's unavoidable fragility. These fragilities are compared with the anticipated distribution environment demands.

Where there are shortcomings, protective packaging must be provided. As a final check, a number of prototype packages should be submitted for a laboratory evaluation of their suitability for the intended distribution environment.

Agencies Sponsoring Preshipment Test Methods

Preshipment test procedures and container performance requirements are prepared by many agencies. Only the most important are listed here.

ASTM International (ASTM)

ASTM has a membership of about 34,000 and publishes voluntary consensus standards on a variety of subjects in its annual standards books. Standard test methods and procedures related to packaging are developed through committee D-10, which meets twice a year to consider new proposals and to upgrade old standards. Most packaging test methods are published in Volume 15.10, General Products, Chemical Specialties and End Use Products. Volumes 08.01 and 08.02 deal with plastic materials and contain some methods related to plastic packaging materials and containers.

ASTM standards are thorough and timely. They are the prime North American reference for all preshipment testing procedures and are widely used internationally. ASTM D 4169, Practice for Performance Testing of Shipping Containers and Systems, is the industry standard for specifying testing and evaluation procedures.

International Safe Transit Association (ISTA)

ISTA has about 500 members—shippers, carriers, manufacturers and laboratories interested in reducing handling and shipping damage to products.

ISTA issues widely followed preshipment test procedures that have formed the basis of most preshipment testing to date. ISTA's Procedures 1A and 1B are two of the oldest preshipment testing procedures in continuous use. The methods are simple and popular with corrugated box suppliers. Other ISTA testing protocols are more complex and are intended to simulate various distribution environments and occurrences. The actual individual tests are done according to ASTM standards with ISTA detailing specific performance levels based on industry observations of damage levels.

Carrier Classifications (United States)

The Uniform Freight Classification (UFC) is prepared by rail interests under authority from the Department of Transportation. It described tariffs, ratings, rules and regulations pertaining to the transport of goods by rail. Rule 40 (containers other than fiberboard), Rule 41 (solid or corrugated fiberboard containers), Rule 54 (barrels, drums, pails or greaseproof-waterproof tubs), and Rule 55 (synthetic resin containers, inner or shipping) primarily describe material characteristics but also list some package performance requirements.

The National Motor Freight Classification (NMFC) is similar in scope to the Uniform Freight Classification but applies to movement over the road. It is maintained by the National Motor Freight Traffic Association.

National Motor Freight Classification (NMFC) Rule 180

Both NMFC and UFC require container materials to meet minimum specifications as detailed in Item 222 and Rule 41 of their respective carrier rules. In 1995 NMFC approved Rule 180, an alternative to Item 222, which would allow shippers using truck common-carriers to use any material as long as the package passes a series of performance tests. The rule applies to all less-than-truckload (LTL) package shipments except drums, pails and bags.

The performance requirements are a two-part sequence: a compression/vibration test simulating over-the-road travel followed by an impact/handling test simulating the hazards of loading and unloading trailers. The tests are based on a similar series of packaging performance tests developed by the ASTM International.

Carrier Classifications (Canada)

RAC 6000, prepared by the Railway Association of Canada, describes ratings, rule, and regulations pertaining to the transport of goods by rail. RAC 6000 is similar to, but not identical to, its U.S. counterpart, the Uniform Freight Classification. Generally, Canadian authorities try to maintain reciprocity with the United States. Complying with RAC 6000 has little if any impact on damage claims. Canada has no equivalent of the National Motor Freight Classification.

Canadian General Standards Board (CGSB)

A CGSB committee convenes whenever industry or government perceives a need to publish a Canadian standard of practice. The committee is normally made up of a producers, users and other interested parties who meet until a consensus standard can be issued. CGSB (an office of the federal government) arranges for the meetings and publishes the standard.

CGSB packaging standards are issued under the 43-GP series. They include standards for dangerous goods packaging and other specialized packaging and container systems. CGSB usually references an ASTM test procedure and then specifies the test's severity or level.

In principle, CGSB is for the service of industry. In practice, industry tends to support standards developed through industrial associations or the better-known standards bodies. CGSB standards, therefore, are inclined to be convened by the government for issues in which the government has a specific interest.

Hazardous Goods Packaging Regulations

While routine package-shipping tests are typically voluntary and based on statistically likely occurrences, dangerous or hazardous goods code tests are mandatory and are based on a "catastrophic incident" concept. A plastic bottle filled with shampoo may have to withstand a number of drops from 0.5 metre (20 inches), but if the same bottle were used to contain an infectious substance, it would be required to survive a 10-metre (32-foot) drop.

The United Nations publishes Transport of Dangerous Goods: Recommendations of the Committee of Experts on the Transport of Dangerous Goods. Many countries and organizations have adopted the performance standards outlined by the United Nations in total.

Some countries (such as Canada and the United States) have regulations covering the packaging of dangerous goods that predate the U.N. issuance and are not in total agreement with it. Moves have been made to bring the national standards of both countries into line with the U.N. standards.

In the United States, the Code of Federal Regulations, C.F.R. Title 49, describes performance requirements of containers for hazardous goods. In Canada, transport of dangerous goods is the responsibility of Transport Canada. Actual performance standards are issued by CGSB.

The Inter-maritime Consultive Organization (IMCO) and the International Air Transport Association (IATA) issue performance standards for their respective transport modes. Generally, they follow the U.N. recommendations; however, there are important exceptions.

Determining the exact required test procedure can be difficult for some combinations of package and product. Care should be taken to identify the product and hazard level precisely.

International Organization for Standardization (ISO)

ISO is an international consensus standards body. ISO standards are particularly important to those countries that do not have established national documents. North America, while contributing heavily to ISO standards, tends to refer to national or ASTM documents.

Preshipment Testing Equipment

Vibration Tables

Vibration tables are used to assess product and package responses to the various ranges of vibration that they will experience in the field. They are available in two basic types:

Repetitive-shock vibration tables operate at about 1.1 G (acceleration), one inch amplitude, and about 4.5 Hertz (Hz). These tables are used in tests specified by the Dangerous Goods Code and in procedures recommended by the ISTA and by ASTM D 4169. These fixed frequency, fixed amplitude tables are very limited in their ability to simulate vibrations as encountered in the distribution environment. They are useful for determining relative scuff resistance.

Variable-frequency vibration tables are programmable to sweep through all common transport frequencies between 3 and 100 Hz. They can more realistically represent the true distribution environment. They are useful for searching out resonance susceptibility in the packaged and unpackaged product and to locate stack resonance points for stacked packages. Programmable tables can also be set up to cycle through actual recorded road travel random vibrations. Chapter 17 discusses the problem of vibration in more detail.

The following vibration tests are described by the ASTM:

D 999, Vibration Testing of Shipping Containers

D 1185, Pallets and Related Structures Employed in Materials Handling and Shipping

D 3580, Vibration (Vertical Sinusoidal) Test of Products

D 4728, Random Vibration Testing of Shipping Containers

D5112, Vibration (Horizontal Linear Sinusoidal Motion) Test of Unpackaged Products and Components

D 4169, Performance Testing of Shipping Containers and Systems

Drop Testers

The principal feature of all drop-test devices is the ability to produce repeated drops at selected orientations and from selected heights without imparting rotation or other influences. Drop heights can be selected from drop probability tables, from standards set by the ISTA or ASTM, or by the requirement of a dangerous or hazardous goods code.

Drop tests are described in the following standards:

ASTM D 5276, Drop Test of Loaded Containers by Free Fall

ASTM D 1083, Mechanical Handling of Unitized Loads, Large Shipping Cases and Crates

ASTM D 3071, Drop Test of Glass Aerosol Bottles

ASTM D 5487, Standard Practice for Simulated Drop Tests of Loaded Containers by Shock Machines

ASTM D 5265, Bridge Impact Testing

Horizontal and Incline (Conbur) Impact Machines

The incline impact machine simulates horizontal shocks such as those experienced in rail shipment. The shock can be controlled by changing the impact velocity and by using impact programmers. By using suitable backloads during the test, the effects of dynamic horizontal compression can also be assessed. With modifications, the incline impact machine is also used to determine the durability of pallets to repeated forklift entries.

Incline impact tests are specified by ISTA and ASTM preshipment test methods and are described in the following:

ASTM D 880, Incline Impact Test for Shipping Containers

ASTM D 1185, Pallets and Related Structures Employed in Materials Handling and Shipping

ASTM D 4169, Performance Testing of Shipping Containers and Systems

A newer, more controllable method of producing horizontal shocks is with horizontal impact machines. These machines accelerate the load along a horizontal track and into a programmable backstop.

ASTM D 4003, Programmable Horizontal Impact Testing for Shipping Containers and Systems

ASTM D 5277, Performing Horizontal Impacts Using an Inclined Impact Tester

Environmental Chambers

Good packaging laboratories provide a wide range of climatic conditions with environmental chambers. They are typically used for preconditioning prior to physical testing. For example, to determine the ability of a plastic pail to survive drops at subzero temperatures or to identify whether a corrugated box loses stack strength at high humidity, both packages would require preconditioning in the appropriate environment.

Such chambers are also used to accelerate aging for such things as long-term storage tests and for environmental stress-crack tests on plastic containers (ASTM D 2561, Environmental Stress-Crack Resistance of Blow-Molded Polyethylene Containers).

All standard paper tests should be conducted at $23 \pm 2°C$ and 50% R.H. $\pm 2\%$. The highest humidity normally recommended for routine testing is 85%. Beyond this humidity, it becomes very difficult to control the temperature with the accuracy needed to prevent condensation. To simulate a particular environmental condition, the conditions listed in Table 16.4 are the normal choices.

Environmental conditioning is described in:

ASTM D 685, Conditioning Paper and Paper Products for Testing

ASTM D 4332, Conditioning Containers, Packages or Packaging Components for Testing

Table 16.4
Recommended standard atmospheric conditions as provided in ASTM D 4332.

Simulated Environment	Temperature	Relative Humidity
Cryogenic	−55 ± 3°C	—
Frozen food storage	−18 ± 2°C	—
Refrigerated storage	5 ± 2°C	85 ± 5%
Temperature, humid	20 ± 4°C	85 ± 5%
Tropical	40 ± 2°C	85 ± 5%
Desert	60 ± 3°C	15 ± 2%

Compression Testing

Compression strength is directly related to warehouse stacking ability. Compression testing is used to determine a package's load-carrying abilities. Sizes vary from small, for measuring the compression strength of plastic bottles, to units large enough to measure the stacking strength of entire pallet loads. Fixed-platen testers tend to cause the specimen to fail at its strongest point. Swivel platens tend to cause the specimen to fail at its weakest point.

Compression tests can be either dynamic, using hydraulically or mechanically driven platforms, or static, wherein a dead load is stacked on a subject container and the system observed over a period of time. Compression tests are required by most preshipment test procedures and are described in:

ASTM D 642, Compression Test for Shipping Containers

ASTM D 2659, Column Crush Properties of Blown Thermoplastic Containers

ASTM D 4577, Compression Testing of Shipping Containers Under Constant Load

Shock Machines

Shock machines are used to develop fragility boundary curves and to determine G levels (see Chapter 17) used to calculate cushioning requirements or to assess a product's design fragility. A shock machine consists of a rigid table that can be raised and dropped onto a programming device. By controlling the programming device and the drop height, different G levels, pulse durations and pulse shapes (sine, square wave, etc.) can be achieved.

Tests using shock machines are described in the following:

ASTM D 3332, Mechanical Shock Fragility of Products Using Shock Machines

ASTM D 4168, Transmitted Shock Characteristics of Foam-in-Place Cushioning Materials

ASTM D 5487, Standard Practice for Simulated Drop Tests of Loaded Containers by

ISTA and ASTM Preshipment Testing Procedures

In the late 1940s the Porcelain Enamel Institute's members were experiencing considerable shipping damage. They conducted studies to identify a standard preshipment test procedure that would assess the protective characteristics of packaging. A requisite was that damage created in the lab should closely duplicate that observed in the field. The procedure that was developed was found to be useful by other industries and soon was widely adopted.

Modified and updated, these test methods continue in use today. Briefly, for Procedure 1A, packages under 68 kg (150 lb) are subjected to 14,200 vibratory impacts on a repetitive shock vibration table moving in a 25.4 mm (1 in) rotary motion at a cycle rate that just causes the package to momentarily lift off the table. The actual cycle rate will vary slightly but is in the general range of 4 Hz. Subsequently, the package is dropped 10 times from a height determined by the package weight (see Table 16.5) and in specified orientations. (See Figure 16.12) As an option, packages over 27.7 kg (61 lb) can be tested on an incline impact machine.

Procedure 1B is similar but is intended for packages or load of over 68 kg (150 lb).

The original ISTA methods were quick, economical and simple. However as knowledge of the shipping environment increased, drawbacks became apparent. Damage that could not be duplicated by the basic ISTA methods was commonly observed, and it was recognized that the basic methods (Procedures 1A and 1B) had a limited ability to simulate distribution hazards.

In response to the need for more flexible and predictive preshipment testing methods, ASTM developed and published a number of focused Preshipment tests and the all-encompassing ASTM D4169, Practice for Performance Testing of Shipping Containers and Systems.

Table 16.5

Drop heights and orientations for ISTA preshipment tests.

Package Weight	Drop Height	Drop Number	Orientation
1–20.99 pounds	30 in.	1	2/3/5 corner
21–40.99 pounds	24 in.	2	Shortest edge leading out from that corner
41–60.99 pounds	18 in.	3	Next shortest edge from that corner
61–100.00 pounds	12 in.	4	Longest edge from that corner
		5, 6	Flat on one of the smallest faces and on opposite small face
		7, 8	Flat on a medium face and on opposite medium face
		9, 10	Flat on one largest face and flat on opposite large face

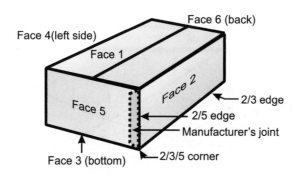

Figure 16.12

Identification of box features. With the box placed so that the manufacturer's joint is at the front right, number the faces clockwise with the top being face 1. The front face is 5 and the back is 6. Corners and edges are identified by the faces meeting there.

Parallel to the ASTM developments, ISTA increased the number of test procedures it sponsored to meet a variety of shipping situations including: Unitized Loads (Procedure 1E and Project 3E), Closed Reusable Transport Containers for Loads up to 68 kg (150 lb) (Procedure 1F), Parcel Delivery System Shipments (Project 3C), and Small Packaged-Products 453.6 g (1 lb) or Less (Project 3D).

The two examples of preshipment tests given here have been chosen to illustrate the simplest ISTA test (Procedure 1A) and a more complex test based on ASTM D 4169.

The ASTM method recognizes that different distribution elements impose different hazards on the product and package. (See Table 16.6.) It further recognizes that different products might require different levels of assurance against product damage. (See Figure 16.13) A 1% loss of household cleaning sponges may not warrant an increase in packaging, whereas a 1% loss of large flat-screen monitors might be a financial disaster.

The ASTM procedure essentially outlines the elements needed to tailor a preshipment test procedure to a specific need.

To use the procedure, you first identify the nature of the distribution environment you wish to simulate in the laboratory and what the shipping unit will

Table 16.6

Summary of ASTM D 4169 distribution testing elements.

Shipping Occurrence	*Hazard Element*
Handling—manual and mechanical	drop, impact, stability
Warehouse stacking	compression
Vehicle stacking	compression
Stacked vibration	vibration
Vehicle vibration	vibration
Loose load vibration	repetitive shock
Rail switching	longitudinal shock
Environmental hazard	

Figure 16.13

Preshipment test severity is related to the value of the contained product, or in the instance of certain hazardous products, the negative consequences of a package failure.

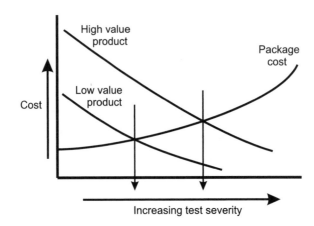

be for different stages of the journey. For example, a unit load may constitute the test unit for part of the program, and an individual container may be used for the remainder.

The elements representing those events anticipated in the identified shipping environment and the appropriate assurance level are then selected. A decision as to what constitutes an unacceptable level of damage must be made. The test procedure describes different shipping modes, or elements and provides for introducing atmospheric factors at any point in the test program.

Table 16.7 shows an example of an ASTM test cycle for an 11.4 kg (25 lb) box. Each distribution element has an appropriate simulation of the hazard associated with it. For this example, test conditions are taken from Assurance Level 2, the most commonly used Assurance Level for general merchandise. Assurance Level 1, the most severe, would require drops from 21 in., while Assurance Level 3 would require 8-in. drops. All other test conditions would be similarly adjusted to match the desired Assurance Level.

Table 16.7

An example of an ASTM D 4169 test protocol that simulates the given distribution cycle.

Distribution Element	Test Simulation
Manually palletized	5 drops from 13 inches
Warehoused	compression at 4.5 times anticipated load
Road transport of unitized product	vibration: 3 to 100 Hz—10 min. dwell at resonance points
Rail transport	longitudinal shock: two at 6 and one at 4 mph
Warehoused	compression at 4.5 times anticipated load
Manual handling	5 drops from 13 inches
Road transport (loose load)	repetitive shock for 40 minutes
Manual handling	5 drops from 13 inches

The entire sequential test would be performed when evaluating a new shipping container. Where the package response to a single condition might be needed, only that element needs to be performed. The operator has the option of designing a custom sequence or using one of the 18 predesigned sequences describing the most common distribution cycles.

Preshipment testing is a valuable tool in the development of a suitable distribution package or for resolving specific problems. Whatever tests are chosen, the damage observed in the laboratory should be similar in appearance to that observed in the field. One fallacy that must be avoided is that a particular dwell time or exposure in the laboratory is equal to a certain number of kilometers or miles in the field. Finally, it should be understood that the ultimate and true test is a successful shipping history.

Other Test Methods and Standard Practices

The following are selected other standards related to packaging materials:

ASTM D 6198, Standard Guide for Transport Package Design

ASTM D 4649, Selection of Stretch, Shrink, and Net Wrap Materials

ASTM D 5118, Fabrication of Fiberboard Shipping Boxes

ASTM D 5168, Fabrication and Closure of Triple Wall Corrugated Fiberboard Containers

ASTM D 4919, Testing of Hazardous Materials Packaging

ASTM D 3951, Standard Practice for Commercial Packaging

ASTM D 1974, Methods of Closing, Sealing and Reinforcing Fiberboard Boxes

REVIEW QUESTIONS

1. At what point in a package design program should distribution packaging be considered?

2. Discuss the dangers of using a sequential approach to package design.

3. What do we mean by the term "fragility" when describing a product? Give specific examples.

4. Define "distribution environment."

5. What do we mean when we say that a load is 87% area efficient?

6. List some of the considerations you would take into account when designing a distribution package.

7. Shock and vibration are typical distribution environment hazards. List six more.

8. Package damage and loss is normally greater in summer than in winter. Explain why.

9. How would you ensure that your distribution packages are neither overdesigned no underdesigned?

10. What is the size of the most commonly used standard pallet?

11. Many products are designed with the use of environment in mind. Comment on this practice.

12. Under what distribution circumstances might the planned shipping container not be used?

13. The distribution packaging cost is not just the cost of the distribution package. Explain.

14. What problem is inherent to odd-shaped shipping containers?

15. Name three methods of unitized load handling, and comment on the advantages and disadvantages of each.

16. Why should pallet overhang be avoided?

17. What are the extra costs incurred when a product has poor pallet area utilization?

18. List methods of increasing the shipping stability of a palletized unit load.

19. What should be the minimum storage capability of a pallet load according to the Food Manufacturer's Institute?

20. ASTM D4169 has become the most widely used standard for preshipment testing. Discuss the methods advantages.

21. You are investigating a product that has a poor shipping history. There are three things that might be changed to improve the shipping experience. What are they?

CHAPTER SEVENTEEN
SHOCK, VIBRATION AND COMPRESSION

CONTENTS

Shock

Definition, sources, free-fall shock, predictability, generalized drop-height probabilities, manual handling characteristics, damage to package and product, rail transport and shock, small-parcel environment.

Quantifying Shock Fragility

Forces, acceleration of gravity, ratio of observed acceleration and acceleration of gravity, "G," practical effects of G, examples of the acceleration and G calculation, reducing G with resilient materials.

Cushioning Against Shock

Basic shock-cushioning principles, estimating required deflection, static stress, dynamic cushioning curves, required information for calculating protective cushioning geometry, cushioning materials, basic selection criteria, typical shock of factors.

Vibration

Description, occurrence, problem frequencies, typical sources of truck vibration, damage due to relative motion, prevention of relative-motion damage, resonance, identify natural frequencies, typical damage due to resonance, resolving resonance damage problems, stack resonance spurring/mass relationships, isolating vibration.

Compression

Occurrence, static compression, dynamic compression, compression strength and load-application rate, relationship of dynamic (or laboratory) compression strength to static (or warehouse) loading requirements, compression strength and humidity, distribution of load variability around the wall perimeter, factors affecting available compression strength, palletizing patterns, overhang, contributions from content and components.

Estimating Required Compression Strength

Using safety or stacking factors, typical industry stacking factors.

SHOCK, VIBRATION AND COMPRESSION

SHOCK

"Shock" is defined as an impact, characterized by a sudden and substantial change in velocity. For example, a dropped object gains velocity on its way down, which is rapidly lost when it meets the floor.

Shock is encountered in many places in the distribution environment:

- Accidental and deliberate drops during manual handling.
- Drops from chutes, conveyors and other machinery.
- Falls from pallet loads.
- Sudden arrests on conveyors.
- Impacts occurring when vehicles hit potholes, curbs or railroad tracks.
- Impacts occurring when a package is rolled or tipped over.
- Shock due to rail shunting.

Shock Resulting from Drops

Free-fall drops, regardless of the cause, are identical in effect and can be treated as manual drops. Thousands of detailed observations—using instrumented packages or by direct and discreet visual monitoring—determine typical manual handling patterns in a range of shipping situations. One set of data is given in Figure 17.1. This and other studies show a basic predictability in package handling. Details vary somewhat from study to study in the actual number of drops experienced and the drop heights encountered. These reflect differences in handling modes and practices in the actual distribution environment.

Many such studies have been combined to provide generalized drop probability curves such as those shown in Figure 17.2. This figure illustrates another predictable feature of manual handling: the lighter the package, the higher the probable drop height. This reflects human nature: Larger packages are more likely to be carried in groups and more likely to be tossed or thrown. Heavy packages cannot be thrown far and are usually handled more carefully to avoid personal injury.

Figure 17.2 and similar correlations determine the probable drop height a given package should be designed to withstand. They are also the basis of preshipment test procedures and provide information for the development of protective packaging systems.

Fundamental lessons learned from such studies are as follows:

- The probability that packages will be dropped from a height of greater than 1 metre (m) (40 in.) is minimal.

- Packages receive many drops from low–heights, while few receive more than one drop from greater heights.

Figure 17.1

Drop height vs. occurrence for a 25 lb. fiberboard box, 16 × 12 × 20 in. Data summarizes 15 test packages sent on 80 trips through various shipping modes. (Source: Ostrem, F., and Godshall, W., FPL Report 22.)

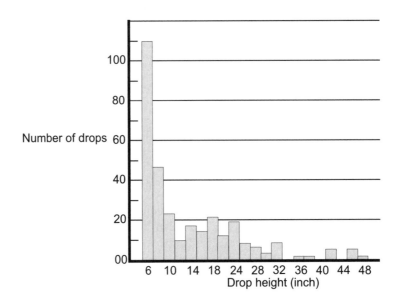

- Palletized, wrapped or otherwise unitized loads are subject to fewer drops than individual packages.

- There is little control over drop orientation with small packages. With larger packages, about half of the drops are on the base.

- A heavier package has a lower probable drop height.

- The larger or bulkier the package, the lower the probable drop height.

- Handholds reduce the probable drop height by lowering the container relative to the floor.

Figure 17.2

Generalized drop-height probability curves. The curves flatten out at the point where mechanical handling predominates.

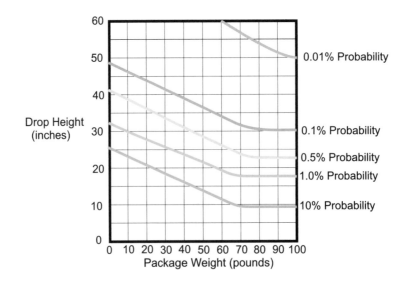

- Cautionary labeling (e.g., "Fragile," "This side up," "Handle with care") has only a minor effect. Cautionary labeling does not make up for inadequate packaging.

- Address labels tend to orient the drop to a label-up position regardless of other instructions.

The usual results of drops and shocks fall into two categories:

- Damage to the package that reduces its protective or containment qualities.

- Damage to the product, typified by bending, distortion, or ultimately, breakage.

Typically, the greatest damage to the container is from edge or corner drops. The greatest damage to the contents is from a flat drop onto one of the faces. Shock can frequently damage the contents without adversely affecting the enclosing container. Usually this suggests the need for greater cushioning protection rather than an increase in the strength of the enclosing container.

Shock During Rail Transportation

A special shock condition is experienced during railcar coupling. Boxcars are assembled into trains by moving individual cars at some speed against other cars. The average "shunting speed" is 8.4 kilometres per hour (km/hr) (5.2 miles per hour). This is the average speed: Some of the impacts are at greater speeds! (See Figure 17.3)

Shipper experience suggests that damage is greater for rail than for truck shipment. Rail's higher damage rates are probably due not so much to the actual shock forces as to load shifts and the effects of dynamic compression. Good loading, bracing and securing practices can substantially reduce rail damage. Trailer-on-flat-car (TOFC) shipping may be gentler than regular boxcar shipping, because TOFC trains are not assembled by shunting. Instead, they are loaded after the cars have been assembled into a train.

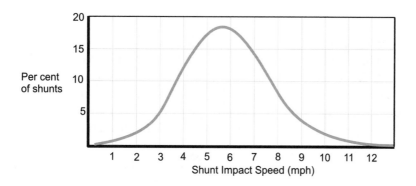

Figure 17.3

Distribution of rail coupling speeds. (Source: New York Central Railway)

Other Shock Conditions

Shock also occurs during the bumps and bangs typical of mechanical handling and transport. Usually, the degree of shock is not as great as that experienced during manual handling and free-fall drops. Generally, a package that will withstand manual handling shocks will survive mechanical handling.

"Repetitive shock" describes the low-frequency bouncing or rattling around that a product experiences if shipped as an unsecured load. The shock input of "loose-load" conditions is low and not likely to cause typical shock damage. However, abrasion can occur, and if the product is in resonance with the input frequency, various forms of mechanical damage may develop. These, however, are better described as vibration-induced damage.

The small-parcel shipping environment (parcel post and parcel courier) represents a special environment. The packages are almost entirely less than 20 kilograms (kg) (44 lb.), and are not unitized. They undergo considerable manual handling, resulting in a higher average number of impacts. This presents both the user and transporter with the most unfavorable situation possible. The use of highly automated conveying and sorting systems complicates matters further. Automatic handling systems do not read cautionary labeling.

QUANTIFYING SHOCK FRAGILITY

Essential to the design of packages that will provide protection against shock damage is the knowledge of the product's fragility or sturdiness. A suitable, cost-effective cushioning system is an engineered structure based on the product's quantified ability to withstand shock.

One way to quantify shock fragility is to measure the drop height at which damage starts to occur. However, quantifying shock fragility in terms of drop height is useful only if no additional protection is anticipated. This is helpful for products that may experience drops in their use environment, such as cell telephones, consumer electronics and laptop computers.

For products that are to be cushioned, packaging engineers use "critical acceleration" or "G" levels to describe an object's tendency to break when subjected to shock. An object will break when it is subjected to a force greater than its structure can bear.

Force is described by Newton's second law as:

$$F = ma$$

Where: F = force, m = mass, a = acceleration.

Acceleration and decelerations are measures of the time rate of velocity change, and the forces are the same whether the object is accelerating or decelerating; only the direction changes. The most common measure of acceleration is "g," or gravity, determined to be 9.81 m/s² (32.2 ft./s²).

"G" is the ratio of observed acceleration to the acceleration due to gravity:

$$G = \frac{\text{observed acceleration}}{\text{acceleration of gravity}}$$

A person encountering 2 G would experience an acceleration twice that of normal gravity. The physical sensation would be a feeling of weighing twice as much as normal. At 3 G, a person would experience three times his or her normal weight. Since mass is constant for a given packaging problem, force is directly proportional to G.

If a coffee cup was dropped from 1 m (39 inch), at the moment it reached the floor, its velocity would be 4.43 m/sec. If in hitting the floor, it lost its velocity (decelerated) in 0.002 seconds, the deceleration could be calculated to be 2,200 m/sec. Expressing this as a ratio to normal gravity would give a G level of 224. At the moment of impact, the cup would, in effect, weigh 224 times normal—44.8 kg. Unless it was a very unusual cup, it would break.

If the cup were dropped onto a sponge pad, the impact velocity would remain the same. However, on impact the sponge pad would deflect, and the time over which the cup lost velocity would be extended. The deceleration would not be as severe, the stop not as abrupt. If the cup now stopped in 0.008 sec., the G level would be 56. Another sponge layer might increase the deceleration time to 0.01 sec., and the cup would experience 44 G. Adding still more layers would eventually reduce the G level to the point where the cup would not break. This would be one way of determining what cushioning protection the cup needed to protect it from a 1 m drop.

However, if the G level that would break the cup was known in advance, that is, if its fragility factor in G was known, it would not be necessary to conduct the drop experiments. The cushioning needed could be determined by simple mathematics. The cup example shows that time is needed over which to dissipate the impact velocity, and that this time is gained by the deflection of a resilient cushioning material. This is the basic principle of cushioning against shock.

A quick estimate of cushioning material thickness can be made if the cushion material is treated as a linear, undampened spring. The deflection necessary to maintain a desired acceleration is calculated as follows:

$$D = \frac{2h}{(G - 2)}$$

Where:

D = required deflection,
h = anticipated drop height,
G = fragility level (critical acceleration)

This formula provides the minimum distance over which the deceleration must take place in order not to exceed the critical acceleration. For example, for a product with a fragility factor of 40 G and an anticipated 1 m drop,

$$D = \frac{2 \times 1 \text{ m}}{(40 - 2)} = 0.053 \text{ m (2.1 in.)}$$

The 53 mm (2.1in.) deflection is the minimum stopping distance consistent with maintaining 40 G or less. Stopping in any lesser distance would raise acceleration to more than 40 G and cause damage. The 53 mm deflection is the theoretical deflection distance, not the cushion thickness. To determine actual cushion thickness, it is necessary to know how far the proposed material will compress before reaching maximum strength, or "bottoming out."

"Static-stress working range" refers to the load-per-unit area that will cause a resilient material to deflect, but not flatten out completely. Static-load ranges can be found in supplier technical data sheets. With the correct static-stress level, the cushion estimate can be completed. For this example, typical optimum strains for three commonly used cushioning materials are on the order of the following:

Expanded polystyrene	40%
Expanded polyethylene	50%
Expanded polyurethane	70%

The theoretical deflection distance arrived at above can now be used to estimate the required thickness for three different materials: 132 mm (5.2 in.) of polystyrene, 106 mm (4.2 in.) of polyethylene or 76 mm (3 in.) of polyurethane foam.

More accurate estimates of cushioning thickness can be made using dynamic-cushioning curves available for most cushioning materials. The information necessary to make these calculations using dynamic cushioning curves is:

- Product size and mass.
- Product fragility, expressed in G.
- Anticipated drop height.

To use dynamic-cushioning curves, locate the curve that is crossed in two places by the critical acceleration (G) line. For example, if a device had a critical acceleration of 50 G, then the 3 in. curve would be selected from the curves in Figure 17.4. This curve tells us that a 3 in. thickness of the cushioning material represented by the curve would provide the required protection, providing that the material was loaded to at least 0.4 psi (the first crossing of the G line), but not more than 1.8 psi (the second crossing of the G line).

Figure 17.4

An example of a dynamic-cushioning curve. A complete set of curves would have dynamic-cushioning curves for a range of drop heights.

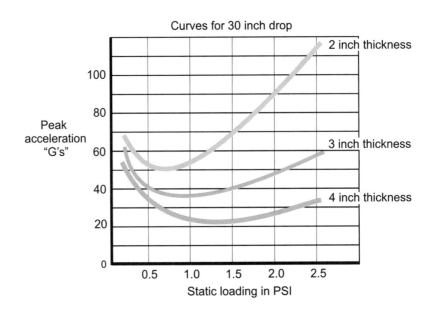

If a chosen cushion area resulted in less than a 0.4 psi load, then the product would not have enough mass to cause the cushion to deflect. On the other hand, if a small cushioning material area gave a loading of more than 1.8 psi, then the cushion would be partially or completely flattened and no longer capable of sufficient deflection. For this example, we might choose to load the cushioning material to 1.5 psi. If the product weighed 15 lb., then a cushioning area of 18 square inches (sq. in.) would provide the required deflection.

Understanding shock and G will help you to understand many shipping damages. For example, a refrigerator shipped by rail has a compressor-motor assembly weighing 15 kg (33 lb.). The designer felt safe in securing this assembly to the frame with three fasteners capable of holding 120 kg (264 lb.), an ample safety factor. However, during shipping, the refrigerator experiences a 10 G shock, and during that brief moment, the motor behaves as if it had a mass of 150 kg (330 lb.). Since the three mounting fasteners can hold only a total of 120 kg (264 lb.), they may shear off.

The refrigerator sidewall, with a bearing area of 1.5 square meters (m²) (15.7 sq. ft.), and the shipping box are able to distribute the load of a unit suddenly weighing ten times more. With no external evidence of damage, the refrigerator is accepted at the receiver's dock and by the retailer. The problem is discovered only when the consumer plugs it in.

Sophisticated manufacturers know the G factor for all their products. In many instances, they will redesign products to accept higher G levels, knowing that savings in protective materials, and the goodwill generated by satisfied customers, will more than repay the added engineering costs. Table 17.1 shows some typical G factor ranges.

Fragility may greatly depend on how the force is transmitted to the product. And egg on a flat surface has a fragility of 35 to 50 G, depending on the axis of the impact. If the egg is supported to a conforming surface, its fragility can exceed 150 G.

Table 17.1

Typical fragility factor classes. A manufacturer would be advised to consider redesign of any product with a fragility level of less than about 30 G. (Source: Robert M. Fiedler, Robert M. Fiedler and Associates.)

G Factor	Classed as	Examples
15–25 G	Extremely fragile	Precision instruments, early computer hard drives
25–40 G	Fragile	Bench top, floor-standing instruments, electronics
40–60 G	Stable	Cash registers, office equipment, desktop computers
65–85 G	Durable	Television sets, appliances, printers
85–110 G	Rugged	Machinery, durable appliances, power supplies, monitors
110 G	Portable	Laptop computers, optical readers
150 G	Handheld	Calculators, telephones, microphones, radios

Cautionary Note:

The explanations for shock provided in this text are simplified. Proper consideration of shock protection takes into account not only peak G but also velocity changes. (These two factors are usually represented by a "damage-boundary curve." For more information on damage-boundary curves, see ASTM D 3332.) The proper method of quantifying shock fragility is through the use of a shock test machine. This device is capable of providing a shock pulse of an accurately defined amplitude, duration and shape.

CUSHIONING AGAINST SHOCK

Any material that will deflect under applied load can act as a cushioning material. By deflecting, the cushioning material attenuates the peak G level experience by the product compared with the shock pulse at the package surface. (See Figure 17.5) Many materials are capable of attenuating shock. Limitations imposed by the product, process or environment generally reduce the choices to a manageable few.

Premolded shapes are one option, but the cost of molds, typically starting at $8,000, restricts their use to high-volume production. Fabricated shapes, those cut and assembled from flat planks, are usually the choice for intermediate volumes. Loose-fill, foam-in-place and bubble pads are used for low-volume requirements or situations where nearly every shipment is unique.

Cushioning materials can be divided into those based on cellulosic materials and on synthetic or polymeric materials. Cellulose-based cushioning materials are generally the most economical and include:

cellulose wadding	excelsior fill	corrugated inserts
molded pulp	indented kraft	newspaper

The shock absorption, resiliency and cleanliness of these materials range from poor to fair. Some paper-based products are corrosive and should not be used with bare metal parts. Since all cellulose materials are hygroscopic, the cushioning characteristics will change as humidity changes.

Many cellulose-based materials, particularly corrugated fiberboard, are quite abrasive and can scuff or polish finished surfaces. Corrugated fiberboard and rigid foams provide product protection by virtue of their own collapse. Their effectiveness is reduced after one major shock.

Polymeric-based materials include:

expanded polyethylene	expanded polypropylene
expanded polystyrene	polystyrene loose-fill
air bubble sheet	expanded polyurethane foam
foam-in-place polyurethane	

Figure 17.5

A cushioning material attenuates the initial shock pulse at the package's surface, so that the product's response takes place over a longer period of time. The areas under the curves represent energy.

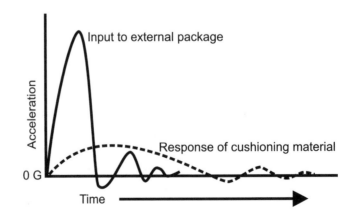

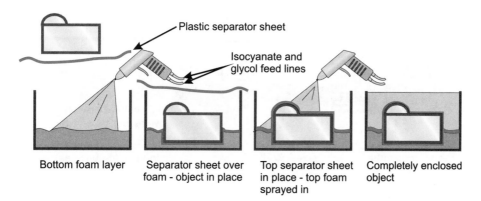

Plastic separator sheet

Isocyanate and glycol feed lines

Bottom foam layer | Separator sheet over foam - object in place | Top separator sheet in place - top foam sprayed in | Completely enclosed object

Figure 17.6

Application of foamed-in-place urethane cushioning.

Polymeric materials have wide design latitude, and most polymeric cushioning materials can be produced in a range of densities and resiliencies. As a class, they are clean materials and have few or no corrosive properties. All plastic materials contribute to static problems unless they are specially treated. The resiliency of some plastic materials can change dramatically with temperature and altitude.

Polymeric cushioning materials are not hygroscopic; however, some open-cell foams (typically polyurethane) will absorb liquid if they are wetted.

Loose-fills are useful for random product packing, but they are difficult to get under large overhangs and are subject to settling during transport. In some instances, loose-fill can be recovered for reuse. In response to environmental issues, loose-fills based on expanded starches have been proposed. Starch-based fills will have shortcomings similar to other cellulose-based products, with the addition that they may attract rodents and other vermin.

Foam-in-place urethane cushioning material is made by mixing two reactive liquid chemicals (an isocyanate and a glycol) as they are ejected through an applicator. The two materials react almost immediately and begin to expand into a foam-like structure. During the foaming stage, the urethane is soft and pliable, but it quickly stiffens to a more semirigid state.

In use, urethane would be sprayed into the bottom of a box, and a protective plastic film would be draped over it (See Figure 17.6). The object to be enclosed would be pressed into the still soft, yielding foam. A second protective sheet would then be draped over the object and more foam applied to create the protective form's top half.

Foam-in-place urethane cushioning is versatile and custom-made; form-fitting shapes are easily fabricated. However, it is labor intensive and generally used only in lower volume or "one-off" applications.

VIBRATION

"Vibration" describes an oscillation or motion about a fixed reference point. The distance moved about the reference point is the "amplitude," and the number of oscillations per second, expressed as hertz (Hz), is the "frequency."

Vibration is associated with all transportation modes, with each mode having characteristic frequencies and amplitudes. Typically, the higher the frequency,

Figure 17.7

Typical sources of truck-bed
vibrations.

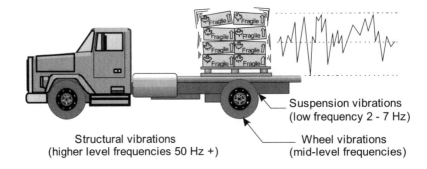

Suspension vibrations
(low frequency 2 - 7 Hz)

Structural vibrations
(higher level frequencies 50 Hz +)

Wheel vibrations
(mid-level frequencies)

the lower the amplitude. Frequencies above 100 Hz are of little concern to most packagers, because in most packaging situations, the product will be isolated (i.e., its vibrational output will be less than the input received) at these higher frequencies. The most troublesome frequencies are below 30 Hz, because they are the most prevalent in vehicles, and it is difficult to isolate products from them.

Vehicle vibrations may come from many sources. Truck vibrations (see Figure 17.7) occur predominantly at the natural frequencies of the load on the suspension system, of the unsprung mass of the tires against the suspension system and of the trailer and body structure. They are excited by the condition and irregularities of the roadbed, the engine and drive train, tire and wheel imbalance, and the dynamics of lading (freight).

During vibration, an object is constantly being accelerated and decelerated as it moves through the vibration cycle. Since an acceleration can be described by its G level, one dimension of vibration is its G level. Vibrations at identical frequencies will have greater G levels at greater displacements or amplitudes.

Vibration Damage Due to Relative Motion

Vibration damage can take several forms. Scuffing and abrasion can occur when one part is free to move against another. Designs affording point contact and those allowing movement against corrugated fiberboard surfaces are particularly prone to abrasion. Abrasion is sometimes aided by external substances, often dust from the product itself (e.g., detergent powders). Scuffing is primarily objectionable on labels and graphics.

Reducing or eliminating relative motion lessens this type of vibration damage. Tight box dimensions, particularly in the vertical axis, are preferred wherever this is compatible with top-load compression of the product and package. Good bottle design incorporates recessed label areas. In other instances, hard surface varnishes protect graphics. Some printing inks are soft and particularly prone to scuffing. In designs where scuffing may be a problem, these inks should be avoided or protected.

Soft, nonabrasive plastic or cellulose wraps can protect finished and painted parts. Coatings are available to reduce the abrasive character of corrugated board surfaces. Wax coating is the simplest and most economical of these.

Many particulate products sift or settle when vibrated. This leaves open voids at the tops of bottles and paperboard cartons that consumers invariably interpret as an underfill. Many products are shipped inverted so that settling and compaction takes place against the container top. Consumers opening such containers usually see a fill almost level with the top.

Vibration Resonance

The spring/mass relationship between an input vibration and the response of a mass can have three outcomes:

- Output equals input   direct coupling (e.g., input amplitude = 6 mm, output amplitude = 6 mm).

- Output is greater than input   resonance (e.g., input amplitude = 6 mm, output amplitude = 12 mm).

- Output is less than input   isolation (e.g., input amplitude = 6 mm, output amplitude = 0).

"Resonance," the condition where a vibration input is amplified, is the key packaging concern. In some instances, the end result is an output out of all proportion to the input. For example, at resonance, a 10 mm (3/8-in.) input amplitude might be amplified to produce a movement of 25 to 40 mm (1 to 1-1/2 in.).

A property of all spring/mass systems is that they have a unique frequency at which they will go into resonance. Resonance occurs whenever the "forcing" (input) frequency is the same as the product's or packaging system's natural resonance frequency. Resonance exists not only for the total assembly, but also for parts or subsections within the total structure.

For protective packaging purposes, all resonance points should be located and quantified . This is done by subjecting the product to a range of frequencies using a programmable vibration table and observing the frequencies at which resonance occurs. For packaging, a typical resonance search might sweep frequencies between 3 Hz and 100 Hz at 0.5 to 1.0 octave per minute (refer to ASTM D 999). The search should be done in all axes.

Identifying resonance damage is usually straightforward once the principles are understood. As with shock, resonance damage can occur without visible external signs of abuse.

The energy developed on the output side during resonance can do many things:

- Fatigue and eventually fracture metal cans and pails.

- Flex and crack delicate circuits on circuit boards.

- Disintegrate or otherwise alter the texture of food products.

- Separate and settle granular components in a food product or settle loose protective fill.

- Aggravate scuffing and abrasion problems by several orders of magnitude.

- Cause individual containers or components to bang into one another.

- Disturb pallet patterns or dunnage (load-securing) systems.

- Initiate stack resonance.

- Unscrew bottle caps and threaded fasteners.

The greatest vibration input in a typical truck is directly over the rear wheels and tailgate. If damage is restricted to or is the severest in this section of the vehicle, vibrational inputs are almost certainly the cause. Vibrational inputs are usually the source if damage seems to occur only in the product layer next to the pallet or on the top layers.

Damage caused by resonance vibration can be difficult to resolve. The problem is complicated in that all cushioning materials are resilient, and while they are acting to attenuate shock, they are also acting as a spring in response to vibrational input. For many applications, redesigning the product to eliminate critical resonance points is the most cost-effective method of decreasing damage. The last resort is a vibration-isolating cushioning system.

Stack Resonance

Occasionally, entire loads go into a "stack resonance" condition, where each succeeding container goes into resonance with the previous container until the entire stack is bouncing, creating conditions of extraordinary destructiveness. (See Figure 17.8)

For example, if a truck bed moves at an amplitude of 5 mm and the bottom container goes into resonance, it might reach an amplitude of 10 mm. The input into the second container in the stack is now 10 mm, and when it goes into resonance, movement might be 20 mm. That amplitude is multiplied as it goes up the stack until the top container actually bounces off the top of the load.

Figure 17.8

In stack resonance, the entire stack is bouncing, creating a destructive condition.

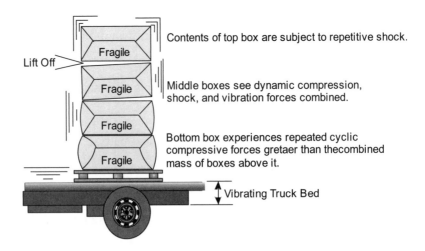

Contents of top box are subject to repetitive shock.

Lift Off

Middle boxes see dynamic compression, shock, and vibration forces combined.

Bottom box experiences repeated cyclic compressive forces gretaer than thecombined mass of boxes above it.

Vibrating Truck Bed

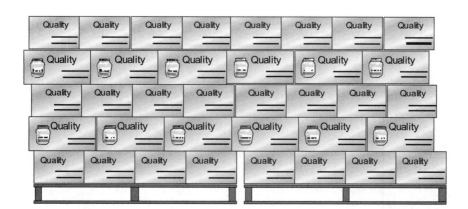

Figure 17.9

Skewing of a load may cause boxes in adjacent loads to interlock.

The dynamic load on the bottom container in such a system can be several orders of magnitude greater than the actual weight resting on it. The top container is subjected to extremes of repetitive shock and vibrations. Since the top layer in a unitized load is essentially weightless for short periods of time, small side loads, such as a bump from the side, will cause it to "float" or move. In a stretch-wrapped load, this tendency for the top layer to move can lean or skew the entire pallet load to one side. Individual boxes will sometimes interlock into the adjacent pallet, making it difficult to pick up a pallet without disrupting or damaging neighboring loads. (See Figure 17.9)

Isolating Vibration

Materials used to isolate vibration are for the most part the same as those used to isolate shock. However, cushioning materials, like all other springs, also have characteristic resonance points. Vibrational response curves are available for many resilient materials.

A material with the characteristics such as those shown in Figure 17.10 could be used effectively to isolate vibrational inputs over 100 hertz (Hz). The amplification between 40 and 100 Hz is not necessarily a problem, provided the product has no response in that range. If by bad choice this is where the product resonates, damage is almost certain. Below 40 Hz there is direct coupling, and the product will not see any worse vibration than the input level.

A properly selected isolation material resonates at an input frequency that is less than half of the product's for resonance frequency. For example if a product has a major resonance at 48 Hz, the isolation material should resonate at less than 24 Hz.

COMPRESSION

Static and Dynamic Compression

Most products are stacked during warehousing and shipping. It is important for a container to bear static compression loads safely without damage to the product

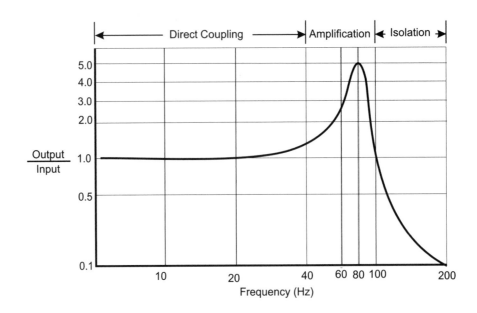

Figure 17.10

Vibration response curve for 175-pound, C-flute pad at 0.5 psi static load. The three conditions—direct coupling, resonance (amplification) and isolation—can be clearly identified.

or container. Static compression is determined by conducting dead-load stacking tests.

"Dynamic compression" describes a condition where the compression load is applied at a rapid rate. Dynamic compression is experienced during clamp-truck operations, rail shipping and stack resonance, as well as during normal transit conditions. According to railroad authorities, longitudinal dynamic compression forces, developed by the movement of backload against a railcar bulkhead, can exceed 1,400 lb./sq. ft. in a standard draft boxcar at typical shunting speeds.

Most standard laboratory compression tests are dynamic in nature. Fiberboard containers are able to bear dynamic loads almost as high as the determined compression strength, but only for a short duration.

Apparent compression strength is affected by the load application rate. Rapidly loading a viscoelastic material will give a higher apparent strength than when the material is loaded slowly. To ensure that data are comparable among laboratories, compression test load rates have been standardized to 12.7 mm per minute (min.), ± 2.5 mm/min.

Compression Strength and Warehouse Stack Duration

The warehouse condition is one of static loading over time, and a true test would involve replicating the warehouse condition. However, quick answers are usually needed for predicting safe warehouse stack duration or evaluating new container designs. The laboratory compression test is completed within minutes; it is a dynamic test.

Compression strength (a dynamic value) is not the load that can safely be applied in the warehouse. Stacking strength (a static value) for a given situation can be estimated from Figure 17.11, which relates dynamic and static loading conditions. The initial part of the figure's curve shows what the container will bear under dynamic, or short-term, load applications. If 85 kg of product were

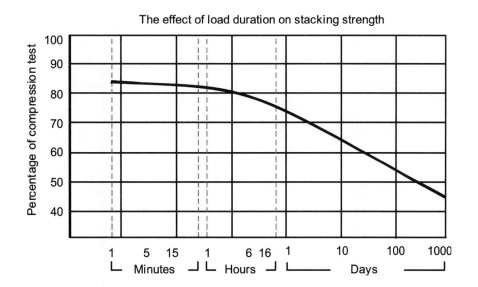

The effect of load duration on stacking strength

Figure 17.11

The compression strength
of corrugated board falls off
with time. This graph relates
dynamic compression
(laboratory) to static
compression (warehouse).
(Source: Kellicutt and
Landt, *Basic Design Data
for the Use of Fiberboard
Shipping Containers*, Forest
Products Laboratory,
Madison, Wis. FPL D 1911.)

stacked on a box with a compression strength of 100 kg load, the box would fail after about ten minutes. The same container would fail in about 10 days if loaded to 60 kg. If the container is to last 100 days, the stack load should not exceed 55% of the dynamic compression-test value.

Compression Strength and Humidity

Paper is a hygroscopic material, and the paper's moisture content can range from about 3 to more than 18%, depending on the surrounding atmosphere's humidity. A change in relative humidity (R.H.) from 40 to 90% can result in a loss of about 50% of a corrugated container's stack strength. (See Figure 17.12) Corrugated

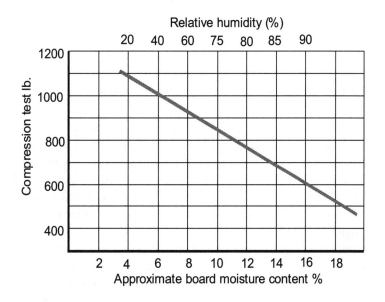

Figure 17.12

The compression strength
of a corrugated box will
drop off rapidly as humidity
(and corresponding board
moisture content) goes up.

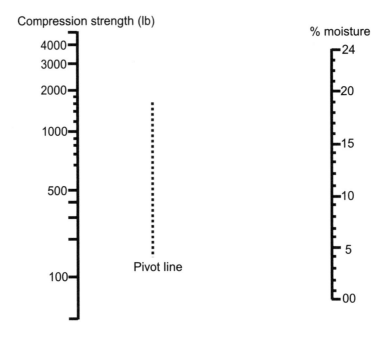

Figure 17.13

Chart for estimating compression strengths at different board moisture contents. (Source: FPL.)

containers destined for humid conditions may need excess stack strength to allow for this loss.

Since the physical properties of paper change dramatically with moisture content, all paper tests are conducted at standard temperature and humidity conditions. Container compression strength is normally given as a load to failure at 50% R.H. and 23°C.

Figure 17.13 is a chart for estimating the compression strength of corrugated board at different moisture levels. To use this chart, make a line from the compression strength to the board moisture content. Mark the point where the line crosses the pivot line. Now project the line from the new moisture content through the pivot line mark, and read the new compression strength. (The moisture content of paper at different relative humidities can be found in Chapter 5, Table 5.3)

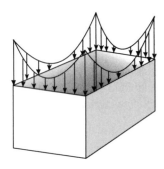

Figure 17.14

Distribution of load-bearing ability around a box perimeter. The length of the arrow is proportional to the load-bearing strength at that point.

Other Factors Influencing Box Stack Strength

In situations where the contents do not contribute to the compression strength of a container, compression strength is mostly a function of the wall perimeter, with the greatest contribution being made by the four corners. (See Figure 17.14) A box will fail at loads far below the measured compression strength if loads are applied unevenly at points away from corners or in a concentrated area. Thus, in addition to the total compressive load, one must also consider the load per unit perimeter length and load distribution.

Laboratory compression tests are conducted on new, undamaged containers. Consider, however, the effect on stack strength of clamp-truck handling that creases container side panels, or of strapping used to secure the pallet load that cuts into the edges of all corner boxes. Such damage, precisely at the container's most important point, dramatically reduces available load-bearing ability. Higher initial compression strength is needed when warehousing follows a long journey or rough handling, since the container will have experienced attrition factors that will have an accumulated effect on load-bearing ability. Lower initial compression strengths can be used only in those instances where the product has a short distribution cycle.

Compression strengths are normally measured as the full bearing area on both the container top and bottom. However, most pallets are decked with boards, and therefore, the bottom container does not have full support over its base. Without this full support, a proportion of the stack strength is lost. Single-face pallet stringers produce a much greater unit-area load on the topmost container of a pallet underneath it. Such loads may be three to four times greater than that assumed for the bottom container in a stack, resulting in unanticipated damage.

Most shipping containers are designed to provide maximum vertical stack strength, since this is the common warehouse condition. Dynamic compression by clamp trucks and rail shunting is in the longitudinal direction, normally the container's weaker axis.

The best possible use of container load-bearing ability is when boxes are stacked directly on top of each other in a vertical column. Unfortunately, column stacking is the least stable technique, and other stacking patterns are used to provide better load stability or cube utilization. Each palletizing pattern has a different total stacking strength.

Allowing boxes to overhang the edge of the pallet leaves the load-bearing walls of the boxes suspended in midair. Pallet overhang is often deliberate, but is rarely a good idea. Inadvertent overhang can occur internally because of pallet board geometries relative to container size. Typical loss of available compression strength as a result of overhang is shown in Figure 17.15. The asymmetrical nature of the oil bottles shown in Figure 17.16 can result in overhang of the major load-bearing bottle wall segment. The available bottle compression strength is a fraction of the measured value.

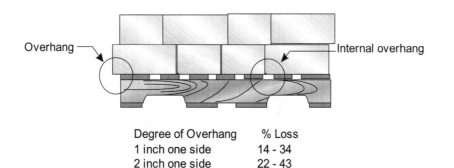

Figure 17.15

Effect of overhang on compression stack strength.

Degree of Overhang	% Loss
1 inch one side	14 - 34
2 inch one side	22 - 43
1 inch one end	4 - 28
2 inch one end	9 - 46
1 inch side & end	27 - 43
2 inch side & end	34 - 46

Figure 17.16

Overhanging of asymmetrical supporting contents can have a major impact on a container's calculated ability to hold a load.

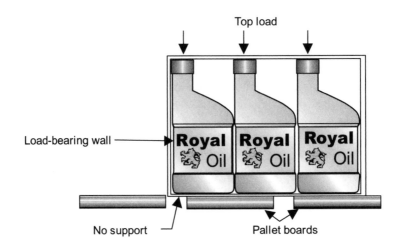

Contents' Effect on Compression Strength

Often times, the shipping container's contents provide some portion of the load-bearing ability. For shrink-wrapped trays, the contents must bear all the stacking load. Contents sometime increase apparent compression strength even though they do not apparently support a load. The usual reason is that the contents prevent the container sidewalls from buckling inward, thus delaying the failure point.

Contents can also reduce compression strength. Bag-in-box systems and flexible primary packages containing liquids or semisolids such as cheese or premixed grouting exert varying degrees of hydrostatic pressure perpendicular to the vertical container wall. Hydrostatic pressure appears as an outward bulge slightly below the sidewall's midpoint and is greatest at the bottom of the box. Supporting walls become bowed rather than perpendicular, with a corresponding loss of compression strength. (See Figure 17.17)

Where various components contribute to total compression strength, good design calls for the individual components to act collectively. Maximum strength

Figure 17.17

Bag-in-box systems reduced compression strength by bowing out the sidewalls.

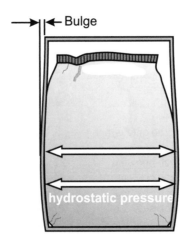

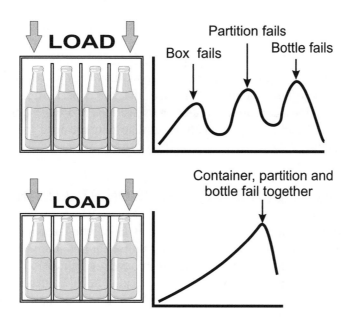

Figure 17.18

The highest compression strength in a multicomponent system is achieved when all components act together. Top example shows separate failures, while the bottom example shows simultaneous failure at a higher compression.

is gained when all components have the same failure point. For example, if a plastic bottle and a partition are expected to contribute to a corrugated container's overall compression strength, the three should be sized so they fail as a single unit. (See Figure 17.18)

Plastic Bottle Stacking Factors

Plastic bottles are expected to contribute compression strength in some shipper designs. This practice is acceptable provided that the plastic's viscoelastic, "or creep," property is taken into account. With plastic, as with corrugated board, the dynamic compression strength must be related to static warehouse conditions.

Stack duration for polyethylene bottles can be estimated using the bottle-to-load ratio shown in Figure 17.19. This ratio consists of the expected load over the compression strength. A bottle with a compression strength of 10 kg and

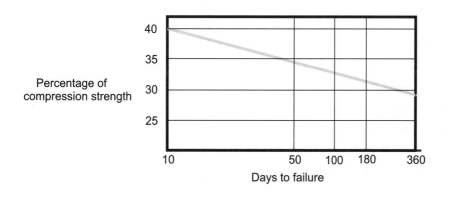

Figure 17.19

Warehouse stacking and load ratios for polyethylene bottles. (Source: Society of the Plastics Industries.)

loaded with 3.1 kg would have a load ratio of 0.31. It could be expected to last about 180 days under this loading.

Carefully review the design of any proposed plastic container. Avoid features such a sharp corners, edges or small-radius curves since they act as stress concentrators and promote flex cracking. Containers that are expected to contribute to load bearing usually incorporate circular cross-sections and large finish surfaces to spread the load and shallow transitions to distribute the load from the finish to container walls.

ESTIMATING REQUIRED COMPRESSION STRENGTH

Assessing all the factors discussed above and calculating a reasonable stack strength requirement for corrugated shipping units requires judgment and experience. Typically, boxes should be designed to have a compression test value of three to seven times greater than the stacking load anticipated during warehousing. This is frequently referred to as the "stacking factor" or the "environmental stacking factor." (See Table 17.2)

The Fibre Box Association has developed a systematic method of determining a stacking factor shown in Tables 17.3 through 17.6. Environmental multipliers are assigned according to the conditions the corrugated boxes will experience in a specific distribution cycle. The product of the multipliers is divided into the anticipated maximum load a box will have to hold (the stacking strength) to give the design compression strength.

Example of Calculations

A box will have 76 kg (168 lb.) stacked on it in the warehouse. Boxes will be arranged in an interlock pattern and will be required to hold the load for 30 days at 80% R. H. The pallets are in good condition; there will be no overhang. What should the design compression strength of the box be?

Table 17.2

Suggested stacking factors. These should be regarded only as starting points. Actual required stacking factors should be calculated for each application.

Condition	Stacking Factor
Column stack, no overhang, minimum warehousing	3.5
Column stack, no overhang, normal warehousing	4.0
Interlock stack, no overhang, normal warehousing	5.5
Column stack, overhang, normal warehousing	5.5
Column stack, no overhang, freezer storage	5.5
Interlock stack, overhang, normal warehousing	6.0
Interlock stack, extended distribution and warehousing	7.0

Table 17.3

Stacking strength multipliers that compensate for storage time. (Source: Fibre Box Association.)

Days Storage	Compression Loss	Multiplier
Up to 10 days	37% loss	0.63
30 days	40%	0.60
90 days	45%	0.55
180 days	50%	0.50

Table 17.4

Stacking strength multipliers that compensate for humidity. (Soource: Fibre Box Association.)

Relative Humidity	Loss	Multiplier
50%	0% loss	1
60%	10%	0.90
70%	20%	0.80
80%	32%	0.68
90%	52%	0.48
100%	85%	0.15

Table 17.5

Stacking strength multipliers that compensate for palletizing conditions. (Source: Fibre Box Association.)

Palletizing Condition	Loss	Multiplier Best Case	Worst Case
Aligned columns	Negligible	1	
Misaligned columns	10–15% loss	0.9	0.85
Interlocked columns	40–60%	0.6	0.4
Overhang	20–40%	0.8	0.6
Deck-board gap	10–25%	0.9	0.6
Excessive handling	10–40%	0.9	0.6

The multipliers for this example are:

30 days stack duration	0.60 (Table 17.4)
80% R. H.	0.68 (Table 17.5)
Interlock stack (best case)	0.60 (Table 17.6)
Multiplier product (environmental stacking factor) = 0.245	

$$\text{Required box compression strength} = \frac{\text{anticipated load}}{\text{stacking factor}} = \frac{76 \text{ kg } (168 \text{ lb.})}{0.245}$$

$$= 310 \text{ kg force } (686 \text{ lb. force})$$

Now that the actual compression strength is known, this value can be plugged into the McKee formula (see page 413), and the required edge crush test (ECT) value of the corrugated board can be calculated.

REVIEW QUESTIONS

1. Define the terms "shock" and "resonance."

2. What is the typical shunting speed of a rail boxcar?

3. Drops resulting from manual handling are influenced by the nature of the package. Describe five relationships between the package and manual handling drops.

4. A product arrives damaged. Inspection of the shipping container reveals no marks or clues that the package had been dropped or otherwise mishandled. Describe two mechanisms by which the damage could have been caused.

5. What is the vibration frequency range that is of the greatest concern to packagers?

6. What are the two basic mechanisms by which vibration can damage goods?

7. Describe how stack resonance occurs.

8. Renumber to suit

9. A box falls off a conveyor. What orientation will cause the greatest damage to the container, and what orientation is likely to cause the greatest damage to the contents? Why?

10. What effect does address label location tend to have on the orientation of a package?

11. Vibration is described as a spring/mass relationship. What are the three conditions that can result from a vibrational input?

12. What are two units of measurement most commonly used to describe vibration?

13. What is the difference between compression strength and stacking strength?

14. A technician measures the compression strength of a corrugated box to be 600 kg load. The room conditions are 30% R. H. and 21°C. What is the actual compression strength if measured at the proper conditions? (Use Figures 17.13 and 15.6.)

CONTENTS

Automated Production

Options for increasing production, factors that dictate the course for increasing production.

The New Production Line

Custom nature of packaging machinery, conventional and unconventional machines, industry's global nature, commissioning or debugging, general considerations, single-purpose and multipurpose lines, effective servicing.

Package Design and Machinability

Designing for production.

Speed

The filler as a benchmark, speed as related to the filler, dynamic machine settings, rate of operation and output, utilization, machine speed and product variations.

Buffers

Isolation of the slowest station, example of using a buffer to increase output, bringing a line under control, run speed.

Straight-line and Rotary Systems

Intermittent in-line production lines, rotary machines, turrets, timing screws, starwheels.

Changeovers

Changeovers on intermittent and rotary machines. The relationships between changeover and economic order quantity, just-in-time manufacturing. Fast changeover, implementing fast changeover, the ideal fast changeover.

Machine Controls

Optimum settings, microelectronics, control concepts, monobloc lines.

Upgrading Existing Equipment

Advantages of upgrading in-house equipment. Advantages and cautions when buying used equipment.

Filling Systems

Dry-product categories: free-flowing, non-free-flowing, discrete, fragile, mixed. Liquids. Impact of rigid, semirigid, flexible containers on filler selection, filler accuracy.

Liquid Filling

Constant-level and constant-volume requirements/applications, carbonated beverages, bottom-up filling, vacuum fill, gravity fillers, pressure fillers, pressure-and-vacuum fillers, piston fillers, rotary piston fillers, diaphragm fillers, metering pumps.

Dry-product Filling

Volumetric-cup filler, vacuum-volumetric filler, auger fillers, net weighing, computer-combination weighing, number counts, electric-eye counting, rotary perforated disks, chute and channel fillers.

Introduction to Statistical Process control

Terminology, standard deviation, standard deviation characteristics, SPC and control charts, example X-bar and R chart correlations.

PACKAGING MACHINERY

AUTOMATED PRODUCTION

Early packages were preformed paper bags, crude cans and glass bottles of rather doubtful dimensional tolerance. Shipping containers were usually wooden crates or casks. Most factory equipment was operated by belts driven from central line shafts, and it was difficult, if not impossible, to match machine speeds or even maintain a constant speed on a single machine. It was natural that early packaging lines were labor-intensive, discrete operational units. In many cases, workers became so dexterous at routine jobs as wrapping or gluing labels that savings from installing inconsistent machines were hardly worthwhile.

Today, automated production is essential. Neither volume nor product consistency can be achieved in any other way. Increasing production in a cost-effective manner is a difficult and complex undertaking. The production engineer must have strong support from management, production, maintenance and vendors. Delays, errors and higher costs will result if this support is not totally integrated, with all concerned playing an active role.

The critical people should be exposed to trade shows, vendors, trade literature, seminars and tours of related facilities. This will ensure a full understanding of the technologies and options involved.

Increasing Production

Four options to increase production are:

- Buy new state-of-the-art equipment.
- Do something with existing equipment.
- Buy refurbished equipment.
- Hire a contract packager.

Factors that influence this choice are as follows:

- *Availability of in-plant equipment:* Producing a package similar to an existing one can conceivably be done on existing production lines, but an all-new package type must be produced by other means.

- *Market demand for the product:* Temporary surges would best be met by hiring contract packagers. Slow, steady growth might initially be contracted out while a new line is being established. Careful analysis is needed to determine whether the product line will live long enough to provide a return on investment.

- *The time frame in which the product must be produced:* Lead times for new machinery can be considerable. In some situations, it may not be acceptable to wait for the delivery and commissioning of a new line. Upgrading existing lines, purchasing used equipment or hiring contract packagers are possible solutions.

- *Production volume:* A slight increase over existing capacity may best be achieved by upgrading existing production machines. Significant increases in volume, however, must be treated in other ways.

- *Quality standards:* Market expectations are continually changing. Dated equipment and technology may not meet these needs.

- *Equipment technology:* New materials and manufacturing technologies are being introduced every year. Refurbishing outdated machinery is not a wise investment.

THE NEW PRODUCTION LINE

The Packaging Machine Industry

Unlike the manufacture of household appliances or automobiles, packaging machinery manufacture is a highly specialized business that does not produce large numbers of identical machines. It is, therefore, not possible to visit a few stores, compare prices, buy a unit and plug it in.

Products and packages come in such an infinite variety of materials and forms that even though a machine manufacturer may specialize in a particular machine class—for example, piston fillers—it is likely that almost every order has some small difference to accommodate a product, package or customer need. In this respect, packaging machinery is a custom business, and every packaging machine is built to a specific customer's specifications. Since construction of a packaging machine does not begin until design specifications are prepared and the order placed, long lead times are common. Construction and delivery times of a year and sometimes more are not unusual.

However, even though individual orders are custom, they are built within a standard frame or configuration that is targeted at a conventional package format. This standard machine is then adapted to the particular dimensions and needs of the conventional package. If you create an unconventional package design, the entire machine will need to be designed from the floor up, and costs will soar.

For example, cartoning machine companies provide machines that will erect and fill an infinite range of standard tube-style cartons. They can fit on extra stations to date-code, insert leaflets, attach deal labels and so on. Despite these differences, the cartons are still conventional or standard. Asking for a machine to form and fill a seven-sided carton, however, requires original (and costly) design.

Most packaging machinery companies are relatively small, often individually or family owned, and tend to be built around the present or past skills of an innovative mechanical specialist. The markets are specialized enough that the majority need an export market to survive, making packaging machinery a global business. While all industrialized countries have some domestic machine production, Italy and Germany are the most significant producers on the world market.

Given that a complete packaging line may consist of six functional stations from suppliers located in six different countries, connected by conveyors and buffers made by still another supplier, it is not likely that a new line can be plugged in and expected to work instantly and perfectly. New lines have to be debugged and brought up to operating speed or "commissioned." It has been reported (Ben Miyares) that about 70% of all packaging machine projects do not reach their objectives after one year. Good production engineers can usually coax a bit more speed out of a line given time and experience with the process.

General Considerations

Broad decisions as to machine class need to be made early and are usually obvious. For example:

- *Space constraints:* It is often useful to construct a three-dimensional model of the proposed line. In addition to the physical space occupied by the equipment itself, ensure that operators have adequate space to tend the line safely and effectively. This includes ergonomic placement of all controls and adequate access for changeover and maintenance. Allow for the storage and flow of input materials, the removal of input dunnage or packaging and the removal of finished product.

- *Installation requirements:* What services (electrical, water, air, steam, waste disposal) will be needed? What are the required floor loadings? How will the machines be moved to their fixed locations (e.g., do you need to remove walls)? Who will do the installation?

- *Power and control:* What level of automation is appropriate? How will machine movements be actuated and controlled? Using power and control systems similar to existing machinery can reduce training and maintenance times.

- *Special requirements:* Is the product highly flammable? Does the machine have to be explosion-proof? Are particular standards of cleanliness and sterility necessary? Are active chemicals needing special corrosion protection procedures a factor? Should the machine flow be from left to right or right to left?

When examining candidate machines, remember that good packaging lines accomplish their objective with a minimum of vibration and noise. Vibration indicates out-of-balance components or questionable forces acting in an asymmetrical way. Such forces translate directly into wear and stress on the machine. The machine's mainframe should be heavy enough to hold all the moving machinery adequately and stiff enough not to twist or deform under operational stresses.

The transfer and flow of product and material through the production process should be smooth, with the minimum of directional changes. Mechanical motions should be rotary rather than reciprocating, wherever practical. Heavy drive trains should be mounted low or on the floor with easy access for maintenance. Motors and gearboxes overhanging the product line should be avoided, as lubricants or debris may drop on the product during routine maintenance.

Before calling on machine suppliers, make a thorough and critical analysis of what exactly needs to be accomplished. Purchasers commonly request broad performance ranges, believing that the machine is thus more versatile and could be adapted to more operations in the plant. While it may be possible to design a filling machine that will handle 4 millilitre (ml) vials and 4 litre (l) pails, compromises will be necessary. The machine will not likely do either job well.

Be realistic in the range of tasks that your machine will be required to perform, and resist the temptation to compromise the main objective. The more dedicated a machine is, the more efficient it will be. *Versatility should not be purchased at the expense of output efficiency.*

All machines need to be adjustable, and those machines that will be running multiple product types and/or multiple package types will require a changeover capability. A basic tenet to remember is that *the more things that can be adjusted, the more things there are that will go out of adjustment.*

Adjustments are those machine features that accommodate the natural variations inherent in the product and package being run. For example, the viscosity of pancake syrup will vary depending on the ambient temperature. A folding carton will be stiff when the humidity is low, but soft and pliable when it is high. Packages themselves will have a range of tolerances within which a machine must be able to work.

Changeover capability requires that the machine can be significantly reconfigured to run a completely different product, package or both. In general, change parts are preferred for fixed, required changes (e.g., a product that is filled into three different package sizes). If there are a great number of package/product combinations, then a machine must be completely adjustable, within the overall range of possibilities, to handle numerous package or product combinations.

Capital outlay for machines can be heavy. Is the proposed product line going to live long enough to repay this investment? Is there a new technology on the horizon that will make your product or package obsolete? (Some bakeries, for example, invested in waxed paper bread wrappers when it was obvious that polybags offered a superior alternative.)

Effective servicing and parts supply is a key vendor issue. Does the proposed machine supplier have a local office and local parts supply, or will you need to wait for parts to be flown from Greece? If you are purchasing equipment from abroad, browse the instruction manuals. Sometimes these are translated by local staff, who have dictionary knowledge of English. Technical terms take a beating, and sometimes are unrecognizable. If the technology is new, your service people will need to be retrained.

And finally: At what point does the line become "yours"?

PACKAGE DESIGN AND MACHINABILITY

The typical package design process tends to focus on marketing, containment and protective values. Machinery's role in bringing product and package together, often at great speeds, is frequently overlooked. A survey conducted by the Packaging Machinery Manufacturer's Institute about packaging line productivity and material issues reported that, among respondents:

- Nearly half had reduced scrap and rejects by redesigning packages.
- Over a third had shifted to better quality packaging materials.

Contribute to trouble-free machining by ensuring that a package shape can be easily conveyed without jamming. Also, keep centers of gravity low, and ensure an appropriate level of package robustness. Common dimensions for products offered in several sizes can substantially reduce changeover time and costs. For example by keeping the footprint dimension of a 500 ml and a one l bottle of vegetable oil the same, (see Figure 18.1) a changeover between sizes will not require adjustment of conveyor guide rails and will not need replacement of infeed timing screws and star wheels. By keeping the labeling panel in the same geometric location, the labeler will need no adjustment; simply a replacement of labels to the size being run.

Good package design makes for efficient production.

Figure 18.1

An example of two bottle sizes with the same footprint and similar label placement.

SPEED

Terminology

The lack of specific and consistent terminology often makes discussions of productivity confusing. In this discussion, the following definitions (based on the recommendations of Paul Zepf, Zarpac, Inc. will be used:

Packaging line	A group of integrated special-purpose machines that combine product and package inputs and produce a new product. The individual machines, each performing a different function, are referred to as stations.
Input	Specific product and package items required for package assembly.
Design speed	The theoretical capacity under perfect running conditions. The speed of the machine as designed, running empty, is the design cycle rate.
Capacity	The upper sustainable limit of quality packages passing a point just before warehousing.
Run speed	The instantaneous operating rate at a point in time.
Output	A packaging line's output is the exact quantity of quality product passing a point just before warehousing or shipping in a given time. A machine's or station's output is the exact quantity of quality product leaving that machine in a given time.
Efficiency	Efficiency is a ratio of output over input, but in packaging production, this definition has many subtle variations. For this discussion, efficiency is used to describe a station's or a packaging line's actual operating time over the available time. (Other authorities call this "capability.")

The speed hierarchy would be as follows:

1. Design speed
2. Capacity
3. Run speed
4. Output rate

When discussing machine speeds, one must consider the credibility of the vendor. One experienced machine integrating specialist reports that on average, the vendor's quoted speed is 80% of what is achieved.

Output and Machine Design Speed

The first step in considering a new line is to determine and quantify accurately the desired output. Be specific and realistic in determining the numbers that will serve today's needs, and if necessary, provide a contingency for future sales increases. Bear in mind that a machine that goes twice as fast is sometimes more than twice as expensive. Excess production speed is an expensive luxury.

Vendor literature will quote a "machine design speed" or "cycle rate": the theoretical containers per minute (cpm) at which the machine has been designed to run. Machine design speed is not "output rate," which is a measure of actual quality product output over time. An empty machine will cycle indefinitely; it is the material passing through it that causes problems. A line capable of 30 cpm may in theory produce 14,400 completed packages in an 8-hour shift. However, the real output might be more like 11,000 units, a 0.76 efficiency based on the theoretical output.

A complete packaging line is typically composed of a number of discrete machines that are connected together. These individual stations will likely come from different suppliers, and each will need to have an assigned design speed. Evolved practice uses the most critical station in the line, usually the filler, as the benchmark, and all other stations are specified to run at a higher design speed than this unit. Machines preceding the filler are specified at a higher design speed than the filler in order to ensure that the filler is never "starved" for containers. Post-fill machines must also run faster in order to pull product away from the filler and not create a backup problem. The design speed of each machine past the filler increases as the line gets farther from the filler. (See Table 18.1) This creates a "pulling" effect on the filler. In this approach, individual machine run speeds are set to balance the flow of product through the entire line.

A more modern approach is to work with dynamic speed settings. Any machine in such a line will vary in speed at any instant in time in relation to upstream and downstream conditions. This may be compared to automobiles traveling down a congested highway—individual cars will be constantly changing their speeds depending on the conditions ahead of them. At any instant of time, the cars in any group may all be traveling at different speeds, but as a group they are making progress. Progress would be interrupted if a single car elected to travel at a fixed speed.

Selection of the design speed required for a new line starts with consideration of final market needs. For example, a proposed filling line needs to produce

Table 18.1

The filler is usually the most critical operational unit in a production line and is frequently used as the benchmark from which all other machine speeds are derived.

Unit	Speed (cpm*)
Bottle supply station	230
Bottle dump station	220
Unscrambler	210
Cleaner/fill station	200 (benchmark speed)
Cappe	205
Labeler	210
Inspect/date-code station	215
Six packer	220
Caser/packer/sealer	225
Palletizer	230

*cpm = containers per minute

57,000 sellable containers per 8-hour shift, or 120 cpm. However, the time in which the line is actually available and producing is affected by many other factors. While the staff may be in the plant from nine to five, the line does not run nine to five every day. Incidental time (see Figure 18.2) reduces the working time. Non-equipment-related problems, such as product shortage or out-of-specification containers, subtract more minutes from the time the line should be running but isn't, through no fault of its own. Finally, more time will be lost from full run-speed production due to various problems directly associated with the equipment.

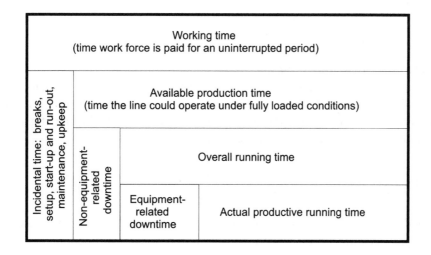

Figure 18.2

Actual production time is working time minus equipment-related downtime, non-equipment-related downtime and incidental time.

Figure 18.3

The line illustrated in this block diagram cannot be run faster than 90 cpm, the filler's maximum speed. The line's actual output would be the product of each machine's efficiency (eff.): 0.96 × 0.93 × 0.98 × 0.92 × 90 cpm = 72 cpm.

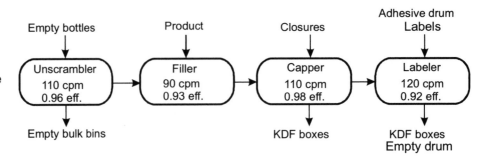

Obviously, specifying a filler with a design cycle rate of 120 cpm would be a mistake for many reasons, not the least of which is that the machine may not cycle at 120 cpm once the product and package are introduced. Start-up and shutdown times, changeovers, breaks, and routine lubrication and maintenance will all eat into the available production time. In other words, the actual running time available on an 8-hour shift might average out to 7 hours, in which case the filler cycle rate would need to be about 136 cpm.

Next, consider what happens when the machine is running for the 7 hours remaining for actual production. To start with, the filler will not always be running at its full 136 cpm limit. There will be run-ups and slowdowns. There will be periodic slowdowns or stoppages, because of either other stations in the line or irregularities in the product or package. This might bump up the required design speed to 150 cpm.

Finally, will every package produced be a sellable unit? And what about a contingency for growing sales? In the end, a filler capable of 200 cpm or even more might be the best choice.

Machine design speed alone should not be a gauge for specifying a purchase. A filler operating 98% of the time at 50 cpm will outperform a 70 cpm machine running 65% of the time. As a general rule, the faster the machine, the less tolerant it is of input variations. A faster machine usually requires tighter input material tolerances to run at full capacity.

Once new line expectations and the required levels of output and design speed have been determined, a block diagram showing the respective machines and activities can be made. (See Figure 18.3.) As the project evolves, the inputs (empty bottles, closures, labels, adhesive drums) and outputs (empty boxes, empty drums) of every station can be entered to provide information on space needed to service the line properly.

The output of every machine in a line is critical, since line output can never be greater than the output of the slowest station. Output inefficiencies are cumulative in lines with directly connected machines, such as the one illustrated in Figure 18.3, since whenever one machine stops, the whole line stops. It is vital that the output capabilities of each station be understood.

BUFFERS

The additive effect of individual station inefficiencies can be reduced by isolating the different stations with product accumulation areas. "Buffers" are conveyor storage devices that hold a calculated amount of product between operational units. Their capacity should be calculated to provide an accumulation large enough to hold a station's output or continue to feed other stations in line as needed. Buffers are generally used to isolate the least efficient stations on the line.

Using the line in Figure 18.3 as an example, if the typical problem at the filling station (misaligned bottles, no bottles, bottles that are out of spec) requires one minute to clear, then a buffer located after the filler should be able to hold at least one minute's production at the filling station—in this example, about 90 bottles.

As Figure 18.4 shows, the buffer effectively isolates one part of the line from another, allowing each to run for short periods without the other. An output efficiency can be calculated for each subunit:

$$\text{Efficiency of Subunit A: } 0.96 \times 0.93 = 0.89$$

$$\text{Efficiency of Subunit B: } 0.98 \times 0.92 = 0.90$$

The output of Subunit A is

$$0.89 \times 90 \text{ cpm (the maximum filler speed)} = 80.1 \text{ cpm}$$

But Subunit B can be set to run at a speed of up to 110 cpm, the maximum capper speed. Subunit B at an efficiency of 0.90 and running at 110 cpm could handle up to 99 cpm. If Subunit B is set to run at 89 cpm, then, adjusting for its efficiency factor:

$$0.90 \times 89 \text{ cpm} = 80.1 \text{ cpm}$$

Subunit B will be able to handle 100% of the output from Subunit A. Therefore, line output with the buffer will be the 80.1 cpm output of Subunit A. This is an improvement of 8 cpm, or 480 extra sellable units per hour.

In this example, the least efficient machine was the labeler. Looking at the efficiency figures alone, one might be tempted try to improve the performance of the labeler. However, looking at the calculations in this simple example demonstrates quite clearly that improving the efficiency of the labeler would not have a significant effect.

As a line's run speed increases, the buffer's size must also increase proportionately. Well-designed lines should not require extensive buffering areas and should have a capacity run speed approaching 100%. No one would accept a capacity run speed of 85% from their car, and yet a similar run speed from a vital production machine is often considered "normal."

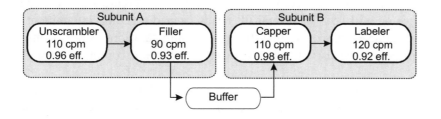

Figure 18.4

Using a buffer to divide a packaging line into two subunits, each of which can run independently of the other for short periods.

Buffers need to be placed after noninterruptible operations. A baking oven full of muffins with a 20-minute bake time cannot be stopped if the muffin wrapper goes down. The alternative is to scrap that amount of production.

To operate properly there must always be some product in the buffer. This requires that operations before and after the buffer be capable of short periods of higher speed in order to partly refill the buffer when it has been emptied or to partly empty the buffer when it is filled to capacity.

It may appear that buffers are a great way to increase a production line's output, but it should be kept in mind that the buffer itself is a machine with its own efficiency factor. A good buffer installation will have a 0.99 efficiency. Efficiency below 0.98 can potentially slow down the production line, as would the installation of too many buffers. For example three buffers in a production line, each operating at 0.97 would as a group have an efficiency of 0.91.

Do not install buffers to compensate for a defective or improperly operating machine or poorly specified input components. Fix the machine or change the input specifications.

Run Speed

A line is best run at the speed at which it can produce quality product, even if that is below the line's rated speed. Driving a machine at the rated speed, with periodic stoppages and occasional off-spec product, is usually counterproductive. Several things are typically going wrong at once, and problem solving becomes difficult.

The general rule is to slow the line down until it is brought under control, then increase the speed in increments until a problem starts to occur. When this problem is resolved and the line is brought under control again, the line speed can be increased in increments until the next problem area is discovered. Comprehensive production data and statistical process control data records are valuable sources of information for improving a line's operating efficiency. Operator consistency and skill level are critical.

STRAIGHT-LINE AND ROTARY SYSTEMS

Packaging machines, such as fillers, cappers and labelers, can be designed in straight-line (intermittent) and rotary configurations. Straight-line machines usually index a product into an operational station, and then hold it there until the operation is completed.

For example, intermittent-motion straight-line fillers move containers under the filling heads and then stop for the fill cycle. (See Figure 18.5) The machine may have one fill head or several fill heads ganged together. Intermittent fillers have operating speeds of up to 150 units per minute. (Some straight-line fillers move the filling heads with the container to achieve a continuous straight-line fill.)

Continuous-motion (rotary) machines do not index a container into a station and stop, but instead feed the container into a rotating turret, where the operational

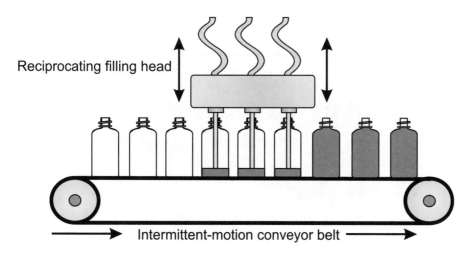

Figure 18.5
Intermittent-motion
straight-line filler.

heads work on the moving container. Rotary machines require a timing screw on the conveyor feeding into the starwheel to separate the containers to the correct pitch. (See Figures 18.6 and 18.7) The starwheel changes the direction of the container flow and either inserts the containers into the filling turret or moves them back out onto the conveyor as needed.

As the turret diameter increases, more stations can be placed on the circumference. The turret can be turned faster and still provide enough time for proper fill.

High-speed rotary turret fillers can be several metres in diameter and can have in excess of 100 filling heads. Rotary fillers operating at 80 cpm are common, and special machines of 2,000 cpm and more have been built for the beverage industry.

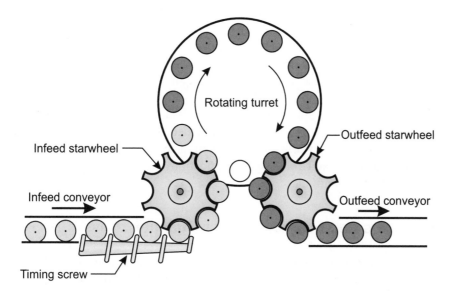

Figure 18.6
Rotary machines are able to operate at higher speeds than intermittent machines.

Figure 18.7

A rotary filling machine showing infeed timing screw (also called a helix), the infeed star-wheel and the filling stations.

CHANGEOVERS

Generally, the faster a machine operates, the more complex the changeover. Intermittent-motion machines, for example, need repositioning of the guide rails and timing adjustments. Change parts are minimal. A rotary machine will almost always require change parts, such as additional infeed timing screws, infeed and outfeed starwheels, and sometimes the turret itself.

For applications where several different products will be run on the same line, ease of changeover becomes important. The simplest change is when only the product needs to be replaced. Sometimes the product remains the same, but the volumes required may vary substantially, ranging from unit of use to institutional quantities. Systems using cylinders, metering cups or other similar volume fixturing usually have a fairly fixed range within which they can be adjusted. Auger feeds and metering pumps, on the other hand, have broader adjustment ranges because one simply increases the fill time period.

Changeovers can be an important part of output calculations. Where changeovers are frequent, ease of changeover, rather than actual machine speed, may dictate machine choice. A fast machine requiring excessive changeover time will be a handicap.

Ideally, changeovers should require no tools and should be done from one side of the machine and from one end to the other. It should be possible to make critical or time-consuming adjustments or settings off-line. Parts and adjustments should be clearly marked for easy identification and setup by personnel. All settings should be quantified.

Changeovers and Economic Order Quantity

Rapid changeovers are important for efficient production. Just-in-time (JIT) manufacturing, in many instances, depends on the ability to make fast changeovers.

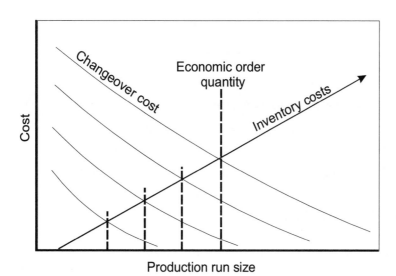

Figure 18.8
As changeover time and cost are reduced, so is the economic order quantity.

Packagers need to balance the inventory cost of larger and larger production runs against the per-unit cost of doing changeovers.

Producing smaller lots with more frequent changeovers reduces inventory costs but increases the per-part changeover cost, while long runs decrease manufacturing cost but increase inventory costs. (See Figure 18.8) The most economical point is where the two costs are at a minimum. This point is the "economic order quantity" (EOQ).

Fast Changeover

Some level of fast changeover is built into most current packaging machinery. Many older, still reliable machines and lines are being rebuilt to increase production by reducing changeover time.

Introducing fast changeover to existing lines starts with listing all the elements in a changeover. These should be listed by time from "going" to "going," that is, from the last sellable part off the old configuration to the first sellable part made at production speed on the new configuration. It includes both the "hang time" (i.e., the time that the machine is off) and the "run-in time" (i.e., the time required to bring the line up to capacity run speed). Total changeover time can be grouped into four main categories:

- Preparation or organization: get parts, get tools, locate mechanics/operators.

- Changeover: remove and remount change parts.

- Measurement: settings, calibrations, centering.

- Trial run: run-in, final adjustments.

Make a histogram (i.e., a detailed bar chart showing where time has been spent to effect the changeover). Focus on the histogram's long time elements.

> The ideal changeover
> takes no time,
> no tools, no talent,
> no muscle
> and
> you can sell "first off."

Determine ways to accomplish time reductions:

- Eliminate the need for tools.

- Externalize or "off-line" as much as possible.

- Make all settings to a quantified scale (no "eyeballing").

- Perform the changeover from one side of the machine and in one direction.

- Have a single documented procedure for all operators.

MACHINE CONTROL

The motions of machine components are achieved, timed and controlled by various methods. They may be mechanically actuated by levers, cams, chains, push rods or gears. Motions can be controlled and implemented by microswitches, timers, electromagnetic relays, hydraulics, pneumatics and electronic means. Each method has its advantages and applications.

Maintenance is an important aspect of machine motion and control systems. In a plant where the machines are controlled by electrical relay logic or mechanical systems, the change to a hydraulic/electronic system will require considerable re-education of the maintenance and operating staff.

A machine runs best when all components are at their optimum settings. These settings should be determined and quantified, *not* left to operator discretion. Running a machine should not depend on the anonymous turn of a temperature control knob or on moving a feed roll "just a touch."

For example, critical heat-sealing stations should have direct temperature readouts taken at a specific location or several locations. Critical mechanical adjustments should be made to a scale or vernier. Quantified machine adjustments provide a better understanding of what the machine is doing and make line operation a science rather than an art.

Microelectronics and microprocessors have provided packaging engineers with endless possibilities for continuous monitoring of station variables, such as fill weight, throughput, production speed and machine settings. With programmable controllers, feedback circuits and servo-stepping drives, in-process changes can be controlled by the microprocessor. Machine settings can be retained in memory, and changeover between different production runs can be made automatically at a considerable savings in setup time.

"Control" is also a concept that applies to the package itself. A bottle traveling freely on a conveyor belt is not in control; it moves with minimal limitations. Yet, the bottle must be precisely located to apply a closure to it—that means bringing it under control. A package traveling along a production line may go in and out of control several times as it passes through different machines and functional stations.

Earlier, it was mentioned that a machine's design speed (running empty) is greater than the speed it will run at when loaded with product and packages. This difference comes about partly because every component in a machine is always under control, whereas the package and product are not.

Gaining and maintaining package control is an important part of packaging machinery design. On a rotary machine, control is gained by the infeed timing screw. On a typical rotary filling machine, the package is then handed off (in control) to the starwheel, which changes the direction of movement and then hands off the package to a filling stage. On most contemporary machines, the filled package would then be placed (now out-of-control) onto a conveyor that goes to the capper. At the capper, the whole process of gaining control must be repeated, a process that occurs again at the labeler.

Current packaging line design thinking proposes that once you have gained initial control of the package, you should maintain control until all operations are completed (a "monobloc machine"). In the above example, the filled bottle would be indexed directly, in control, to the capper and again to the labeler. In other words, instead of several machines being linked together to form a line, where control is gained and lost at each machine, the entire filling/capping/labeling process is accomplished on one extended machine.

A monobloc machine, as described, would require only one infeed timing screw, would occupy a significantly smaller footprint, and at least in principle, be more reliable. On the negative side, the machine is not as versatile, and because it does not include buffers, the entire machine must stop with any malfunction.

UPGRADING EXISTING EQUIPMENT

Refurbishing existing in-house equipment, if possible, has definite benefits:

- You are working with proven technology (for in-house equipment).
- There are no capital costs for upgrading existing equipment.
- Initial training and commissioning problems are reduced.

Existing equipment can also be purchased from one of the many used-machinery brokers. Advantages cited are 30% or more savings against new equipment of equal performance and shorter delivery and start-up times.

Remember that packaging machines tend to be highly specialized, complex pieces of equipment and that each machine has been custom built to a particular customer's specifications. Furthermore used-machinery brokers are generalists, not specialists, in the kinds of machinery you are seeking. They may not be fully aware of the machine's history. In purchasing used machinery, as with used cars, let the buyer beware.

FILLING SYSTEMS

Product Categories

Selection of a filling system requires careful consideration of several key factors. Depending on a project's scope, one or two of these factors will have overriding importance. The obvious product division is "liquid and solid" or "liquid and dry," but within each of these categories exists a range of possibilities.

Figure 18.9

Types of dry products include free-flowing, non-free-flowing and agglomerated dry products.

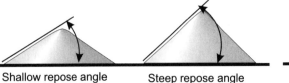

Shallow repose angle   Steep repose angle   Agglomerate

- Free-flowing
- Relatively constant density
- Can be measured by volume

- Does not flow freely
- Variable density
- Equal volumes will vary in weight
- Must be weighed

"Dry" products include discrete items such as candies, fasteners, pills and nuts. Discrete items are often counted for filling. Free-flowing powders or granules are powders that have a reasonably consistent density and pour readily to form a fairly flat cone when dumped on a plane surface. The flatter the angle of repose, the more readily the material will flow and the more consistent the density. (See Figure 18.9) Because of their free-flowing character and consistent density, they are fairly easy to measure by a variety of methods, including simple free-fall gravity feeders.

Unlike free-flowing powders, other powdered and granular products do not flow readily and have a steep angle of repose when poured out on a table. They frequently bridge and clog passages. Some have a tendency to agglomerate, pack or entrain air, and therefore, the density is not consistent. These materials cannot be fed by gravity alone; provision must be made for physically moving them through the filler. Since their densities vary, volumetric fills are inappropriate.

Finally, products such as potato chips, dry cereals and some other granular compositions are fragile and must be handled gently. Vibratory feed systems and net weighing are typically used for these products.

"Wet" or liquid products range from low-viscosity free-flowing liquids to viscous "semiliquids" to extremely viscous products that might better be classed as semisolids. Liquid-fill characteristics vary widely, depending on such factors as temperature, tendency to entrain air, surface tension and frothing or foaming tendencies. Carbonated beverages form a class of their own.

Some products contain a mixture of ingredient types. Instant soups may contain noodles, assorted dried vegetables, dried meat and powdered soup base. It is impossible to premix these and ensure a consistent fill in proper proportions, since the ingredients will always separate according to their densities and geometries. Such products need a separate filling station for each ingredient. Mixed solids and liquids, such as canned peas or stew, are similarly filled at two stations: one for the solids and one to top up the fluid portion.

Other Considerations

Rigid glass, metal or heavy plastic containers can be accelerated and decelerated at high rates. They can have significant force applied to the finish during filling or to the sidewalls during conveying. Vacuum or pressure levels during the fill cycle are not critical considerations.

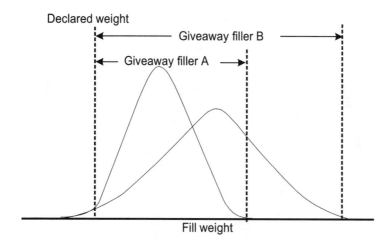

Declared weight

Figure 18.10

The more accurate the filler, the smaller the standard deviation and the closer the filler can be set to the declared fill.

Semirigid containers, typically blow-molded plastic bottles, cannot withstand the same stresses. This places limitations on the vacuum or pressure level that can be used during the fill, and also limits the means of moving the container from station to station.

Flexible pouches or bags cannot maintain their dimensions in all axes, and therefore, must be retained in a fixture while being filled. Since flexible containers cannot be filled to a specified level, piston volumetric fillers are often used to push the product into the pouch.

No filler is perfectly accurate, and fillers must be considered in terms of accuracy relative to product value. The challenge is to satisfy legal fill requirements without having excessive "giveaway." The more accurate the system, the closer the machine can be set to the declared fill, and the less giveaway there will be. (See Figure 18.10) Accuracy is generally accepted to mean that 99% of all fills meet the declared fill statement. As a practical matter, for quality-assurance purposes, it is the average fill and the standard deviation that are often calculated. Average fill should be at least three standard deviations (sigma) above declared fill.

LIQUID FILLING

Constant-Volume and Constant-Level Fillers

Liquids can be metered into containers so that they reach either a constant level or a constant volume.

"Constant-level filling" is used for most low- or moderate-cost products such as soft drinks, beer and ketchup, where accurate volume is not as important as keeping a visually constant-fill level. Containers can have slightly inconsistent volumes due to variations in wall thickness. (See Figure 18.11) Fill height levels will, therefore, vary if the containers are filled to a constant volume. Customer satisfaction demands that all containers be filled to the same level. Constant-level filling achieves this regardless of the actual liquid volume.

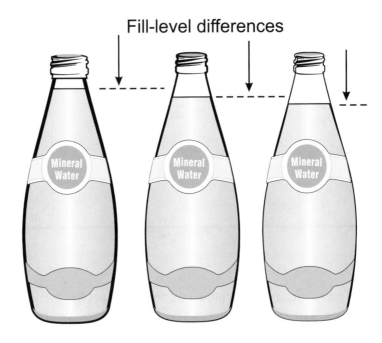

Fill-level differences

Constant-level filling is achieved by using gravity, vacuum, pressure or combinations of pressure and vacuum. The level is controlled by drawing off excess liquid when the required level is reached or by using electronic or pneumatic controls to shut off the filling valve.

With "constant-volume filling," an accurate product volume is placed into the container, usually with pistons or other accurate metering systems. Uses for constant-volume fills:

- High-cost products.

- Products where net weights must be maintained because the product is sold by weight.

- Products whose end use demands accurate weight or volume control (such as paint tint bases).

- Pharmaceuticals or chemicals requiring accurate dosage rates.

- Non-free-flowing viscous and paste products.

"Top filling" is done by inserting the filling tube into the container's neck to the fill-height level and by either allowing the product to drop to the bottom or directing the liquid to the container sides so that it will run down the sides with a minimum of turbulence and air entrapment.

The more common method, "bottom-up filling," inserts the filling tube down to the container bottom and allows it to recede gradually upward as the container fills. Bottom-up filling inhibits frothing, minimizes product aeration, eliminates air pockets in semisolids and avoids undue vaporization of volatile products. Rigid filling-line connections are used when the containers themselves are raised

Filler tube
withdraws

Cleansing
Cream

Cleansing
Cream

Figure 18.12

Bottom-up filling can be done by lowering the tube into the fixed container and gradually withdrawing it as filling proceeds, as illustrated here, or by putting the container on a stage that can be elevated and then gradually lowered as the container fills.

and lowered. Flexible connections are used when the filling stems are inserted into the containers and gradually moved upward. (See Figure 18.12)

Filling carbonated beverages requires a special approach to eliminate foaming and ensure retention of desired carbonation levels. Product is supplied to the filling heads from a chilled supply bowl that is pressurized with carbon dioxide. (See Figure 18.13) The container is brought up against the filling-head seal, and a multiposition valving system opens to the supply-bowl headspace. When the pressure inside the container is at about the same elevated pressure as the supply bowl, the valve repositions to allow product to flow from the supply bowl into the container. When the liquid level reaches the bottom of the vent tube, a check valve stops the filling process. A vent then opens to the atmosphere while sealing off the pressure equalization tube. This allows the container pressure to come down to atmospheric levels. The process is virtually foam-free.

"Vacuum fillers" operate by lowering the stem, consisting of the filling tube and a vacuum line, into the container neck and sealing the stem into place with a seal ring. Air is drawn from the container so that air pressure on the product in the supply tank forces product into the container. When the product reaches the vacuum inlet, suction draws it into the overflow tank, preventing it from rising

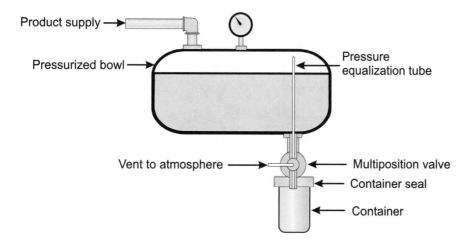

Product supply →

Pressurized bowl →

Pressure
equalization tube

Vent to atmosphere →

Multiposition valve

Container seal

Container

Figure 18.13

Carbonated beverages are filled cold and under pressure to ensure minimum loss of carbonation. Rotary carbonated-beverage fillers can have 100 or more filling heads.

above the fill-height level. Excess product drops to the bottom of the overflow tank, and air is sucked through the tank outlet tube through the vacuum pump.

Vacuum-fill systems are used for putting free-flowing liquids into glass containers. They are fast, flexible and relatively low in cost. However, they are limited to rigid containers and the constant-level method. They are not used with products that are affected by agitation.

"Gravity fillers" have a filling stem with a spring-loaded outer tube and a rubber seal that fits over the bottle finish. The outer tube is raised by the bottle to open the filling valve. This eliminates drip before and after filling. Gravity filling is slower than vacuum filling, and for this reason, it is used primarily for some foaming products, since agitation is minimal. Very foamy products demand bottom-up filling. Flow rate is controlled by the height of the product in the supply tank above the filling tubes. Gravity filling cannot be used with slow-flowing products. Few products are filled by gravity alone.

"Pressure filling," which is similar to gravity filling, uses a pump to provide the force to move the product. This makes an elevated supply tank unnecessary and results in a faster product flow. Pressure filling is ideal for viscous products requiring minimum agitation.

Pressure-and-vacuum combinations (see Figure 18.14) are used to dispense viscous foaming products into plastic containers. The pressure gives faster product flow, and the vacuum draws off overflow. The system prevents containers from bulging under the filling seal, which would create an overfill or overflow condition when the seal was removed.

Some of the systems described above require a seal ring on the container finish and an excess-product return line. These may be eliminated by product-level sensing devices. Pneumatic systems use a stream of low-pressure air flowing through an inner tube in the filling stem. The product level exerts a back pressure when the fill height level is achieved. This actuates a high-pressure pneumatic system, which closes the valve and retracts the filling stem from the container. This provides a drip-free cutoff and eliminates the need for a seal or return line.

Sonic systems bounce high-frequency sound waves off the surface of the rising liquid and cut off the flow valve when the fill-height level is reached.

Figure 18.14

Pressure-and-vacuum fill system.

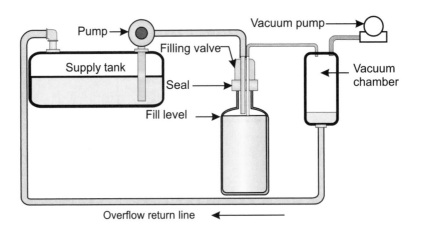

Piston Volumetric Fillers

Simple "piston fillers" (see Figure 18.15) consist of a cylinder fitted with a plunger and a valve. Product is drawn from the supply tank when the plunger is drawn back and is forced into the container when the plunger is pushed forward. A valve rotates 90° with each cycle. Suction draws the product through the valve duct and into the cylinder during the first part of the cycle. Then the valve rotates, shutting off the supply tank and allowing product to be forced into the filling spout when the plunger pushes forward.

Piston fillers usually have a control device that prevents the valve from rotating if no container is in the filling station. Product is pushed back into the supply tank without spillage. The amount of product ejected depends on the cylinder's diameter and the piston stroke length. The stroke is adjustable while the machine is in operation.

Piston fillers are available as single, manually actuated pistons or as fully automatic rotary machines with twelve or more pistons. (See Figure 18.16) Many ingenious valve arrangements have been designed for piston fillers. Continuous-motion rotary-head piston fillers are used for high speeds of 500 to 2,000 cpm. They are ideal for viscous or paste products, such as honey, peanut butter, creams and jams, as well as for free-flowing liquids such as fruit juices.

Diaphragm Volumetric Fillers

"Diaphragm fillers" (see Figure 18.17) are used to fill a premeasured volume of fluid rather than for filling to a level. A rolling diaphragm in a cylindrical chamber moves up to charge the cylinder with product. Valves then open to allow discharge into the container when the diaphragm moves down. Precise volumes are attained by adjusting diaphragm movement. The use of a rolling diaphragm eliminates the need for seals between piston and cylinder, as would be needed on a piston filler. Such sliding seals can cause abrasion and particle generation, though.

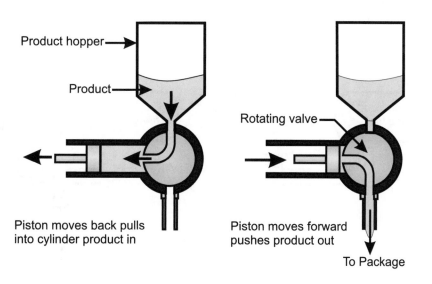

Figure 18.15

A simple piston filler. Piston fillers are able to dispense accurate product volumes.

Figure 18.16

Cross-section of a rotary piston filler.

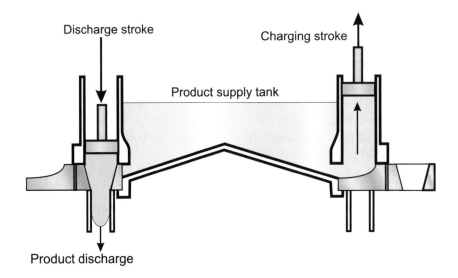

Metering Pumps

"Metering pumps" can be used as fillers. These use positive displacement pumps or constant output impellers to measure a preset amount of product. To control the amount dispensed, the pump usually operates for a preset number of revolutions and then stops. Timed pumps are also available, but are said to be less accurate. Pump fillers are used for aerosol propellants and single portions of ketchup, mustard and other liquids.

DRY-PRODUCT FILLING

The three principal methods of metering dry fills are by:

- Volume
- Mass or weight
- Count

Each is described in the following sections.

Figure 18.17

Diaphragm fillers dispense accurate volumes of product.

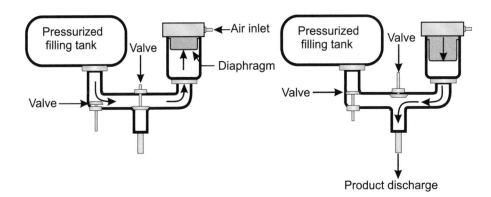

Volumetric-cup (or Flask) Filling

In its simplest form, a "volumetric-cup" filling machine consists of a flat, circular plate fitted with open-top cups at regular intervals. As the plate revolves, the cups fill by passing under a product hopper. Scrapers or brushes ensure that the cup is even and level. The cups revolve to a discharge station where the product discharges to the container. (See Figure 18.18)

The simplest discharge system employs a stationary disk under open-bottom cups. This disk has a single opening at the discharge station, and the product is contained in the cups by the disk until the discharge opening is reached. The alternative system employs a trap door under each cup, eliminating the stationary disk. The trap doors open at the container-filling station and close again before the cup-filling station is reached. Volumetric adjustments are made by using telescoping cups, with the bottom half of the cup sliding up over the top half. The maximum adjustment cannot be more than a 2:1 ratio.

Cup- or flask-filling is used for free-flowing solids of consistent density. It is advisable to maintain a constant level in the feed hopper in order to maintain consistent density and an even flow of the product into the flasks.

Vacuum-volumetric Filling

"Vacuum-volumetric filling" is accomplished by means of a rotating wheel with adjustable volumetric cups. When a cup is in the top position, product is fed from a feed hopper. As the product flows into a cup, a vacuum is drawn from the center of the wheel, through a very fine filter. The vacuum removes the air from the product, making it more dense and compact.

The wheel rotates to the discharge station, where the vacuum is released. The slug of product is discharged into the container either directly or, when a small-mouthed container is used, through a funnel. This filling method proves accurate

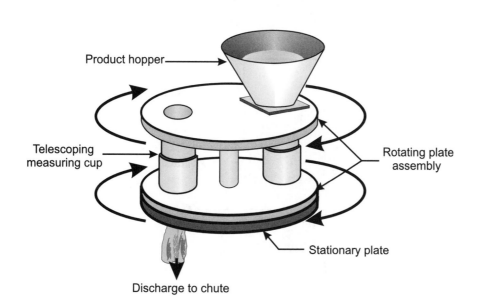

Product hopper

Telescoping measuring cup

Rotating plate assembly

Stationary plate

Discharge to chute

Figure 18.18

Volumetric cup filling is the simplest form of volumetric filling for dry products. Moreover, it is the least expensive and requires minimum maintenance and changeover.

with products that are normally light and fluffy and entrain large quantities of air. Talcum powders and cocoa powders are typical examples.

Auger Fillers

"Auger filling" is a volumetric form of product measure. Generally, auger fillers are used for products that are non-free-flowing in nature. This type of filler consists of a supply hopper and an auger, or "worm," running in an outer sleeve. (See Figure 18.19) The sidewalls of the hopper are funneled to form the sleeve in which the auger runs, and the product is discharged from the end of the tube into the container.

When the machine stops, product is prevented from falling through by a saucer or disk attached to the lower end of the auger. As the auger spins, the centrifugal force throws product off the disk. The amount measured from an auger filler can be controlled either by a time cycle or by counting its revolutions. Accuracy is to a large degree dependent on the mechanism used to start and stop the auger rotation.

Product characteristics determine auger construction. A straight auger is most suitable for products that do not tend to pack in the hopper. Tapered augers are used with loose product. The larger auger flutes are capable of handling more product than the smaller flutes running in the sleeve. This also ensures that the auger at the discharge point has a continuous supply of product. Auger fillers are commonly used in the spice industry.

Although used primarily for dry products, auger fillers can also be used with many semisolids such as ointments, thick sauces and patching pastes.

Net Weighing

"Net weighing" employs weigh cells and tared weigh buckets to weigh the product accurately and then transfer it to the container. In older systems, product

Figure 18.19

An auger filler.

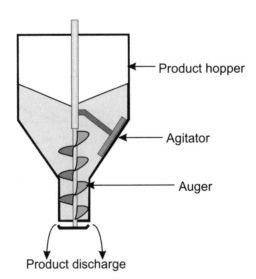

is fed from a hopper, usually by a vibratory feeder, to a scale bucket. An electrical contact stops the feed when the required product weight is in the bucket and trips it to discharge the product into the container. A single-station net-weigh scale cannot work at speeds much higher than 20 or 22 weighings per minute.

An inherent problem of net weighing is the presence of product in midair between the feeder and the scale at the time that the correct weight is reached in the scale bucket. The "bulk-and-dribble" system reduces this problem by splitting the feed into a fast-flowing bulk stream and a slow-flowing dribble line. Both lines feed the scale bucket until the required weight is nearly reached. The bulk feed then stops, and the dribble feed continues until the final weight is obtained. This minimizes the amount of product suspended between the feeder and the scale bucket, but slows the filling process.

That amount of product above the declared weight, or "giveaway," is an important cost factor. Product cost and legal requirements justify the higher price of accurate scale systems rather than volumetric measure. These considerations have spurred many improvements to the basic net-weighing system.

Bulk-and-dribble filling methods have been replaced by computerized "staged-weighing systems." In these systems, final product weight is based on combining product from several weighing stations to fill the container. Approximate quantities of product are distributed among a number of holding buckets. The amount dropped in each bucket is usually between 20 and 33% of the required fill. The product in each bucket is weighed by a load cell integral to the bucket. Then, a microprocessor selects the three, four or five buckets that will provide the fill nearest to the declared weight.

In the system illustrated in Figure 18.20, product is brought by vibratory feeders from the main supply hoppers to the filler's circular dispensing cone, and then along individual vibratory feed trays to one of a number of staging buckets. (Most machines have between nine and fourteen buckets. Fillers may be based

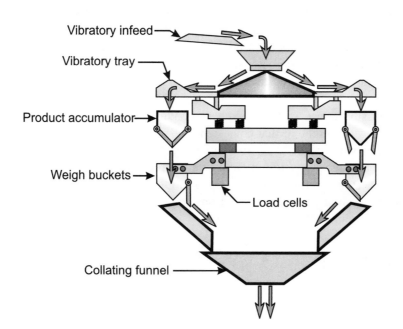

Figure 18.20

Cross-sectional view of a computer-combination or statistical-weighing filling machine. A weigh bucket and a product accumulator bucket are shown in the open position. Some machine variations have another set of holding buckets underneath the weighing buckets. Computer-combination fillers can do 120 weighings per minute.

Figure 18.21

There are 511 possible bucket combinations on a nine-bucket computer-combination weigher. The fifteen combinations closest to the 100 gram (g) target weight are shown here. The machine will combine the product in buckets 2, 4, 7, and 9 to get exactly 100 g.

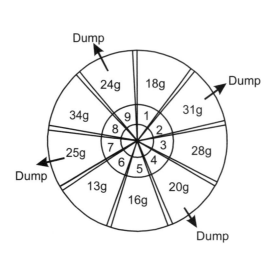

BEST COMBINATIONS		
Weigh Buckets	Total Grams	Computer Decision
2,4,5,7	92	X
2,4,5,8	101	X
2,4,5,9	91	X
2,4,6,7	89	X
2,4,6,8	96	X
2,4,6,9	88	X
2,4,7,8	110	X
2,4,7,9	100	yes
2,4,8,9	109	X
2,5,6,7	85	X
2,5,6,8	94	X
2,5,6,9	84	X
2,5,7,8	106	X
2,5,7,9	96	X
2,5,8,9	105	X

on a circular-flow dispensing pattern, as shown in this text, or may have a linear-flow pattern.) The vibratory feed trays operate on a demand-timed cycle, only when a staging bucket is empty. The staging buckets empty their contents into their respective weigh buckets whenever one is available. Load cells determine the weight in each bucket and enter these data into the filler's microprocessor memory system.

When a package becomes available for filling, the microprocessor searches through the available weights and releases a combination of weigh buckets that is closest to the declared weight but not under. An example of computer-combination weighing is given in Figure 18.21.

For example, an assortment of chocolate-covered confections has pieces weighing from 2 to 8 grams (g). With bulk-and-dribble systems, the average giveaway is about 20 g in a 350 g package (0.7 oz. in a 12 oz. package). Staged-weighing divides the feed stream into ten holding buckets, each typically holding about 70 to 120 g. The computer selects whatever combination of buckets comes closest to but not under the declared fill weight. Giveaway is reduced to 0.5 g (0.02 oz.).

It is possible to use load cells to check container tare weight and automatically adjust the gross weight so that consistent net weights are obtained. This system requires two weigh cells. The first cell weighs the empty container and relays the weight to a receiver and a memory unit, which adjusts the reference voltage so that an accurate net weight is obtained. Sophisticated systems record weights continually; compute averages, deviations and ranges; adjust fillers through feedback; and eliminate off-weight packages.

Number Counts

Electric-eye counting, perforated-disk counters and measuring from chutes or channels are used for products requiring exact numbers of discrete pieces in a package. "Electric-eye counting" is ideal for hardware and tablets, where versatility and quick changeover are required. A photocell counts the items passing in a single file along a belt or conveyor. Usually a gate diverts the stream of items from one channel to another as soon as a required count is completed.

"Rotating perforated disks" provide a simple, inexpensive method for counting tablets or capsules. The mechanism consists of a metal or plastic plate that revolves over a fixed plate. The revolving plate has holes that are appropriate to the tablet size and are grouped according to the desired count per container. As the plate revolves through a feed hopper, the holes fill up with product. An orifice in the stationary bottom plate allows the items to drop out of the holes into a discharge spout. An inspector will check to ensure that all the holes are full.

"Chutes" and "channels" are the most popular counter device for tablets or pills of consistent size. The product travels single file down the channels and is measured linearly to give the correct number. High-number counts are obtained by releasing the required number of single-row counts into a single container. For instance, a fill of 100 tablets might require five counts of twenty tablets. Continuous-motion rotary-head machines can fill 450 such bottles per minute. These machines use rotating turrets with vertical chutes, and the bottles are automatically indexed.

An adaptation of the "perforated-disk-type counter" involves the use of a series of slats moving on an inclined plane. The openings in the slats are designed to the product shape. The slats move through the hopper area, where they pick up the product, then carry the count to a discharge section, where it is discharged into a bottle chute.

Orientation devices are needed for irregularly shaped items such as screws, nuts, bolts or other hardware items. Usually bowl-shaped vessels act as hoppers. The unoriented items tumble or vibrate in such a way that they settle into a track leading out of a hopper. Unoriented items are detected and blown back into the hopper. The track leads to a conventional counting station.

INTRODUCTION TO STATISTICAL PROCESS CONTROL (SPC)

Terminology

assignable cause	Identifiable changes in the relationships of materials, methods, machines or people.
attribute	A characteristic quality that can be directly quantified in numerical units. The mean, range and standard deviation of the numbers can be calculated.
average	Not a commonly used term in statistics. See mean.
bell curve	A curve or distribution having a central peak and tapering off smoothly and symmetrically to either side.

common cause	Those sources of variability in a process that are truly random and inherent in the process itself. The standard distribution bell curve of a machine running at stable steady state can be said to represent common cause variations.
control limits	The limits within which a product or process is expected to remain. When a process goes beyond these limits it is said to be out of control. On control charts, the limits are designated as upper control limit (UCL) and lower control limit (LCL).
mean	The value or statistic that is the result of the sum of the observations in a sample divided by the number of specimens in the sample. The mathematical average. The mean is abbreviated as $\overline{x}$, pronounced x-bar.
median	The value in a set of measurements that divides the set into two groups having equal numbers. If the sample size is odd, the median is the middle value.
mode	The value of the variable in a set of statistical data at which the greatest concentration of observations occur.
population	In statistics, the total of all possible objects of the same kind from which a statistical sample is drawn.
sample	A quantity of a product, drawn from a specific lot or process and being reasonably representative of the product for purposes of testing or evaluation.
random	Variations that have no discernable pattern.
range	The difference between the least and the greatest values in a group of attribute measurements.
sigma	A number representing the standard deviation of a data set from the average. Sigma is abbreviated σ.
stability (of a process)	A process is said to be stable if it shows no recognizable pattern of change.
standard deviation	A measure of the dispersion of a set of values relative to the mean.
standard distribution	A distribution of values that can be represented by a standard bell curve.
specimen	An individual unit in the sample is a specimen.
variables	Quantities that are subject to change or variability.

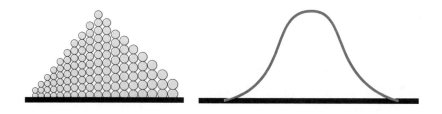

Figure 18.22

A pictorial representation of pea sizes and a standard distribution bell curve that would mathematically describe the distribution around the average size. The mean, mode and medium values of the curve are all at the same point and the slopes on both sides are symmetrical about the mean. The tails of the sloped side continue to infinity.

Standard Deviation

Numbers representing average values are a common and useful part of our lives, but in terms of science and engineering, "average" is often not specific enough for critical calculations and at times can be completely misleading. (Lying down with your head in the refrigerator and your feet in the oven, your average temperature would be a comfortable 22°C.)

Furthermore, average as a single point, provides little information on the range or dispersion of values around that point. Median and mode are other terms used to describe data dispersions, but have limited statistical use.

In the 1860s, English scientist Francis Galton, observed that if you graded peas according to their size, there was an equal distribution to either side of the average size. After observing various other natural phenomenon he proposed the idea of standard distribution and developed mathematical formula to quantify his observations. Transferring the data from a pictorial image to a mathematical representation, resulted in a uniform bell-shaped curve such as that illustrated in Figure 18.22. Moreover it was soon realized that Galton's bell curve represented many other natural random distributions. For example, the speed of 100 cars on an expressway, the shoe size of 60 male university students, or the fill weight of a peanut package could be represented by similar bell curves. The bell curves became known as standard distributions (because they seemed to apply to so many common phenomenons) and the dispersion about the main peak became the standard deviation or sigma.

(In a reverse application of his theories, Galton tabulated the submissions of a contest where local farmers were trying to guess the weight of a large bull. The tabulated results formed a standard bell curve and the average value of all the guesses was the closest to the bull's actual weight).

In more recent times the standard distribution concept was found to be useful for quantifying, controlling and improving production processes. Using packaging as an example, closure torques, fill weights, dimensional variations and other production attributes can be described with standard distribution bell curves and the calculation of standard deviations. The practical application of this technology to production processes has come to be known as statistical process control (SPC).

Calculating the Standard Deviation

The shape of the bell curve can be described numerically by the standard deviation or sigma, a value that quantifies the dispersion of data about the mean.

For example, if we wished to find the standard deviation of the spread of values 2, 4, 6 and 9.

Step 1. Find the arithmetic mean. $\frac{(2+4+6+9)}{4} = 5.25$

Step 2. Find the deviation of each number from the mean

$$2 - 5.25 = -3.25$$

$$4 - 5.25 = -1.25$$

$$6 - 5.25 = 0.75$$

$$9 - 5.25 = 3.75$$

Step 3. Square each of the deviations. (This amplifies the larger values)

$$-3.25^2 = 10.56$$

$$-1.25^2 = 1.25$$

$$0.75^2 = 0.56$$

$$3.75^2 = 14.06$$

Step 4. Sum the calculated squares = 26.43

Step 5. Divide the squared sum by the number of values added together $\frac{26.43}{4} = 6.61$

Step 6. Take the square root of the result.

The standard deviation (σ) of this group of numbers is = 2.57.
In standard mathematical terms the formula is expressed as:

$$\text{standard deviation } (\sigma) = \sqrt{\frac{\sum_{i=1}^{n}(x_i - \overline{x})}{n-1}}$$

Where n = number of values etc.

Calculating standard deviation using this formula is a long and laborious process. Fortunately, all statistical and many scientific hand calculators incorporate the formula so all that needs to be done is enter the numbers and press $\sigma-$.

Standard Deviation Characteristics

The characteristics of a normal distribution as shown in Figure 8.23 are:

- 68.25% of all measurements will fall between minus one σ and plus one σ.

- 95.46% of all measurements will fall between minus two σ and plus two σ.

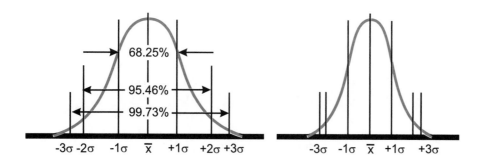

Figure 18.23

Two standard distribution curves, showing wide and narrow standard deviations. About 0.1% beyond 3σ would account for another 0.1% on each side of the curve.

- 99.73% of all measurements will fall between minus three σ and plus three σ.

- Other values such as the percent of values higher than -one σ can be calculated.

Suppose 20 packages are removed from a filling line and the following weights in grams recorded:

95	97	105	103	98
96	104	102	99	100
100	99	98	101	102
99	100	101	101	100

The average and standard deviation is calculated.

Average fill weight $= 100$ g (target weight)

Standard deviation $= 2.53$ g

The client has called for a minimum fill weight of 94 g.

What is shown in Figure 18.24, left is that the filling process is not capable of meeting the client's fill requirements. Furthermore, at the other end, anything over 100 g is a costly give-away.

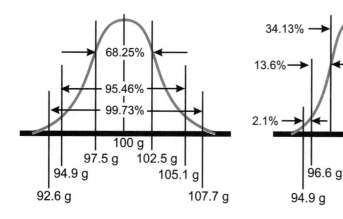

Figure 18.24

The left curve shows the gram weights at each standard deviation. The right curve shows the change when a more accurate weighing system is installed.

By installing a more accurate weigh cell, the lowest and highest fill weights are eliminated. Now the 20 fill weights are:

100	97	100	103	98
97	103	102	99	100
100	99	98	101	102
99	100	101	101	100

Average fill weight $= 100$ g

Standard deviation $= 1.7$ g

The new filler is able to easily meet the 94 gram specification at three sigma, and has reduced the giveaway by 1.6 grams.

SPC and Control Charts

The first step in applying SPC principles is to ensure that the process is capable of producing product within the required specification. Quality cannot be "inspected in", quality must be produced.

The next step is to ensure that the production process is stable and will reliably produce quality parts. As long as the machine is stable and running at a steady state, the measured attributes of samples removed periodically for quality assurance will fall within the boundaries of the established standard deviation. Data outside the established standard deviation will occur only when some changes have occurred that will take production outside of the established steady state. (For example a machine component coming out of adjustment, wear on bearings and other machine parts, changes in the materials being handled and so on.)

Histograms, (a bar chart arranged by frequency of an event occurring) Pareto charts (a bar chart arranged by the relative importance of a number of events that occur) and process analysis diagrams are useful tools to provide a visual basis for an investigation. Histograms focus attention on the most frequent occurrences. Pareto charts focus attention on the incidents that are the most serious. (The Pareto rule of thumb is that 20% of occurrences will cause you 80% of your headaches.) Process analysis documents the entire material and process flow. Some problems that come to light may actually have their origin several process steps ago.

To become aware of changes that might be taking place requires keeping a continuous record of the product characteristics using SPC control charts. Sampling is done at predetermined times based on the nature of the product and the production speed. Most usually, a group of three or more specimens are drawn, the measurements made and their average is plotted on the control charts.

X-bar charts are a data record of values as they are grouped around the average value; in other words the bell curve excepting that the actual curve is not drawn in. An R chart records the range of values for every particular specimen group that was drawn for assessment. X-bar and R charts are usually drawn together so that any correlation between the two charts can be seen. The charts will have X-bar and the designated upper and lower control limits.

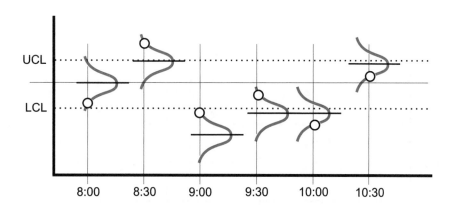

Figure 18.25
A lack of understanding standard deviation principles can lead to costly errors.

A good understanding of sampling and understanding statistical distributions is a key factor in not committing the type of errors illustrated in Figure 18.25.

8:00 — The operator weighs a box from production and finds it is holding 95.1 g of product. The lower limit is 95 g so to be safe the operator increases the machine's fill weight. In actual fact, the machine is properly adjusted; this particular package happened to be at the lower end of the distribution curve.

8:30 — The operator hasn't realized it yet, but a fair percentage of product is over the UCL. At 8:30, the operator weighs another package and discovers it's considerably overweight. The fill weight is drastically reduced.

9:00 — Between 8:30 and 9:00, all fills are below LCL. Not knowing what is going on the operator increases the weight upward a little.

9:30 — Finally at 9:30 the operator thinks fill weight are finally correct so no adjustments are made. In actual fact the distribution curve is partly below the LCL limit and so half the packages are under-filled.

10:00 — Now the operator is cursing the machine. It was perfect at 9:30, and now it's filling below LCL again. Actually the machine hasn't changed at all ... the distribution curve is in exactly the same place as it was at 9:30. The operator increases the fill again.

10:30 — At the end of the day, everyone is wondering what's wrong with the machine.

X-Bar and R Charts

A basic tool in tracking down problems is to find significant correlations between data sets. Figure 18.26 illustrates a normal X-bar chart while Figures 18.27 to 18.32 illustrate examples of patterns that indicate that a problem exists or that there is a forewarning that the process is drifting out of control and that remedial action is advisable.

Figure 18.26

A normal X-bar chart with a random distribution of attribute points about the mean. A single point outside the standard distribution would indicate a lack of stability and should be investigated.

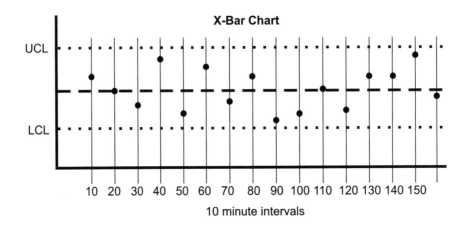

Figure 18.27

A run of seven or more points to one side of the centerline calls for an investigation.

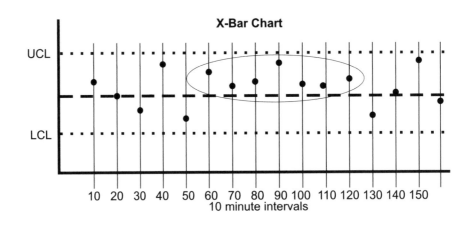

Figure 18.28

A directional trend is a warning that the machine is drifting out of control.

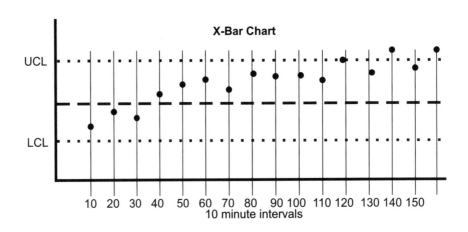

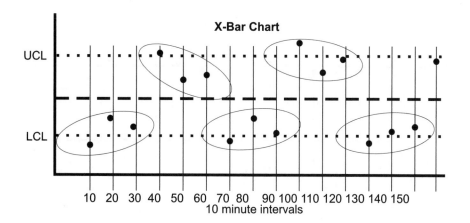

Figure 18.29

Cycles are patterns that repeat; a sure sign of instability. In this example each cycle is preceded by a point beyond the control limits.

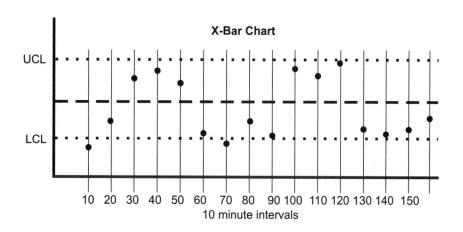

Figure 18.30

Mixtures usually indicate that there are two processes working at different levels.

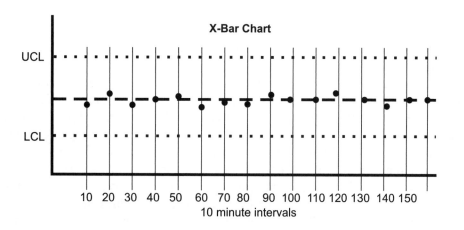

Figure 18.31

Stratification may happen when improperly calculated control limits or chart scales are used. It is also possible that the specimens in any given sample group are constantly averaging out to the median line.

Figure 18.32

Correlations between the range of values in the sample and the deviation are possible. In a positive correlation the X-bar and range points tend to follow each other up and down. In a negative correlation the points move in opposite directions.

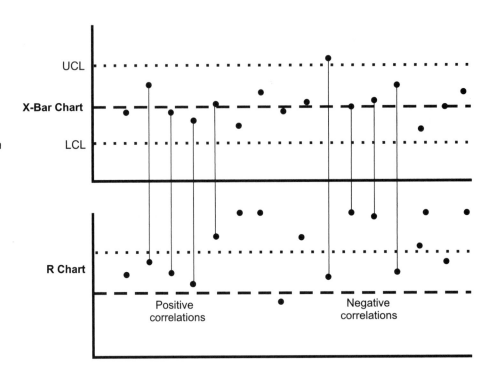

SOURCES OF INFORMATION

Gathering information on machinery and production methods should be an ongoing task. Production engineers must be aware of the state-of-the-art technology and should not get caught in a mad scramble when a decision is made to replace or upgrade a production line. Sources of information on packaging machinery include:

- Trade literature buyer's guides, including online guides
- Trade shows
- Associations
- Recommendations from other packagers
- Recommendations from consultants

There are many national and regional trade shows in North America, as well as international expositions, at which operating machines can be examined and features discussed. The largest comprehensive North American show, Pack Expo International, is held in the fall of even-numbered years in Chicago. Canada's Pac-Ex show is held in Toronto in odd-numbered years. In addition to these comprehensive shows, industry-specific shows such as those focusing on plastics, food and beverage and other sectors feature specific packaging systems.

Most other industrial countries hold packaging trade shows as well. The Düsseldorf International Packaging Exposition in Germany is the world's largest packaging trade fair, occupying upward of a dozen buildings. It is held every three years and is an excellent place to get introduced to international packaging. For information about a product made in another country, contact that country's embassy or consulate and ask to speak to the commercial officer.

REVIEW QUESTIONS

1. A buffer is a conveyor mechanism where an amount of manufactured product can be held. Describe two reasons for specifying a buffer for a production line.

2. For what applications are piston fillers used, and what specific features of a piston filler are particularly useful?

3. Why and where would you use fill-to-volume systems? Give examples.

4. Dry products can be classed into several different categories according to the product's nature. Each type would require a different filler system. Describe four product types and a filler that could fill each product.

5. Why and with what kind of product would you use fill-to-level systems?

6. What four options are available for increasing production? Describe a situation that would favor each option.

7. Why is the packaging machinery business essentially custom in nature?

8. Discuss the possible advantages and disadvantages of a rotary machine compared with a straight-line machine.

9. What does "angle of repose" mean, and what does it suggest to you in terms of filler election?

10. A filler, a capper and a tamper-evident band applicator are all connected inline. Calculate the theoretical throughput of this production line if the machine speeds and station uptimes are as follows:

Station	Machine Speed	Efficiency
Filler	275 cpm	97.5%
TE applicator	260 cpm	99.7%
Capper	290 cpm	91.6%

11. What are the operating principles of an auger filler, a volumetric-cup filler and a vibratory-feed filler?

12. Bulk-and-dribble-type weighing systems have largely been replaced by net-weighing fillers. Describe the operating principle of computer-combining techniques used in net weighers, and tell why these are an advantage over bulk-and-dribble systems.

13. Where and why are bottom-up fillers especially important?

14. What are the limitations of a gravity-type filler?

15. What kind of product would be filled using a vacuum-volumetric filling machine?

16. How does container type affect your choice of filler?

17. Why is rapid changeover often a critical part of JIT, or "just-in-time," manufacturing?

18. New production lines sometimes need a significant debugging time. Why is this so?

19. What is the advantage of upgrading existing equipment? What advantages might be gained by purchasing used equipment?

20. In a typical production line, how would you estimate the speed required from each operating station in the line?

21. What is the purpose of an infeed starwheel and a timing screw?

22. What steps would you take to implement a rapid changeover program for a packaging line?

23. Define design speed, capacity, run speed and line output.

24. Both volumetric-cup fillers and diaphragm fillers fill to predetermined volumes. What might be some advantages of a diaphragm filler compared with the volumetric-cup filler?

25. What are working time, available production time, overall running time and actual productive running time?

26. Why is it desirable to have machines before and after a buffer to be capable of temporary increases in speed?

27. A buffer can be useful for increasing production, but installing too many buffers can slow a production line down. Explain why.

28. Define population, sample and specimen.

29. Describe the attributes of a standard distribution.

30. What does a standard deviation quantify?

31. Approximately what percentage will be one sigma, two sigma and three sigma away from the mean?

32. What information is recorded on x-bar and R charts?

CONTENTS

Carded Display Packaging

Blister and skin packaging compared, pegboard displays.

Blister Packaging

Blisters on card, foldover sliding blister and clamshell designs. Blister materials and caliper, paperboard backing cards, assembly.

Carded Skin Packaging

Process, applications, films, paperboard and porosity.

Chub Packages

Description, applications.

Fiber Cans

Definition, round and oblong shapes, applications, materials, spiral winding and convolute winding, proprietary systems.

Collapsible Tubes

Comparison of metal, extruded plastic, co-extruded plastic and laminated tube types.

Plastic and Paper Bags

Dimensioning, single-wall and multiwall paper bags, gussets, closure styles. Plastic bag materials and variations.

Bar Codes

Responsible authorities, overview of types, UPC elements, scanning, colors, printing, scannability.

Security Labeling

Retail losses, electromagnetic and radio frequency systems, benefits of EAS tagging.

Durable Goods Packaging

Furniture, appliances. Environment, protective steps.

Wood Packaging

Pallets, skids, boxes, crates. Packaging wood groups, nailing.

Pharmaceutical Packaging

Regulations and jurisdictions, basic intent of regulations, drug stability, degradation mechanisms, manufacturing practices.

Creative Designs

Heated packages, double-chambered packages, squeezable toothpaste and valved containers, case-ready modified-atmosphere beef packages, printing inks.

Molded Pulp Containers and Forms

Forming methods and applications.

CHAPTER NINETEEN
APPLIED PACKAGING

The greater part of this text has concerned itself with the materials of packaging and the most common package forms made using those materials. There are, of course, many other mixed material applications and many nonmaterial concerns that occupy a packager's time. This chapter will discuss some of these.

CARDED DISPLAY PACKAGING

Carded display packaging offers maximum product visibility and self-service convenience, while at the same time it provides reasonable product protection against contamination and shipping damage. The backing card discourages theft of smaller articles, provides convenient space for product identification or instructions, and is useful as a means of retail display. Although staples, ties or other physical means can be used to attach the product to a backing card, blister and skin packaging offer additional protection by covering the product and are more adaptable to automated production.

"Blister packaging" uses a preformed plastic shape that holds the product and is heat-sealed to a backing card. "Skin packaging" places the product on a backing card and uses a vacuum to draw a plastic film into close conformity to the object. A heat-sealable coating bonds the film or (blister) to the backing card. (See Figure 19.1) Inks used to decorate the cards must withstand the temperatures involved with either process.

The majority of carded packages are displayed on pegboards. A significant problem with suspended display packs is inadequate strength in the pegboard, or "butterfly," hole area. The backing card should be able to hold several times the product weight and accommodate being readily removed and replaced on a pegboard without special care. Cards narrower than 50 millimetres (mm) (2 in.) are probably better displayed by other means. Where permitted by the manufacturing process, card corners should have a radius to reduce curling or ply separation.

Most retailers follow standard dimensions for spacing the hangers for carded display packages. The length and width of the backing card should be selected to provide maximum usage of available display space and should require minimum hanger relocation.

Package depth is controlled by product geometry and placement. Heavy blister and skin packages, with a center of gravity significantly in front of the

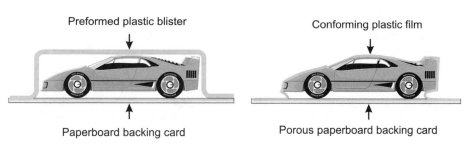

Preformed plastic blister

Conforming plastic film

Paperboard backing card

Porous paperboard backing card

Figure 19.1

A paperboard-backed blister pack (left) and a skin pack (right).

backing card, will hang on an angle facing downward from the viewer's eyes. Such designs tend to twist the pegboard hole against the hanging peg, often tearing the backing card.

BLISTER PACKAGING

Blister packaging is composed of a rigid, preformed thermoformed plastic shape that is typically attached to a paperboard backing card. Usually, the plastic shell is bonded to the backing card by an adhesive.

The most common blister package is the blister-on-card type shown in Figure 19.1. A perforated backing card provides a convenient opening feature. "Foldover" or "sandwich" cards effectively increase the backing card's thickness. (See Figure 19.2, left) "Sliding designs" offer repeated or easy access to a product, and do not require heat-sealable coatings.

The advantages of "double blisters" and "clamshells" (see Figure 19.2, right) are the ability to view the product from all sides, hold an irregularly shaped product and keep a design's center of gravity close to the package midpoint. Clamshell designs can also be used as a hinged storage container. Information is usually provided on a paper or card inserted into the blister along with the product.

Plastic blisters are produced by thermoforming: heating a plastic sheet to a temperature at which the sheet can be shaped to a mold with the desired configuration. The key properties of blister material are cost, moldability, impact resistance, scuff resistance, low-temperature performance and clarity. While most thermoplastics can be thermoformed, most blister packages are made from one of the following:

- Poly(vinyl chloride) (PVC)
- Poly(ethylene terephthalate) copolymer (PETG)
- Polystyrene (PS)

Typical thermoforming temperatures are listed in Table 19.1.

Most blisters and clamshells are thermoformed from PVC. Its performance varies depending on formulation, and PVC characteristics should be verified for the application. PETG has recently become more cost competitive and offers superior stiffness. In some applications, PETG is considered to be the more environmentally friendly choice. Styrenics have excellent clarity, but low impact

Figure 19.2

Examples of foldover, slide and clamshell blister design variations.

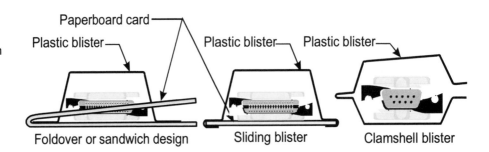

Foldover or sandwich design   Sliding blister   Clamshell blister

Table 19.1

Typical thermoforming temperatures for the most common blister packaging plastics.

Material	Thermoforming Temperature °C
poly(vinyl chloride)	139–176
polystyrene	143–176
polypropylene	148–199
poly(ethylene terephthalate) glycol	129–162
poly(ethylene terephthalate)	148–176

resistance unless an impact grade is used. The blister material caliper varies depending on the material, blister geometry and product nature. Most blister package materials are in the range of 0.12 to 0.18 mm (0.005 to 0.007 in.).

Paperboard is selected according to the weight of the product being packaged, and it must be suitable for the intended graphic presentation. Paperboard for quality blister packaging should be about 500 micrometres (μm) (0.020 in.) thick and can go up to 800 μm (0.030 in.) for heavier or larger objects. Suitable paperboard thickness can be achieved by doubling a lighter sheet rather than by using a single heavy stock. This technique is particularly useful for reinforcing pegboard holes. Lighter boards would be used only for small items, items not displayed on pegboards, or for designs that incorporate structural integrity differently. Most paper backing for carded blister packs is flat and does not require that the paperboard have good folding properties.

The board surface must be receptive to the printing process and must have enough internal bond strength to resist ply separation under use conditions. Clay-coated newsback or its equivalent is a good choice for most hardware applications. Double-white-lined board stock would be used for applications where the back of the sheet will be printed or decorated. Solid bleached board stock is used where an overall high-quality appearance is necessary.

After printing, the card is coated with a heat-sealable top coating that's compatible with the blister material being used. Most PVC blisters are attached with a PVC-based heat-sealing material. Acrylic and ethylene-vinyl acetate-based formulations are also used. Heat, applied either from the blister side or the paperboard side, seals the blister to the board. A properly produced blister package will have a fiber-tearing bond between the blister and paperboard backing card.

In the packaging operation, the product is usually dropped into the open top of the blister. The paperboard card is placed over the blister and heat applied to form the seal.

CARDED SKIN PACKAGING

A "carded skin package" is made by first placing the product on a flat paperboard sheet. A plastic film mounted in a frame above the substrate card is heated to softening and then draped over the product. A vacuum applied through the substrate card draws the film down to conform intimately around the product. The hot film activates an adhesive coating that has been preapplied to the paperboard, bonding the film to the board wherever contact has been made.

An alternative to blister packaging, skin packaging is more economical since it doe not require special tooling or a mold—the product becomes the mold. Plastic film is used rather than thicker sheet stock, a factor that increases in importance with larger parts. The process adapts readily to small or large production runs. Unlike blister packaging, skin packaging immobilizes or secures the product to the backing sheet. Skin packaging can be designed to hold several parts securely and in such a manner that each part can be inspected individually.

Skin-packaging films are usually polyethylene or ionomer (e.g., DuPont's Surlyn). Ionomers have good clarity, are abrasion resistant, are exceptionally tough and have rapid cycle times. This makes ionomer the material of choice for retail display applications, despite its premium price.

Polyethylenes are more economical, but they are not as clear and are easily abraded or scuffed. Polyethylene requires more heat (and a longer cycle time) and has a higher shrinkage factor than other films. High shrinkage can curl board edges. The advantage of polyethylene's material economy is largely lost to the longer cycle times. Industrial applications where clarity and appearance are not critical use polyethylene.

Since a vacuum needs to be drawn through the board to create the conforming skin, paperboards used in skin packaging must be porous. Clay-coated paperboard is rarely used since the clay seals the board surface. If a clay-coated or other nonporous board is selected for appearance reasons, the board must be perforated to ensure that air can be withdrawn from the skin enclosure. Perforating a high-quality board tends to defeat the appearance objective, and a weakness of skin packaging—from a presentation point of view—is the difficulty of creating a high-quality graphic image. In some instances, the product is large enough or the geometry is such that perforations can be concealed behind the product.

Paperboards need to be stiff enough to provide a good display card and not curl or delaminate when the skin is applied. Thicknesses of 450 to 635 μm (0.018 to 0.025 in.) are most common.

The heat-seal material must not seal the board's surface so completely that a vacuum cannot be quickly drawn. Heat-seal materials are usually formulated from ethylene-vinyl acetate.

CHUB PACKAGES

The term "chub packs" originated with the processed meat industry and describes short, chubby sausage-like forms. (See Figure 19.3) Modern chub packs are made on vertical form-fill-seal machines (see Chapter Fourteen, "Flexible Packaging Laminates") from a variety of laminated materials. The flat stock is unrolled, pulled over a forming collar and heat sealed into a tubular shape. In its most common variation, one tube end is sealed with a metal clip, the product is pumped into the tube and the other end is similarly clipped shut.

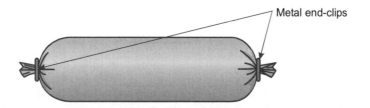

Figure 19.3

A chub pack. A typical package might hold a pound of breakfast sausage.

Chub packaging is versatile. Package sizes can range from miniature tubes up to 150 mm diameter and 1220 mm in length (6 in. diameter and 48 in. long.) Virtually any pumpable paste can be filled into a chub pack. In addition to various ground and sausage meats, chub packs have been used to contain processed cheese, drywall compounds, explosive slurries, lard, frozen juices, icing, pastry dough and sandwich spread.

FIBER CANS

"Fiber cans" are also called "composite cans." In this discussion, the terms refer to cans made by winding overlapping layers of paper, sometimes with plastic film, foil or other laminated materials, to produce an open-ended tube. (See Figure 19.4) Single wrap containers produced from a sheet blank are not usually included when discussing fiber and composite cans. The tube could be round, oblong or other cross-section. The tube ends are plugged or sealed with metal, plastic, composite or paperboard end pieces. Providing a liquid-tight seal is somewhat easier with a round cross-section tube than with an oblong tube, so round cans tend to be used for most liquid products and products requiring a hermetic end seal. Can shape is not as critical for dry products. Fiber cans are relatively low in cost compared to similar metal, plastic and glass containers. The production machinery is simple enough that many users manufacture their own fiber cans in-house.

The main body component of a fiber can is paperboard, usually a kraft or similar paperboard selected for its stiffness and strength. Body plies might be plain kraft, while the innermost plies may be coated or laminated in advance to

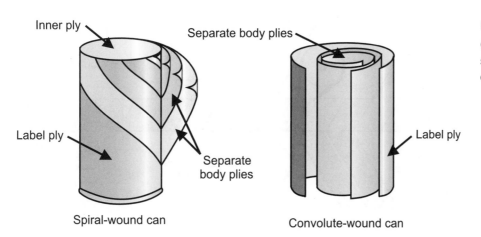

Figure 19.4

Construction of spiral-wound and convolute-wound fiber cans.

Spiral-wound can

Convolute-wound can

Figure 19.5

General layout of a
convolute can-winding line.

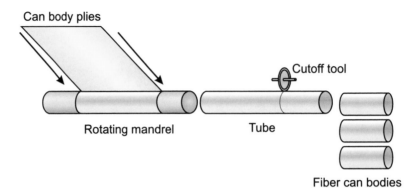

provide appropriate product contact surfaces. Where high barrier is required, the inner material would be an aluminum foil laminate, while for lesser demanding barrier applications a poly(vinylidene chloride) coated polypropylene might be used. Polyethylene and other coatings are used when gas barrier issues are not a concern.

Although the details vary, can bodies are made by one of two basic processes: convolute and spiral wound. In the convolute production method, sheets of paper and body materials are wrapped around the forming mandrel at right angles to form the body tube. (See Figure 19.5) The mandrel can be round, oblong or any other shape. In the spiral-wound production method, the body plies are brought in at an angle to the mandrel and spirally wound in staggered overlapping layers to form the body tube. (See Figure 19.6)

Either wet adhesives or heat-seal systems can be used to join the body plies. Typical wet adhesives are poly(vinyl acetate)/poly(vinyl alcohol) blends or dextrin. Synthetic blends offer somewhat better water resistance than dextrin, whereas dextrin is more economical. Hot melts and polyethylene require heat to create the ply bonds, but have significantly better moisture resistance.

Metal can ends are applied by a double-seaming technique similar to that used for metal cans. Paperboard and plastic ends are used for less demanding applications. Fiber can size is given as the diameter and length in whole inches

Figure 19.6

General layout of a
spiral-wound fiber can line.

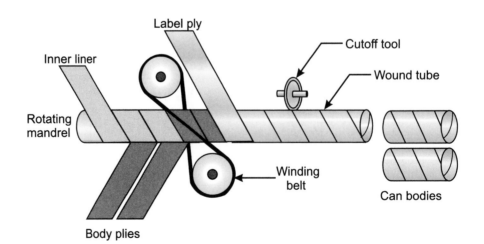

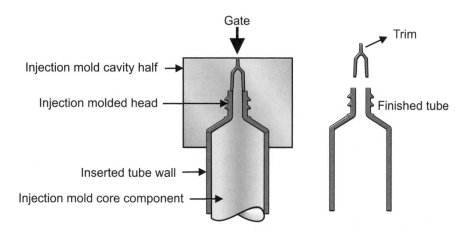

Figure 19.7
The heads of laminated and extruded tube bodies are injection molded on. The molten injected plastic fuses to the preformed tube body.

and sixteenths of an inch, identical to the procedure used for sizing metal cans. (See Chapter Seven, "Metal Cans and Containers")

COLLAPSIBLE TUBES

Collapsible tubes can be made of impact-extruded metal, (see Chapter Seven, "Metal Cans and Containers") extruded and co-extruded plastic (see Chapter Ten, "Shaping Plastics") or laminated stock, (see Chapter Fourteen, "Flexible Packaging Laminates"). In the instance of extruded tubes and laminated tubes, the tube head is injection molded onto the tube body as shown in Figure 19.7. Each of the methods produces a tube with different application properties. These are summarized in Table 19.2.

"Dead fold," the ability of the tube to stay flattened when the product is ejected, is an important consideration for many pharmaceutical applications, where sucking air back into a partially emptied tube might result in product contamination. Superior dead fold characteristics and absolute barrier property make metal the material of choice for many pharmaceutical applications. Laminated tubes made with an aluminum foil layer are almost as good as metal for these properties. Co-extruded tubes incorporating barrier layers provide sufficient barrier for many less demanding applications, but have poor dead fold characteristics. However, in many cosmetic and other general applications, the lack of

Table 19.2

Comparison of collapsible tubes made by different methods.

Property	Metal Tubes	Extruded Plastic	Co-extruded Plastic	Laminated
Barrier	best	lowest	good	very good
Dead fold	best	poor	poor	fair

dead fold is viewed as a positive feature, since it allows for attractive display of the company graphic throughout the product's life.

Formed metal and plastic tube bodies are decorated by offset letterpress (dry offset). A limitation of this method is that process printing is difficult to achieve; hence, most formed tube decoration is restricted to line art. Laminated tube stock is printed flat so that, in principle, any printing method can be used and full color process art is feasible. Laminated tube-stock is commonly printed by gravure.

Metal tubes can allow the body metal to show through the printing as a distinctive decorative feature. Extruded plastic tubes can be made clear to show off the contents or the body can be extruded as a colored tube.

PLASTIC AND PAPER BAGS

Definitions

There is no distinct dividing line between what is a sachet, a pouch, a bag or a sack, and there are many regional variants on how the terms are applied. The predominant usage would be:

Sachet

A small flexible container intended to hold single-serve portions, samples or any other small quantity of product. Similarly, a pouch is a relatively small flexible-packaging format. (Production of sachets and pouches is covered in Chapter 14, "Flexible Packaging Laminates.")

Bag

A flexible container that opens or fills at one end that may subsequently stay open or be sealed. One authority refers to any such container as a bag if the contents weigh less than 22.7 kilograms (kg) (50 lb.). When the contents weigh more, it is called a "sack."

Sack

"Sack" is often used as a synonym for "bag" or as a heavy-duty bag as noted above. In some instances, sack refers to any large bag made from natural or synthetic fibers.

Bags can be made from single-layer plastic, plastic-based multilayer laminate and single-wall or multiwall paper constructions. Regardless of construction material, bag dimensions are given in order of face width and length, with finished length being the dimension of the tube. Note that this dimensioning convention is opposite of that used for folding cartons and corrugated boxes, where length and width identify the box opening. For gusseted bags, the gusset width is the second dimension listed; the length dimension is always last. (See Figure 19.8)

Paper-based bags have a price advantage over plastic bags. However, plastic-based laminates offer weather resistance and specific high-barrier properties. In the instance of carry-out retail bags, plastic bags are more tear resistant and carrying handles are easily incorporated.

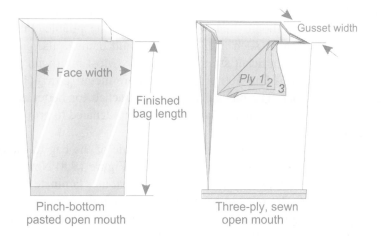

Figure 19.8

Dimensioning conventions are the same for plastic or paper bags. They are given in this order: face width and finished bag length for flat constructions and face width, gusset width and finished bag length for gusseted bags. Bags with a length to width ratio of 2:1 can be efficiently interlocked on a pallet.

Paper-based Bags

The simplest paper bag is a flattened paper tube with one end folded over and pasted (glued). The open end may be left open after filling or pasted shut. Incorporating gussets into the sidewalls can increase the bag's volume. (See Figure 19.8) When filled and sealed, the bags assume a pillow-like geometry and are sometimes referred to as "pillow packs." This geometry, while simple to produce, can form an unstable pallet load.

Heavier paper bags and multiwall paper bags use a taped and stitched end form. (See Figure 19.8, right)

Squaring up the bag ends creates better load stability. (See Figure 19.9) A gusseted bag would use the seal geometry shown in Figure 19.9 (left), while a tube-form bag without gussets would use the geometry show in Figure 19.8 (middle). Valve-type multiwall bags shown in Figure 19.9 (right) are sealed at both ends, except for an extended sleeve (the valve). The extended sleeve projects out from a top corner through which the bag can be filled. When filled, product pressure tends to flatten the valve to form an acceptable closure.

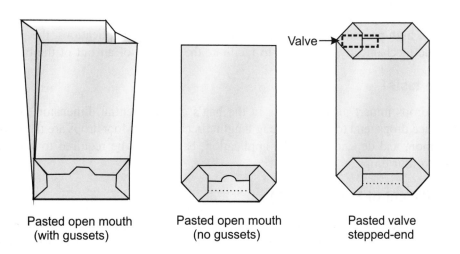

Pasted open mouth (with gussets)   Pasted open mouth (no gussets)   Pasted valve stepped-end

Figure 19.9

Three common bag end-closure designs.

Multiwall paper constructions are used when the expected load requires a single thickness of paperboard that would no longer be pliable. Furthermore, the folding and creasing of such a thick sheet would damage the paper's fiber structure and result in significant strength reduction. Most multiwall paper bags use 3 to 5 paper plies of 65 to 100 grams per square meter (g/m^2) (13 to 20 lb. basis weight) kraft paper. The outer ply may be bleached for better appearance, and any of the plies could be coated, laminated or impregnated to provide specific additional properties.

Multiwall bag plies are numbered from the inside of the bag to the outside; that is, the ply touching the product is "ply 1." (See Figure 19.8) Note that this is opposite to flexible-packaging laminate convention that lists laminate construction from the outside face. The plies in most bags are generally of equal grammage. If a heavier ply is required, it will be put in the inside or ply 1 position.

Major paper bag markets for large multiwall bags are cement and other minerals, grain products, pet foods, industrial chemicals, polymer resins and related materials. "Bailer bags" are large bags intended to hold a group of smaller bags. Smaller bags of essentially similar design are used for consumer products such as sugar, salt and cookies.

Paper Tests

Following are commonly used paper tests:

Tensile Energy Absorption

The Tensile Energy Absorption (TEA) test, combining both tensile strength and elongation factors, is commonly used to specify a paper's toughness. Increasing the TEA values increases the bag's ability to absorb shock during filling and handling.

Porosity

A paper's porosity is reported as the time in seconds for 100 millilitres (ml) of air to flow through a 2.54 mm (1 in.) square of the paper. Porosity requirement will vary with the product being filled and the bag design. For example, the filling of valve-style bags can be slowed by the time required for air to escape from the bag. A high-porosity paper would be preferred. In some applications, the paper will be mechanically perforated to facilitate the passage of air out of the bag.

Drop tests

Butt drops impart major stresses in the bag's circumferential dimension, while flat-face drops tend to stress the bag length direction. Two-foot drops are the most common, and depending on the application, bags would be required to survive two to four drops.

Coefficient of Friction (CoF)

A bag's coefficient of friction should be high enough to produce stable pallet loads. The CoF is usually measured using a slide-angle-type test in which the

Table 19.3
The CoF for selected slide angles.

Slide Angle	Coefficient of Friction
17	0.30
22	0.40
26	0.50
31	0.60
35	0.70
39	0.80

angle of a ramp is increased until the bag placed on it begins to move. Table 19.3 gives the CoF for selected slide angles.

Water-vapor Barrier

Water-vapor barrier properties of paper-based bags are usually achieved by extrusion coating a paper ply with low- or high-density polyethylene (high-density polyethylene offers better grease barrier) or polypropylene. A bag's seals are a critical area when barrier properties are required, so final evaluation should be done on the completed bag, filled with the product and sealed as for shipment. Water-vapor barrier properties are best determined by placing bags into conditioning chambers at the test humidity and following the gain or loss of water by periodic weighing of the bags.

Plastic Bags

The majority of plastic bags are made from various linear low-density polyethylene (LLDPE) grades and blends. For more high-performance applications, metallocene PE might be used entirely or as a blend. Coextruded bag materials are used to provide such properties as custom heat-seal layers or differential coefficients of friction between the inside and outside of the bag. Laminated constructions for high barrier and other special qualities are based on the same material criteria discussed in Chapter Fourteen, "Flexible Packaging Laminates."

Cross-laminated plastic film (e.g., Valeron by Van Leer) provides the highest performance and extreme toughness, but at a substantial cost. Other plastic bag materials include woven polypropylene, used for many grain product bags, and Tyvek (DuPont trade name), a strong ultra-clean material having a porosity similar to paper and sometimes used for critical chemical packaging. Woven polypropylene bags and bags made of Tyvek are typically taped and stitched.

The majority of plastic bags are heat sealed to form a pillow-pack shape. However, pillow-pack shapes can be squared up to form more stable loads similar to what is done with paper-based bags. The typical thickness of a heavy-duty plastic bag ranges from100 to 150 μm (0.004 to 0.006 in).

Plastic bags are particularly suited for applications where outdoor storage and use is a factor. Well over half of all large plastic bags produced are used in the lawn and garden care market. Chemicals and insulation are other large markets.

BAR CODES

A "bar code" is a machine-readable symbol whose value is encoded in a sequence of high-contrast rectangular bars and spaces. The Uniform Code Council (UCC) is the North American body that controls the Universal Product Code (UPC) and other North American machine readable codes. The European Article Numbering (EAN) system is the standard machine-readable bar code system that is used in Europe for retail food packages. In Canada, bar coding information can be obtained from the GS1 Canada. Readability standards are maintained by ANSI.

A number of different bar code systems are available depending on the application. Some can record only numerical data, while others can reproduce the entire ASCII character set. Fixed-length codes have a specific number of characters that can be encoded, and the scanner looks for this number. Variable-length codes have no specific number of characters.

- **UPC-A.** The Universal Product Code (UPC) is the common retailing code in North America. It is a two-part, fixed-length machine-readable code used for individual items, or SKUs, sold to consumers. It can be run 200% of size. UPC-A should meet the retail scanning guidelines of ANSI C grade.

- **SCC-14.** Interleaved 2 of 5 (Shipping Container Code) is a fourteen-digit machine-readable code used primarily to provide information on goods packed in corrugated containers. It would be scanned at manufacturing warehouses and distribution centers. The code is 6.0 in. wide × 1.63 in. high and surrounded by bearer bars. An ANSI D grade allows it to be effectively printed on natural corrugated and other substrates that lack contrast.

- **SSCC-14.** Interleaved 2 of 5 (Serial Shipping Container Code) is a machine-readable code that uses UCC/EAN 128 symbology, and is applied as a secondary bar code along with SCC 14 on shipping containers or as the primary bar code for variable or serial information. The compact format allows for added information such as weight and count to be included in the scanned information.

- **UCC/EAN-128.** The Uniform Code Council/European Article Numbering is a standard international, machine-readable variable-length code that is able to encode all 128 ASCII characters. This complex code provides the maximum amount of scanable information, including the expiration date, lot number, origin, etc. EAN requires an ANSI C grade or better read. This cannot be achieved on natural kraft, and corrugated washboarding further aggravates the problem. Accordingly, EAN 128 is usually printed on label stock, which is then applied to the shipping container.

- **Code-39.** This is a machine-readable bar code where each character is made up of nine elements (four bars and five spaces). Separate characters are defined by inter-character gaps. Code-39 is a variable length code in that no fixed number of characters makes up a code. Standard Code-39 can encode forty-four different characters, while an expanded version can encode the entire 128-character ASCII set.

The Universal Product Code (UPC)

The UPC found on retail packages started in the early 70s as a twelve-digit, machine-readable, fixed-length numeric code that uniquely identifies retail products. A five-digit group (manufacturer's identification number) identifies the manufacturer or organization controlling the product label. A second five-digit group (item code) identifies individual items within the company or organization controlling the product label. These main identification numbers are bracketed by two more digits: a number-system digit and a scan-check digit.

It was soon realized that with global adoption of UPC it was only a matter of time before the available manufacturer's numbers would be used up. To provide for future new companies, steps were taken to meld the 12 digit UPC code with the thirteen-digit EAN code. (EAN-13 is the global counterpart of UPC). The intent was that current users of the twelve-digit UPC should not be affected by this shift. Advance planning allowed ample time for retailers to acquire equipment capable of recognizing both twelve and thirteen-digit codes. In the more distant future, it is expected that the code will move to a fourteen-digit UCC/EAN-14 code.

The company identification number, assigned by the UCC or its representatives, and the product identification number are the central components of a UPC. (See Figure 19.10) Guard bars at either end of the code tell the scanner

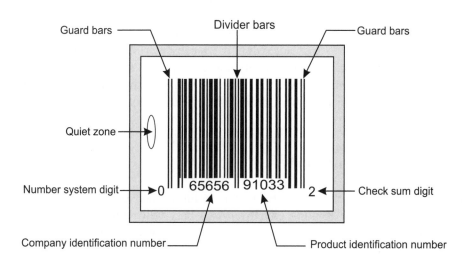

Figure 19.10
A representation of UPC components.

where the code starts and ends; a pair of divider bars separates the company and product halves of the code.

The check character or check digit at the end of the UPC bar code is a value used for performing a mathematical check to ensure the accuracy of the scanned message. The number system digit identifies particular categories of scanned product. All bar code values are also presented in human readable form underneath the machine-readable bars in the event that manual entry or verification is required.

The "quiet zone" is a specified area that must be kept clear of any other printing or features that the scanner might mistake for a bar code element. This might include other text, graphic designs, the package edge, creases and seams. For some bar code applications, the quiet zone will be framed by a printed frame or "bearer bars." These ensure that printing plate pressure is even across the bar code. Bearer bars are particularly recommended when printing corrugated board.

Bar Code Scanners

UPC bar code scanners use a helium neon (red) laser (emitting at 660 nanometres) to determine the contrast between the reflected light from the dark bars and light spaces. The scan determines the ratio of bar width to space width. Using a ratio allows the scan to cross the code at any angle and also allows codes to be enlarged or reduced slightly as required by particular packaging applications.

The scanner does not see color as such, but rather either the presence of red reflected light (space) or its absence (bar). When a black bar is printed on a white surface, the scanner detects red light reflected from the white spaces and no light reflected from the black bars. A black bar printed on a red background would also be scannable. In summary, colors can be used in bar codes providing that a high enough contrast, from the scanner's point of view, can be maintained.

- White, yellow and red are seen by the scanner as a "space."
- Black, blue and dark green are seen by the scanner as a "bar."

Light greens are combinations of yellow (space) and blue (bar). These should be avoided or at least thoroughly tested for scannability.

Foils and metal surfaces reflect incident light away from the scanner and would be seen as a bar. An opaque white patch can be printed under the bar code to eliminate this problem. Alternatively, the code printing can be reversed, and white spaces can be printed over the reflective surface leaving the bare metal to represent the bars. Clear plastic films also require an opaque patch to be printed under the bar code symbol.

Printing and Scannability

High levels of scannability require precise printing, and print gain will affect scannabilty, since the printing gain from two bars will reduce the size of the space between them. This double reduction of space width can seriously affect the bar-to-space width ratio and result in a misread. All printing processes have some gain, but older flexography, in particular, requires care to ensure good scanning. Since gain tends to be greatest in the printing machine direction, it is best to locate UPC codes so that the bars are aligned in the machine direction. Gain in bar length is not as detrimental as bar width gain.

Each printing press has its own particular printing characteristics. For purposes of bar code printing, each printing press needs to be "fingerprinted" to determine its printing attributes on any particular ink and substrate. Fingerprinting is used to determine the amount of gain inherent in the process for the purpose of producing a high-quality bar code film master. Film masters for bar code symbols will be size reduced to make up for subsequent gain during the printing on that press.

SECURITY LABELING

It is estimated that shoplifters account for a $10 billion annual loss in the North American retail trade. Retailers have struggled to reduce these losses by various means. Initially, this meant careful watch with mirrors and keeping theft-prone goods in locked display cases. Early electronic devices were cumbersome.

Technological advances have reduced the cost of "electronic article surveillance" (EAS) tags, and the devices themselves have become almost paper-thin and the size of a commemorative postage stamp. As more retailers are asking their suppliers to include EAS tags in their products (source coding), the problem of tagging merchandise is shifting from the retailer to the package supplier. In short, the reduction of shoplifting losses has become a packager's problem.

Two basic technologies are currently in use: Sensormatic systems employ acoustomagnetic technology, while Checkpoint systems use radio frequency technology. Both technologies revolve around a label or tag attached to the merchandise. If the tag is not deactivated at a checkout counter, it will respond to a signal sent when the article is moved between sensor gates at the exit and trigger an alarm.

In the acoustomagnetic system, the sensor gate emits low radio frequency 58 kilohertz (kHz) pulses. The EAS tag has a built-in resonator that will begin to vibrate at 58 kHz, identical to the transmitted frequency. A receiver inside the sensor gates listens for a response in the 11 milliseconds between emitted pulses. If it receives a signal at least four times, it will set off an alarm.

A magnetized strip next to the resonator ensures that the resonance response is at precisely 58 kHz. A device at the checkout counter can deactivate the label by demagnetizing the strip or altering its magnetic properties so that it resonates at some other frequency.

Radio frequency (RF) technology revolves around a circuit that is etched from aluminum foil and laminated to a paper carrier. The RF circuit is tuned to resonate to an 8.2 megahertz (MHz) transmitted signal. The deactivation device generates a RF field that alters the tag's resonance frequency.

EAS devices are small enough that they can be incorporated into backs of price tags or pressure-sensitive labels. They can be laminated into multilayer constructions, attached to the inside of a folding carton, attached to the product itself or simply dropped into the package with the product. In these applications, the

EAS tag is not visible to the prospective shoplifter. Depending on the situation, all merchandise or a selected percentage can be tagged.

Discouraging shoplifting is only one of the benefits of EAS tagging. With an effective detection system, retailers will be able to move theft-prone products out from behind the counter and into open displays, so customers can make hands-on purchasing decisions.

DURABLE GOODS PACKAGING

The packaging of durable goods such as appliances and furniture is directed more at containment and protective qualities than marketing and graphic display qualities. Corrugated board, often double-wall, is the main structural material, sometimes in conjunction with wood battens, skids or platforms. Internal securement and protective forms can be made from any of the expanded plastics or from cellulose-based materials. Surfaces that can be polished or abraded are wrapped or covered with a nonabrasive isolating material. An example of furniture packaging is shown in Figure 19.11.

Do not assume that the appliance or furniture item will be shipped in its normal use position or that directional arrows will be respected. Couches, desks

Figure 19.11

An example of a furniture package.

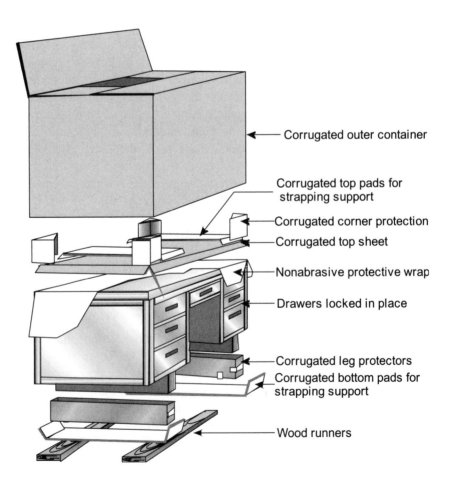

Corrugated outer container

Corrugated top pads for strapping support

Corrugated corner protection

Corrugated top sheet

Nonabrasive protective wrap

Drawers locked in place

Corrugated leg protectors

Corrugated bottom pads for strapping support

Wood runners

and long dressers are frequently upended to make use of carrier vehicle space. Packages can end up on their sides, faces or ends to utilize equipment and space more effectively. Product needs protection from all directions.

Wherever possible, provide handling holes or grips. A heavy item without good gripping points is more likely to be dragged, rolled and otherwise abused. Strategic placement of gripping points will also tend to control package orientation.

Suggested good appliance and furniture packaging practices are as follows:

- Cover all woodwork and polished surfaces with a protective nonabrasive material.

- Protect all edges to at least 75% of their length with inner protective forms.

- Protect all corners and projections with protective forms.

- The outer package should provide at least 20 mm (0.75 in.) clearance between the package and the goods for all surfaces.

- Base, plinths and legs should not be used as bearing surfaces. Suspend pieces off their legs or bases. A separate skid or resting surface attached to the base or legs is another alternative.

- Contain all hardware separately and secure it firmly to an appropriate component. Wrap loose shelves, legs and other finished pieces in protective material and fasten in place. Secure all drawers, doors and other moving parts. Nonmarring tape is convenient.

- Corner drops are common. If the object being packaged does not have a great deal of diagonal rigidity, brace the container to provide additional needed support.

- The final package should be tight, with no opportunity for movement of the principal object, subassembly items or interior packaging.

- Verify your designs with suitable preshipment test procedures.

WOOD PACKAGING

A small amount of wood is used for upscale and novelty packaging. For these applications, wood is usually selected for its aesthetic properties. Most often, these would include attractive close grains, good color, absence of resinous materials and absence of objectionable odors.

The single biggest packaging application for wood is for the manufacture of pallets, skids, boxes and crates. For these applications, structural properties such as stiffness and fastener-holding ability become of paramount importance. Although all woods are chemically similar, the amount and nature of the cellulose fiber component results in a broad range of properties. The amount of cellulosic material in a wood species is related to its density. It follows that a denser

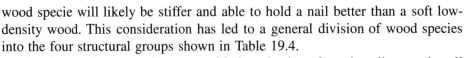

Table 19.4

The four structural wood groups. The densities in kilograms/cubic metre are given for selected woods. For comparison, balsa, the least dense wood, is 40 kg/cubic metre (m^3) while lignum vitae, the densest wood, is 1,400 kg/m^3.

Group 1	Group 2	Group 3	Group 4
Aspen	Douglas Fir (545)	Ash (most) (560)	Beech (750)
Basswood (469)	Hemlock (465)	California Black Oak	Birch (650)
Cedar (335)	Southern Yellow Pine	Soft Elm (629)	Hackberry
Cypress	Tamarack	Soft Maples (530)	Hard Maples (740)
Firs (most) (358)	Western Larch	Sweetgum	Hickory (800)
Pine (most) (415)		Sycamore	Oak (750)
Redwood		Tupelo	Pecan
Spruce (480)			Rock Elm (735)
Poplar (465)			White Ash

Group 1 woods are lower density woods of both coniferous and deciduous species. These woods have moderate nail-holding ability and are relatively free from splitting. They have low to moderate beam and shock strength. Species in this group are easily cut and fastened and are the most economical.

Group 2 woods are all medium-density coniferous species. They are heavily grained woods with the springwood being much harder than the summerwood. While stiffer and better at holding nails than group 1 woods, group 2 woods have a greater tendency to split or to deflect nails from their intended path.

Group 3 woods are medium-density hardwoods. Their structural properties are similar to group 2 woods, with the important exception that they are less likely to split when nailed or impacted. Group 3 woods are useful for box ends and cleats, and when rotary cuts are used, to make wirebound boxes and plywood panels.

Group 4 woods are high-density hardwoods and have the greatest stiffness, nail pullout resistance and shock resistance. They are the heaviest and hardest of the commonly used wood species, which makes them more difficult to work with. Driving nails, for example, takes some effort, and there is some tendency to split.

Figure 19.12

A three-way corner joint eliminates the need for weak end-grain nailing.

wood specie will likely be stiffer and able to hold a nail better than a soft low-density wood. This consideration has led to a general division of wood species into the four structural groups shown in Table 19.4.

Sturdy wood constructions start with the selection of good quality wood; well seasoned, dry, and free of excessive warp, knots, splits and dry rot. Assembly should follow good nailing practice:

- Drive nails through the thinner piece into the thicker wherever possible.

- A nail should have twice the length in the thicker piece than in the thinner or at least 40 mm (1.5 in.).

- Never nail into the end grain. Nail withdrawal resistance from the end grain is very low. Figure 19.12 illustrates the proper method of making

100 units   120 units   667 units   1130 units

Figure 19.13
The rigidity of a structure is most significantly improved by diagonal bracing members.

a three-way corner that avoids end-grain nailing. "Toe" nailing is only marginally better than end-grain nailing.

• Design containers so that that nailed joints are in shear since this offers the greatest resistance to nail withdrawal.

• Clinch nails where the joined pieces are less than 75 mm (3 in.) thick.

• Avoid placing nails closer than the thickness of the board from the end or half the thickness from an edge.

Good crate and box designs make extensive use of diagonal members to increase the structure's rigidity. Figure 19.13 illustrates the effect of perpendicular and diagonal bracing.

ASTM D 6039, Standard for Crates, Open and Covered, is a guide to the design and construction of open and closed wood crates.

PHARMACEUTICAL PACKAGING

Regulations

It is essential that drugs be taken in the prescribed amount and at the prescribed time periods for them to achieve their desired effects. Furthermore, a high degree of confidence is needed that the drug, as taken by the patient, is actually the one that was prescribed and that it has not lost or changed in potency. Any departure from these conditions could result in an ineffective treatment, or since many drugs are potentially harmful or even toxic when improperly administered, could have more serious consequences.

The packaging and sale of drugs is a highly regulated business. The primary responsibility for drug regulations falls under the jurisdiction of the Food and Drug Administration (FDA) in the United States and the Health Protection Branch (HPB) in Canada. The spirit and intent of regulations in both countries is similar although regulation details vary. Section 505 (b) of the Federal Food, Drug and Cosmetic Act (U.S.A.) establishes the basic regulatory framework:

Any person may file with the secretary an application with respect to any drug subject to provisions of section 505 (a). Such persons shall submit to the secretary as part of the application (1) full reports of investigations which have been made to show whether or not such drug is safe for use and whether such drug is effective in use; (2) a full list of the articles used as components of such drug; (3) a full statement of the composition of such drug; (4) a full description of the methods used in, and the facilities and controls used for, the manufacture, processing, and packing of such drug; (5) such samples of such drug and of the articles used as components thereof as the secretary may require; and (6) specimens of the labeling proposed to be used for such drug.

For regulatory purposes, packaging is regarded as part of a drug, so a drug approval application also requires a full and detailed disclosure of the intended packaging. Package information will often call for explicit information on the composition and manufacture of a material. To reduce approval times and costs, and to protect proprietary material constructions and manufacturing methods, the FDA maintains a Drug Master File (DMF). The file contains proprietary information submitted by the material manufacturer and can be accessed only when authorized by a New Drug Application (NDA) submitter.

A manufacturer who wants to change an existing approved package format will usually need to submit a supplementary application to approve the change.

Drug Stability

Most drugs are complex organic compounds. The chemical nature of many of them is such that their exact composition can be easily altered, resulting in significant changes in the drug's potency. Proper packaging should not contribute any influences stemming from the nature of the materials used that would encourage chemical changes and should protect the drug from outside influences that might promote changes. Some preparations are inherently chemically unstable, and almost any outside influences, including heat and light, can cause detrimental changes. In addition to the usual protective packaging, these products will typically require refrigeration.

Many pharmaceuticals, particularly those containing ester or amide functional groups, are prone to hydrolysis. Hydrolysis of these breaks the molecules down into acid and alcohol or acid and amide species. For these products, an ultimate moisture barrier, such as one provided by a blister package made from polychlortrifluoroethylene (Aclar), is necessary. Glass bottles also provide a superior barrier, but the opening and closing of the bottle will repeatedly introduce more moisture into the headspace, continuously degrading the product over time.

Many vitamins, steroids, antibiotics and other preparations are adversely affected by oxidation reactions. Often, only small amounts of oxygen are needed since the oxygen acts as an initiator that sets off a chain ("free radical") reaction. Superior oxygen barriers are required for these products. In some instances, packages will be flushed with inert gases.

Light is an energy source, and when an organic molecule is exposed to light, the molecule's energy level is increased. Shorter light wavelengths have greater energy levels. (See the discussion on color in Chapter Four.) Ultraviolet (UV) light is more energetic than visible light and can rupture chemical bonds to form free radicals. The free radicals encourage a chain reaction, continuing and accelerating degradation. Oxidation reactions are often photochemically initiated where both UV light and oxygen are present.

Of the furnace glass colors, only amber glass offers a significant filter to UV light. Opacity of a plastic material to visible light does not necessarily mean it is opaque to UV light. Specific UV barrier pigments must be incorporated into plastics used for light-sensitive preparations. Similarly, a plastic can be clear and still offer some UV barrier. Poly(ethylene naphthalate) is a clear plastic cited to have a good UV barrier.

Glass, normally considered to be an inert material, has many water-extractable ions that can interfere with a drug's efficacy or the body's normal function, particularly with parenteral (injectable) drugs. Glass used for many pharmaceutical applications and particularly parenterals must be as free as possible from extractables. The pharmaceutical industry classifies glass as types 1, 2, 3 or NP according to the measured amount of extractables (see Chapter Eight, "Glass Packaging"). Most ampoules and vials used for parenteral drugs are made from Type 1 borosilicate glass rather than the usual soda-lime container glass.

Figure 19.14 illustrates glass container designs peculiar to the pharmaceutical industry. These containers are turned from preformed glass tubing rather than being made by the more usual blow-and-blow or press-and-blow methods. (See Figure 8.11).

Ampoules (see Figure 19.14) have a score or an applied ceramic frit around the ampoule neck (constriction). This acts as a stress riser and makes it easy to snap off the ampoule's top. Liquid contents can then be withdrawn with a syringe. Since they have no separate closure system, ampoules provide 100% barrier and sterility confidence.

Vials (see Figure 19.14) are sealed with an elastomeric stopper held in place by an aluminum ferrule. The vial may contain either a liquid or a powder that must be dissolved in water. Water can be introduced into the vial by inserting a syringe through the elastomeric stopper; in a similar fashion, the contents can be withdrawn from the vial. Selection of an appropriate elastomer for the stopper is a critical design issue and depends heavily on the nature of the contents. In some instances, stoppers are lined with Teflon.

The dual-chambered glass bottle shown in Figure 19.14 is used in hospitals to deliver injectable solutions that, due to their solution instability, must be made up immediately prior to injection. The dry powder and liquid diluent are kept in

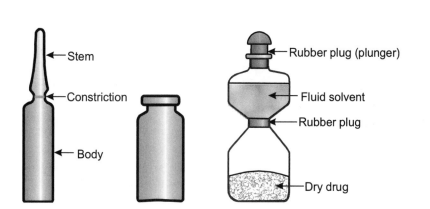

Figure 19.14

An ampoule, a vial and a dual-chambered glass container particular to the pharmaceutical industry.

two chambers separated by an elastomeric plug. When pressure is applied to the top plug/plunger, the elastomeric plug separating the chambers is dislodged, and the two components can be mixed.

Another system for mixing pharmaceuticals just prior to application, inserts a glass ampoule containing one component into a squeezable polyethylene bottle. The ampoule can be broken while inside the plastic bottle and the contents then administered.

In addition to this brief review about the nature of drugs, most of the discussed degradation mechanisms can be catalyzed or initiated by trace quantities of other impurities or very slight changes in pH level. The package is one possible source of these inputs. Thus, it can be readily appreciated why the nature of pharmaceutical packaging materials is the focus of so much scrutiny.

The concern for knowing the packaging material's exact nature and guarding against any possible sources of contamination impacts heavily on the materials that can be used. That is particularly true for recycled plastics. Even new plastics can contain very low molecular weight prepolymer fragments that can leach into a contained product. Suppliers of polymers will sometimes designate particular resins as being "pharmaceutical grade." This designation means that care has been taken to minimize low molecular weight components and no additives (antistatic agents, process aids, etc.) that might affect the drug have been added.

By definition, recycled plastics have an unknown history, so their use is restricted to secondary packaging roles, if used at all. Even in-plant regrind is not allowed for many applications, since there is a possibility of some molecular breakdown during the harsh conditions of regrinding, remelting and extrusion.

Manufacturing Practice

The manufacture of packaged pharmaceutical products is also the subject of scrutiny. Producers must validate their production process, meaning "... establishing documented evidence which provides a high degree of assurance that a specific process will consistently produce a product meeting its predetermined specifications and quality attributes." (FDA definition.)

In essence, it must be proven and documented that the manufacturing process does not in any way change the drug and packaging from what has been approved.

This intense focus has led to many manufacturing procedures unique to the drug packaging industry. For example:

- Gang printing of packaging (the printing of several designs on one press sheet) for different drug products or of the same product in different strengths is prohibited, with the possible exception of items that are absolutely differentiated by size, shape or color.

- Reconciliation requirements, (e.g., the tabulation of quantities of packaging system components such as labels, cartons and other components used in production, removed from production and disposed of) are so strict that the use of cut labels has essentially been eliminated. Almost all pharmaceutical labeling is done from pressure-sensitive roll stock.

Machines can automatically count labels, and the possibility of a loose label slipping into the wrong pile is eliminated.

- On-line, 100% verification of packages or labels is a feature of pharmaceutical production. Typical of these are optical character recognition systems that inspect a simple bar code on each label or package to ensure that it matches with the product being packed.

CREATIVE DESIGNS

It is all too easy to conclude that most packages are represented by variations on rectangular boxes or Boston round bottles. But the most creative part of packaging is problem solving, whether that problem is technical or creative in nature. This section will look at a few of the more unusual packaging designs.

Heated Packages

Figure 19.15 shows a package designed to provide a timed release of insecticide fog for fumigating buildings. The packaging system is composed of a metal fumigant cup inserted into an outer metal can that has holes punched in its bottom. A felted textile pad blocks the holes enough so that an exothermic chemical in the bottom of the outer can does not fall through, and when in use, controls the ingress of water. The system is activated by pouring water into the plastic water cup. Water seeps through the bottom holes of the metal outer can through the felted textile pad. The reaction between the water and the chemical develops enough heat to vaporize and provide a controlled release of the insecticide retained in the fumigant cup.

Self-heating packages have been developed for a variety of heated-food applications. A self-heating instant coffee (or other beverage) container (see Figure 19.15, right) is activated by pushing a button that ruptures the thin, foil separator membrane, allowing water to make contact with the quicklime. The coffee will be heated to about 60°C (140°F) in three minutes. In Japan, sake is heated by a similar method. Figure 19.16 shows a plastic and a metal self-heating beverage containers.

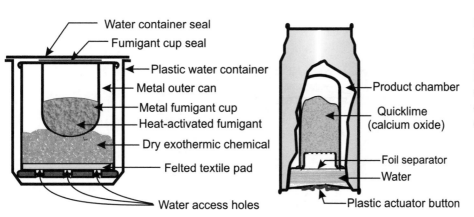

Figure 19.15

Self-heating fumigant and beverage can packages. Both are activated by allowing water to come in contact with an exothermic chemical.

Figure 19.16

A plastic self-heating
container of tea from Italy
(left) and a metal
self-heating can of coffee.

Self-chilling cans are made by replacing the exothermic chemical with an endothermic chemical.

Shoulderless Jars

Ideally, the inside of a skin cream jar would have straight walls with no undercut. This can be done only if the closure threads are placed around the exterior of a straight-walled cylinder, which would result in a closure larger in diameter than the jar. For aesthetic reasons, some designs call for a perfectly smooth match between the closure exterior and the jar body. One way of achieving this is shown in Figure 19.17. The injection-molded product jar has a smooth-walled bowl to hold the product. The closure threads are on the jar. The product jar is snapped into an outer shell that provides the smooth surface that will give an exact uninterrupted match with the closure. The locking collar and the bottom extension of the product jar have a matching series of vertical serrations to stop the inner product jar from turning inside the outer shell when the closure is being rotated.

Figure 19.17

A two-piece cosmetic jar
body designed to provide a
smooth uninterrupted
exterior surface.

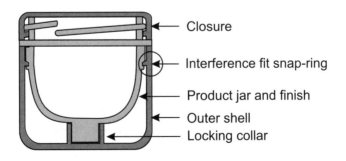

Double-chambered Packages

Packages that have two separate chambers in one overall package have been designed for various applications. Several designs have incorporated threads into the bottoms of jars, in effect making the bottom of the jar a closure. A second jar can then be screwed into the bottom of the first jar. Additional jars can be added to produce a "stack" of jars. The dual-bottle package shown in Figure 19.18 is composed of two blow-molded bottles that fit together along a curved side. The two bottles are held together by adhesive and top and bottom snap-on collars. The upper collar is part of the dispenser pump housing. The pump outlets face in opposite directions.

A similar concept, but assembled from glass, has been used to market a specialty liquor.

In another variation, the pump draws a metered amount of product from the two separate containers, but delivers it through one exit nozzle. This is a useful system for products that must be mixed immediately prior to use.

Two standard collapsible tubes can be inserted into a larger third tube to provide simultaneous ejection of two components. While simpler than pumps, getting the last bit of product out can be a challenge.

Hair coloring kits often have components that must be mixed immediately before use. One common approach is based on having the first component bottle screw into the bottom of the second component bottle. (See Figure 19.19) A plug in the bottom of the upper bottle is forced open as the first bottle is screwed in, allowing the two fluids to mix. Since the product is intended for single use, the upper bottle has a breakaway applicator tip rather than a threaded closure.

The Squeezable Toothpaste and Valved Containers

Dental creams have been offered in a wide selection of package formats, including aerosol cans and more recently in a complex paste-pump. Despite these innovations, the convenience and low cost of a simple squeeze tube makes it

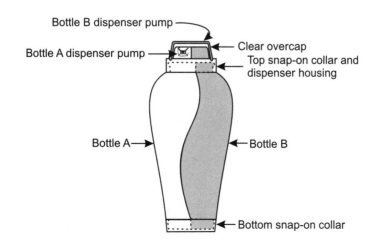

Bottle B dispenser pump

Bottle A dispenser pump

Clear overcap

Top snap-on collar and dispenser housing

Bottle A

Bottle B

Bottom snap-on collar

Figure 19.18

A dual-bottle package with dispensing pumps. (After a Lever Ponds design.)

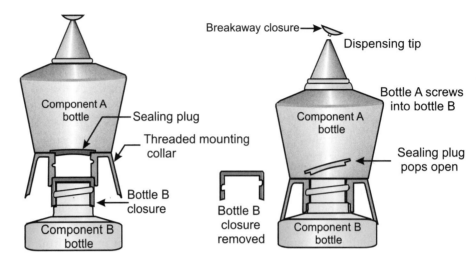

a mainstay in the category. The system shown in Figure 19.20 combines the convenience of a squeeze tube with the aesthetic appeal and stand-up advantage of a bottle. The paste, in a high-barrier laminated bag, is sealed into a soft plastic outer shell. When the shell is squeezed, air pressure forces paste out of the bag. When the pressure on the outer shell is relaxed, a one-way valve opens to the outside to allow the pressure inside the shell to equalize back to atmospheric.

Simple, small one-way valves have been applied to many package types for various purposes. For example, fresh-ground coffee releases significant amounts of carbon dioxide immediately after grinding. Where flexible packaging is done directly from the grinder, a small one-way valve allows internal outgassing pressure to vent the package, while preventing entry of outside air and a shorter shelf life. In another application, a microwavable pouch has a pressure-release valve that allows the venting of excess steam during heating.

Figure 19.20

A flexible product bag inside a valved, squeezable outer shell.

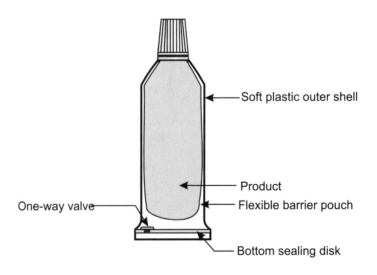

Figure 19.21

Egg trays are most typically molded by the basic process and incorporate recycled fiber.

Molded Pulp Containers and Forms

Molded pulp refers to three-dimensional packaging articles that are manufactured by pouring a slurry of cellulose fiber and water into a mold made from a fine screen material. As in paper-making, the water runs through the screen, usually helped by the application of a vacuum, leaving the matted cellulose fiber caught on the screen. In the basic molding process the completed form travels through a drying oven to remove the remainder of the water.

In the more advanced (but slower) precision molding process, the part is molded in a similar way, but the drying takes place between heated matched mold surfaces. Precision molding provides a more exactly dimensioned, smoother and denser surface.

Familiar applications of molded pulp forms made by the basic method are the common egg tray, corner protectors and berry boxes. (See Figure 19.21). Most commonly these are molded from low cost mechanical pulp or from recycled feedstock.

Precision forming is used to make a variety of disposable dishware products. More recently, significant inroads have been made in applications the protective forms such as shown in Figure 19.22. Higher grade pulps including bleached pulps are used for many of these applications.

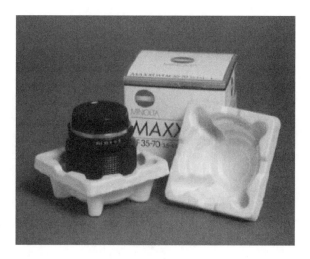

Figure 19.22

A precision molded protective form for a camera lens.

Case-ready Modified-atmosphere Beef Packaging

Modified-atmosphere packaging is an attractive option for increasing the shelf life of many food products, including red meats such as beef. However, the absence of oxygen, while improving shelf life, gives the myoglobin a deoxygenated deep purple color. This does not present a problem with commercial beef, but the North American consumer is not accustomed to seeing purple beef in the supermarket display case. This problem has been overcome by a modified-atmosphere trayed beef package that has a conventional breathing plastic film sealed over the tray, and then over this breathing film is a second high-barrier film that prevents oxygen permeation. In the back of the store, the beef cuts are all purple. However, when the retailer strips away the high-barrier film, the beef reverts to its oxygenated bright red color in a few minutes. The availability of such as system allows for more efficient central processing and packaging.

Printing Inks with a Difference

Not all packaging innovations concern the package's physical design. Thermochromic inks that change color with temperature have been used to indicate when a microwavable product has reached a suitable temperature. Another application features a graphic of a wolf on a beer bottle label. When the label is cold, only the wolf's glowing red eyes can be seen. As the bottle warms (presumably as the contents are consumed) the rest of the wolf's image develops and becomes visible.

Doctors occasionally need to conduct certain procedures (for example, when using a video endoscope) in dimly lit rooms. At the same time, they need to be able to read labels on catheter and other medical supply packages. One line of devices used under these conditions improves readability under dim light by using a phosphorescent ink for the essential information.

REVIEW QUESTIONS

1. Explain the structural difference between a blister package and a skin package.

2. What plastic material is most commonly used for thermoforming the blister of a blister package? Name two other materials that are also used.

3. What two materials are used for the film component of a skin package? Which is the preferred film for consumer retail applications? Why?

4. Explain why clay-coated boards are not normally used for skin packaging. What disadvantage arises from this fact?

5. What are the two processes used to make fiber can bodies?

6. Why are metal collapsible tubes preferred for many pharmaceutical applications?

7. What decorating advantages might be gained by specifying a laminated tube?

8. Compare the barrier qualities of the four collapsible tube constructions.

9. List three design features that would be applied to a bottle for a semisolid product.

10. Discuss aspects of neck design and its relationship to product, filling and distribution.

11. What problem might be encountered if a bottle design has deep circumferential rings molded around the body?

12. What is the "quiet zone" on a bar code?

13. What does a scanner actually measure when it scans a code? Why was this particular method chosen?

14. The divider bars in a UPC(EAN) code separate two major digit groups. What do the two groups represent?

15. What would happen if you printed red bars on a white background?

16. What three colors are recognized as a bar by a UPC scanner?

17. What problems must be overcome when printing a bar code on a metal can? A clear plastic bag?

18. What two significant advantages could be gained with effective EAS tagging?

19. For the purpose of structural applications, woods are classed into four groups. What is the basis of this classification system?

20. What is the design advantage of a three-way wood corner construction?

21. Why do most large wood crates make extensive use of diagonal members?

22. Name the three main avenues of degradation when discussing drugs.

23. What is "gang printing," and why is this method of printing generally disallowed for pharmaceutical packaging applications?

24. What does the term "validation" describe?

25. Why are recycled and regrind plastics not allowed for direct-contact applications in many drug packages?

26. What are the advantages and disadvantages of precision molding compared to the basic method of molding pulp forms?

27. Concerning paper bags: a) What is the convention for dimensioning a paper bag? b) How are multiwall paper bag plies listed?

CHAPTER TWENTY
THE PACKAGE DEVELOPMENT PROCESS

CONTENTS

Managing the Packaging Function

Importance of a strong product/package combination, market failure, complexity, different needs, packaging as a system, positioning of packaging in different sized companies, packaging as a coordinated activity.

Project Scope

Graphic changes, repositioning, changing existing structures, new products in established marketplaces, introduction of new products, understanding where familiarity is needed.

Package Development Process

Package design functions as a central clearing point, generation of ideas, idea sources, packaging-objective statements, new product risks, launch as a team effort. Project planning charts, quantifying packaging objectives, the general design process. Package design briefs, typical responsibilities, facts to be assembled, importance of a design brief. Developing and screening alternatives.

Specifications

Importance of documenting requirements, quality defined, what a specification does, performance factors and tolerance levels, problems with tolerances that are too broad or too tight, specifications as joint documents, "capable" processes, test methods, rejection categories.

Case Study: Redesign of an Oil Battle and Shipping System

Initial goals, project concept, information development, calculating stacking potential for a tray, selecting the optimum resin, changing closures, programming for optimum resin distribution, modifying the design to increase strength. Stacking strength contribution from tight packing, resolving warehousing and hot-filling concerns. Palleting problems, improving stack strength by changing bottle-nesting pattern, increasing pallet stacking strength by changing pallet board patterns, convincing the distributors. A shipping problem, vibration and skewing, possible solutions, resolution.

An Example of Graphic Design Development

Designing a new instant milk package, chord of familiarity and the producer's name, identifying consumer perceptions, isolating target markets, point-of-difference statement. Point-of-difference examples targeting economic, health and weight conscious, elderly and home-baker markets. Cluttering the message.

Package Designer's Checklist

List of the facts the package designer needs to compile for a product launch. Package Design Brief Example packaging design brief summarizing what the package should achieve.

THE PACKAGE DEVELOPMENT PROCESS

MANAGING THE PACKAGING FUNCTION

The Successful Package

Throughout this work, the word "system" has been used on many occasions to link a package to other essential activities that are part of the packaging universe. The relationship between the package, product and purchaser is one of these systems. Most purchasers tend to view package and product as a single entity, so having a superior product is not enough. The message of superiority, convenience or other benefit associated with that product must be clearly communicated to the prospective purchaser. Sadly, many excellent products never reach their market potential for lack of a suitable package. (See Figure 20.1)

On the other hand, an occasional spectacular package is developed for a product that does not live up to the promise made or implied by the package. It is true that such a package will stimulate at least one sale, but an inferior product, once exposed, will not generate a second purchase. Success will be short-lived.

The goal for long-term success is, therefore, to have a strong product showcased in an effective package. Many examples show how excellent package designs have lifted ordinary products into the unusual, and in some instances, created a whole new product category. Many of these designs probably started with the questions, "How can this be made easier?" or "How can I get rid of this problem?" or even, "There must be a better way of doing this." In highly competitive markets, often the package makes the difference between a successful product and market failure.

Sources differ on the exact number, but as many as 30,000 to 40,000 new consumer products are launched every year. Few of these generate respectable sales, and indeed, the failure rate of new launches is very high. Katrina Carl, Mark Oliver Inc., suggests that about 58% of new launches fail because the customer cannot recognize any significant differences between the new product and an existing competitor's product. A further 32% fail because of poor product positioning. It is perhaps significant that product performance accounts for only 12% of launch failures.

Indeed, many so-called "new" products are more often relaunches of products that have failed in the past. The "new" is as often as not, a repositioning, a package redesign or both.

Packaging Development Has Many Stakeholders

It would be convenient to be able to draw a tidy flowchart of the steps needed to develop a package, accompanied by another block diagram detailing who was responsible for each activity. However, this is just not possible. There are about as many ways of developing and managing the packaging function as there are companies.

Figure 20.1

A good product and a good package ensure long-term success.

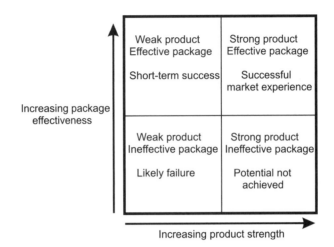

Packaging is an extraordinarily complex endeavor that must be viewed as a part of a larger system, within which every activity has some impact or demand on the package. Thus, purchasing, receiving, warehousing and materials handling, production, marketing, shipping, distribution and sales each has its own particular demands on the package. Quite often, these demands are not mutually compatible:

- Purchasing wants a good price and reliable suppliers.

- Product development wants a package that contains, protects and preserves.

- Production wants trouble-free operation on existing equipment.

- Warehouse staff wants to stack three pallets high.

- Shipping wants packages that will withstand every shipping hazard.

- Marketing wants a unique seven-sided package printed in eleven colors.

- Sales wants a package that will impress retailers into providing more shelf space.

- Legal wants protection against all real and imaginable possibilities.

- The retailer wants the highest possible sales turnover for every square metre of store space.

To complete the picture, add environmental and sustainability concerns, and lastly, the needs of the final consumers.

No part of the product production system can be altered without affecting other parts. The purchase of a faster packaging machine may require tighter packaging specifications. A small change in package size may have a detrimental impact on palleting and transport efficiencies. A change from corrugated distribution boxes to shrink-wrapped trays may require an increase in a plastic bottle's compression strength. The most economical package to purchase may be the most difficult to fill. A unique design having superior shelf impact may require extensive production machinery retooling. The packaging challenge is to meet all of the individual system requirements, including the company's long-term strategy and profit objectives.

How the packaging process is managed is primarily a function of the company's philosophy and its view of packaging's role in the enterprise. Company size and packaging cost relative to total cost are other important factors. In a small company, packaging responsibility may be a part of some other officer's job, typically a purchasing agent or the production supervisor. Time constraints or lack of in-depth knowledge usually forces a heavy reliance on the package supplier.

As company size or expenditures on package material increase, a full-time packaging specialist may be appointed to oversee packaging activities. This person may report to the production manager, marketing or other departments, depending on company structure. The person may have total responsibility for organizing, coordinating, directing and implementing the packaging process, or he or she may work under the direction of a committee or senior manager. Companies with professional packaging staff and facilities are less dependent on suppliers.

Packaging responsibilities at very large companies are typically divided among various departments. Package development, quality control and testing, graphic design and package purchasing are typical divisions. The management and inter-relationships of the individual departments vary. If a single universal statement is to be made, it is that product and package must be developed in a parallel, closely coordinated fashion, with all parties contributing, rather than developed sequentially, as is sometimes the case (i.e., "Here's the product—now figure out a package.").

PROJECT SCOPE

Package development can take from a month to several years, depending on a project's scope and complexity. The simplest situation is one where graphic changes are made to an established line to change the demographic/psychographic appeal, add a seasonal or holiday note or announce a promotional offering. These changes are invariably restricted to copy or graphics. Whatever the change, the product parentage remains obvious, and because the change affects only the graphics, most of the work centers on the marketing function. With few exceptions, new suppliers do not have to be located, production line changes are not needed and material compatibility or shelf-life studies are not necessary. (See Table 20.1, Situation 1)

Repositioning is primarily a graphics change, assuming that the package's physical structure does not need significant alteration. The usual challenge is to reposition the product to appeal to a new demographic/psychographic market while still retaining the identity or equity of the original product. Obviously, this is a more risky undertaking.

A second situation is somewhat more complex and might involve changing the package's physical design. (See Table 20.1, Situation 2) The package size might have changed, the new graphics may include a hologram or the design may have been altered to accept a promotional/bonus compact disk. Now, the

Table 20.1

Package development projects vary in complexity depending on the project's scope. Project complexity increases (more people have to be involved and more problems need to be resolved) as you go down the table.

	Product	*Physical Design*	*Materials*	*Graphic Design*
Situation 1	same	same	same	change
Situation 2	same	similar	same	similar
Situation 3	similar	same	same	similar
Situation 4	same	different	same	different
Situation 5	same	different	different	different
Situation 6	all new	unknown	unknown	unknown

changes affect more than just the marketing and graphics functions. Production needs to check if such a package can run on existing machinery, and if not, what changes are required.

Formulation changes, changes in the package's physical design or changes to different packaging materials (see Table 20.1, Situations 3, 4 and 5) might trigger the need for product/package shelf-life tests, material compatibility studies or material specification changes. The number of stakeholders who must be involved increases, too. The impact on production, warehousing, shipping container size, distribution, customer acceptance, and other parts of the system will need to be determined.

Situation 6 in Table 20.1 illustrates the most complex packaging project—a truly all-new product. No consumer is going to the supermarket with this item on a shopping list. For such a product, there is no history of consumer attitude toward the product, nor is there any existing marketplace experience (competitors) on which to base package design directions. At the beginning of such a project, there is, at best, only a general feel for the demographic/psychographic audience and a limited idea of what the package material should be and what form the package should take.

Packaging form is sometimes dictated by technical necessity, similar existing product lines or the consumer's preconception of what the packaged product should look like. For example:

- There is no technical reason why a breakfast cereal or a detergent could not be offered in a round, spiral-wound paperboard container. (In its early years Quaker Oats did just that) However, today many consumers would not recognize the product because it was not in a familiar container.

- Canadian smokers expect cigarettes to come in rigid paperboard slide boxes; U.S. consumers prefer a soft pack. Using either nation's packaging form in the other country would be going against established consumer perceptions.

Notwithstanding, some package designs have successfully challenged convention. The Pringles potato chip and L'eggs ladies' hosiery packages (that originally came in a package shaped like an egg) are examples of designs that challenged established convention. Such moves must be taken with caution and with some evidence that consumers will respond to the unfamiliar form.

Some product fields are relatively insensitive to material or package format. Spices and condiments, for example, are offered in a wide assortment of containers:

Spiral-wound paperboard composites	Plastic bottles
Aluminum cans with plastic end pieces	Ceramic decorator jars
Impact-extruded aluminum cans	Glass bottles
Round and rectangular steel cans	Flexible pouches

PACKAGE DEVELOPMENT PROCESS

An Overview of the Package Development Process

The figures in this section offer generalized models for the package development process. It is important to understand that the model does not have an orderly information flow from left to right or top to bottom. Rather, information flows continuously among the respective bodies; it passes or is coordinated through the "package design function" several times during its course. (In this text, "package design function" does not imply major technical and graphic activity by a specific design department. Rather, it implies important milestones at which some person or body must give serious thought to some aspect of the final package.)

It is obvious that the package design function, whatever its form, acts as a central clearing point and a vital communication channel through which ideas are assembled and evaluated and a consensus established.

Generating Ideas

Ideas for change can come from many sources inside or outside the company. (See Figure 20.2) Some companies have specific product development departments. Such departments continuously scan the field for new product ideas and work on new product concepts. Some projects might be internally motivated. For example, company growth may be stagnant, and management may have been brainstorming for a major new market offering. The following are some ways in which companies generate new product ideas:

- Many concepts, particularly in the fashion industries, are developed in the marketing department or consumer research department. Perhaps some color trend can be applied to cosmetic offerings. A competitor's success or consumer perceptions of some issue can motivate new product ideas.

- Company R&D laboratories generate new technologies that can be used to create products with market possibilities. This is an important source

Figure 20.2

Ideas for change can come
from many sources.

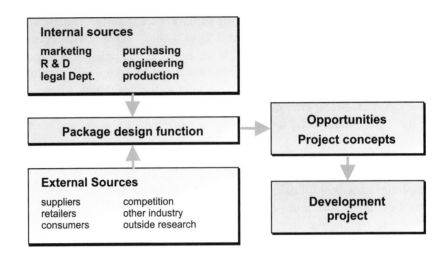

of ideas for technology areas. Alternatively, technologies and product ideas can be licensed or purchased from outside sources.

- Suppliers are often good sources of ideas. Most suppliers are actively involved in getting that little edge on the competition, and their efforts often lead to cost-cutting innovations or new possibilities.

- Observation of techniques used in other industries or countries. For example, can some technique used in the cosmetics industry be used to enhance a food product? Is a business product finding increased home use?

Whatever the origin, management must judge project ideas in view of manufacturing expertise and limitations, corporate goals and financial capabilities. In a dynamic field such as packaging, there are literally thousands of options available at any point in time.

Any package change or development must have clearly stated objectives. Change simply for the sake of change is not a valid reason for altering a package. The following are some examples of specific, quantified objectives for new or revised packaging:

- To successfully launch a new product, with success being identified by specific sales targets.

- To revitalize a dormant brand and raise sales to a specified level.

- To increase sales by providing a new convenience or utility to the consumer.

- To respond to environmental concerns, whether voluntarily or mandated.

- To respond to newly identified customer needs.

- To reposition an existing product in response to changing market conditions.

- To reduce costs by changing to more efficient packaging or processing.

- To maintain market share by responding to a competitor's initiative.

Not having a specific reasoned objective does not focus the design on those elements that will be needed to realize some benefit. (If you don't know where you're going, any road will take you there.) Changes or designs made under such circumstances are as just as likely to be detrimental as beneficial.

The objective of all business, of course, is to create profitable sales. Every proposed option must be tested against that prime objective. New product developments are notoriously risky and expensive undertakings. It is said that of 100 concepts developed to a working stage, only ten are actually offered to the consumer. Of these ten, only one or two will still be available two years later.

The most effective way of decreasing risk is to do your homework first. Marketing analysis, product mapping studies, focus group sessions, exhaustive development trials and market tests are costly, but their cost is minimal compared with the cost of a failed product launch.

A new product/package launch represents a team effort, with each team member wanting something different from the package. All stakeholders, including the final customer, must be consulted and actively involved in screening out the insignificant many from the significant few. The significant few are the real business opportunities.

The Package Design Brief

The ideas generated in the project initiation phase are not enough to form the basis of a full development program. Perhaps the most important first task is to expand and quantify the project objectives. The next task is to generate a comprehensive catalog of all possible information related to the new product launch.

Among others, the various departments and groups listed under "Information Development" in Figure 20.3—and further expanded in Figures 20.4 through 20.7—will contribute information according to their needs and expertise. Compiling the required information for the brief is an excellent example of the kind of interdisciplinary, interdepartmental role a packaging professional may be expected to fill.

The information is compiled in a comprehensive document, sometimes called the "package design brief." The brief summarizes what the proposed package design is supposed to achieve:

- In what marketplace
- With what product
- By what means
- Against what competition
- Targeted to what group
- In conjunction with what other activities

The objective is to document as many facts about the proposed launch as possible, and that each stakeholder be aware of all the project details. The design brief ensures that all needs are met and any necessary compromises are acceptable. A checklist for compiling the project details and a hypothetical design brief blank form is at the end of this chapter.

Figure 20.3

The general package design process.

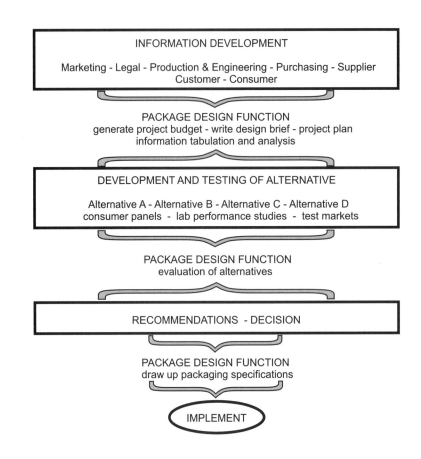

Figure 20.4

Package design: technical responsibilities.

PRODUCT SPECS	PACKAGE SPECS	INFORMATION	PERFORMANCE
protection required form required handling characteristics hazards	material requirements testing requirements storage data field conditions	ingredient lists instructions legal claims government	trials and tests field evaluations hazards

Figure 20.5

Package design: manufacturing and engineering responsibilities.

EQUIPMENT	PACKAGE	STAFF	SCHEDULE
available capacity new machines product performance package performance production methods layout required modifications production costs	production trials size specification storage specification receiving specification pallet patterns rejection criteria shipping tests plant hazards inspection	quality control machine operators handling staff occupational hazards	supplier plant seasonal

CONCEPT	MARKET FACTORS	INFORMATION	MARKET TESTING
Product 　form 　arrangement 　features Package 　type 　unit size or sizes 　artwork and copy 　features	identification buying habits product exposure market practice competition seasonal factors distribution positioning targeted customer	use instructions storage instructions safety recipes pricing environmental sustainability	customer consumer

Figure 20.6

Package design: marketing responsibilities.

LEGAL	PURCHASING	TRAFFIC
brand names trademarks patents net weight ingredients tamper evidence child resistance NDC/DIN number government	company-supplier liaison materials availability package type alternatives graphic art alternatives cost estimates prototype samples supplier identification specification agreements quality control standards government approvals delivery schedules	freight classifications rates gross weights distribution costs customer practice shipping hazards coding handling and warehousing

Figure 20.7

Package design: legal, purchasing and traffic responsibilities.

The design brief can be compared to a musical score in that it ensures that all participants are playing the same tune. The brief is not a static document. As a project evolves, information on the initial brief may change and new information may be added. The important thing is that everyone involved with a project should clearly understand the objectives and the means by which they will be achieved. It is vital that input be sought from everyone involved in the launch. Finding out after several months of intensive packaging design work that the hot new material has not been FDA approved is costly. Input from suppliers should be sought as early as possible in any project. They are aware of new technologies on the horizon, as well as knowing the arts and tricks that will keep costs in line and quality at its peak.

Not all the facts will be readily available at this early stage. Depending on the nature of the launch, some consumer focus-group studies may be conducted in order to better quantify market potential or product parameters. The group responsible for the package design function assembles and coordinates this information for presentation to management.

The Development Timetable

Assuming favorable management response to the project concept, a timetable is developed that lists activities, milestones and critical decision points. Gantt charts,

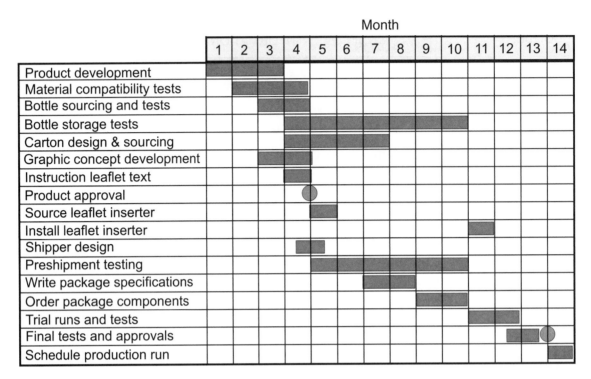

Month

	1	2	3	4	5	6	7	8	9	10	11	12	13	14
Product development	▓	▓	▓											
Material compatibility tests		▓	▓	▓										
Bottle sourcing and tests			▓											
Bottle storage tests				▓	▓	▓	▓	▓	▓	▓				
Carton design & sourcing				▓	▓	▓	▓							
Graphic concept development			▓	▓										
Instruction leaflet text				▓										
Product approval				●										
Source leaflet inserter					▓									
Install leaflet inserter											▓			
Shipper design				▓										
Preshipment testing					▓	▓	▓	▓	▓	▓				
Write package specifications							▓	▓						
Order package components									▓	▓				
Trial runs and tests											▓	▓		
Final tests and approvals													▓ ●	
Schedule production run														▓

Figure 20.8

Example of a Gantt chart. A more complete chart would include time allocations for legal clearances, closure sourcing, accompanying promotional activities and so on.

or critical path charts, are popular project scheduling and tracking methods. The simplified Gantt chart in Figure 20.8 shows only the most general details. Gantt charts clearly identify those activities that can start only after the completion of another, and they allow staff and resource allocation planning over the project time period.

Development and Testing of Alternatives

Based on the information provided in the package design brief, the package design group will generate ideas for how the product might be packaged. Some organizations conduct wide-open brainstorming sessions, at which all ideas, regardless of their apparent practicality, are considered. From these, choices are narrowed to those most likely to succeed. Others use a strictly logical and practical step-by-step scientific approach. Both approaches have their merits.

Eventually, the possibilities are narrowed to a few options, all of which, on the surface, appear good. Laboratory evaluations are used to detect the not-so-obvious flaws or problems in the approaches. Product compatibility tests, shelf-life studies and simulated shipping tests are three of the most important types of laboratory evaluation. This part of the program may also include pilot product runs and consumer test panels or markets. Laboratory evaluation data are often useful when writing the package specifications.

If the data are positive, the project may proceed to the last phases: recommendations, final decisions, drawing up the specifications and implementing the design. As often as not, new information may send a project back to an earlier position. A whole new set of package alternatives may need to be explored, developed and tested.

SPECIFICATIONS

The last step in the development process prior to actual production is to negotiate a supply of packages and packaging components of adequate quality from suitable suppliers. "Quality" is often defined as "conforming to requirements." Requirements fall into three broad categories:

Machinability

When a package is introduced into a production line, it essentially becomes a part of the machine. While the tolerances of a machine's moving parts are fixed within a very small range, the tolerances of cartons or bottles introduced into the production lines can vary by several orders of magnitude. Production problems are encountered when a package tolerance range goes beyond what the machine can do. For example the centrality of a plastic bottle finish must be within the very small range within which the liquid filling tube moves. If the filler is one that employs a vacuum to assist filling, the finish land area must be flat and free from parting lines or other irregularities. At the capping station, any ovality of the finish may give a false torque reading and result in a leaking closure.

The requirements that need to be established are those dimensions and values that will provide the most trouble-free production for the intended production line. (usually referred to as a package's "runnability). As has been noted in Chapter 18, Packaging Machinery, faster machines tend to require tighter specifications.

Performance

These are values that pertain to containment, preservation, protection and provision for efficient transport and use of the product. Performance may include such values as chemical compatibility, barrier qualities, shock (drop) resistance, stacking strength, water resistance, openability, dispensability and so on. Another factor of concern is the readability of bar codes.

Aesthetics

Maintaining an acceptable appearance in the eye of a prospective customer is an important merchandising factor. Cleanliness is an issue with all packaging. The acceptable ranges of a graphic's color and overall appearance must be established along with the acceptable levels of hickeys, misregister, scuffs and other defects inherent to the printing process. Aesthetics also includes the placement accuracy of labels.

In well-run companies, "requirements" are documented in the company's specifications. This is essential for defining and communicating corporate expectations of quality. Without such written definitions, your suppliers and your own staff will adopt the quality standards that are most convenient to them.

When dealing with suppliers, the production of a quality package rests finally on good communication, as formalized in the incoming packaging material specification. This specification:

- Communicates your exact needs to your supplier.
- Provides your supplier with a basis for judging their production.
- Provides your staff with a basis for accepting packages and components.
- Allows for supplier bids on a fair and identical basis.
- Serves as the contractual benchmark in where there is dispute.
- Serves as a benchmark for package improvement.

Great care should be taken to establish the correct tolerance level for every critical package performance factor. Too broad a tolerance can cause machine or aesthetic problems. On the other hand, establishing unreasonably tight tolerances may limit the number of potential suppliers and can significantly increase costs.

A complete product specification system is not a single document, but rather three groups of documents. (See Figure 20.9) The documents describe all the materials and activities that will result in the efficient production of a product possessing the characteristics that have been identified as representing the appropriate quality.

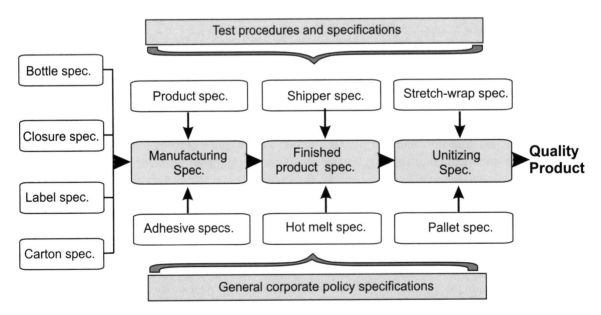

Figure 20.9

A product manufacturing specification is a set of documents that defines a quality product and all of the materials and activities that will result in a quality product.

Corporate policy standards and specifications are those documents that govern the entire specification process. For example, they will identify:

- A consistent corporate specification format.
- Who is responsible for writing specifications.
- How the specifications are written.
- How they are issued, who gets copies and where they are kept.
- How a specification is revised and how a specification is withdrawn.
- Implementation.
- Courses of action when events occur that are outside of the specifications.

Material and manufacturing specifications identify the critical properties of all raw materials, packages and components that are used in the manufacturing process, as well as the production sequence that will lead to the desired quality level. It ensures that every manufacturing step receives quality material from a previous step and forwards a quality item to the next production step.

The final group of standards and specifications will detail the sampling protocol and test methods used to quantify the attributes identified as being critical in the material and manufacturing specifications. For example, an adhesive material specification may call for an adhesive of a particular viscosity, open time and peel strength. These values would be determined using established test methods. This group of documents should also specify the instrument calibration methods that will be followed to ensure measurement accuracy. Such thoroughness is essential for International Organization for Standardization (ISO) certification or any other certification or accreditation.

A good specification is a joint document drawn up in close consultation with the supplier. The supplier must have production facilities that are capable of producing product within the tolerance range set by the purchaser. For example, a purchaser requires that a plastic bottle have a weight tolerance of $\pm 2\%$, but the supplier's machine, because of wear, inadequate controls, untrained staff or other reasons, has an actual production tolerance $\pm 4\%$. There will always be a percentage of production that is out of specification. We would say that such a supplier is not capable.

In such an instance, the purchaser must consider lowering the specification or the supplier must improve the manufacturing process. Or, the purchaser must seek a capable supplier. Evidence that a supplier is actively engaged in a statistical process control program is usually a good sign that the company is working toward establishing better levels of production control.

As well as spelling out the critical values, the method of measuring these values must also be agreed to. In the majority of instances, standard methods such as those spelled out by ASTM International (ASTM) should be referenced.

Causes for rejection of a shipment should be clearly spelled out. In some instances, where appropriate, defects may be classified into three categories:

A. **Critical defects.** Those defects that prevent the package component from fulfilling its purpose. For example, an incorrect dimension.

B. **Major defects.** Those defects that will likely seriously reduce the performance of the packaging component under stressed conditions, although it may perform adequately under most conditions. For example, a corrugated box with compression strength slightly below specified levels.

C. **Minor defects.** These are mostly aesthetic defects that do not substantially reduce a package function.

A specification may, for example, allow up to 1% of category C defects, 0.01% of category B defects and reject any deliveries with more than 0.01% category A defects.

WRITING A SPECIFICATION

A specification for a new package typically begins with the specialists developing the product and those responsible for the packaging function in the company. (See Figure 20.10). This initial draft is often based solely on the tests, observations and experience of the specialists. This draft will be subjected to a broad review by all the parties concerned with the project, and in particular in consultation with those who will be using it.

Work closely with your suppliers ... they know their business best just as the product packager knows their business. If the company is working with dedicated suppliers the review would include the supplier representatives. If a dedicated supplier is not being used, a corrected and updated draft should be forwarded to the best potential supplier(s). Since the launch of a new product is usually a confidential matter, the chosen prospective supplier(s) should have credible trustworthiness and reliability.

In the normal sequence of events, the project might be on its third or fourth draft. By this point the draft will have progressed as far as it can, given current knowledge. In some instances a small number of the proposed package or package

Figure 20.10

A representative package specification process.

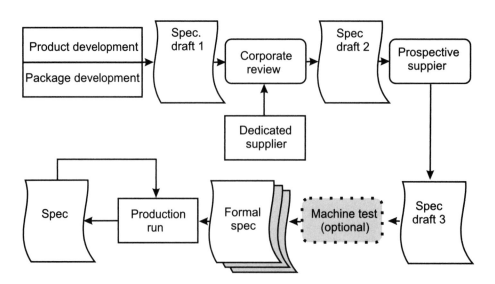

component might be made for purposes of a trial run on the actual production line. For such machine tests the package may not need to be printed.

The formalized company specification with an appropriate identification system would be produced at the end of these activities and the first full production run would be scheduled.

It is normal with new product launches and particularly when the launch also includes new machinery, that other issues will be identified. These may require adjusting a characteristic value, changing a quantification method to more realistically reflect actual conditions or adding a new requirement to the specification.

A specification must provide sufficient detail to minimize the risk of failure while still being flexible enough to permit change and improvement. Specification details can't be open to interpretation; there can only be one version of meaning. Use numbers, drawings, visual samples (for graphic art) and photographs along with clear descriptive language to communicate the message.

Do not include non-essential details. In some few instances where selected background or explanatory notes are desirable, these should be in an appended section that is clearly not part of the specification.

Specifying by a company brand name, for example, *Superply 101,* limits you to buying stock from the company who owns the brand. Stating *Superply 101 or a comparable, equal performance metallized PP/mLDPE laminate*, opens the door to other suppliers who are able to produce such a material. Furthermore, what assurance is there that the manufacturer of Superply 101 won't change **their** specification for the product (for example by changing their supplier of mLDPE or altering their manufacturing procedure in some way) without informing you.

Specify commodity or market grade materials wherever possible. Clay-coated newsback (CCNB) is a generic description of a common folding carton stock made in large quantities and available from many paper mills. Altering the construction of a CCNB board in some unusual way would require a paper mill to reconfigure a $550 million dollar machine ... hardly likely, unless the order is for several hundred thousand tons a year or the willingness to pay a considerable upcharge. Similarly metals are offered in industry standard alloys and tempers, corrugated boards are assembled from standard linerboard and medium grades.

And finally, a specification is a continuously evolving document; there is no such thing as a final specification.

Measuring Quality

The basic steps for writing a specification are:

- Identify those factors and characteristics that are essential to meeting acceptable machinability, performance and aesthetic levels.

- Identify the range within which the individual characteristics can vary and still meet acceptable machinability, performance and aesthetic levels.

- Select a test or evaluation procedure suitable for quantifying or otherwise describing each required characteristic.

Material Specifications and Performance Specifications

Material specifications provide indicators for materials that, with proper treatment, are capable of producing a quality product. A performance test verifies that the desired end result has been successfully met. One advantages of citing performance rather than material specs is that it transfers some responsibility to the supplier and encourages supplier input.

A material specification for a high barrier plastic bottle might specify the density and glass transition temperature of the polypropylene to be used; the thickness profile of the bottle walls; the grade of ethylene-vinyl alcohol barrier layer and its thickness and so on, covering every detail of the material used to make the bottle. However, it is still possible that even using the best materials, a deficient product can be had. The real interest is to have a bottle with a given barrier level toward oxygen and enough strength that it won't rupture if accidentally dropped on the floor.

A performance test would state the required barrier and specify a drop test from one metre to ensure proper material distribution and closure integrity. The performance test has the advantage of allowing the manufacturer the leeway to make whatever changes might be advantageous without compromising the desired performance levels.

Knowing when to use material or construction specifications and when to use performance testing is a skill in itself.

Specification Format

All specifications start with a common header page bearing the specification title, the intended application and pertinent dates as shown in the example header in Figure 20.11.

Sections following the header will vary depending on the material, package or process being described. A specification for a folding carton may contain the following headings and sub-headings:

1. Scope (as described above)

2. Construction
   2.1 Material description
   2.2 Testing
       All paperboard testing will be conducted after conditioning for 24 hours at 23°C and 50% R.H. Reference method ASTM D 685)
       2.2.1 Paperboard caliper shall be _____ ± _____ (Reference method TAPPI T 410)
       2.2.2 Elmendorf tear strength measured in accordance with TAPPI T 414

       Machine direction   Cross direction
       _____ ± _____   _____ ± _____

2.2.3 Taber board stiffness measured in accordance with TAPPI T 451

Machine direction　Cross direction

_____ ± _____　_____ ± _____

2.2.4 Brightness measured in accordance with TAPPI T452 Minimum value *80 bright*

2.3.5 and so on …

3. Carton dimensions
   3.1 Carton dimensions shall be as specified in appended drawing D 5618-3A

4. Graphics and printing
   4.1 Printing shall be done with inks that are free of heavy metal-based pigments
   4.2 Color rendition shall be within the limits of the sign-off samples dated _____
   4.3 Printed cartons shall be able to withstand 500 cycles on the Sutherland Ink Rub tester.

5. Consumer function
   5.1 The tear strip shall pass the following performance tests ….

6. Product protection

7. Packing and delivery
   7.1 Cartons will be shipped within 7 days of folding and gluing.

And other quantified factors as required.

The above example describes specifications that inform a supplier of what is required, and for receiving staff to judge whether the specifications have been met. Another group of specifications and protocols is now necessary for within the packaging plant to ensure that the various packaging components and the product are brought together in a proper manner.

Manufacturing specifications for a bottled shampoo might include such items as

- All incoming materials to be checked and released for production by QA
- Each product batch to be checked and released for production by QA
- Production cleanliness standards
- Fill level tolerances, frequency of check
- Application closure torque tolerances, frequency of check
- Label placement accuracy and appearance, frequency of check
- Recording of time, cause and duration of line stoppages
- Remove 4 bottles every two hours for 24-hour removal-torque test.
- Remove two bottles per hour for archiving.
- Batch and fill date coding at beginning of every shift.
- Shipping box codes, pallet RFID devices
- Palletizing patterns.
- Stretch wrapping.

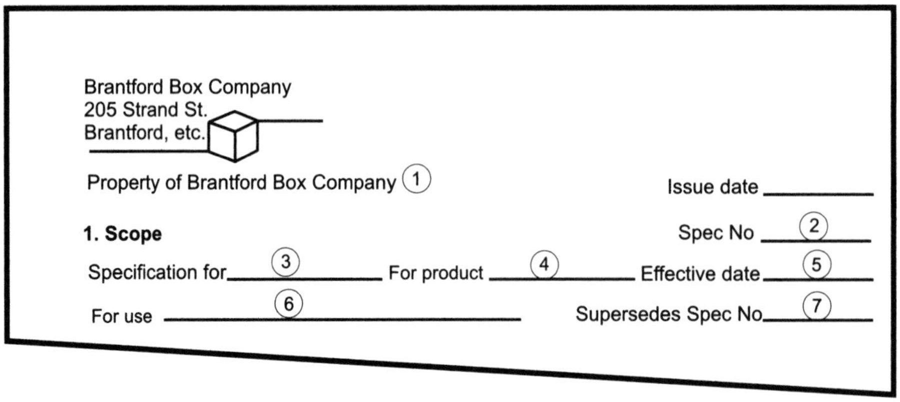

Figure 20.11

Example of a specification header page.

1. Statement that the specification is the sole property of Brantford Box Company. As the sole property of Brantford Box, the specification cannot be altered by the converter, nor be used for any other purpose other than for the specific order that it relates to.

2. Every specification needs a unique identification number. A company with 400 products on the market might have upwards of 2,000 specifications on file. A consistent alpha-numeric coding system is essential to rapid identification, filing and retrieval.

3. A brief title identifying what packaging component the specification is for. (e.g. die-cut label)

4. A descriptor for the product that it is intended for.(e.g. 300 ml bottle: Pepe's Chili Sauce) The product UPC code could be included as a further identifier.

5. The exact date on which the specified labels will be put into production and remaining old labels removed from inventory.

6. Production locations and labeling machinery may vary. These might require slightly different label treatments. For example different language and legal declarations for U.S. and Canadian plants. Some labels may be wet-glue applied while others might be pressure sensitive applied. Locations may have several labeling machines made by different manufacturers. (e.g. For Krones labeler, Minneapolis plant).

7. In the instance that this is a revised specification, the number of the specification that is being replaced. Normally a superseded spec is removed and filed in an archive record.

Specification Identification

Specifications could simply be numbered in the order that they are written. However for any manufacture other than a one-product in two sizes operation, simple sequential numbering is not flexible and detailed enough to allow quick location of a specification or to accommodate cross referencing.

Most specification-keeping today is computerized and allows for searches by package type or component, by product type, issue date, UPC code or any other of a large number of attributes.

CASE STUDY: REDESIGN OF AN OIL BOTTLE AND SHIPPING SYSTEM

The following case study provides examples of how changes at one point in a system dramatically affect packaging at another point. The leading role of a good packaging test capability is also highlighted.

In the case study, the initial project objectives were limited to optimizing an existing plastic bottle design. As data were developed, other opportunities became evident and were taken advantage of. The most significant change, from corrugated board to a shrink-wrapped distribution container, was initially rejected. It was, however, reinstated as bottle performance improved.

Project Concept and Organization

A motor oil marketer had begun manufacturing its own high-density polyethylene (HDPE) bottles in-line with the filling department. As a short-term goal, the company wanted to optimize performance of the existing design. However, an enthusiastic supplier had convinced a few staff members that switching from corrugated shippers to shrink-wrapped trays would reduce distribution costs substantially.

The initial project scope covered only optimization of current bottle production, using the bottle's top-load compression strength as a key indicator. A program was put into place to screen potential bottle-grade HDPE resin suppliers and determine the most efficient HDPE distribution within the bottle. However, as the project evolved, new opportunities became apparent, and other tasks were added to the original project scope.

The project involved an existing product line in current production. All changes, of necessity, had to he calculated to give the absolute minimum production downtime. This required close contact with production and scheduling staff.

The company had installed a number of small blow-molding machines, half of which could supply the filling lines, while the remaining machines were on standby or were undergoing preventive maintenance. Since blow molding bottles entails a large number of subtle variables, including the molding machine and the molds being used, care had to be taken to ensure that bottles submitted for testing were produced from the same molds and on the same machine.

Information Development

Initially, most information came from the manufacturing and engineering departments, with input from purchasing. However, as the project's scope expanded, all major departments became involved in various aspects of the project.

Figure 20.12

For shrink-wrapped trays (left), the primary package alone must bear the top load.

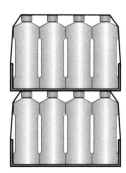 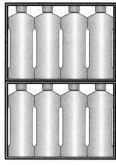

Shrink-wrapped trays   Corrugated boxes

The possibility of shrink-wrapping was answered fairly quickly. Distribution indicated that the pallets could be stacked up to three high for up to 90 days. Unlike corrugated boxes, shrink-wrapped trays of plastic bottles rely entirely on the compression strength of the plastic bottles. (See Figure 20.12) Since plastic is a viscoelastic material, the material will flow and distort with time, the essential result being that the bottle's ability to hold a load will decrease with time.

To be able to hold a load for the stipulated time, the bottle compression strength would need to be at least three times the anticipated load, according to the SPI data for plastic bottles. (See Chapter Seventeen, Figure 17.19) The existing bottle's compression strength was not even close to this value. It was decided that this approach had no chance of success.

Development and Testing of Alternatives: Resin and Design

Selected HDPE suppliers submitted resin samples, and several hundred bottles of each resin were produced for evaluation.

Good communication had to be maintained between the testing group and manufacturing to ensure that inadvertent variables were not introduced. For example, manufacturing, in a mistaken bid to make identification easier, color-coded each supplier resin, adding master batch colors. Since different coloring pigments have a different effect on a bottle's final performance properties, the entire bottle test run had to be repeated, using only the natural resins.

Top-load and environmental stress-crack resistance (ESCR) tests conducted in accordance with standard ASTM International procedures were the main criteria for selecting the resin suppliers. Care was taken to ensure that each mold number was equally represented. The first round of ESCR tests revealed that the closure— rather than the bottle—was the most vulnerable part. The closure supplier and material were changed.

Several bottle production runs, followed by top-load and ESCR tests, were conducted to ensure that consistent, repeatable data were being produced. The preferred suppliers and resins were specified based on these data. Having specified the materials, the project team now turned to programming the blow-molding machines to provide optimum material distribution. The general approach was to

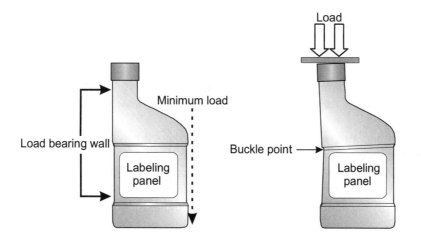

Figure 20.13

Typical compression load
failure of a bottle with an
off-centered neck.

do a top-load test on the bottle, note the typical failure pattern, and determine
areas from which material could be allocated to strengthen the weak point.

Since the bottle had an off-centered neck, top-load forces traveled predominantly down the one side of the bottle. The typical failure point was across the
end panel at the indentation that went around the bottle perimeter and constituted
the bottle's labeling panel. (See Figure 20.13)

The bottle was labeled front and back, but not across the ends. Removing
the labeling recess across the bottle ends (see Figure 20.14) would not change
the labeling, but would produce a straight load-bearing end wall. The mold
manufacturer assured the company that the change could be made at minimum
cost since the change involved removal of metal from existing molds.

A single mold was changed to test the proposition. The redesigned bottle's
top-load ability increased substantially, and an order was immediately placed to
change all of the production molds. With increased top-load ability, the bottle
weight specification could be reduced slightly, providing an economic advantage.
It was also generally felt that the redesigned bottle was more attractive.

This program phase ended with material specifications, a redesigned bottle
and a specification for resin weight and distribution. The substantial increase in
the bottle's top-load ability reopened the shrink-wrapped tray discussion.

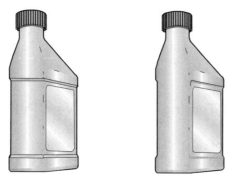

Figure 20.14

The new bottle configuration
(right) eliminated the
labeling recess across the
bottle end.

Development and Testing of Shrink-Wrapped Trays

With the bottle optimized, investigators turned to examining the distribution package. The main question was: Could some of the redesigned bottle's increased top-load strength help reduce the corrugated distribution container's board weight? A second question, although still highly speculative, was: Could a shrink-wrapped tray be used?

Suppliers prepared samples of shrink-wrapped trays holding twelve oil bottles. The investigators were surprised to note that the top-load strength of twelve unitized bottles was significantly higher than twelve times an individual bottle's value. The immediately obvious reason was that the flat bottle sides, when pressed together in the unitized configuration, lent mutual support to one another. The sidewalls were prevented longer from buckling, and therefore, the top load of a shrink-wrapped tray was higher than for twelve individual bottles. It was also determined that a tighter wrap increased the effect.

Subsequent development suggested that the theoretical minimum top-load requirement could be met by inserting a single vertical partition wall down the center of the tray.

Warehousing, however, was concerned. An overlooked fact was that oil was filled hot, and it took considerable time for the mass of oil in a pallet load to come down to room temperature after filling. Meanwhile, the palletized bottles would be detrimentally affected by the heat. Meetings were arranged with production, warehousing and development staff to discuss the problem. Production tests showed that fill temperature could be reduced somewhat, with only minor effects on filling.

The packaging development team prepared a test protocol to determine the stack duration of hot oil bottles. During discussions of what top load should be used to simulate actual warehouse conditions, it was discovered that while company specifications called for a container capable of being stacked three pallets high, only a single regional warehouse used three-high stacks. The main distribution centers palleted two high or used racking. Distribution practice was immediately rewritten to limit stacking to two high. This considerably eased bottle compression performance requirements.

Shrink-wrapped trays were dead-loaded with a mass equal to two pallets high and stored at elevated temperatures. The vertical deformation of the loaded trays was observed over time, with the investigators knowing that failure would occur at about the deflection at failure of a standard dynamic top-load test. The bottles successfully passed the warm stacking tests. With this development, management elected to begin implementing a change from corrugated containers to shrink-wrapped trays. This involved some risk, since no data had yet been developed on how the new shrink-wrapped trays would behave in a palletized load.

Development and Testing of Alternatives: Pallet Loads

The first top-load tests of full pallet loads were alarming; the compression strength they yielded was almost a third lower than expected. The project could fail if

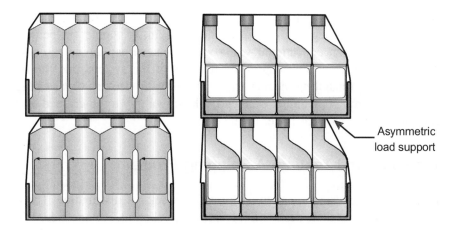

Figure 20.15
Symmetrical bottles (left) compress evenly. Asymmetrical bottles (right) tend to fail toward the less supported side.

Asymmetric load support

this was not corrected. Different pallet patterns were tested, and although some were better than others, none were at the required level.

Data to date were critically reviewed and the compression failure mechanism of the different pallet patterns was studied to answer the following question: Why are some pallet patterns better than others?

Since the bottle necks were off-centered, the trays buckled to the less supported end. (See Figure 20.15) An arrangement that turned every second row of bottles 180 degrees was tried, and it gave a small but important improvement. The major breakthrough came with the observation that most pallet patterns had considerable unintended internal overhang. (See Figure 20.16) This created a condition in which many bottles on the bottom layer actually had the load-bearing wall hanging over empty space. This problem was eliminated by respecifying the positions of the pallet deck boards so that all load-bearing bottle-walls were fully supported.

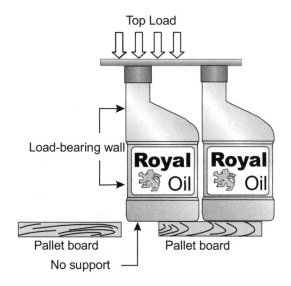

Top Load

Load-bearing wall

Royal Oil   Royal Oil

Pallet board   Pallet board

No support

Figure 20.16
Critical support was lost when the palleting pattern resulted in unintentional internal overhang directly under the load-bearing wall.

Shrink-wrapped trays require different handling methods. In fact, early distributor tests revealed a negative view of the new system. To counter the perceived acceptance problem, an educational video was produced explaining the reason for the change, the many advantages and features of the system, and the most effective methods of handling the new trays. Shrink-wrap geometry was changed to leave a large, strong opening at each end, allowing a tray to be grasped by the end and pulled off a shelf or pallet load.

Development and Testing: A Shipping Problem

A serious problem became apparent within a few weeks of distribution. Trucked pallets would arrive at their destination leaning, or "skewed," to one side. When two pallets leaned into each other, individual trays from the two loads interlocked, making easy movement and stacking almost impossible. (See Chapter Seventeen, Figure 17.9)

From previous experience, the development staff correctly surmised that the problem was likely caused by vibrational inputs during transport. This was confirmed by placing a pallet load onto a programmable vibration table and sweeping through a range of typical transport frequencies. In short order, skewed loads were produced similar to those observed in the field. The vertical stacks of bottles acted as springs, and at particular frequencies, a minor stack resonance occurred in the top layer. This layer would "walk" or "float" to one side, dragging the rest of the stretch-wrapped unitized load with it.

Vibration concerns a spring/mass relationship. To solve a vibration problem, either the spring or the mass has to change. The load mass was relatively fixed within narrow limits, leaving only the spring as a major variable. Several avenues were tried:

- Increasing the amount of stretch-wrapping in order to create a "monobloc" load failed. No practical amount of stretch-wrapping seemed to be able to hold the resonating top layer in place.

- Inserting tier sheets at various points in the load improved the situation somewhat, but did not resolve it. In principle, sufficient isolating tier sheets or other isolating material would have solved the problem. (Incorrectly selected tier sheets could also make it worse.)

As at several other points in the program, detailed observation by development staff solved the problem. After several vibration tests, it was noted that the pallet load always seemed to skew in a particular direction. Further observation revealed that the direction was governed by the tray orientation in the pallet load and the orientation of the off-centered bottles. By reversing the orientations of selected trays, the trays could be made to "walk" into each other, canceling out potential displacement forces. A new pallet pattern was built up around the favored tray orientations, and the problem was solved.

The successful completion of this program resulted in savings in the millions of dollars.

AN EXAMPLE OF GRAPHIC DESIGN DEVELOPMENT

The following example is a hypothetical examination of the process a company might use to determine how best to position a product and create suitable text and graphics for the package.

Establishing Possible Product Positions

Mohawk Dairy Ltd. wants to enter the instant powdered milk market. The product must be identified, and so "Instant Milk" (the chord of familiarity) will appear on the package. The company may also choose to brand the product with the company name, Mohawk.

"Instant Milk" and "Mohawk" can be given equal graphic prominence, or one or the other can be made more prominent. Since Mohawk is not an established brand, it is not likely to be a major purchase motivator. It would make sense to give "Instant Milk" more prominence.

However, the main problem is to differentiate this product from the other eight competitors on the shelf. At this point, Mohawk Dairy needs to decide how to position the product—it needs to decide what the target market will be. In consumer focus group studies, Mohawk discovers the following about consumers and instant powdered milk:

- Many consumers associate instant milk with economy.

- Instant milk is considered healthy on account of its low fat and high calcium and protein content.

- Some consumers find it convenient to cook and bake with instant milk.

- Parents use it for baby formula, but are somewhat concerned about nutritional quality.

- Some consumers feel instant milk is too difficult to dissolve.

- Some consumers associate instant milk with dieting.

Examples of Positioning by Point-of-Difference Statements

With the above information and some added demographic details, target markets can be isolated and point-of-difference statements can be developed to attract the target audience. For example, "Fast Dissolving" could be added to "Instant Milk" to communicate a solution to a commonly voiced problem (providing, of course, that this could be developed).

To attract the economic demographic group, the package must meet their perceptions of economy. Graphics should be simple, using uncomplicated fonts and colors. Photographic illustrations might be counterproductive. Benefit or point-of-difference statements would be selected to emphasize the economic nature of instant milk powder, for example, a flash reading, "Makes 12 Full Quarts!"

To attract the health- and weight-conscious young urban professional demographic group, "Good Dietary Source of Protein" and "Low in Saturated Fats" could be displayed. An accompanying illustration might feature obviously successful young professionals taking a pause from jogging, cycling or tennis to have a cool glass of milk.

Older people are more concerned about calcium, vitamins and minerals. "Excellent Source of Calcium" and "11 Added Vitamins and Minerals" could be featured to attract this group. The accompanying illustration would be the same as above, except the models would be obviously successful older persons.

Home bakers might be further encouraged by illustrations related to baking and "Bonus: Measuring Spoon in Box."

Those who prepare baby formula would be attracted by illustrations of healthy babies. "11 Added Vitamins and Minerals" and "Lots of Calcium for Growing Bones" would be appropriate messages.

The predominant package colors would likely be cool colors, probably shades of blue. White, usually avoided in most packaging, would be quite appropriate for a milk product.

What one would not do is try to appeal to all the mentioned psychographic/demographic groups. The box would be hopelessly cluttered, and no message would be properly delivered through the confusion.

PACKAGE DESIGNER'S CHECKLIST

- Facts about the product's physical form:

mobile fluid	viscous fluid	solid/fluid mixture
gas/fluid mixture	granular material	paste
free-flowing powder	non-free-flowing powder	solid unit
discrete items	multicomponent mix	

- Facts about the product's nature:

corrosive	corrodible	flammable volatile
perishable	fragile aseptic	toxic
subject to odor transfer	odorous	abrasive
easily marked sticky	hygroscopic	under pressure
irregular shape		

- Facts about the competition:

strengths	weaknesses	unit sizes
target markets	sales volumes	pricing structure
package types	market share	marketing strategy
customer loyalty base		

- Facts about the intended consumer:

demographics	psychographics	preferred purchase unit
staple item	impulse item	durable good
seasonal purchase	gift item	

- Facts about the merchandising method:

self-serve	sales clerks	peg-board
shelf display	dispensing machine	door to door
mail order	warehouse outlets	department stores
specialty stores	e-mail purchase	inspect before purchase?

- Facts about how the product is used:

easy-opening features	reclosure features	dispensers
measuring aids	use quantities	table pack
need for instructions	need for attractiveness	need for cautions
storage method	disposal	returnable package
secondary use	environmental features	other special features

- Transport, handling and storage details:

truck	rail	aircraft
cargo ship	carrier rules	weight considerations
unitizing methods	stock-picking	handling methods
storage conditions	storage duration	cold/frozen storage
dimensional considerations		

- Graphic design:

brand name	product name	company name
logos or icons	package "persona"	visibility and impact
color selection	ingredient lists	price panel
UPC code	opening instructions	use instructions
disposal instructions	emergency instructions	hazard warnings
legal text requirements	environmental information	number of facings
language requirements		

- Specifics on what will cause loss of value (damage):

  vibration (determine resonant frequencies)
  mechanical shock (determine fragility factor, drop height)
  abrasion (determine how to eliminate or isolate relative movement)
  deformation (determine safe compression load)
  temperature (determine critical values)
  relative humidity (determine critical values)
  water, oxygen, carbon dioxide (determine required barrier level)
  essential oils, solvents (determine compatibility and required barrier level)
  light (determine whether opaque package needed)
  spoilage (determine nature/chemistry)
  incompatibility (determine material incompatibilities)
  tampering (determine method of providing tamper evidence)
  sterility loss (determine mechanism)
  biological deterioration (determine nature)
  time (determine required shelf life)

- Environmental considerations:

  reduce packaging
  use recycled materials
  do not use heavy-metal pigments
  design for efficient area/cube utilization
  meet all environment rules and mandates

- Legal requirements:

  patents, trademarks and copyrights
  tamper-evidence requirements
  child-resistant packaging requirements
  ingredient listing
  comply with hazardous goods codes
  avoid trade dress infringements
  make only supportable product claims

PACKAGE DESIGN BRIEF

IDENTIFICATION

Project Name

Date Prepared   Issue Number   Replaces

Prepared by

PRODUCT CATEGORY

New Product	Domestic	Institutional
Line Extension	Export	Industrial
Redesign	Retail	Other

PRODUCT PACKAGE

Product will be sold by :   Weight | Volume | Number   No. of sizes

Largest Size   Next Size   Next Size

Product units in primary   Primaries in secondary

Will the package be used to:

Dispense _____

Serve _____

Measure _____

Prepare _____

Possible convenience/unique features _____

Package type preferences or restrictions

Package material preferences or restrictions _____

Other package considerations _____

PACKAGE DESIGN BRIEF   2

SPECIAL REQUIREMENTS

Tamper evidence required?

Child resistance required?

Other

GRAPHICS

Proposed printing method: Flexography   Lithography   Gravure

Additional decorating processes

Other graphic notes

OUTLETS AND DISPLAY (IF RETAIL PRODUCT)

Retail Chains   Mini-markets   Mom & Pop

Vending Machine   Mail Order   Other

Product display

Store location

Shelf location   Number of facings

Single units   Trayed   Case cut

Racks   Pegboard   Bulk bins

Linear stack   Vertical stack   POP display

Retailer size limitations?

Other retailer requirements

LABELING

Required nutritional labeling

Use-before dates

DIN number required

Hazard or cautionary labeling required

Additional language requirements

Other legal requirements

PACKAGE DESIGN BRIEF	3

PRODUCT USE

Main use

How used or prepared

How/where will product be stored?

Package be used for long-term storage?

Does package require resealability?

Product visual/physical/sensory attributes

Considerations arising fromhow the product will be used

Unique product features that can be exploited on the package

TARGETED CUSTOMER Demographic/psychographic description

Gender/age bias

Seasonal bias

Fashion/sport bias

Ethnic skew or appeal

Regional or other bias

Other factors

Other information

PACKAGE DESIGN BRIEF	4

MARKET ENTRY

Details of introductory offers if any

Details of introductory displays if any

Details of advertising tie-ins

Are advertising layouts or storyboards available?

Are models/mock-ups needed for advertising?

DISTRIBUTION

Distribution cycle details

Area/cube utilization requirements

Proposed pallet patterns

Required warehouse stack height   Stack duration

Critical G or expected drop height

Other product fragilities

Special storage or transport conditions

Details of protective packaging if required

Applicable carrier rules

PACKAGE DESIGN BRIEF   5

CURRENT MARKET, CONSUMER, AND TRADE INFORMATION

Current target market

Repositioned target market

What is the main selling proposition of the launched product?

What are the objectives of this launch? (quantify)

Market position relative to competition

Major competitors in order of importance

Name	Market share/Comments

Market, product, or package research available?

If research is planned, nature and date available

Are packages needed for market research?

PRODUCTION REQUIREMENTS

Required annual production   Run on existing line?

Product/package required for trial runs?

Modifications or tooling required

Lead time required

New equipment required

Lead time for new equipment

ENVIRONMENTAL AND WASTE MANAGEMENT FACTORS IF ANY

REVIEW QUESTIONS

1. Package design is a very complex process. What are the factors that contribute to this complexity?

2. What is probably the single most important factor in designing a successful package?

3. What makes the launch of a totally new product particularly difficult?

4. Why is it difficult to draw an orderly flow chart showing the exact steps needed to design a package?

5. A package design should start with a clear statement of what the package is supposed to achieve. What are some examples of package design objectives?

6. What is a package design brief? Why is it important?

7. What facts might you want to know about the competition?

8. Why is supplier contact early in a development program regarded as a good idea?

9. What will likely happen if you do not have adequate written packaging specifications?

10. What are the reasons for maintaining packaging specifications?

11. What are the consequences of having overly tight tolerances in a specification?

12. Why is it important for a specification to be jointly drawn up in consultation with the supplier?

13. What is the difference between a materials specification and a performance specification?

14. Specifications detail the attributes necessary to meet the required quality level in what three areas?

15. What issues are covered in the corporate policy portion of a specifications system?

16. Describe the general classification of defects.

17. What are the three basic steps when writing a specification?

Assignment

Prepare a package design brief for launching a product of your choice. You may make a photocopy of the hypothetical design brief at the end of Chapter 20. Be aware that, depending on your product , special needs that are not mentioned in the design brief example may need to be addressed.

A

abiotic, 35–36
  deterioration, 34
ablation, 102
abrasion, 33, 211, 382, 389, 472, 478
  abrasion damage, 270
abrasive, 379, 382, 476
abrasion resistant, 538
absorption, 35, 89
abusive handling, 447
accelerated aging, 458
acceleration, 472–473, 478
  due to gravity, 472
  observed, 472
acceptable cost, 25
accordion flexible section, 257
acid environments, 45
acidic, 363
  food, 42, 178
acid rain, 22
ACL, See applied ceramic lettering.
Aclar, 390, 554
acoustmagnetic technology, 549
activated, 243
acrylates, 352
acrylic, 355, 387, 537
acrylonitrile, 298
additional surface area, 163
addition polymer, 224, 228
addition reaction, 291
additives, 130, 300–301, 293, 365, 300–301, 556
  heat stabilizer, 353
  wet strength resins, 131
  plasticizer, 362, 365, 293
  processing aides 293
  UV inhibitor, 289
additive synthesis, 84
address labels, 471
adhesion, 345
adhesive, 35, 102, 113, 118, 137, 151, 212, 238, 345–366, 387, 392–395, 410, 540, 578
  application, 356, 361
  bond, 128, 135, 178, 179, 272, 347
  break, 352, 361, 364
  category, 345
  coating, 538
  coverage, 366
  emulsion, 118, 352, 353, 364
  extrusion, 356
  failure, 361, 364, 365
  gravure roll, 256

  hot melt, 118, 353–354, 356, 361, 452, 540
  jelly gum, 351
  mechanical adhesion, 345–346
  metering rolls, 356
  penetration, 345
  pressure sensitive (PSA), 355
  selection, 360
  specific adhesion, 346
  spray, 356
  valved dispensing head, 356
  water based, 136, 351, 353
  wheel applicator, 356
aerobic, 38
  biodegradation, 25
aerosol products, 186, 189
  air fresheners, 190
  cans, 176
  container, 76, 189, 194
  design, 189
  fine spray, 192
  foam dispenser, 192
  fumigating, 192
  insecticide, 189, 191–192
  inverted operation, 192
  multiposition dispensing, 192
  packaging, 188
  markets, 188
aerosol valves, 191–193
aesthetic, 203, 378, 577–578, 581
aflatoxin, 39
aggressive solvents, 177, 187
airborne emissions, 22
air cooled, 203
air/water/soil pollution, 20
alcohol, 45, 222
aliphatic, 45
alkali, 201, 363–364
alloy, 177
alumina, 199
aluminum, 16, 176, 178, 183–185, 258, 320, 392
  can, 176, 191
  deposition, 380
  foil, 112–113, 138, 234–325, 363, 382, 388–389, 392, 398, 540–541, 549
  metallizing, 112, 381
  oxide, 199
amber glass, 199, 202, 555
amplitude modulated, 93
ambient, 225
  temperature, 47
  R.H., 43
American Cereal Company, 9

American Society for Testing and Materials International, (ASTM) 26, 220
American Wholesale Grocers' Association, 452
amplification/ amplified, 479, 481
amplitude, 477–478
amorphous, 230–231, 234, 248
ampoule, 200, 212–213
anaerobic, 38, 41
  bacteria, 45
analog workflow, 94
angstrom, 381
anilox roll, 102
animal glue, 352
anisotropic, 133
annealing, 178, 185, 201, 206–207, 235, 250
ANSI, 546
ASCII, 546–547
anticipated drop height, 474
anticipated maximum load, 488
antioxidants, 45, 353
anti-static, 365, 392
anvil, 184
appearance, 243
application rate (load) 232
applied ceramic lettering, 116, 212
approval, 154, 203
  approved design, 154
AQ4, See DuPont Digital Waterproof
aqueous surface varnish, 106
arable cropland, 20
area utilization, 439, 449–450
aroma, 35, 389
aromatic, 45
arrangement, 439, 450
art department, 256
art reproductions, 92
artwork, 90–91
aseptic, 40, 41
  drink packaging, 40
  beverage packaging, 149
assembly jigs, 440
Association of Independent Corrugated Converters, 25
assurance level, 462
ASTM, 318, 349, 389–390, 409, 412, 452–454, 456–458, 460–463, 578, 582–583
asymmetrical 485
atactic, 289
atmospheric release, 22
atomic bonds, 222, 230
attribute, 578
attrition factors (distribution), 485

auditing, 119
Aunt Jemima, 9
automated conveying, 472
automatic handling, 472
average, 521, 526
average values, 523, 525–526
A_w, 43–44
axis, 211–212, 274, 406, 410, 478, 479, 485

B

baby boom, 10, 11
baby food, 211
baby powder, 177
backing card, 535–537
backing sheet, 538
backload, 482
bacteria, 36, 38–39, 42
bacteriological activity, 44
bacteriostat, 45–46
bag, 542
    bailer, 544
    carry-out, 542
    dimensions, 542
    gusseted 542
    multilayer laminate, 54
    multiwall, 542–544
    paper, 542–543
    plastic, 542–546
    retail, 542
    single layer plastic, 542
bagasse, 13
bagged products, 286, 453
bag-in-box, 40, 486
Bakelite, 9, 10
banding, 440
bar chart, 526
bar code, 546–549, 577
bar contrast, 548
bar scannability, 548
bar scanner, 548
bare metal, 476
barrel, 6, 8
barrier, 24, 37, 44, 226–227, 265, 317,
    324–326, 388, 555
    absolute, 37, 186, 541
    flavour, 246
    high, 40
    packaging, 36–37
    properties, 89, 371, 378–379, 381,
      389–390, 398
    oxygen, 222, 227, 246, 260, 307, 273
    polymer, 222, 246, 251
    water vapor, 44, 222 227, 260, 306
base, 211
    substrate, 393
    web, 393
base box, 178
base surface area, 211
bast fiber, 128
base component, 169
basis weight, 136, 397, 407, 409
bead, 180, 320

preapplied, 354
bearer bars, 548
beer, 34–45, 83, 202, 214, 260, 323
Beers tray, 165–166
bell curve, 521, 523, 526
bellows closure, 161
benzene, 230
beryllium/copper, 271, 258
beverage can, 176
beverage baskets, 149, 166
beverage bottles, 256
beverage cans, 115
beverage packaging, 149
biaxially, 379
biaxially oriented polypropylene (BOPP), 290
bisphenol A, 22
biodegrade, 25
biodegradability, 24
biological, 36
    functions, 34
    biological hazards, 441
    life, 12
biologically active, 22, 35, 46
biological deterioration, 34
biologically inert, 46
blue glass, 199
black and white photograph, 85, 91
black plate, 77
black printer, 90
bladder, 284
blank, 152, 155, 179, 182
blanket roll, 105–106, 115
    cylinder, 135
blank mold, 203–205, 210
bleach, 187
bleached, 544
    fiber, 408
    kraft, 129
    liners, 166
    pulp, 133, 561
bleaching, 130
bleed, 96, 155
blind end, 184
blister, 354, 537
    blister-on-card, 436
    material caliper, 537
    blister pack, 288
    packaging, 535, 538
blistering, 395
boil-in-bag, 371
blow-and-blow, 204, 206, 555
blow-fill seal, 275
blowing agent, 276, 288
blown extrusion, 286
blown film, 248–251, film, 286
blow mold, (glass) 203–204, 206, 208, 210
    bottom plate, 204
    neck match, 204
    neck ring, 204
    parison bottomer, 205
    transfer bead, 204
blow-molded plastic containers, 121
    plastic bottles, 41, 559

body flange, 182
body plies, 539
body taper, 257
body tube, 540
boil-in-bag, 11
boiling point, 225–226
BON, 379
bond, 345, 347
    failure, 345
    quality, 345
    strength 347, 351
bonding agent, 207, 395
book-style, 164
borax, 200, 351
boron oxide, 200
borosilicate glass, 200, 555
Bosch, 40
Boston round, 208
bottle (glass), 199, 203–204, 206, 209–210,
    214
    forming machine, 202, 204
    stability, 211
    nomenclature, 209
bottle design (glass), 266
    design features 208–209
    carbonated beverages, 166, 267
bottle design (plastic), 266–270
    load ratio (plastic), 487
    terminology, 263
bottle-to-bottle contact, 166, 167
bottom end, 175
bottoming out, 474
bottom panel, 165
botulism, 39
box, 405, 483, 485, 488
    compression strength, 405, 420, 427, 483,
      485, 488
    dimensions, 478
    wood, 551
boxcar, 442, 482, 471
box maker's certificate, 405, 416–417
box orientation, 447
box styles (Corrugated), 419–422
    Bliss box, 420
    die-cut designs, 419
    regular slotted boxes (RSB), 419
bracing, 471
branching, 226
    linear chains, 226
brand, 49
    brand mark, name, 8
break (emulsion), 352, 361, 364
breakability, 200
breakage, 207
break-open force, 138
bridge, 410
bridgewall, 202
brilliant metallic surface, 392
brittle cracking, 285
broker, 203
Bruntland Commission, 20
bubble, 247
buckling, 486

bulge, 486
bulk, 382
   bin, 265, 406
   shipping container, 286
   container, 274, 440
   delivery, 11
   packaging, 8
bug bomb, 188
bump, 179
burst strength, 153
burst test, 405, 408
butadiene, 288
butterfly hole, 535–536
by-products, 19

C

CAD, See computer aided design
calcium carbonate, 135, 194, 199, 201
calcium compounds, 199
calender, 135, 397
caliper, 133–134, 136
can, 175–184
   blank, 179, 187
   body, 179, 192, 540
   dimensioning, 186
   ends, 177–178, 180, 182
   lid, 324
   sidewalls, 180
   top, 182
Canada, 19, 194, 456
Canadian General Standards Board (CGSB), 456
Canadian Standards Association (CSA), 334
canned meats, 176
canning, 40–41
   canned food, 118
   canned taste, 41
can maker's quality (CMQ), 177
can making steel, 178
cap, 440, 452–453
capable, 526, 578
carbohydrates, 38, 128–129
carbonated beverages, 45, 182
carbon atom, 219, 221, 223
carbon black, 261
carbon coating, 213–214, 265, 323, 381
carbon dioxide, 21–22, 19, 24, 34, 45–46, 182, 189, 201, 213, 276
   footprint, 21
   emissions, 21
carcinogenic, 22
cardboard box, 406
carded display packaging, 435
carded skin package, 537
cargo ship, 406
carrier web, 112–113
carrier classifications, 417
carrier rules, 48, 407, 416
carrying handles, 152
carton, 153, 156, 406
   blank, 155

body scores, 158
   cartoning, 353
   dimensions, 158
   layout, 155
   production process, 154
carton design, 149–150, 152–153
   beverage carriers, 149, 166
   tray style, 150, 165–168
   tube style, 150, 157–164
   Brightwood tray, 152, 166
carton designer, 154
cartoning machine, 152–153, 155
casein, 351–352
case ready, 562
case study: graphic design development, 591–592
case study: motor oil bottle, 585–590
cascade model, 18
case packer, 406, 410
cast extrusion, 286
cast film, 246, 250–251, film, 286
casting, 249
casting roll – chilled, 248
catalyst, 224, 232, 237, 395
catalyzed, 556
caulk, 180, 246
causes for rejection, 578
   critical defects, 578
   cosmetic defect, 207
   major defects, 580
   minor defects 580
cautionary labeling 471
cautionary markings, 194
cavity, 204, 257, 277
CD and MD, 153
cell, 163–164, 276
cellophane, 9, 221
cellular foam (plastic), 276, 288
cellular plastic, 382
cellulose, 9, 127, 129–130
   fiber, 561
   material, 550
cellulose based plastic 246, 297
cementing, 179
centrality, 577
central processing, 562
center of gravity, 211, 440, 435–436
centipoise, 358
central impression (CI) press, 103, 104, 479
   drum, 103–104
central processing, 13
ceramic, 212
cereal grains, 44
CFC, 22
CFR, 332, 334
CGSB, 456
chain reaction, 554
characterizing plastic materials 301–312
Charlotte flaps, 165
checkout counter, 549
Checkpoint, 549
chemical
   activity, 42

bond
   bleaching, 130
   change, 47
   family, 226
   interference, 353
   properties, 176, 238, 271
   pulps, 129
   reaction, accelerated, 395
   resistance, 101
   treatment, 347
   union, 347
chemically compatible, 190, 276, 317, 325
chemically inert, 347
chemically unstable, 554
chemical preservation, 39, 45
   preservatives, 45
   inertness, 184
   compatibility,
child resistant (CR), 11, 317, 330, 334
child proof, 334
chilling, 36, 39
chilled, 179
chilled mold cavity, 275
chill roll, 246, 378
China, 21
chipboard, 168
chlorine, 221, 130
chlorofluorocarbons (CFC, HCFC), 11, 22, 276, 190
chrome, 177
   coated, 135
   oxides, 177, 199
chub package, 438
chucking station, 330
chuck panel, 180
circuit boards, 479
circular bulls eye, 277
circular cross-section, 486
circumferential register, 115
circumferential rings, 257
clamshell, 536
clamp truck, 448, 482, 484–485
clarity, 200, 221, 231, 246, 249, 260, 371, 380, 391, 536
clay, 135, 346, 365
clay coating, 106, 135, 166
   clay coated, 133, 136
   clay lift, 135, 365, 378
cleanliness, 476
cleaning compounds, 22
clear, 249
clear plastic wrapping, 221
clearances, 152
cliché, 117
climatic conditions, 458
climate change, 21–22
clinching, 179
cling, 293
closure, 11, 178, 204, 210, 212, 238, 246, 285, 317–339
   collapsing core, 329
   cork, 335
   cosmetic, 328

crimped-on, 323
continuous thread CT) 210
crown, 17, 210, 323
dispensing, 327, 337
glass stopper, 335
integrity, 582
lightning, 335
linerless, 325
lug, 210, 321–322
metal, 320, 321–324, 332
roll-on, 210, 322
sealing ring, 256
screw, 49, 185
skirt, 322, 325
stripped core, 329
threaded, 255–256, 320–321, 328
neck bead, 322
press-fit closure base, 328
press-on/twist-off (PT), 322
pry-off crown, 323
silicone valve, 339
snap-fit, 335, 337
thermoplastic, 327
thermoset, 327
twist off crown, 323
unscrewed core, 329
venting closure, 318
closure code groups, 320
closure liner constructions, 325
expanded polyethylene, 324
expanded polypropylene, 324
Closure Manufacturer's Association (CMA),
318
closure rotation, 339
closure standard finish dimensions, 319
closure-less seal, 275
closure panel, 152, 158, 161
CMYK, See cyan, magenta, yellow
coagulate, 353, 364
coal-fired generating stations, 23
coated, 544
coat hanger die, 246
coating, 238, 348, 354
cobalt, 60, 47
oxide, 199
Code of Federal Regulations (CFR), 456
coefficient of friction, 24, 153, 207, 209, 287,
305, 408, 544–545
coefficient of viscosity, 357
co-extruded, 246, 251, 256, 260 273, 541
co-extrusion, 271
cohesion, 345
cohesive bond, 347
cohesive strength, 355, 452
cohesiveness, 346, 365
failure, 365
co-injection, 256
cold cream jar, 211
cold-end coating, 207
cold flow (creep), 232, 289, 327
cold rolled, 178
cold-water resistance, 352
Colgate, 8

collapsing frame, 247
collapsible inner bag, 193
collapsible tubes, 115, 176, 184–185,
541–542, 559
colloid, 352
color, 91
adjustment, 106
consistency, 97
separated, 93
swatch, 91
television screens, 84
temperature, 86
perception, 86
red, green, blue, 84
standards, 256
stations, 103
variations, 102
colorants, 199, 202
color communication, 84
brightness, 86, 90, 135, 137
color memory, 84
hue, 84, 90
observer, 86
saturation, 84
value, 84
verbal, 84
colorimeter, 89
colorimetry, 89
Color Key, 99
cold weather car starter, 91
column stacking, 485
Combibloc, 40, 149, 163
commercial glass, 199
commercial sterility, 41
comingled plastic trim, 260
commodity, 581
commodity polymers, 219, 221
communication, 48–49
compacted volume, 15
company structure, 569
compatibility, 24, 570
competitive market 567
component colors, 93
composite can, 539
composite sheets, 105
composting, 23
compound, 180, 192
compressed air, 189, 243, 253
compression molding, 244, 274–275, 327
compression, 438, 441–442
apparent compression strength, 482
compression strength, 269, 411, 429, 459,
482, 483, 484, 485–487, 568
dynamic, 459
dead load, 459
static, 459
compression test load rate, 482
compression test value, 488
compressive load, 33, 482, 484
compressive force, 207
computer arrangement programs, 450
computer aided design (CAD, 154
computer-to-plate (CTP), 94, 102

condiments and spices, 571
condensation, 36
condensation polymer, 224, 228
condensation reaction, 291
confectionary industry, 166
confections, 176
confidence level, 99
consensus standard, 454, 456
consistent color, 97
consistent properties, 153
constant cross-section, 245–246
Consumer Product Safety Commission
(CPSC), 334
consumer safety, 190
contact angle, 223, 349
contact pressure, 105
contain, 16, 24, 31, 317, 243
function, 32
contained pressure, 194
container, 203–204, 328, 483
plastic, 318
load bearing ability, 485
containerboard, 408
container geometry (bottle), 261–262
container glass, 200
container performance level, 194
container pressure, 189
sidewalls, 486
containment, 31, 550, 577
contaminate, 186
contamination, 541, 556
contaminating material, 106
contaminants, 128
continuous record, 526
copolymer, 291
cook time, 41
consumer attitude, 570
consumer perception, 570
consumer test panel, 576
consumerism, 11
consumer package, 31, 437
society, 12
consumption, 21, 48
continuous decoration, 182
continuous repeat, 102
pattern, 108
continuous thread (CT), 320
continuous tone, 91, 93
contamination, 35, 150
contaminated water sources, 22
continuous thread (CT), 210
contract proof, 98
control charts (SPC), 526
normal x-bar chart, 527–528
R chart, 526
bar chart examples, 528–530
X-bar chart, 526
control limits (SPC), 522
LCL, 527
lower control limit (LCL), 526
UCL, 527
upper control limit (UCL), 526
controlled atmosphere storage (CAS), 45

convection, 201
convection oven, 273
convenient entry, 152
convenience dinners
convenience features, 318
conventional storage, 152
converting, 243
    converter, 354
conveyor, 152
convolute wound, 540
coolant, 252
cooling rate, 256
copolymer, 227, 291
    alternating, 228
    block, 228
    random, 228
    terpolymer, 228
copper wire electrodes, 179
copy and position, 98
corner guards, 452
corporate expectations, 578
corporate identity, 97
    color, 97, 101
correlation, 526–527
corona discharge, 223, 227, 347–348
corrosive, 476, 477
    agents, 187
    protection, 177
    products, 178
corrugated, 25
    container, 405, 452
    fiberboard, 476, 478
    sheet, 407
    shipper, 31–32, 207
    shipping container, 31
    shipping units, 488
corrugated board, 100, 103, 405–406,
    409–410, 418, 439, 484, 487, 489, 550, 581
    manufacture, 350
corrugated board grades, 405, 408, 417–418
    microflute, 408
corrugated box, 270, 405–406, 416, 439, 488,
    568
    suppliers, 455
    industry, 129
corrugated box printing, 425–427
    direct print, 423
    litho labeling, 423, 426
    litho laminating, 424, 426
    preprint, 423
    post print, 426
    washboard appearance, 425
corrugating machine, 406, 409–410
    corrugating rolls, 409
cosmetic, 35, 168, 201–202, 212
cost-effective, 17, 446
    cost-effective distribution system, 449
cost-effective cushioning, 472
cost-efficient, 480
counter, 155
counter-blow, 204
cover, 169
covering material, 169

CPET, 273, 292
CR, 334
cradle to cradle, 23
cradle to grave, 23
crash lock, 161
crates, 285, 551, 553
Cream of Wheat, 9
crease, 95, 152
creep, 138, 411
creosote, 45
critical acceleration, 472–473
critical path charts, 576
critical resonance point, 480
cross-contamination, 17
cross-laminated plastic film, 545
cross-link, 47, 236–238, 243
cross direction, 134–135, 411
cross-section, 214
crowns, 17
crystal glass, 200
crystallize, 354
crystallized poly(ethylene terephthalate)
    (CPET), 273
crystallinity, 221, 227, 230–231 234, 249, 256
    crystalline regions, 234
    crystal sites, 231
    crystallization level, 265
crystal polystyrene, 287
cube utilization, 485
cullet, 201
cup, 182
    wide, 182
cure, 102, 186
curing, 45
curl, 180–181, 186, 192, 535, 538
curling, 138, 275
currency paper, 128
cushion, 48
cushioned, 472
cushion thickness, 473
cushioning characteristics, 476
cushioning material, 473, 476 480, 481
    bubble pads, 476
    cellulosic, 476
    fabricated shapes, 476
    foam-in-place, 476, 477
    high volume production, 476
    loose fill, 476
    polymeric, 476–477
    premolded shapes, 476
cushioning protection, 471, 473
custom, 203
customer, 203
customer appeal, 163
customer approval, 154–155
    responsibility, 154
    signature, 154
custom mold, 258
cut edge, 163
cut glass effect, 211
cut-off, 277
cutout, 160, 163
cutting die, 155

cut-score, 155
cyan, magenta, yellow, key, 90, 92–93, 95,
    97–98, 101
cylinder, 107, 186
cylindrical, 115, 184
cross direction (CD), 133
cube utilization, 439, 449–450
customer acceptance, 570
customer, 573
customer order, 447
cut-in, 452

D

dairy crate, 285
dairy products, 162
damage, 33, 449, 475, 480–481, 485
    excessive, 446
damaged goods, 444
damage investigations, 446
damage mechanism, 446
damp environments, 153
Dangerous Goods Code, 457
dangerous goods packaging, 456
deactivate, 549
dead fold, 186, 541
dead-load, 482
deadplate, 206
dead soft, 178
decelerated, 478
deceleration, 472–473
decked (pallet), 485
decolorizer, 199
decompose, 47, 201
decorate, 182, 208, 210, 212
decorating process, 49, 97, 112
    decorative coating, 113
decoration, 208, 210–212
decorative appeal, 169
deep draws, 176, 178
deflect, 473–474, 476
deflection, 473
deformation, 33, 232, 235, 268
degradation, 45, 238, 555
degrees of rotation, 322
delamination, 133
deteriorating, 35
demographics, 10, 49
demographic/psychographic, 569
de-nest, 257
densitometer, 89
density, 91–93, 190–191, 226, 231, 236, 276,
    285, 362, 477, 551
Department of Transportation, (DOT) 194
depolymerized, 351
deposit laws, 18
designation, 320
design brief, 573, 575–576, 595–599
design compression strength, 488
design flexibility, 113
design fragility, 459
design latitude, 477
design objectives, 203

design verification, 155
desiccants, 44
dextrin, 351–352, 361, 364, 540
DI, See draw and iron
diagonal members, 553
diamine, 230
dibasic acid, 229–230
die, 113, 155, 175, 182, 245
    creasing die, 155
    die bed, 155
    die board, 155
    die cost, 256
    circular, 247
    coat hanger, 246
    lips, 246
    T-shape, 246
die cutting, 96, 103, 155–156, 158, 247
die-cutting (corrugated) 419
die-cutting register, 138
die-making, 15
dilatent, 357
differential thermal analysis, 234
differential tin plate, 177–178
digital technology, 94
    design, 102
    graphic, 95
    image, 93
    printer, 98
    proof, 98–99
    workflow, 94, 95
dilatent, 357
dimensionally accurate, 251
dimensional part, 243
dimensional limit, 416
dimensional stability, 308,
dimensioning (corrugated) 424
dip tube, 189
direct coupling, 479, 481
directionality (paper), 134–135, 153
directionality (plastic), 234
direct-to-press, 94
dispenser pump, 559
dispensing aids, 152
dispersion, 523
display, 152–153, 163
distribution, 24, 48, 568, 570
    container, 417
    cycle, 211, 485, 488
    efficiency, 451
    elements, 461
    normal, 524
distribution environment, 440, 447, 457, 461, 469
distribution environment hazards, 441
    air pressure, 441
    biological hazards, 441
    compression, 438, 441–442
    contamination, 441
    electrostatics, 438
    light, 441
    moisture, water, 43
    puncturing, 441
    racking, deformation, 441

shock, 438, 441–442
    time, 438
    vibration, 438, 441–442
distribution packaging, 13, 31, 48
distribution warehouse, 439, 447
disposable package, 10
doctor blade, 108, 356
documented, 556
Dole process, 40
domed, 211
dots, 91–93
    elliptical, 92
    per linear inch, 92
    pattern, 107
    random, 93
    round, 92
double backer, 410
double bond, 225
double gob, 204
doubled board, 163, 165
double glued end seals, 150
    double gluing, 158
double reduced steel (DR), 178
double seam, 175–176, 179–181, 323
double-seaming, 540
double tight, 177
    doubletite, 177, 324
doublewall board, 406, 550
    boxes, 416
double white lined, 537
Dow Chemical, 219, 276
down-gauging, 23
dpi, See dots
draft, 257, 271
drag, 99
draw, 178, 181
draw and iron (DI), 115, 176, 181–183
draw and redraw, 176, 181–182
drawdown, 91
drawing, 176–177
drawing metal, 175
drawn container, 176
draw-off orifice, 202–204
dried foods, 44
drop height, 33, 460, 472
drop orientation, 470
dropping, 447
drop test, 457, 544
drug 553–554, 556
Drug Master File, 554
dry condiments, 177
    product, 179
drying, 42, 100
    zones, 103
dry offset, 99, 110, 115, 186, 188, 542
DSD, 19
DTP, See direct-to-press
dual chambered glass bottle, 555
dual chambered packages, 559
dual ovenable, 149, 273
dual system 19
ductile metals, 176, 184
ductility, 178

dunnage, 480
DuPont, 190, 387, 538, 545
DuPont Digital Waterproof, 99
durable goods, 13, 550
duration of load, 232
dust flaps, 152, 158, 161, 163, 165
Dymel, 190
dynamic, 482
dynamic load, 481
dynamic compressive strength, 138, 411
dynamic horizontal compression, 458
dynamic compression test, 483
dynamic compression, 482, 485, 487
dynamic cushioning curves, 474
dyne level, 223, 345, 349, 365
dyne solutions, 349

E

EAN code, 547
EAS tag, 549
EAS, 549–550
ease of disassembly, 439
easy-opening tear, 411
EBM, 257, 264, 266
ECCS, See electrolytic chrome-coated steel
ecological toxicity, 22
economics, 15, 16, 17
ecosystem, 24
ecotoxic, 2
ECT, 405, 407–408, 416–417, 454
edge crush test (ECT), 405, 408, 489
edge/corner drops, 471
edge lock, 150, 161
effective package, 567
efficient transport, 577
efficient utilization, 158
eject, 255, 275
elastic, 232, 233
    elasticity, 234
elastomer, 232, 238, 288, 355
elastomeric plug, 193, 556
elastomeric stopper, 555
electricity, 23
electrolytic chrome-coated steel (ECCS), 177
electrolytically tin-plated, 177
electromagnetic spectrum, 83
electron beam, 237
electronic article surveillance (EAS), 549
electrons, 222
electronic image. 98
electrostatic assist, 108
elements, 222
elements (shipping), 461–462
elongation, 232–234
embossing, 49, 112–113, 156, 247
emerald glass, 199
emissions, 19, 22–23
emulsified propellant, 191
emulsions, 191, 352, 364
emulsifier, 353
end-of-life treatment, 22

endothermic chemical, 558
end-piece diameter, 182
energy, 15, 18, 20–21, 23, 47, 200, 202, 234
engaging hooks, 179
engineering polymers, 219, 221
engraved, 91, 100, 102, 107
    die, 113
    etched plate, 117
EPR, See extended producer responsibility
EPS, 276
European Union, 19
eutrophication, 22
environment, 11, 15
environmental, 4, 22, 201, 58
    groups, 18
    issues, 14, 293
    concerns, 572
environmental (distribution), 477
    conditioning, 458
environmentally friendly, 16, 17
environmental multipliers, 488
    humidity, 489
    palletizing condition, 489
    storage time, 489
environmental stacking factor, 488
environmental stress crack resistance (ESCR), 309, 458, 586
enzymes, 47
epoxy, 297–298
equilibrium moisture content, 43, 137, 412
equilibrium relative humidity, 43, 44
equity, 569
ERH, 43, 44
ergonomics, 440
essential oils, 34–35, 317
etching, 212
ethylene acid copolymers, 297
ethylene gas, 36
ethylene glycol, 230, 291
ethylene monoethyl ether, 349
ethylene-vinyl acetate, (EVA), 324, 353, 537–538
ethylene-vinyl alcohol (EVOH), 246, 256, 273
evaluation procedures, 581
evaporation, 35
EVOH, 324, 256, 260
expanded plastic, 169
expanding chuck, 184
expansion panel, 180
expanded plastic, 276, 550
    closed-cell foams, 276
    expanded sheet, 276
    loose polystyrene, 276, 474
    open-cell foams, 276
    polyethylene, 324, 47
    polypropylene, 324
    polyurethane, 474
    steam heating, 276
expanded polystyrene (EPS), 219, 221, 274, 288, 440
evaluating distribution packaging, 454
exothermic chemical, 558
expansion coefficient, 255–256

expansion per degree (plastic), 234
expected load, 487
explosion hazard, 194
extended producer responsibility, 18, 19
external evidence of damage, 475
external pressure, 180
extensible web, 104
extractable, 200, 555
extruded parts, 277
extruded, 247
    tubes, 541
extruder, 244, 245, 251–252
    barrel, 245
    feed hopper, 245
    heater bands, 245
    ram-screw, 252
    reciprocating, 252
    screw, 245
extrusion, 244
    blown film, 244
    cast film, 244
    coextrusion, 244
    profile, 244, 246
    sheet, 244, 246
extrusion blow mold (plastic), 119, 257–258, 264
    blow-fill-seal, 275
    blowhead, 275
    blow-up, 261
    clamp force, 258
    cooling, 259
    flash, 259
    mold halves, 277
    neck finish, 258
    parison, 257, 259–260
    pinch-off, 258–259
    sand blasted, 258
    shear, 258
    steel inserts, 258
extrusion blow molding (EBM), 243–244, 257, 264, 277
    blowing cycle, 259
    bottom tab, 259
    cycle time, 259
    secondary operations, 259
    shuttle blow, 259
    trim regrind, 260
    weld line, 258
extrusion die, 203
eye mark, 100

F

fabric, 169
facing sheet, 406
facing, 406–407
failed product launch, 573
fan-fold, 119, 355
fastener holding ability, 551
fast food, 10, 11
fatigue (damage), 479
faulty transport equipment, 444

FDA, 331, 554, 556, 575
Federal Food, Drug and Cosmetic Act, 553
ferrule, 191, 555
fiber, 106, 127
    bundles, 129
    alignment, 133–134
    fiber distribution, 128
    fiber length, 127
    long fiber, 128
    short fiber, 128
    fiber sources, 127
    fibril, 130
fiberboard, 452
fiberboard characterization tests, 412–415
fiberboard, box, 406
fiber cans, 3, 539
fiber tear, 346, 351, 366, 537
Fibre Box Association, 405, 429, 488–489
field observations, 446
fifth panel, 163
fill level, 210
filling, 210–211
filling machine, 208
filling orientation, 152
fill requirements, 525
film, 246, 538
    blown, 248–250
    cast, 246, 250
    extruded, 246
    thickness, 250
film labels, 187
finish, 204–205, 207, 210, 266, 268, 275, 317–320, 321–322, 330, 336, 339, 488, 577
finish land area, 577
fingerprint, 99, 549
fired, 212
fish, 36, 176
five point scores, 411
flat film stock, 120
flammable, 189, 191, 194
flame treating, 121, 223, 347
flange, 179, 182
flaps, 152
flash, 252
flat drops, 471
flat rounds, 176
flavor, 35
flex cracking, 488
flexible laminate, 454
flexible materials, 41
flexible packaging, 247, 486
Flexible Packaging Association (FPA), 25
flexible packaging laminate, 544
flexible plastic, 103
flexography, 7, 549
flexography, 7, 94, 99, 100, 102, 105–106, 111
    flexo, 99
    printing strengths, 105
    printing limitations, 103
flexographic, 106, 427
    sheet, 110
    web, 110
    printing station, 102

plate, 97, 102
flint, 202, 211–212
flow (plastic), 235, 345
    flowability, 234, 245
flue gas, 201
fluorescent colors, 97, 101
fluorocarbon, 188
fluoropolymer, 355
flute, 406, 408–409
flute integrity, 407
foam, 191, 229
foaming stage, 477
foam-in-place, 276
focus group, 573, 575
foil laminated, 162
fold, 155
folding ability, 128
folding carton, 95, 97, 103, 105, 133, 149,
    157–158
folding carton blank, 138, 168
foldover, 436
font, 49
food, 338
    products, 479
Food and Drug Administration (FDA), 331,
    362, 553
food applications, 362
food dehydration, 39
food loss, 442
Food Manufacturing Institute, 449
Food Marketing Institute, 452
food moisture content, 43
food packaging, 12
food products, 179
food shortages, 20
food spoilage, 34
food taste, 273
footprint, 449, 453
footwear industry, 168
FPA, See Flexible Packaging Association
force, 156, 232, 472
forehearth, 202–203
forklift truck, 448–49
formability, 243
formamide, 349
formation, 128
form-fill-seal, 100, 163
forming collar, 538
forming frame, 152
four-corner Beers tray, 165
fourdrinier paper machine, 406
four Rs, 15
fragile, 438
fragility, 438, 454, 472, 475
    boundary curves, 459
    factor, 33, 438, 473
free-fall drops, 472
free radical, 554
free radical degradation, 353
free water, 42
freeze, 175, 261, 353
freezer, 354, 362
    burn, 39, 40

dehydration, 39
    storage, 153
    temperature, 256, 285
Freight Classification Committee, 405
freight classification, 417
freight rule requirements, 407
frequency, 477–478
frequency, 479
    forcing frequency, 479
    natural resonance
    modulated, 93
friction, 207
friction coatings, 440
friction fit plug, 246
friction lid. 175, lid, 324
friction lock, 161
friction ring, 287
frit, 202
frosted, 212
frost line, 249
frozen juice, 179
frozen product, 256
frozen food, 39, 149, 161
F-style, 177
fruit juice, 162
full-color illustration, 94
full-opening ring-pull top, 177
fumigant, 557
functional coating, 347
functional group, 228
furnace, 201–202
furnace glass, 202, 555
furniture, 550
fuse, 179, 258
fusion, 202, 212

G

g, 472
gable top container, 149, 162–163
gain, 99, 102, 548–549
G level, 459
games, 168
gamut, 92
gamma, 47, 83, 293
gang printing, 556
Gannt chart, 575
garbage, 15, 17
garbage removal fees, 18
gas barrier, 175, 287, 540
gas bubbles, 276
gas mixture, 45
gas permeability, 286
gas permeation, 37
gas transmission rate, 37
gas volumes, 213
gate mark, 257, 275
gate projection, 257
gauge band, 250
gel, 193, 350
generalized drop probability, 469
generic container, 165

gift, 168, 175
give-away, 525
glass, 17, 24, 37, 47, 199, 201–203, 206
    amber, 202, 555
    blue, 202
    borosilicate, 200, 555
    bottles, 116, 166, 191, 554
    brown, 202
    clear, 202
    containers, 204, 208
    dead-leaf green, 202
    distribution, 206
    emerald, 202
    flint, 202, 211
    furnace, 201
    gob, 6
    green, 202
    jars, 8, 41, 47, 49
    markets, 200
    opal, 202
    opaque, 202
    tubing, 555
    glass types (pharmaceutical), 200–201, 555
glass cleaner, 190
glass defects, 207
    bird swings, 207, 210
    spikes, 207, 210
Glass Packaging Institute (GPI), 208, 210, 318
glass transition, 24, 233–235, 265
glassware, 200–201, 203, 207
glassy, 199
G level, 472–473, 475, 478
glue, 345, 152
    glue-assist incisions, 346
    glueability, 153
    glue-bond, 345
    flaps, 447
    glue-line, 159, 345
    glue tab, 158
glucose, 351
German Packaging Ordinance, 19
GHG, See greenhouse gas
Global sustainability, 19–21
gloss, 111, 135
    coating, 114
    label face, 120
glue area, 97
glue joint tolerances, 429–430
glycol, 229, 276, 477
gob, 203–206
gold foil, 97
    gold, 112
    stamp, 49
goniometer, 349
gourmet peanut butter, 49
GPI, See Glass Packaging Institute
gradation, 103
grain, 158, 165
grammage, 127, 136, 179, 396, 407, 409, 411
granular, 152, 479
graphic, 14, 155–156, 163, 478 550, 569
    quality, 110
gravity, 472

gravure, 92, 94, 97, 100, 106, 111, 116
  cylinder, 108
  strengths, 109
  limitations, 109
  printing, 107–108
gray scale, 85, 91
gray balance, 99
grease, 175, 177
grease barrier, 285
grease resistant, 153, 286
green bond, 352
green strength, 361
green dot, 19
greenhouse gas, 19, 22–23
green labeling, 18
green washing, 23
gripping points, 551
Grocery Manufacturers of America, 452
groundwood, 129
GS1 (Canada) 546
gusseted, 149, 161–162, 166, 247
gussets, 543

H

halftone, 90–91, 92, 93, 94, 102, 115
  dot, 92, 188
  printing plate, 93
  reproduction, 116
  screen, 116
halo effect, 103
halogenated hydrocarbons, (CFC, HCFC) 22, 190
ham cans, 176
handleware, 257
hand pump, 188
hand sample, 154
handhold, 156, 440, 470
handling techniques, 48
hand sample, 429
hardness, 178
hardwood, 127
hazardous good packaging, 456
hazardous product codes, 194
HCFC, 22, 190
HDPE, 226, 230
headspace, 163, 189, 210, 554
health and beauty aids, 35
Health Protection Branch, (Canada), 362,) 553
heat activated adhesive, 112, 113
heat
  cured, 106
  deflection temperature, 273
  exchanger, 201
  penetration, 41
  resistance, 41
  sealable polyolefin, 41
  seal, 149, 235, 246, 251, 326, 355, 545
  sealed, 535, 538
  sealing material, 537–538
  seal system, 540

shrink, 47
tolerant, 112
transfer, 112
heated die, 113
heat sealable, 535, 537, 290
  coating, 290
heat-seal medium, 286
heat-seal properties, 287
heat-setting, 265
heat-stabilized, 250, 290
heat stabilizer, 353
heavy ink coverage, 427
heavy metals, 22
heel, 210–211
hermetic seal, 179, 182, 192, 539, 322, 324, 326
hertz, 477
Hexachrome, 95
hicky, 135
hidden damage costs, 443
high barrier, 540, 545
  film, 562
  laminate, 194, 560
    high barrier plastics, 194
high friction coating, 452
high humidity, 444
high impact polystyrene (HIPS), 287–288
high performance board, 407–408
high speed, 153, 156, 175
high tack bond, 452
high quality graphic, 538
Himes lock, 151
  Himes bottom, 161
hinged lids, 169, 175–176
hinged storage container, 436
histogram, 526
homopolymer, 228, 287
hooks, 179
hoop strength, 180
horizontal end-loading, 151–152, 160
horizontal impact, 458
horizontal shock, 458
hospital, restaurant, institutional (HRI), 11
hospital supplies, 47, 83
hot cavity, 274
hot-end coating, 207
hot-fill, 40, 200, 207, 235, 260, 265, 268, 289, 324
hot stamp, 97, 112–113, 156, 392
hot tack, 227, 353
hour-glass sidewall, 212
human color perception
  after image, 87
  color blindness, 86
  fatigue, 87
  human eye, 84
  red, green, blue, 84
human toxic, 22
humid conditions, 484
humidity, 36, 44–45, 412, 427, 476, 483
humidor tubes, 186
hydrocarbons, 193, 224–226, 276
  butane, 224–225

butene, 227
ethane, 224–225
ethylene, 224–225, 227
hexene, 227
isopentane, 276
methane, 224–225
octene, 227
pentane, 224–225, 276
propane, 224–225
propylene, 224–225
hydraulic force, 252
hydrofluoric acid, 212
hydrogen bonding, 346
hydrogen peroxide, 40, 130
hydrolysis, 554
hydrolytic breakdown, 291
hygroexpansive, 138
hygroscopic, 43–44, 137, 411, 476–477, 483
  food, 43
  plastics, 252
hydrostatic pressure 486

I

IBM, 266
ice crystals, 35
ideas for change, 571–572
impact qualities, 288
image quality, 94
imitation leather, 169
impermeable, 354
impression cylinder, 102, 103, 105
impact, 469
  extruded, 185, 191, 541
  extrusion, 176, 184, 186
  programmer, 458
  strength, 258
  velocity, 473
impermeable, 200
impregnated, 544
impression roll, 100
improper handling, 444
improper storage. 156
inadequate packaging, 444, 471
in-case filling, 121
incineration, 18
incline impact, 458, 460
incompatibility, 34
indented container, 211
inert gases, 554
indexing label lug, 208
individual section machine (IS), 204
individual packaging, 8
industrial boxes, 285
industrial chemicals, 286
industrial composter, 25
industrial packaging, 31–32, 439, 286
industry guidelines, 452–454
  bagged products, 453
  container dimensions, 453
  minimum storage capability, 453
Industrial Revolution, 7–8, 12

induction inner seal, 324–327 332
inert, 200, 207, 226
infeed timing screw, 330
inflation ratio, 250
information development, 573, 585
information, 10, 163, 573
information, inner panel, 166
infra-red, 83
inherent design faults, 454
injectable drugs, 200, 555
injection, 200
injection blow molding (IBM), 243–244, 264,
  328
    blow molding station, 264–265
    core pin (rod), 264
    economics, 265
    injection-stretch (ISBM), 265
    mechanical stretching, 265
    one-step, 264
    preform, 265
    thermal history, 265
    two-step process, 265
initiation, 353
injection mold (plastic), 251–252
    assembly, 252
    cavity, 251–253
    clamp, 252
    clamping force, 252
    collapsing core, 255
    core, 320, 252–253, 257, 275, 328–329
    gate, 253, 256, 274, 277
    heating elements, 253
    hot runner, 254
    plug, 253, 277
    runner, 253, 256
    runnerless, 253–254
    sliding frame, 253
    sprue, 253, 274
    stack, 254
    stripping core, 255
    three plate, 253–254
    threaded core, 255
    two piece, 253
    unscrewing core, 255
injection molded, 541, 558
injection molding, 243–244, 251–252, 256,
  264, 271, 277
innovation, 572
instrument calibration, 578
integral measuring chamber, 357
interference-fit, 287
intermodal, 286
ink, 35, 187, 223, 238, 345, 347–348, 358,
  366, 478
    insoluble, 364
    absorption, 128
    consumption, 111
    fountain, 100
    jet printers, 115
    lay-down, 97
    litho, 106, 187
    oil based, 106
    opaque, 112

phosphorescent, 562
thermochromic, 562
thermoplastic, 113
train, 105
transfer, 102, 105
transparent, 86
UV curing ink, 188
in-line, 112
    press, 100, 104
    configuration, 103
inform/sell, 31
infrared radiation, 46
in-mold labeling, 121
input frequency, 472, 479, 481
input level (vibration), 481
input received, 478
irradiation, 237
insecticide mist, 188
insect population, 47
inside liner, 410
inspection, 207
instant cure, 188
Institute of Packaging Professionals (IoPP), 25
institutional packaging, 40
Insurance Company of North America, 442
intaglio, 100
integral hinge, 289, 327
integrated activity, 437
interdepartmental, 573
interdisciplinary, 573
interference layer, 349, 365
interference ridge, 328
Intergovernmental Panel on Climate Change,
  21
interlock pattern, 488
Intermaritime Consultive Organisation (IMO),
  456
intermodal cargo container, 406
internal
    bond strength, 537
    cohesion, 351
    friction 357
    partitions, 163
    lining, 186
    strength, 346
    stress, 206–207, 232, 235
    pressure, 183, 188, 190, 214, 318
    temperature, 206
    vacuum, 180, 323
International Air Transport Association, 456
International Box Code, 405
International Organisation for Standardization
  (ISO), 23, 25, 127, 456, 578
international packaging, 530
International Safe Transit Association (ISTA),
  26, 444
interrupted thread, 322
inventory, 118, 187
inventory reduction, 452
ionize, 348
ionization, 47
ionizing energy, 47
    radiation, 47

ionomer, 297, 387, 538
ions, 200
irradiation, 13, 39, 46–47
irregular shape, 152, 208
iron, 183, 199
    cast, 203
ironing, 176
    rings, 82
ISBM, 265
ISO, 23, 127, 456
isocyanate, 276, 477
isolate, 48, 478, 480–481
isotactic, 289
isolation material, 481
isopentane, 193
ISTA, 452, 455, 457, 460–461

J

jar, 199, 203
jams, 42
jelly gum, 351
jewel boxes, 251
jurisdiction, 17

K

Kelvin, 86
key color, 90, 93
keyline, 95, 98
key opening, 177
kiss, 96
knurled, 211
knocked down, 138
knocked down flat, (KDF), 158, 165–167
Kodak Approval, 99
kraft, 103, 129, 406, 408, 539
    pulp, 129
    bag paper, 128
    natural, 129
    paper, 153
    paperboard, 166
    virgin, 128

L

1–2–3, lock label, 9, 11, 47, 49, 94, 105, 121,
  180, 187, 203, 207–208, 210, 211, 549
    clear, 212
    cut length, 120
    cut and stack. 118
    film, 121
    full body shrink, 120
    glued-on, 119, 353
    in-mold, 121
    label lug, 208
    no label look, 119
    panel, 209, 210–211
    paper, 211
    pick-up adhesive, 212
    plastic, 212

prelabeled cans, 118
pressure sensitive, 103, 115, 118, 212
shrinkable, 119, 212 235, 270
shrink label materials, 120
shrink-on sleeves, 120
stock, 378
labeling, 211
    adhesive, 351
    abrasion damage, 270
    blow on, 119
    non-contact applicator, 119
    orientation, 270
    pad style applicator
    round cross-sections, 270
    register mark, 270
    spot, 208
    square bottles, 270
    stock, 120, 169
labeling (pharmaceutical), 556
labels, (scuffing), 478
L*ab globe, 87
laboratory compression test, 482, 484
laboratory glassware, 200
labor intensive, 477
Lab star, 87
labor intensive, 168
lacquer, 101
    adhesives, 354
laminate 17, 41, 260, 371, 382, 387, 391, 395, 397
    examples, 398–399
    layer, 366
    material, 388, 538–539
    purpose, 384
    stock, 118
    web, 392
laminated, 247, 290, 371, 544–545
    collapsible tubes, 541–154, 186
    sheet, 271
    structures, 286
laminating, 354
laminating machine, 397
land, 210, 325
landfill, 15, 23
lap seal, 386
laser, 102
    cutting, 155
    marking, 114
lathers, 191
launch, 573
    successful product, 567
law, 11, 48
lay-down, 107
lay-flat, 120
L'eggs, 571
LDPE, 226, 231, 336, 387
leach, 200
leachable land-fills, 22
lead (metal), 176, 179, 184
lead time, 105, 109
leaf printing, 113
lehr, 206–207
less developed societies, 13

less than truckload (LTL), 455
letterpress, 99, 103, 115
letterset, 115
levels of assurance, 461
levels of packaging, 439
lid, 257
life cycle, 18, 22, 23
life sustaining resources, 20
light, 554
    barrier, 175, 391
    sensitive, 555
    source, 86–87
light-weighting, 23
lignin, 128–129
LLDPE, 226–227, 381
limestone, 199
linear undampened spring, 473
line art, 90, 97, 101, 102, 103, 106, 108, 110, 115, 116, 542
    copy, 97
liner, 317, 320, 323
    pulpboard, 325
    resilient liner, 324
    retainer ridge, 329
linerboard, 406–410, 581
    basis weights, 405
line screen, 92
liquid density, 189
liquid effluent, 22
liquid penetration, 135–136
liquid phase, 189
liquid propellant, 189
liquid waste, 22
litho, 100
lithographed, 179
lithographic printing, 96, 104, 106
    ink, 106, 187
    limitations, 207
    plates, 105, 106
    strengths, 107
lithography, 91, 94, 97, 100, 103–105, 179, 187
load application rate, 482
load-bearing ability, 485–486
load-bearing walls, 485
load-per-unit-area, 474
load stability, 485
locking tabs, 152
longitudinal direction, 485
longitudinal dynamic compression, 482
longitudinal seal, 384
long-term storage, 168, 458
loose-fill, 477
loose-load, 472
loss of value, 33
low carbon steel, 177
low-cost shipper, 168
low-frequency bouncing, 472
low molecular weight components, 556
low profile cans, 177
low tooling cost, 149
lug, 212
luncheon meat, 187

M

machinability, 24, 153, 159, 345, 371, 391, 577, 581
machine assembled, 166
machine direction (MD), 133–135, 158, 250, 411, 549
machine glazed, 135
machine handling, 211
machine readable symbol, 546
machinery, restrictions, 152
main panel, 158
major flaps, 159
make-ready, 97, 108
maleates, 352
mandates, 17
mandrel, 245, 284, 540
man-made chemicals, 22
manual drops, 469
manual handling, 440, 447, 469, 472
manual set-up, 166
manufacturing cost, 236
manufacture's joint (carton), 163
manufacturer's joint (corrugated), 420
manufacturing sequence (corrugated) 423–424
manual erection, 151, 160
MAP, 45, 46
marketing, 163, 550, 568
    advantage, 318
    analysis, 573
    function, 569
market failure, 567
market potential, 575
market share, 110, 572
market tests, 573
manual erection, 151, 160
market tests, 155
mass production, 118
material
    area, 439
    bans, 18
    characterization tests, 454
    distribution, 208, 258, 260, 264, 269, 271–273, 582
    efficient, 17
    handling system, 447
    levy, 19
    properties, 226
    utilization, 208
    plies, 396
material-combining nip, 393
maximum board utilization (corrugated), 420
maximum stack strength, 439
McKee formula, 413, 489
measurement accuracy, 578
meat products, 35–36, 40, 46
mechanical adhesion, 345–346
mechanical
    bond, 346
    damage, 472
    forces, 221
    handling, 31, 440, 472
    history, 221, 235

pulp, 128–129, 561
 mechanical properties (corrugated), 411
 shock, 33
mechanically clinched, 175
mechanically seamed, 175, 178–179
median, 521, 523
medical, 47, 272, 381, 562
medications, 176
medium, 289, 406–411, 418, 581
melamine formaldehyde, 238, 243
melt flow rate, 244, 251, 257
 melt index, 244
melting point, 231–232
 melt phase, 234
melt strength, 292, 387
melt temperature, 353
memory (plastic), 235, 250
mer, 219
merchandising, 163, 166
metal, 37, 235
 cans, 40, 41, 175
 clip, 538
 cylinder, 102
 packaging, 175
 sheet, 106
 tubes, 186, 542
metal deposition, 379
metallic, 97, 101, 112, 95, 106, 371
 decoration, 113
metallized, 194, 290, 378, 379, 392 393
 carrier, 112
 film, 112, 115
 paper, 378
metallizing, 379, 390, 392
metallocene, 232
 polyethylene, 545
metallurgy, 176
metering, 100, 102, 105
methane, 22
metered, 393
metric (micron), 396
MD, See machine direction
micelle, 352
microbial population, 47
microbial loading. 47
microorganisms, 24, 34, 35, 38–40, 42, 43, 46,
 83, 391
 anaerobic, bacteria, 45
 Aspergillus flavus, 39
 binary fission, 38
 botulism, 39
 Claviceps purpurea, 39
 Clostridium botulinum, 39, 41
 ergotism, 39
 Escherichia coli, 38
 fungal growth, 36
 fungi, 38
 mesophilic, 36, 38
 mold, 38, 39, 42, 45
 multicellular, 38
 mycelia, 38
 nutrient source, 38
 pathogen, 40, 42

psychrophilic, 36, 38
Shigella dysentaria, 38
spores, 41
Staphylococcus, 38
thermophilic, 38
unicellular, 38
yeast, 34, 42
microprocessor, 94
microwave, 11, 46, 273, 379
 compatible plastic trays, 273
 energy, 379
microwavable, 562, 291
 pouch, 560
microwaved, 371, 381
microwave transparency, 292
migrate, 365
mils, 397
milestones, 571, 575
minimum burst pressure, 194
minor flaps, 150
mixed-load pallets, 447
mock-up, 155
Mocon, 390
mode, 521, 523
modern industrial society, 12
modified atmosphere packaging, 39, 45, 562
modular system, 451–452
moire', 93, 95, 378, 483–484
moisture
 barrier, 37, 39, 554
 content, 43, 44, 137
 gain, 35
 loss, 35, 45
mold (glass), 203, 207
 body, 204
 seams, 204
mold (plastic), 235, 261, 536
 molding, 137
 molded, 243
molded-in lettering, 211
molded pulp, 561
mold markings, 277
molecule, 222
molecular
 chain, 225–226, 238
 drag, 226
 flow, 235
 friction, 357
 geometry, 219, 231
 mass, 219
 movement, 231
 realignment, 235
 shape, 221
 weight, 221, 225–226 350, 352–353,
  231–232, 244
molecular chains, 225–226
 linear chains, 226
 side branching, 226
molten state, 231
monolayer, 381
monolithic, 207
monomer, 219, 223–224, 227–228, 230, 236
monostearate, 207

most frequent/serious occurrences, 526
Mottled, White, 408
motivational role, 10
mounting cup, 186, 191
mouthfeel, 34, 43
mulch, 24
Mullen 405, 407–408, 416–417
multiple draws, 176
multiple friction, 177
mutually soluble, 190
multilayer bottles (plastic), 261
 translucent strips, 261
multi-layered, 371, 392
multilayer injection molding, 256
multilayer laminated sheet, 271
multipacks, 120
multiple filling heads, 384
multiple lane FFS, 385–386
multiple trip, 440
multi-ply boards, 133
multi-purpose lines, 397
multiwall bags, 129
municipal solid waste, 16
MXD6, 260
mycelia, 38
myoglobin, 562

N

nail, 551
nailing end grain, 553
nanocomposites, 381
narrow necked bottles, 206
National Motor Freight Classification,
 (NMFC), 405, 415
natural gas, 201
neck band, 330
neck ring, 204, 213
needle cannula, 213
nesting, 257
new convenience, 572
New Drug Application (NDA), 554
new product development, 567, 572–573
Newtonian fluid, 357–358
nipped, 394
nitrocellulose, 392
nitrogen, 46
nitrogen oxide, 201
nonabrasive material, 551
noncrystalline, 199
notions box, 165
multi-layered, 24
natural register point, 188
neck, 185
 necking, 182
 designs, 185
necked cans, 187
netting, 452
nitric oxides, 22
nitrogen, 35, 45, 46, 183
nitrous oxide, 22
NMFC, Item 222, 405, 415, 455

no label look, 115, 119, 121
nonabrasive, 478
noncorrosive, 177
nonspecification container, 194
nonvolatile content, 345, 363
North American Van lines, 443
nostalgia, 175
notch sensitive material
novelties, 176
nozzle, 189, 191
nucleating agent, 231, 276, 289
Nucrel, 387
numerical data, 546
nutrient, 34
nutritional labelling, 11
nutritional quality, 41, 295–296
nylon, 378, 379, 382

O

objectives, 572, 575, 585
oblong, 177
observed acceleration, 472
odor, 371
off-flavors, 395
off-line, 97
offsetting, 105
offset letterpress, 99, 110, 115, 188, 542
offset lithography, 97, 100, 105, 106, 111
   sheet, 110
   web, 110
off-set necks, 177
off-ware, 207
oil, 177
oleic acid, 207
one piece impact extruded, 176
one up die, 155
on-line, 557
Ontario, 19
opacifying agent, 199
opacity, 111, 115, 371
opaque, 102, 231, 380, 555, 548
   ink, 112
open end, 185
open-head pails, 285
open time, 361, 365, 578
operating room supplies, 272
ophthalmic medication, 185
OPP, 378, 379, 383, 391, 392
optical density, 379
optical illusions, 86, 93
optimal distribution packaging, 439
optimum investment, 443
organic coatings, 187
organic vapor, 390
orientation, 97, 232, 234–235, 265
   biaxial, 234, 250–251
   cross direction, 250
   monoaxial, 234, 244
   transverse direction, 250
   unoriented, 234
orientation (package), 440

oriented polypropylene (OPP) 378
orifice, 204, 245
orienting, 250
ordinance, 19
orifice, 353
oscillation, 477
outdoor storage, 546
outgassing, 560
ovality, 577
ovals, 177
oven, 187, 207, 324, 235, 354, 394
overhang, 449, 485, 488
   inadvertent, 485
overlap, 212
over-the-counter (OTC), 332
over-packaging, 14, 443–444
overprinting, 115
Oxford Concise Dictionary, 20
oxidation, 200, 554–555
oxygen, 34, 36, 45–46, 186, 200–201, 389, 554–555
   barrier, 41, 44, 371, 379, 391
   oxidation, 25, 35, 45–46
   oxidize, 34, 40
   oxygen permeability, 390, 380, 390
oxygen absorbers, 45
   scavenger, 44, 260, 323
oxygenless environment, 41
ozone depleting, 11, 22, 190
oxidizing, 223, 227
Oysterboard, 408
ozone, 227, 348

P

PA, 378, 379, 381
package, 115
   alternatives, 577
   design, 97, 571, 574–575
   designer, 10, 24, 175
   designer's checklist, 592–594
   development, 569–571
   filling, 388
   form, 570
   handling, 469
   performance, 578
   printing and decorating, 83, 91
   supplier, 549
   users, 25
packaging, 219, 572
   cost, 443, 569
   drug, 554
   functions, 3, 567, 580
   industry, 21, 22, 25
   materials, 24
   primitive, 4–8
   process, 569
   professional, 12, 573
   responsibility, 569
   specialist, 569
   test capability, 585
Packaging Association of Canada (PAC), 25

Packaging Machinery Manufacturer's Institute, (PMMI), 25, 429
primitive packaging, 4–9
pad printing, 117
paint, 191
   cans, 179
   industry, 177
pallet, 207–208, 285, 47–449, 485, 551, 588
   board geometry, 485
   block pallet, 448, 449
   cleanability, 448
   corrugated board, 448
   deck, 449
   distribution packaging, 437–438, 440, 443
   durability, 448
   footprint, 453
   four way entry, 448
   hardwood, 448
   issues, 449
   load, 543
   metal, 448
   failure, 448
   pattern, 588
   plastic, 448
   reversible, 448
   size, 448
   single face 485
   stringer, 448
   two way entry, 449
   wood, 448
palletized, 451, 439, 470
pallet load, 452–453, 459, 481, 484
pallet overhang, 449
pallet patterns, 440, 480, 485
paneling, 180, 261
Pantone Matching System (PMS), 91–92, 95, 98, 101
paper, 24, 106, 127, 483
   bleached kraft and sulfites, 140
   bonding, 351
   book, 139
   coated, 135
   commercial, 139
   containerboard, 140
   glassine, 130
   greaseproof, 139
   label, 140, 211
   mill, 354
   natural kraft, 140
   newsprint, 128, 129, 139
   pouch, 140
   tissue, 140
paperboard, 39, 47, 103 127, 149, 155, 158, 537, 538, 539
   bending chipboard, 141
   bottom liner, 133
   boxboard, 127
   cardboard, 127
   chipboard, 140
   clay-coated, 538
   cartonboard, 127
   clay coated newsback (CCNB), 141
   coated boards, 136

cylinder board, 133
    double white lined (DWL), 141, 537
    filler plies, 133
    food board, 129, 141–142, 149
    grease resistant, 130
    lined chipboard, 141, 153
    linerboard, 140, 406–410, 581
    medium, 140
    newsboard, 141
    single white lined, (SWL) 141
    solid bleached sulfite (SBS), 141, 153
    solid unbleached sulfite (SUS), 141
    top liner, 133
    underliner, 133
paper caliper and weight, 136
    basis weight, 136
    caliper, 136
    density, 136
    grammage, 136
    pounds per ream, 136
paperboard selection, 153
    requirements, 156
paperboard, trays, 149
paperboard tubs, 149
paper and paperboard, 127
paper carrier, 549
paper-making machines, 131–134
    calendering, 134
    cylinder, 132–133
    drier, 131
    fourdrinier, 131–133
    free water, 132
    furnish, 131
    headbox, 131
    mill roll, 132
    screen drum, 132
    twin wire former, 133
    vertiformer, 133
    wet end, 133
paper mills, 153
paper/poly/foil/poly laminates, 149
paper qualities, 128, 153
    absorbency, 130
    burst strength, 128, 130, 153
    caliper consistency, 134
    folding ability, 128
    fold endurance, 128, 133
    glueability, 153
    mechanical strength, 130
    pick resistance, 131
    puncture, 128, 153
    stiffness, 134, 153
    tear strength, 128, 130, 134, 153
    tensile strength, 128, 130, 134, 153
    z-direction strength, 153
paper testing, 137
paper tests (bags), 544–545
paper brightness, 86
papermaking, 7
papyrus, 6
paraffin, 226, 231
parenteral drugs, 200, 555
Pareto charts, 526

parison, 204, 208, 210, 257, 261, 264, 292
    pre-inflated, 258
    co-extruded, 260
    programmed, 261–262
part assembly, 361
particulate, 191, 479
parting line, 203, 212, 252, 277, 320, 577
paradigm, 23
pascal second, 358
paste, 175, 188
pasteurization, 214
patent, 208
pathogen, 38, 40, 41
pattern applied adhesive, 101, 388
PE, 247, 258, 260
peak G level, 476
pear-shaped ham cans, 177
pedestal base cup, 255
peel test, 578
peer reviewed, 20
pegboard, 153, 163, 535, 537
penetration, 346
perceived value, 335
perforated, 120, 538–539
perforations, 136, 155
performance characteristics, 221
performance properties (plastics), 221
    barrier, 226, 231, 234
    clarity, 231
    elongation, 233
    hardness, 226
    melting point, 221–222, 226
    physical strength, 227
    stiffness, 221, 226, 231, 265
    tensile strength, 226, 233–234
performance, 577, 581
performance test, 582
per capita income, 21
perforations, 136
performance criteria, 24
performance properties, 371
performance requirements, 384
permanent deformation, 384
permanent set, 138, 156
permeability, 37, 390–391, 454
permeate, 35, 381, 388
permeant, 37, 227, 389
permeation, 194
perpendicularity, 207
Perrier, 8
persona, 9, 318, 335
personal care products, 47, 188, 246
PET, 230, 256, 260, 265, 272, 324, 371,
    378–379, 381, 391–392
PETG, 230, 536
petrochemical, 20, 219
petrolatum, 226
pharmaceutical, 105, 118, 184–185, 191, 202,
    212, 266, 275, 355, 386, 388, 448, 541,
    554–556
    glassware, 200
phenol formaldehyde, 9, 238, 243, 327
pH, 40, 42, 353, 363–364, 556

phosphate, 22
phosphorous, 178
photocells, 207
photochemically initiated, 555
photonegative, 94, 99, 102
photopolymer, 102
photo sensitive material, 116
physical properties, 153, 221
physical strength, 153, 371
picking aisle, 447
pigment, 89–90, 191, 236, 293
pillow pack, 543, 545
pilot product runs, 576
pinch-lock tray, 166
pinch-off, 277
pinholing, 389, 390
piston driven dispensers, 193
piston, 252
plasma, 380–381
plastic film, 378, 435, 539
    breathing, 562
    clear, 97
plastic packaging, 75
plastic, 17, 219, 149, 221–222, 232, 235, 243
    bottles, 3, 166–167, 210, 459, 487
    cans, 177
    collapsible tubes, 186
    containers, 116, 121, 488
    film, 348
    industry, 17, 112
    jugs, 177
    material, 119
    packaging film, 234
    strapping, 234
    tubs, 115
plastic resin, 252
plastic and polymer terminology, 220, 224
plasticize, 388
plastics industry, 219
plastisol gasket, 322–323
    flowed in, 323
plastomer, 232
plate, 96, 97, 102
    cylinder, 102–103, 105
    cost, 105
    dampening, 106
plate-making, 94, 99
    maker, 97
platen press, 256
platform quality, 452
plies, 133
    interply bonding, 133
plug, 277
plug gauge, 207
ply, 544
ply separation, 535, 537
point, 136, 397
point of fill, 166
point-of-purchase display, 272
point-to-point scores, 410
poise, 358
polar, 346–347, 349
    attractions, 222

bonds, 346
non-polar, 222, 227
polarity, 221–223, 345–346, 393
contact angle, 222–223
politicized, 18
pollution, 15
polyamide (PA), 224, 228–230, 295–296, 354
MXD6, 295
polycarbonate, 253, 298
poly(chlorobiphenyl), 22
polychlorotrifluoroethylene, (PCTFE), 299, 390, 554
polyester, 228–230
polyethylene, 10, 39, 47, 104, 149, 162, 207, 221–222, 225–228, 232, 246, 249, 251, 260, 276, 283, 347, 382, 387, 387, 391, 393, 538, 540
bottles, 486
laminates, 40
low molecular weight, 226
polyethylene, high density (HDPE), 17, 284–285, 545
polyethylene, low density (LDPE), 226, 230, 283, 285–287, 386
polyethylene, linear low density, (LLDPE), 283, 285–287, 381, 545
poly(ethylene naphthalate) (PEN), 298, 555
poly(ethylene terephthalate), (PET), 17, 41, 112–113, 119, 149, 224, 230, 253, 256, 274, 291–292, 536
poly(ethylene terephthalate) glycol (PETG). 291
polylactide, (PLA), 24, 299
polylactic acid, 24
polyhydroxyl, 230
polyisocyanate, 230
polymer, 219, 221, 224, 228, 231–232
melt, 234, 245, 252, 393
molecules, 221, 234, 250, 265
resins, 236, 243–244
surface, 223
compatibility table, 311–312
polymer chain, 224, 235
branching, 226, 230
random state, 231
shape, 230
structure, 238
polymer phase changes, 231
T_g
T_m
polymer base, 345, 349
polymeric based materials (cushioning), 476
polymeric materials, 408
polymerization, 223–224, 227–228, 237, 243
addition, 224, 228
condensation, 224, 228
fully polymerized state, 337
prepolymer, 237, 276, 395, 556
polyolefin plastics, 18
polypropylene (PP), 10, 18, 47, 112, 119, 212, 222, 231, 234, 236, 249, 256, 260, 273, 289–291, 325, 347, 349, 391, 452
oriented, 391

coated, 440
woven, 545
polystyrene (PS), 47, 230, 231, 273, 276, 287–289, 328, 536
polyurethane (PUR), 276, 298, 354, 474, 477
poly(vinyl acetate) (PVAC), 294–295, 352, 365, 540
poly(vinyl alcohol) (PVAL) 227, 296–297, 352–353, 540
poly(vinyl chloride) (PVC), 47, 221, 292–294, 324, 362, 387, 536
poly(vinylidene chloride) (PVDC), 40, 292, 294, 324, 390, 540
point of purchase display, 116
portion pack, 387
porosity, 544–545
porous, 538
porous screen, 115
post-consumer, 17, 202
potency, 553–554
pot life, 361
pouch, 384–385, 542
pour spouts, 152
powdered products, 152, 158
PP, 273, 257–258, 381–391
preapplied, 538
prebreak, 156
preconditioned, 410
precut salads, 37
predictability, 469
prefold, 156
preform, 256, 264
preformed part, 112
preformed plastic shape, 535–536
preformed tubing (glass), 212
preglued, 151
preprint, 408
preprinted, 188
film, 378
preshipment testing, 268, 452, 454, 460–461, 463, 469
test severity, 462–463
press approval, 256
press sheet, 99, 105, 106, 155, 158, 160
pressure, 225, 271
prepress, 95, 96
prepress proofing, 98
preprinted image, 113
preserve, 16, 31, 33, 317
preservation, 14, 577
press-and-blow, 204, 206, 555
press set-up, 97
pressure, 41, 243
pressure differential, 180
pressure sensitive roll stock, 556
pressure sensitive adhesive (PSA), 355
pressure sensitive label, 103, 349, 355, 549
pressure test, 179
pressurized container, 188
pressurized products, 214
pressurized vessel, 194
primary colors, 90, 93
primary container, 417

primary package, 31, 150, 152, 439, 449–450
primer, 207, 360
Pringles potato chips, 571
printability, 24, 128
printed sheet, 96
pattern, 113
stock, 112
principal display panel, 158
print, 392, 393
printing, 97, 187, 247, 537
cost, 105
gravure, 100
industry, 25
methods, 99
planographic, 100, 104, 106
plate, 106, 156
processes, 49, 153, 542
relief, 99, 101, 102, 104
printing inks, 86
reflectance curves, 89
printing plate, 83, 90, 91, 94, 97, 98, 100, 102, 155
printing presses, 95–96, 100, 188
printing processes compared, 111
printing processes, 25
printing surface, 166
pristine, 207, 429
probable drop height, 440, 469
process analysis diagrams, 526
process color, 90, 93, 97
art, 90, 101, 188
processed food, 13
process printing, 92–93, 103, 115–116, 212
process scrap, 237
process waste, 398
produce, 36, 46
fruits and vegetables, 36, 45
herbs and spices, 47
maturation, 36
respiration, 36–37, 45–46
ripening, 36
sprouting, 47
producer, 203
product
compatibility, 576
damage, 461
degradation, 389
fragility, 446, 474
filling, 384
mapping, 573
parentage, 569
loss, 443
protection, 476
release, 188
residues, 24
sediment, 211
sleeves, 157
visibility, 535
production, 568
attributes, 523
die, 155
line, 569, 577, 581

machinery, 539
  processes, 523
product-propellant interface, 190
professional packaging staff, 569
profile, 245
profile extrusion, 243
programmable (shock machine), 459
programmable vibration table, 479
project cost, 97
project objectives, 573
project scheduling, 576
project scope, 569–570, 585
promoter, 224
proof, 98, 256
  press, 98
propagate, 38
propane, 18
propellant, 189–193
  charge, 193
proprietary, 163
protect, 16, 24, 31, 33, 317
protection, 14, 243, 371, 577
protective, 550
  coating, 113, 188
  fill, 479
  forms, 288, 550–551, 561
  materials, 475
  wrapping, 406
  packaging, 276, 437–438, 447, 454, 469,
    479, 554
prototype, package, 454
PT (closure), 322
PS, (polystyrene) 258, 272–273
pseudoplasticity, 358
psychographics, 49
pulping methods, 128–129
pump, 257, 338
punch, 184
puncture, 382
puncture resistance, 371
purchase preference, 18
purchase motivation, 12
purchaser, 203, 567, 578
purchasing 569, 568
push-up, 211
PVAC, 361
PVC, 236, 257–258, 272, 387, 537
PVDC, 391, 393
post consumer waste, 128
printing surface, 133
Pyrex, 200

Q

Quaker Oats, 9
quality, 526, 577–579
quality control 569
quality graphics, 408
quantify, 523
quartz, 199
Quebec, 19
quicklime, 557

R

RAC 6000 (Canada), 405, 455
radiant heat, 379, 392
radiation, 46, 47
radioactive isotope, 13, 47
radio frequency (RF), 549
radura symbol, 47
rail shipment, 471, 482
rail shunting, 485
railcar coupling, 471
rancid, 34
rapid chilling, 248
ream, 136
reactive components, 237
reactive thermosets, 361
recess, 212
recessed cap, 211
recessed cell pattern, 108
recessed label, 478
reclosability, 317
recognizing molding methods, 277
reconciliation, 556
recover, 16
recoverable elongation, 384
recycle, 15, 16, 17, 19, 24, 237, 561
  mandates, 18
recyclable, 17, 121, 243
recycled plastic, 251, 261, 556
recycled fiber, 128, 406, 408
  kraft, 128
  newsprint, 128
  paper, 360
  pulps, 133
  target levels, 23
recycling, 9, 21, 200, 260, 440
  paper, 354
red meat, 35, 36
  myoglobin, 34, 35
  oxymyoglobin, 35
redrawn, 182
reduce, 15
reduce costs, 572
reduced shelf life, 37
reduced temperature, 39
  chilling, 36, 39
  freezing, 39
  freezer burn, 39, 40
reducing losses, 443
refined, pulp, 130
reflectance, 89
refraction, 231
reflective aluminum, 378
reflective glossy metallic, 112
reflective values, 378
refractory material, 201
register, 90, 94, 96, 97, 99, 113, 115, 138,
  212, 384, 391
  circumferential, 115
register lug, 212
regenerated cellulose, 221
registration marks, 99, 100
regrind, 243, 253, 260, 266, 556

regular slotted box (RSB), 406, 410, 417
regular slotted container (RSC), 405
regulated, 553
regulations, 18
reheated, 265
relative humidity, 33, 35, 43, 390, 408, 411
relative movement, 33
release, 187
  coated, 113
  paper, 119, 349, 355
  sheet, 112
relative motion, 478
remedial action, (damage), 446
removable lids, 151
repeats, 98
repetitive shock, 472, 481
reposition, 572, 569
reprocessed, 243
residential waste, 15
residual metal, 178
resilient foam 276
resilient material, 113, 474, 481
  rubber, 115
resiliency, 476, 477
resilient, 473, 480
resin, 245
resistance to flow, 226
resolution, 94
resonance, 457, 472, 479–481
  damage, 479
  frequency, 33, 268, 481
  point, 481
  search, 479
  stack, 480, 482
resources, 22
respiratory functions, 45
  rate, 46
  natural, 46
retailer, 152, 166
retail display, 535
retailer, 549, 535
retail trade, 549
retooling, 569
retort, 41, 180
retortable, 200
retort pouch, 41, 42, 382, 399
retorting 180
reunitized, 447
reuse, 16
reverse printing, 114, 120, 290, 392
reverse reading, 97
reverse scores, 410
revitalize, 572
rewind, 392
RF, 549
R.H. 408
rheology, 357–358
rigid foams, 476
right reading, 97
rigid solid, 229, 233
ring and ball, 354
ring-pull top, 176
ripening rooms, 36

risk of failure, 581
Rockwell, 178
roll, 107, 247, 250
    bowed, 392
    roll-fed, 103, 371
      roll-formed, 355
      herringbone, 392
      stock, 101, 103
rolling, 178
rotary die cutting, 156
rotary screen printing, 116
rotary machine, 330
rotational molding, 244, 274
rotogravure, 100
rough handling, 485
round bottles, 208
round container, 188
rubber, 101
runnability, 155, 577
rubber, 354
rubber latex, 355
Rule 41, 405
Rule 180, 455

S

sachet, 385, 542
sack, 542
safety factor, 475
sales display, 440
Salmonella, 38
salt, 42
sampling protocol, 578
sand, 199
sand blasting, 212
sandwich card, 536
sanitary food can, 175–176, 179–180
Saran, 390
saturation, 84, 91–92
sauce bottles, 211
scan, 548
scanned, 546
scuff resistance, 457
seafood products, 177
sealability, 371
sealant, 180
seal integrity, 386
sealing jaw pressure, 386
seal strength, 227
seam, 179
seamed, 191
seaming collet, 193
seamless appearance, 186
seamless tubes, 184
second draw, 182
self-chilling packages, 558
self-heating packages, 557–558
self-service, 535
semisolid, 175, 226, 287
Sensomatic, 549
sensor gate, 549
separations, 94

sequential approach (design), 437
set, 237, 394
setup cartons, 133
scavengers, 45
Schweppes, 8
scientific community, 20–21
score, scored, 154–56, 410
score lines, 138
scratches, 211
screen, 92, 103
screen printing, 115, 117, 212, 427
screw, 252
scuff/scuffing, 210, 476, 478
scuffing/abrasion, 480
scum, 202
seal, 324
    sealing, 210
    sealing collar, 323
seal-end cartons, 158–159
seam, 246
seamless plastic bag, 247
secondary fiber, 408
secondary package, 31
secondary trimming, 243
securing practices, 471
security, 161, 163
semi-solid, 358, 364, 486
sensory active agents, 34
septum, 213
serrations, 329
serum, 212–213
setback, 152, 158
settle blow, 205–206
setup boxes, 149, 152, 167–169
shallow cup, 182
shallow draw, 175, 178, 182
shallow profile can, 181
shaped can body, 284
shears, 204
shear, 357–358
shear strength
sheet, 101, 246–247
    fed, 103, 106, 392
shelf appeal, 392
shelf life, 12, 33, 35, 36, 37, 39, 44, 562,
    569–570, 576
    extended, 38
    natural, 34, 46
    reduced, 37
shelf stable, 175
shellac, 392
shelving, 152
shingling, 269
shipper, 31, 438–439, 450
    designs, 486
    experience, 471
shipping, 152–153, 166
    box, 439
    container, 438, 486, 541, 570
    damage, 449, 435
    efficiency, 439
    sacks, 286
shock, 438, 441–442, 469, 471, 473, 475

absorption, 476
attenuating, 476, 480
fragility, 472
shock machine, 459
    pulse, 476
shop air, 258
shoplifting, 549–550
short-term load application, 482
short wave-length radiation, 47
shot, 252, 275
shoulder, 284–285
shoulder-less jars, 558
shoulder ridge, 210
shrink, 188, 235
    allowance, 255
    labels, 119, 235
    neck bands, 119, 330
shrinkage rate, 255
shrink plastic, 250, 265
    properties, 235
    strength, 235
shrink wrap, 235
shrink-wrapping, 452, 586
shrink wrapped, 453, 486, 568, 588
shunt speed, 442
shunting, 471, 482
sidewalls, 543
sigma, 521, 523
silica, 199
silicone, 207
silicone oxide, 380–381
side panel, 165
sidewall, 175, 182, 184, 186
    beading, 180, 182
sifting, 150
sift proof, 150, 158
sign-off, 98, 154
silicone pillow, 117
silk screen, 115
Simplex tray, 166
simulated shipping tests, 576
single draw, 182
single face, 406, 410
single face pallet, 485
single glued, 151
single rule, 156
single service, 10, 385
single wall, 406, 416
single white-lined board, 168
sink mark, 255–257
SI unit, 396
six corner tray, 165–166
six-color process, 95
sizing, 130, 133
    surface size, 135
skew, 481, 590
skids, 550–551
skin packaging 535, 538
SKU, 546
sleeve, 169
slit lock, 150, 160–161
slit score, 166
slit, 247

slip agent, 293
slip angle, 453
slip cover, 175–176
slip sheets, 440, 448, 453
slot orifice, 246
slug, 184
slur, 99
smell, 34, 35
small parcel shipping, 472
Smith Brothers, 8
snack food, 35, 43–44, 115
snap-lock, 161
snap-on cap, 287
snap-on lid, 49, 327
Society of the Plastics Industry (SPI), 318
soda ash, 199
soda lime glass, 199–201, 555
sodium, 200
sodium carbonate, 99
sodium silicate, 199
soft drinks, 183, 202, 212, 214
softening point, 227, 354
softwood, 127
solder, 179
soldered, 175, 179
solid color, 103
solid bleached kraft, 408, 537
solidify, 350
solidification method, 345, 351
solidifying, 100
    solidified, 106
    temperature, 199
solid paperboard, 417
solids content, 345, 351–352, 363
solid waste, 22
solubility, 46, 226–227, 238, 352
    solubility rule, 222
    in water, 189
solvent, 226, 345, 354, 394–396
    adhesives, 354
    bonding, 246
    resistance, 238
    solvent type, 345
solventless laminating, 395–396
Soudronic, 179
source coding, 549
sources of information (production machinery), 530
source reduction, 440
SPC, 526
special colors, 97
specific adhesion, 346
specification, 89, 194, 203, 231, 526, 570, 568, 576–585
    aerosols, 194
spice cans, 177
spectrum, 85
SPI code, 17, 19
spin welding, 272
spiral wound, 540
spores, 38
spot labeling, 210, 212, 426
spray paint, 191

spring, 232, 480–481
spring-back, 361
spring/mass relationship, 479
square breasted cans, 177
squeezability, 287
squeeze tube, 560
stable, 211, 439
stabilizing material, 453
stability (of a process), 521, 526
stacking factor, 488
stacking features, 211
stacking load, 232, 486
stack duration, 487
stack press, 103, 104
stack resonance, 480, 482
stacking ring, 257
stacking strength, 407, 482–484, 485, 488
stakeholder, 567, 570, 573
stamped, 180
standard atmospheric conditions, 459
standard alloys, 581
standard deviation, 521, 523, 525–527
standard distribution, 521, 523–524
standard flute configurations, 409
standard temperature and humidity, 484
starch, 345, 350–352
starch based adhesive, 406, 408
starwheel, 330
static (electricity), 292
static compression strength, 411
static compression, 482
static load range, 474
static loading, 482
static problems, 477
static stress, 474
static value, 482
static warehouse conditions, 487
stationary position, 253
statistical description, 442
statistical distribution, 527
statistical process control (SPC) 521, 523, 578
statistical process control terminology, 521–522
steel, 175, 183
    stiffer, 178
standard viewing illumination, 86
standard temperature and pressure, 390
stand-up pouch, 386
starch, 131, 135
static compressive strength, 138.
static electricity, 392
stationary supplies, 168
stay tape, 168
    stayed box, 168–169
steady state (machine), 526
steam purges, 384
steel cylinders, 107
steel rules, 155
stencil screen, 116
steric hindrance, 226
sterility, 33, 47, 275, 339, 555
sterilize, 40, 47
stewardship, 18

stitched, 543
stiffness, 24, 285, 382, 406–408
stippled, 211
stock
    jar, 335
    screw cap, 335
    containers, 318
    closures, 210
    glassware, 203, 208
    metal cans, 176
    molds, 244
stock-picking, 447
storage conditions, 48
storage container, 151
storage life, 363
STP, 390
strain, 357
strength-to-weight ratio, 208
strapping, 452, 484
stress, 214, 234, 258, 321, 345, 357
stress concentration, 212, 488
stress riser, 268, 555
stress point, 210
stretch wrap, 286, 453
stretch-wrapped load, 481
stretch wrapping, 440, 452, 590
structural properties (wood), 551
structural requirements, 153
styrenics, 536
Styrofoam, 219, 221, 276
styrene-butadiene, 299
sublimate, 39
substrate, 98, 102, 105–106, 108, 112–113, 345–346, 349, 354, 393–395
subtractive synthesis, 85
suck-back, 186
sugar, 42
sulfur, 199, 201
sulfur containing foods, 187
sulfur dioxide, 22
summary of carrier rules 416
supplier, 474, 569, 572, 578, 580, 582
support, 163
surface area, 252
surface contamination, 349
surface irregularities, 250, 346
surface tension, 347–349
surface texture, 211
Surlyn, 381, 387
susceptibility to damage, 438
susceptor, 379
suspended, 188
suspension, 352
sustainable, 21
    development, 21
sustainability, 19, 22–24, 163, 440
synthetic polymer, 345
Svante Arrehenious, 21
syringe, 555
system, 567
    analysis, 451
    cost, 443
    systems approach, 437

System International Tinplate Association (SITA), 179

T

tack, 351, 361
tack and range, 361
tackifier, 353
tacky, 395
tag, 549
take-away speed, 250
take-out tongs, 206
take-up factor, 408
tamper evident (TE), 3, 11, 33, 120, 235, 293, 318, 320, 322–323, 325, 330, 332–334, 339
tamper proof, 322
tank, 202
tape, 411
taped, 543
targeted audience, 49
TAPPI, 26, 582–583
taste, 34, 35
tax incentives, 18
tear propagation, 381
tear resistant, 163
tear strength, 153, 303
tear strips, 120, 134, 158, 161
tear tapes, 152
Technical Association of the Pulp and Paper Industry (TAPPI), 26, 138, 412, 413–414
temper, 177–178, 581
temperature, 33, 231, 233–235, 238, 249–250, 268
    application, 354
    elevated, 354, 441
    end use, 362
    extreme, 382
    melt temperature, 353
    reduced, 441
tensile energy absorption, 544
tensile properties, 302–303
tension control, 392
tension, constant, 392
tensile bond, 346
tensile properties, 405
tensile strength, 234, 347
tenter frame, 250
terephthalic acid, 230, 291
terminology (machine), 499
test methods, 578
Tetra Pak, 40, 149, 163
theft, 550, 535, 549
theoretical deflection distance, 473–474
thermal conductivity, 271
thermal processing, 40–41, 175, 179–180, 182
    heat sensitive, 47
    overcooking, 41
    pasteurization, 40
    ultra-high temperature, 40
Therimage, 113
thermal analysis, 234
    differential (DTA) 234

    mechanical analysis (DMA), 234
    Scanning colorimetry (DSC), 234
thermal conductivity, 271
thermal expansion, 200, 210
thermal expansion coefficient (plastic), 235
thermal history, 221, 231, 235, 248, 265
thermal processing, 354, 362
thermoelastic, 233
thermoforming, 243–244, 247 270–272, 277, 288, 536
    billow forming, 273
    blister or clamshell, 272
    draw-formed packaging, 270
    enclosed containers, 272
    materials, 271
    plug assist vacuum forming, 273
    temperatures, 537
    trays, 272
    vacuum forming, 272
thermoform molds, 271–273
thermoformed containers, 40
thermoplastic, 179, 219, 221, 229, 232–233, 236–238, 243–244, 251, 257, 275, 327–328, 351, 353
    sheet, 270–271
thermoset plastic, 219, 229, 236–238, 243, 274, 327, 351, 353
tier sheets, 452
thin-walled containers, 251, 291
thixotropic, 358, 364
three-point scores, 410
three-sided edge seal, 386
thread, 204, 246, 255, 319, 320, 327–329
    dimension, 210
    interrupted, 329
    L-style thread, 318
    mismatch, 318–319
    modified buttress, 318
    M-style thread, 318
    multiple lead, 336
    multiple pitch, 336
    profile, 210, 319
threaded closures, 320–321, 328
three-phase system, 190
three piece, 175–178, 182, 184
three-sided labeling, 210
three-way corner, 551–552
throughput, 508
tie layer, 260, 391–392
tier, 207–208
tier sheet, 590
time dependent, 232, 358
timetable, 575
timing screw, 505–506
tin, 176–179, 184, 187
tin-free steel, 177
tinplate, 175, 321
titanium tetrachloride, 207
tips (collapsible tube), 184–185
titanium dioxide, 135, 137
titratable alkali, 200
tolerance, 96, 208, 266, 498, 577–578
tonal scale, 99

tongue lock, 150
tooling cost, 243, 245, 251, 272
top end, 175
top-load compression, 478, 586
top-loading tray, 152, 165
top-to bottom compression, 165, 180
torque, 230–231, 232, 319, 330–332, 577
    retention, 324
totes, 285
toughness, 382, 389
tracking damage, 446
tracking losses, 444
tracking, (laminating), 392
traction device, 382
trade economy, 21
trademark, 208
trade name, 219
trailer-on-flatcar (TOFC), 471
trial run, 581
train, 105
training, 497–498
transfer bead, 204–205
transition, 232, 234
    elastic state, 233
    glass transition, 233, 265
    melt phase, 234
    melt transition, 233–234
    phase changes, 233
    point, 232
    temperature, 233–234
    T_g, 233–235
    T_m, 233–235
    zone, 231, 249
translucent, 231
transport, 16, 31, 48, 472
    and handling, 270
    efficiency, 568
    environment, 437
    vibrations, 268
transportation, 14, 21
    modes, 477
Transport Canada (TC), 194, 456
Transport of Dangerous Goods, 456
trapping. 96, 99, 106
trays, 149, 163, 165, 452–453, 588
    tray-style carton
triple gob, 204
triple tight (tripletite), 177
triplewall board, 406, 418
triplewall boxes, 416
Tri-seal International Inc., 325
trouble free, 153, 577
troubleshooting bond failure, 246
truck shipment, 471
truck vibration, 478
tubular sleeves, 119, 120
turnaround time, 110
TV dinners, 11
two phase system, 190–191
two piece can, 115, 175–176, 184, 188
typography, 9, 71–72
tympan, 155
tubes, 186

dimensioning, 185
tube and slide, 169
tube style, 152, 157–158, 162–163
tube forming rate, 250
tube, 245, 271
    body, 541, 542
    caulking tubes 246
    collapsible, plastic, 246, 274
    heavy walled, 246
    injection molded head, 246
    laminated, 541–542
    thin-walled, 246
    seamless, 247
tubs, 244, 257, 327
    dairy, 244, 256
tubular shape, 176
tuck closure carton, 159, 160
tuck cover, 165
tuck flaps, 150–151, 161
tuck-and-tongue lock, 161
turret, 505–506
typical fragility factor classes, 475
Tyvek, 545

U

UCC, 547
UFC, 408, 415, 455
UHT, 40
ultrasonic bonding, 272
ultra-high temperature (UHT), 40, 187
ultraviolet, 83, 102, 106, 115, 202, 237, 371, 395, 554
unbalanced construction, 411
undecorated, 185
undercut, 253, 255, 271, 277, 558
underfill, 479
underlayer, 392
under-packaging, 443
uneven fill height, 211
unglued tray blanks, 152
Uniform Code Council (UCC), 546
Uniform Freight Classification, (UFC), 405, 415
United Nations, 14, 456
United States, 23, 19, 144, 456
United States Pharmacopeia (USP), 200
unit load, 31, 439, 462
unit package, 8
unitized, 447, 472
unitized load, 48, 470, 481
Universal Product Code (UPC), 547
unpacking, 152
unprinted line, 115
U.N. recommendations, 456
unscrambler, 329
unsecured load, 472
unsprung mass, 478
unwind, 392
UPC (code), 99, 547–548
upcharge, 581
upgrading existing lines, 495–496

upscale, 115, 168, 175, 200, 212 335
upstream conditions, 500
urea, 243
urethane, 228–230, 477
urethane foam, 276
U.S. Code of Federal Regulations, (CFR) 194
use conditions, 98
use environment, 472
used equipment, 495
used machinery brokers, 509
utility, 572
utilization, 160
UV, 380, 555
UV cured, 106, 188
UV light barrier, 261, 379
UV sensitive products, 202

V

vacuum, 243, 271, 538
vacuum forming, 247
vacuum metalized aluminum, 113
vacuum metallizing, 380
vacuum pack, 389
vacuum packaging, 45
validate, 556
valve, 188, 190, 560
valve cup, 176
valve-type, 543
Van der Waals' forces, 222, 225, 346
vapor phase, 189
vapor pressure, 189
variables, 208
varnish, 101, 106, 187, 393, 478
Vaseline, 226
vat-lined paper, 132
vegetable polymer, 350
vehicle vibration, 478
velocity, 473
vent holes, 38
venting closure
ventilated packaging, 36, 46
verification, 557
versatile, 498, 509
vertical column, 485
vertical end-loading, 151–152
vertical form-fill-seal (VFFS), 382, 384, 538
vertical stack strength, 485
VFFS, 384–385, 388
vial, 212–213, 555
vibrated, 479, 481, 477, 478
vibration, 33, 438, 441–442, 477–481
    direct coupling, 479, 481
    frequency, 477–478
    repetitive shock, 457
    resonance, 457
    stack resonance, 457
    random vibrations, 457
    programmable tables, 457
    test, 590
    vibration tables, 457, 460
vibration (machinery), 497

vibrational input, 478, 480
vibrational response curves, 481
vibration-induced damage, 472
vibratory feeder, 519–520
viscoelastic, 138, 322, 327, 330, 411, 482, 487
viscometers, 359
viscosity, 191, 199, 345, 353, 355, 357–358, 498
viscous fluids, 287
visible spectrum, 83
vitamin, 34, 47
vitreous 199
voids, 479
volatile, 35, 36, 200, 362, 389, 395
    loss of, 39
volatile organic compound (VOC), 351
vignette, 93, 101, 103
vinyl, 169
viscoelastic, 232
viscosity, 226, 578
    flow, 232, 235
visible light, 231
volume fixturing, 506

W

Walker tray, 166
wall perimeter, 484
wasp spray, 191
waste management, 17–19, 21, 22
warehouse, 438, 449, 482, 485, 488
    damage, 445
    stacking ability, 459
warehousing, 45, 48, 568, 569
warpage, 410
waste management 440
water based adhesive, 351, 353
water glass, 199
water proof, 362
water receptive, 105
water reduction, 39
water resistant, 161, 354, 362, 540
water shortage, 19
water vapor, 35
water vapor barrier, 288, 545
water vapor transmission, 305–306, 371
water vapor transmission rate (WVTR), 287, 390
wavelength, 46
wax, 177, 207, 353, 386, 393
    coating, 478
    laminating, 394
    paperboard, 39
wax (corrugated), 427–429
    cascading, 428–429
    curtain coating, 428
    direct water contact, 427
    dry waxing, 427
    waxed, 408
    treatments, 411
    wet waxing, 428
weather patterns, 19

weather resistant adhesive, 408
web, 384, 388
web-fed, 392, 106, 108
web material, 398
web speed, 378
weigh cell, 518, 526
weightless, 481
welding, 179
   weldability, 177
    welded body, 176, 179
    weld edges, 179
welded cans, 179, 284
    seam, 179
wet adhesive, 540
wet bonding, 394–395
wet end, 133
wet laminating, 397
wet products, 161

wetting, 361
wet out, 223, 226, 345, 347–349
white enamel, 186
wide-mouthed, 206
wide mouth jar, 266
window, 150, 156, 160, 163, 190
windowed, 97, 112
   window material, 120
windshield washer fluid, 177
wire basket, (cage), 339
wood battens, 550
wood distillation products, 45
wood packaging, 551
wood structural groups, 552
work-hardened, 178, 184
working scores, 157
working time, 501
World Packaging Organisation (WPO), 25

wrapper stock, 103
wraparound caser, 408
wrap-around labeling, 210, 212
wrap-around lithography, 179
WVTR, 390

X

X-rays, 46, 47

Y

Yardley's, 8
yeast, 38
yield, 236, 397
yield point, 384